INTERNATIONAL SERIES OF MONOGRAPHS IN
ELECTRONICS AND INSTRUMENTATION
GENERAL EDITORS: D. W. FRY, L. COSTRELL, AND K. KANDIAH

VOLUME 9

STATISTICAL THEORY OF SIGNAL DETECTION

STATISTICAL THEORY OF SIGNAL DETECTION

SECOND EDITION, REVISED AND ENLARGED

by

CARL W. HELSTROM

Professor of Applied Electrophysics,
University of California, San Diego

PERGAMON PRESS

OXFORD · NEW YORK · TORONTO
SYDNEY · PARIS · BRAUNSCHWEIG

U. K.	Pergamon Press Ltd., Headington Hill Hall, Oxford OX3 0BW, England
U. S. A.	Pergamon Press Inc., Maxwell House, Fairview Park, Elmsford, New York 10523, U.S.A.
CANADA	Pergamon of Canada, Ltd., 207 Queen's Quay West, Toronto 1, Canada
AUSTRALIA	Pergamon Press (Aust.) Pty. Ltd., 19a Boundary Street, Rushcutters Bay, N.S.W. 2011, Australia
FRANCE	Pergamon Press SARL, 24 rue des Ecoles, 75240 Paris, Cedex 05, France
WEST GERMANY	Pergamon Press GmbH, D-3300 Braunschweig, Postfach 2923, Burgplatz 1, West Germany

First edition 1968

Reprinted 1975

Library of Congress Catalog Card No. 68—21386

Printed in Great Britain by A. Wheaton & Co., Exeter

ISBN 0 08 013265 0

To Floyd A. Brotzman

a thorough and inspiring teacher of mathematics

CONTENTS

PREFACE TO THE SECOND EDITION

A TECHNICAL book cannot aspire to be a κτῆμα ἐς αἰεί; "diuturnity is a dream and folly of expectation". A few years span its useful life, and relentless Progress carries us beyond. This new edition is not offered with any hope that oblivion will be long escaped.

Nevertheless, much of the book has been rewritten. Old topics have been treated more efficiently; new ones have been undertaken. A chapter on digital communications and sections on sequential and nonparametric detection have been added. Problems now appear at the end of each chapter.

The bibliographies at the end of each chapter list both primary sources of the material and titles of books and articles with which the reader can begin further study. No attempt has been made to be complete, nor should the omission of a citation be considered a disparagement. We recommend the following to those seeking additional references:

STUMPERS, F. H. L. M., "A Bibliography of Information Theory: Communication Theory—Cybernetics", *Trans. I.R.E.* **PGIT-2,** 1–60 (Nov. 1953); **IT-1,** 31–47 (Sept. 1955); **IT-3,** 150–66 (June 1957); **IT-6,** 25–51 (March 1960).

CHESSIN, P. L., "A Bibliography on Noise", *Trans. I.R.E.* **IT-1,** 15–31 (Sept. 1955).

GREEN, P. E., Jr., "A Bibliography of Soviet Literature on Noise, Correlation, and Information Theory", *Trans. I.R.E.* **IT-2,** 91–94 (June 1956).

GREEN, P. E., Jr., "Information Theory in the U.S.S.R.", *IRE Wescon Record,* pt. 2, 67–83 (1957).

MIDDLETON, D., *An Introduction to Statistical Communication Theory,* McGraw-Hill Book Co., New York, N.Y. (1960).

ELIAS, P, *et al.*, "Progress in Information Theory in the U.S.A., 1957–1960", *Trans. I.R.E.* **IT-7,** 128–44 (July 1961).

ZADEH, L. A. (ed.), "Report on Progress in Information Theory in the U.S.A., 1960–1963", *Trans. I.E.E.E.* **IT-9,** 221–64 (Oct. 1963).

In this book citations are made by the name of the author and the year of publication. Equations are referred to by giving the numbers of chapter and section, as "eq. (III, 2.10)" for the tenth equation in the second section of Chapter III. For equations within the same chapter, the roman numeral is omitted.

Most of this book should be easily understood by first-year graduate students in electrical engineering, mathematics, or physics. An introductory course on probability is presupposed. Special topics such as integral equations and Gram–Charlier series are introduced as need arises. For a brief survey of the basic theory, the first four chapters may be read, with the omission of the following sections: Chapter I, Sections 3, 4, 5, 6; Chapter II, Section 6; Chapter IV, Sections 3, 4, 5. Starred sections may be skipped on first reading.

Concurrently with its application to physics and electrical engineering, signal detection has contributed to the study of human perception, a topic outside the scope of this book. For a survey of the subject we refer the reader to *Signal Detection Theory and Psychophysics*, by D. M. Green and J. A. Swets, John Wiley & Sons, Inc., New York, N. Y., 1966.

This revision was started at the Westinghouse Research Laboratories, Pittsburgh, Pa. I wish to thank Dr. Robert Hooke, manager of the Mathematics Department, for his encouragement. I am grateful to Dr. Albert Nuttall for compiling a careful list of corrections of and comments on the first edition. The new version has benefited by my experience in teaching detection theory at the University of California, Los Angeles, 1963–4. I am indebted to Professor A. V. Balakrishnan for his hospitality on that occasion.

FROM THE PREFACE TO THE FIRST EDITION

THE present work is intended as an elementary introduction to the theory of statistical testing of hypotheses as applied to the detection of signals in radar and communications technology. We have tried to steer a middle course, in the hope of making the book useful to both the mathematician and the engineer. In behalf of the former we have tried to present the application of decision theory to problems in signal detection without burdening him with technical details of radar and communications practice. For the latter we introduce statistical decision theory stripped of mathematical subtleties that often make texts and papers on the subject uninviting. The engineer will miss the practical embodiment of the theory and may long for a circuit diagram or two. The mathematician will object to the violence that has been done to much delicate theory and will point to certain oversimplifications (in particular, the concept of randomization has been deliberately omitted). Our intention, however, has been to convey to each some feeling for the subject, so that each can exploit it for his own purposes.

We should like to thank Drs. W. Altar, J. W. Coltman, and D. P. Gaver for reading and commenting on portions of the manuscript. Deep appreciation goes to Dr. G. W. Klotzbaugh for his careful reading and checking of the entire work, and to Miss Juliana Selchan for her patience and industry in typing it. We are grateful to Dr. M. Ostrofsky and the Westinghouse Research Laboratories for encouragement and support of this effort.

I

SIGNALS AND FILTERS

RADAR is a device for discovering distant objects such as aeroplanes and ships. The transmitter generates electromagnetic energy of a few centimeters' wavelength in the form of pulses of large amplitude and brief duration, which are emitted periodically through an antenna that produces a fairly narrow beam of radiation. An object in this beam scatters the radiation in all directions, and a small part of the scattered radiation excites the receiving antenna to create a signal that is led to a receiver, amplified, and applied to the vertical deflection plates of a cathode-ray oscilloscope.

A spot moves rapidly from left to right across the face of the oscilloscope, and when an echo pulse is received, a vertical pip appears with a height proportional to the strength of the signal. The horizontal sweep of the oscilloscope is synchronized with the transmitted pulses, and the echoes from a stationary target are always registered at the same position. The interval between the beginning of the sweep and the echo pip is proportional to the time taken by the radar pulse to travel to the target and back, and this time is in turn proportional to the distance to the target.

The energy in the echo from a remote target may be very small; it is inversely proportional to the fourth power of the distance. One might think that a target arbitrarily far away could be detected by simply increasing the amplification in the receiver. When this is done, however, a dense, fluctuating array of pips appears all along the trace on the oscilloscope. Radar men call this crowd of spurious targets "grass". It is caused by random interference, or "noise", that originates in the surroundings and in the receiver itself. Too weak an echo will be lost in the grass and become indistinguishable from the noise.

In seeking distant targets the observer has to decide which of the pips on the oscilloscope result from echo signals and which are caused by random noise. The receiver should be designed to enable him to ferret out the weakest possible echoes without an excessive number of incorrect decisions. How this can be done is the subject of the statistical theory of signal detection. It can be most clearly understood by first studying simplified or idealized situations, and that is the purpose of this book. For details of the construction of actual radar systems the reader may consult the numerous textbooks on radar, a few of which are listed in the bibliography at the end of this chapter.

Communication systems that must carry messages over great distances with only a limited power also present the problem of detecting weak signals in the midst of random noise. The receiver must distinguish the information-bearing electromagnetic signals from the noise and from each other, and to attain the most reliable communication it must do so as efficiently as possible. Similar problems arise in physics, where it is often necessary to measure weak voltages or other small quantities in the unavoidable presence of background noise. In all such cases the theory of signal detection is a useful guide.

What is given in a typical detection problem is a variable voltage such as might appear between the terminals of a receiving antenna. We mentally divide this voltage into two parts, the signal and the noise, according to our concern. The signal bears information of value, and the noise opposes our efforts to extract it. In this first chapter we shall review various ways of describing signals and the filters by which they are transformed. The next chapter will deal with the noise, introducing the statistical methods appropriate. Then the goals of a detection system will be defined through an analogy with the testing of statistical hypotheses, after which the methods of attaining them will be explained.

1. SIGNALS AND THEIR SPECTRA

In studying signals we must distinguish between the transitory and the permanent. A transitory signal $s(t)$ is a function of time that may be assumed precisely known, that takes the value 0 up to an initial time t_0,

$$s(t) = 0, \quad t < t_0,$$

and that approaches 0 as the time increases without bound,

$$s(t) \to 0, \quad t \to \infty.$$

It is quadratically integrable; the quantity

$$E = \int_{-\infty}^{\infty} [s(t)]^2 \, dt \tag{1.1}$$

is finite. If, for instance, $s(t)$ is the voltage across a resistor of R ohms, the current in the resistor is $s(t)/R$, and a finite energy

$$\int_{-\infty}^{\infty} [s(t)]^2 \, dt/R = E/R$$

is dissipated in the resistor. Such a transitory signal is usually in the form of a pulse or a succession of pulses.

The output of a broadcasting transmitter exemplifies a signal that cannot conveniently be described as transitory. It is most expedient to represent it as a function $s(t)$ of time that has neither beginning nor end and is not quadratically integrable. Such signals might be called "permanent". The simplest ones are the periodic functions. Communication theory, requiring a broader class of permanent signals, draws upon stochastic processes of the kind to be studied in the next chapter. For the time being we shall concern ourselves mainly with transitory signals.

A signal pulse can be described not only by a function $s(t)$ of time, but also by its Fourier transform or *spectrum* $S(\omega)$, defined by†

$$S(\omega) = \int_{-\infty}^{\infty} s(t)e^{-i\omega t}\, dt. \tag{1.2}$$

The spectrum of a quadratically integrable signal always exists and is itself quadratically integrable. The quantity that we denoted by E and shall often refer to as the energy of the signal is also given by the formula

$$E = \int_{-\infty}^{\infty} |S(\omega)|^2\, d\omega/2\pi, \tag{1.3}$$

which is a consequence of Parseval's theorem (Appendix A, eq. (A.9)).

From the spectrum $S(\omega)$ the time dependence of the signal can be recovered by the inverse Fourier transform

$$s(t) = \int_{-\infty}^{\infty} S(\omega)\, e^{i\omega t}\, d\omega/2\pi. \tag{1.4}$$

This formula represents the signal as a superposition of infinitely many sinusoidal oscillations $e^{i\omega t}$ of frequency ω and complex amplitude $S(\omega)\, d\omega/2\pi$. As $s(t)$ is real, the spectrum is subject to the condition $S(-\omega) = S^*(\omega)$, the asterisk denoting the complex conjugate function.

The Fourier integral is an extension of the familiar Fourier series, which represents a periodic function of period T as the sum of a countable infinity of sines and cosines, whose frequencies are integral multiples of $2\pi/T$.

† In this book the variable ω will be called the *frequency*. It is measured in radians/second and is 2π times the quantity, measured in hertz or cycles per second, that is usually termed the frequency. We make this convention so that factors of 2π appear in our formulas in typographically convenient places, the familiar concept of frequency being retained. The variable ω is sometimes called the *pulsatance*. Only the most elementary aspects of the theory of Fourier transforms will be needed here; they are presented in Appendix A, which also lists a bibliography of the subject.

One can think of the integral in eq. (1.4) as arising when T becomes very large and the number of sinusoidal components becomes uncountably infinite. The energy E as given in eq. (1.3) can be regarded as the sum of the strengths of all those sine waves.

A common type of signal is the rectangular pulse of duration T,

$$s(t) = A, \quad 0 < t < T; \qquad s(t) = 0, \quad t < 0, \quad t > T, \tag{1.5}$$

which can be generated in a circuit by connecting a battery for a time T. The spectrum of this signal is

$$S(\omega) = A(1-e^{-i\omega T})/i\omega. \tag{1.6}$$

It is instructive to work out the inverse transform, eq. (1.4), of this spectrum. The analysis is presented in Appendix A.

Signals whose spectra differ significantly from 0 only over a range of frequencies in the neighborhood of $\omega = 0$ are often called *video* signals. The term originated in radar and television technology, in which this type of signal was applied to the deflection plates of a cathode-ray oscilloscope and so made visible. The extent of the spectrum of a video signal is measured by its *bandwidth*, several definitions of which are in use. If the spectrum has a single peak in the range $-\infty < \omega < \infty$, it must for reasons of symmetry lie at $\omega = 0$. The bandwidth can then be defined as the distance between the "half-power points"; it is $2\omega_1$, where $|S(\omega_1)|^2 = \frac{1}{2}|S(0)|^2$. Alternatively it can be defined as the root-mean-square deviation $\Delta\omega$ of the spectrum,

$$\Delta\omega = \overline{(\omega^2)}^{\frac{1}{2}}, \quad \overline{\omega^2} = \int_{-\infty}^{\infty} \omega^2 |S(\omega)|^2 \, d\omega \Big/ \int_{-\infty}^{\infty} |S(\omega)|^2 \, d\omega,$$

which resembles a radius of gyration. Still a third definition is as the ratio $\int_{-\infty}^{\infty} |S(\omega)| \, d\omega / S(0)$. Which definition is used is largely a matter of mathematical convenience.

To be contrasted to video signals are those signals in which oscillations of high frequency predominate. If the spectrum of a signal is concentrated in two narrow, symmetrical peaks, one lying near a frequency $\omega = \Omega$, the other near $\omega = -\Omega$, and if the width of the peaks is much smaller than Ω, the signal is termed *narrowband* or *quasiharmonic*. Such signals are of great importance in this work and are discussed in later sections of this chapter.

2. FILTERS

In the systems we shall study, signals are transformed by devices known as *filters*. In general a filter is an electrical network having a pair of input terminals and a pair of output terminals. It may contain resistors, inductors, capacitors, vacuum tubes, relays, or other components. When we apply across the input terminals a variable voltage, or "input signal", $s_i(t)$, we measure between the output terminals a voltage, or "output signal", $s_o(t)$. The output signal, we shall assume, is uniquely determined by the input signal. The filter can then be defined by the set of all possible pairs of input and output signals; we write these symbolically as $\langle s_i(t) \rightarrow s_o(t)\rangle$. In this section we shall briefly describe some of the properties of filters.

No filter can respond to a change in its input before the change occurs. Symbolically, if for two input–output pairs given by $\langle s_i^{(1)}(t) \rightarrow s_o^{(1)}(t)\rangle$ and $\langle s_i^{(2)}(t) \rightarrow s_o^{(2)}(t)\rangle$, $s_i^{(1)}(t) = s_i^{(2)}(t)$ for $t < t_0$, but $s_i^{(1)}(t) \neq s_i^{(2)}(t)$ for $t > t_0$, then $s_o^{(1)}(t) = s_o^{(2)}(t)$ for $t < t_0$. This statement expresses the principle of causality, and a conceptual filter that fulfils this requirement is said to be "physically realizable".

A filter containing no energy sources is said to be *passive;* otherwise it is called *active*. A vacuum-tube amplifier is an active filter; a transformer is a passive one. A filter whose components do not change with time has the property that if $\langle s_i(t) \rightarrow s_o(t)\rangle$ is an input–output pair, so is $\langle s_i(t+a) \rightarrow s_o(t+a)\rangle$ for all real values of a. It is called a *time-invariant* or *stationary* filter.

An important class is that of the *linear* filters. The output of a linear filter is always a linear transformation of the input, by which we mean that if $\langle s_i^{(1)}(t) \rightarrow s_o^{(1)}(t)\rangle$ and $\langle s_i^{(2)}(t) \rightarrow s_o^{(2)}(t)\rangle$ are any two pairs of inputs and outputs, then

$$\langle As_i^{(1)}(t)+Bs_i^{(2)}(t) \rightarrow As_o^{(1)}(t)+Bs_o^{(2)}(t)\rangle$$

is also a possible input–output pair for all values of A and B. The same rule holds for linear combinations of any number of inputs and outputs.

True signals are real functions of time, but it is sometimes convenient to think of introducing a complex signal

$$s_i(t) = s_i^{(1)}(t)+is_i^{(2)}(t)$$

at the input. From a linear filter the output is the same linear combination,

$$s_o(t) = s_o^{(1)}(t)+is_o^{(2)}(t).$$

When the input signal is real, the output must also be real. If every bounded real input signal produces a bounded output signal, a linear filter is said to be *stable*.

A linear, stationary filter can be regarded as transforming the input $s_i(t)$ in the manner described by the integral

$$s_o(t) = \int_0^\infty K(\tau)\, s_i(t-\tau)\, d\tau. \tag{2.1}$$

The function $K(\tau)$ is known as the *impulse response* of the filter. If the input is a very sharp impulse, which can be represented by a Dirac delta-function occurring at time $t = 0$, $s_i(t) = \delta(t)$, the output of the filter is $s_o(t) = K(t)$. Any input signal can be considered as a linear combination of delta-function impulses by the formula

$$s_i(t) = \int_{-\infty}^{\infty} s_i(t')\, \delta(t-t')\, dt'.$$

By the definition of a linear filter, the output signal must be the same linear combination of the delayed impulse responses $K(t-t')$,

$$s_o(t) = \int_{-\infty}^{\infty} s_i(t')\, K(t-t')\, dt' = \int_{-\infty}^{\infty} K(\tau)\, s_i(t-\tau)\, d\tau.$$

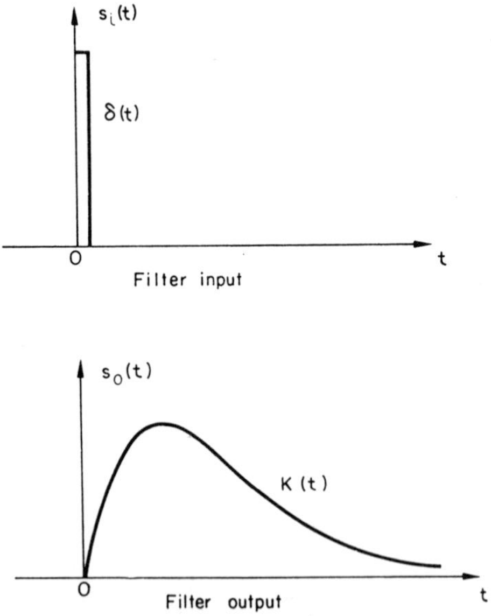

FIG. I.1. The impulse response of a filter.

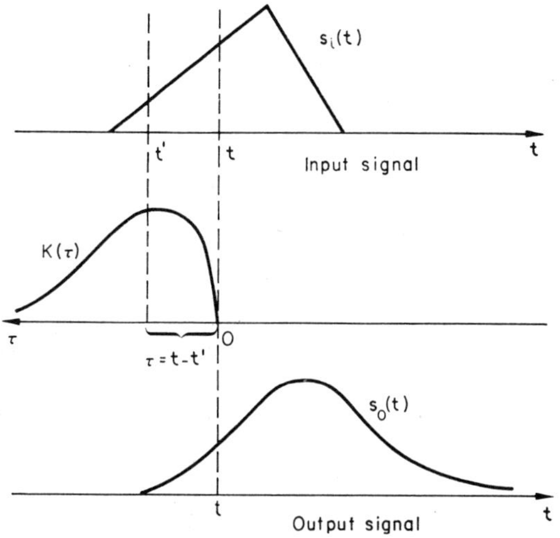

FIG. I.2. The action of a linear filter.

ince the filter cannot respond in advance of its input, $K(\tau) = 0$ for $\tau < 0$; nd we obtain eq. (2.1). For a passive filter containing elements like resis- ors that dissipate energy, the response to an impulse ultimately dies away, nd $K(\tau) \to 0$ as $\tau \to \infty$. A typical filter might have an impulse response ke that shown in Fig. I.1.

The effect of a linear filter can be thought of as an integration over the ast of the input, with the contribution from τ seconds in the past multi- lied by the weight $K(\tau)$, as illustrated in Fig. I.2. In that figure the value of ie output at time t is formed by multiplying the corresponding ordinates f $s_i(t')$ and $K(t-t')$ and integrating to obtain

$$s_o(t) = \int_{-\infty}^{t} K(t-t')\, s_i(t')\, dt', \qquad (2.2)$$

formula equivalent to eq. (2.1). As time goes on, the weighting function (τ) slides along to the right, progressively acting on new portions of the nput signal $s_i(t)$.

In the rest of this section we deal mostly with linear, stationary filters. or more thorough treatments of this topic the reader should consult such extbooks as those of Gardner and Barnes (1942), Guillemin (1953, 1957, 963), and Carlin and Giordano (1964).†

† References to the bibliography—to be found at the end of each chapter—are desig- ated by the date of publication and listed in that order.

The Fourier transform of the impulse response is known as the *transfe* *function* of the filter and will be designated by $Y(\omega)$:

$$Y(\omega) = \int_0^\infty K(\tau)\, e^{-i\omega\tau}\, d\tau,$$
$$K(\tau) = \int_{-\infty}^\infty Y(\omega)\, e^{i\omega\tau}\, d\omega/2\pi. \tag{2.3}$$

(For some filters it is convenient to take the input as a voltage and th output as a current, in which case $Y(\omega)$ is called an *admittance;* if th input is a current and the output a voltage, it is an *impedance*. These dis tinctions are unimportant in the present discussion.) If the input is th complex function of time $e^{i\omega t}$ with frequency ω, the output of the filter i $Y(\omega)e^{i\omega t}$, as one can show by substitution into eq. (2.1) and use of eq. (2.3) The Fourier integral

$$s_i(t) = \int_{-\infty}^\infty S_i(\omega)\, e^{i\omega t}\, d\omega/2\pi$$

represents any input signal as the superposition of a number of such com plex sinusoids, with amplitudes given by the spectrum $S_i(\omega)$. By the defi nition of a linear filter, the spectrum $S_o(\omega)$ of the output must, therefore be given by the formula

$$S_o(\omega) = Y(\omega)\, S_i(\omega). \tag{2.4}$$

This result also follows immediately from eq. (2.1) by use of the convolu tion theorem for Fourier transforms (Appendix A, eq. (A.8)).

Since the impulse response $K(\tau)$ is a real function of τ, the transfer func tion $Y(\omega)$ is subject to the condition

$$Y(-\omega) = Y^*(\omega).$$

For $\tau < 0$ we could evaluate the integral

$$K(\tau) = \int_{-\infty}^\infty Y(\omega) e^{i\omega\tau}\, d\omega/2\pi$$

by completing the contour of integration in the lower half of the comple ω-plane (see Appendix A). Therefore, the vanishing of the impulse respons $K(\tau)$ for $\tau < 0$ implies that the transfer function $Y(\omega)$ can have no singula ities in the region Im $\omega < 0$. If the filter is stable, $|Y(\omega)|$ must be bounde for real values of ω as well, and all singularities of $Y(\omega)$ must lie above th Rl ω-axis.

The commonest kind of linear filter is made up of a network of resistors, inductors, and capacitors, or so-called "lumped" circuit elements. It is shown in books on circuit theory that the transfer function $Y(\omega)$ of such a filter is a rational function of ω; that is, it is the quotient of two polynomials of finite degree in ω. Because of unavoidable capacitances between components and wiring, a real filter cannot pass very high frequencies without an attenuation that increases with frequency: $|Y(\omega)| \to 0$ as $\omega \to \pm\infty$. In a rational transfer function representing such a filter, the degree of the polynomial in the denominator must be at least one unit greater than that of the polynomial in the numerator.

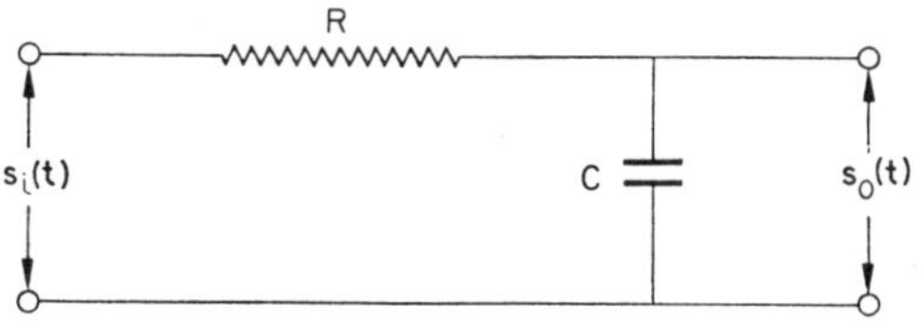

FIG. I.3. An *RC* filter.

As an example consider the simple filter of Fig. I.3. If the input and output signals are voltages measured across the terminals shown, the transfer function is, according to elementary circuit theory,

$$Y(\omega) = \frac{-i/\omega C}{R - i/\omega C} = \frac{1}{1 + i\omega RC}. \tag{2.5}$$

The impulse response of such a filter is easily shown to be a decaying exponential:

$$K(\tau) = \mu e^{-\mu\tau}, \quad \mu = 1/RC, \quad \tau > 0, \tag{2.6}$$

with a "time constant" $(1/\mu) = RC$. If the input is a rectangular pulse like that of eq. (1.5), the output is

$$\begin{aligned} s_o(t) &= A(1 - e^{-\mu t}), \quad && 0 < t < T, \\ s_o(t) &= A(e^{\mu T} - 1)e^{-\mu t}, && t > T, \end{aligned} \tag{2.7}$$

where T is the duration of the input pulse. This output signal is illustrated in Fig. I.4. The spectrum of the output is, by eqs. (1.6), (2.4), and (2.5),

$$S_o(\omega) = A\,\frac{1 - e^{-i\omega T}}{i\omega(1 + i\omega RC)}, \tag{2.8}$$

and $s_o(t)$ could be found by taking the Fourier transform of this expression; but it is much easier to use the impulse response, eq. (2.6), in the basic formulas (2.1) or (2.2).

For a more complicated network than that of Fig. I.3 the procedure in determining the impulse response is similar. One first works out the transfer function $Y(\omega)$ by using standard techniques to solve for the voltage across the output terminals when there is an alternating voltage $e^{i\omega t}$ across the input terminals; the ratio of these voltages is $Y(\omega)$. The impulse response is then obtained by a Fourier transformation, as in eq. (2.3). Since for a lumped network $Y(\omega)$ is a rational function of ω, this inverse trans-

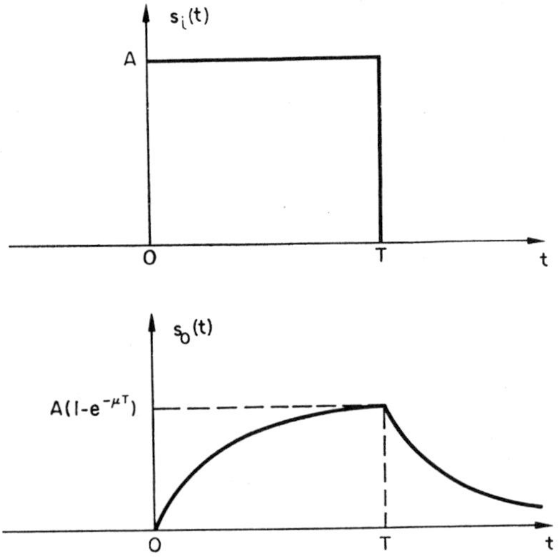

FIG. I.4. The response of an RC filter to a rectangular pulse.

formation is facilitated by determining the roots ω_j of the denominator of $Y(\omega)$; these roots are called the "poles" of the filter transfer function. If there are no multiple roots, one can use the method of partial fractions to write $Y(\omega)$ in the form

$$Y(\omega) = \sum_j A_j/(\omega-\omega_j). \tag{2.9}$$

The impulse response is then simply

$$K(\tau) = i\sum_j A_j e^{i\omega_j\tau}, \quad \tau > 0. \tag{2.10}$$

(When multiple roots occur, a slightly more complicated form is obtained.) This analysis is sometimes carried out using the Laplace transform, with a variable $p = i\omega$. The mathematics involved is the same; one is merely looking at the plane $z = \omega + iy$ from a different direction.

Nonlinear filters have been classified and discussed by Zadeh (1953) and others. The simplest type is a filter whose output $s_o(t)$ is some monotone function of its input: $s_o(t) = F[s_i(t)]$, where $y = F(x)$ is nondecreasing or nonincreasing. The variety of possible nonlinear filters is boundless, and no single method is available for analyzing them all.

3. NARROWBAND SIGNALS

The signals received in radar and in most communication systems consist of a high-frequency carrier modulated in amplitude or phase by functions of time that vary much more slowly than the cycles of the carrier.

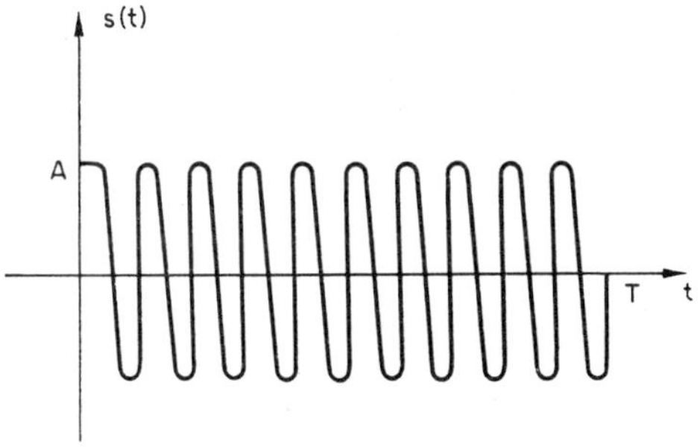

FIG. I.5. A narrowband pulse.

A radar pulse, for instance, usually contains a large number of cycles of the radiofrequency carrier; it looks somewhat like the signal in Fig. I.5, for which $s(t)$ can be written as

$$\begin{aligned} s(t) &= A \cos \Omega t, \quad 0 < t < T, \\ &= 0, \quad t < 0, \quad t > T, \quad \Omega T \gg 1. \end{aligned} \tag{3.1}$$

For a typical pulse the carrier frequency Ω may be $2\pi \cdot 10^9$ rad/sec (a 1000-MHz carrier), and T may be 1 μsec $= 10^{-6}$ sec. This kind of signal is said to be *amplitude modulated.* The outputs of certain broadcasting transmitters are also amplitude modulated and can be described by the expression

$$s(t) = A[1+m(t)] \cos \Omega t. \tag{3.2}$$

Here the function $m(t)$, which changes only slightly over a period $2\pi/\Omega$ of the carrier $\cos \Omega t$, represents the voices and music being transmitted. If care is taken to prevent the factor $1+m(t)$ from becoming negative, the signal in eq. (3.2) looks like a sinusoid with an irregularly fluctuating amplitude.

The output of a transmitter modulated in frequency can be written in the form

$$s(t) = A \cos \left[\Omega t + \int_0^t \psi(s)\, ds \right]. \tag{3.3}$$

The instantaneous frequency of this signal is $\Omega + \psi(t)$, and the slowly varying function $\psi(t)$ carries the information being broadcasted. Such a wave has a constant amplitude, but the times at which its value equals 0 shift about with the modulation.

A high-frequency carrier with the most general kind of modulation can be represented by the equation

$$s(t) = M(t) \cos [\Omega t + \phi(t)]. \tag{3.4}$$

The function $M(t)$ we shall call the *amplitude modulation*, the function $\phi(t)$ the *phase modulation;* the derivative $d\phi/dt$ is the *frequency modulation* of the signal. If the amplitude modulation $M(t)$ has the form of a pulse, the signal $s(t)$ is transitory; the broadcasting signals in eqs. (3.2) and (3.3) are of the kind we called "permanent". The bibliography includes some books on the theory of modulation.

By expanding the cosine in eq. (3.4) we obtain

$$\begin{aligned} s(t) &= M(t)[\cos \phi(t) \cos \Omega t - \sin \phi(t) \sin \Omega t] \\ &= X(t) \cos \Omega t - Y(t) \sin \Omega t \end{aligned} \tag{3.5}$$

with

$$X(t) = M(t) \cos \phi(t), \quad Y(t) = M(t) \sin \phi(t). \tag{3.6}$$

We call these functions $X(t)$ and $Y(t)$ the "quadrature components" of the signal. They too change only slightly during a cycle of the carrier $\cos \Omega t$. The function $X(t)$ can be obtained by multiplying the signal $s(t)$ with a signal $\cos \Omega t$ and filtering off the components of the product with carrier frequency 2Ω:

$$\begin{aligned} s(t) \cos \Omega t &= \tfrac{1}{2} X(t)(1 + \cos 2\Omega t) - \tfrac{1}{2} Y(t) \sin 2\Omega t \\ &\rightarrow \tfrac{1}{2} X(t). \end{aligned}$$

A device that accomplishes this is called a "mixer" or a "homodyne detector". It is said to "mix" or "beat together" the signals $s(t)$ and $\cos \Omega t$. The other quadrature component $Y(t)$ can be obtained by mixing $s(t)$ with the signal $\sin \Omega t$.

By combining these quadrature components in a complex number we obtain a convenient representation of a modulated signal in terms of its "complex envelope",

$$F(t) = X(t)+iY(t) = M(t)\, e^{i\phi(t)}, \tag{3.7}$$

namely

$$s(t) = \text{Rl}\, F(t)\, e^{i\Omega t}, \tag{3.8}$$

where "Rl" stands for the real part of the complex number following it. The complex function $F(t)$ can be pictured as a vector at the origin of the XY-plane. The end of the vector moves about in the plane, and all the while the plane itself rotates with an angular velocity Ω. The signal $s(t)$ is the projection of this rotating vector on a fixed line. Thus the complex envelope of a modulated signal is a natural generalization of the vector representation of alternating currents and voltages. When the motion of the vector $F(t)$ with respect to the rotating plane is much slower than the rate of rotation, the signal $s(t)$ is quasiharmonic.

If the signal is transitory, its complex envelope has a Fourier transform

$$f(\omega) = \int_{-\infty}^{\infty} F(t)\, e^{-i\omega t}\, dt, \tag{3.9}$$

in terms of which the spectrum $S(\omega)$ of the signal is

$$\begin{aligned} S(\omega) &= \tfrac{1}{2} \int_{-\infty}^{\infty} [F(t)e^{i\Omega t}+F^*(t)e^{-i\Omega t}]e^{-i\omega t}\, dt \\ &= \tfrac{1}{2}[f(\omega-\Omega)+f^*(-\omega-\Omega)]. \end{aligned} \tag{3.10}$$

Because the quadrature components of $F(t)$ vary much more slowly than the carrier $\cos \Omega t$, the width in frequency of the modulus $|f(\omega)|$ of its Fourier transform will be much smaller than Ω. The modulus $|S(\omega)|$ of the spectrum of the signal will then exhibit two narrow peaks, one near the frequency Ω, the other near $-\Omega$. Because of this structure $s(t)$ is called a "narrowband" signal.

The spectrum in eq. (3.10) satisfies the condition $S(-\omega) = S^*(\omega)$ imposed by the reality of the signal $s(t)$. The Fourier transform $f(\omega)$ of the complex envelope satisfies a similar condition if $F(t)$ is real and the signal is purely amplitude modulated. Only then will the modulus $|f(\omega)|$ be an even function and the peaks of $|S(\omega)|$ be symmetrical about the carrier frequency Ω. Indeed, the carrier frequency is quite arbitrary. Shifting it by an amount k simply introduces a factor e^{-ikt} into the complex envelope,

$$F(t)\, e^{i\Omega t} = [F(t)e^{-ikt}]\, e^{i(\Omega+k)t},$$

without changing the signal $s(t)$. A proper choice of the carrier frequency Ω sometimes simplifies a calculation.

A transitory signal $s(t)$ can be written as the sum of a positive-frequency part $s_+(t)$ and a negative-frequency part $s_-(t)$. These are defined by

$$\begin{aligned} s_+(t) &= \int_0^\infty S(\omega)\, e^{i\omega t}\, d\omega/2\pi, \\ s_-(t) = s_+^*(t) &= \int_{-\infty}^0 S(\omega)\, e^{i\omega t}\, d\omega/2\pi. \end{aligned} \tag{3.11}$$

If as for a narrowband signal the function $f(\omega - \Omega)$ in eq. (3.10) can be neglected when ω is negative, the positive-frequency part of the signal is given in terms of the complex envelope by

$$s_+(t) = \tfrac{1}{2} F(t)\, e^{i\Omega t}. \tag{3.12}$$

This so-called "analytical signal" $s_+(t)$ was introduced by Gabor (1946). It is more general than the complex envelope, for it can be defined for any signal that possesses a spectrum. In terms of the signal $s(t)$ itself it is given by the integral

$$s_+(t) = \frac{1}{2\pi i} \int_{-\infty}^{\infty} \frac{s(z)\, dz}{t-z}, \tag{3.13}$$

in which z has an infinitesimal negative imaginary part. The real and imaginary parts of the analytical signal are related by the Hilbert transform, for which we refer the reader to McDonald and Brachman (1956) and Guillemin (1963, ch. 18). The definitions in eqs. (3.11) and (3.13) are of small practical value, however, and the analytical signal is useful mainly when the signal $s(t)$ is quasiharmonic, whereupon the complex envelope serves as well.

A filter whose output is a function of the amplitude modulation of a narrowband signal applied to its input is known as a *rectifier*. It must be nonlinear, for a linear filter could never remove the oscillations of the carrier without destroying the envelope as well. A typical rectifier whose output is related directly to the amplitude modulation of its input is the quadratic rectifier. The action of this rectifier is to square its input, yielding by eq. (3.5)

$$\begin{aligned} [s(t)]^2 &= \tfrac{1}{2}\{[X(t)]^2 + [Y(t)]^2\} \\ &\quad + \tfrac{1}{2}\{[X(t)]^2 - [Y(t)]^2\} \cos 2\Omega t - X(t)\, Y(t) \sin 2\Omega t, \end{aligned} \tag{3.14}$$

after which a low-pass filter removes the terms with frequencies in the vicinity of 2Ω, so that the final output is proportional to $|F(t)|^2 = [M(t)]^2 = [X(t)]^2 + [Y(t)]^2$. Rectifiers having other than a quadratic characteristic can be considered to produce some other monotone function of the absolute value $|F(t)| = M(t)$; thus a *linear* rectifier yields $M(t)$ itself.

A device to produce an output proportional to the instantaneous frequency deviation $\phi'(t)$ of the input is known as a *discriminator*; its output can be taken as proportional to $d\,\mathrm{Im}\,[\ln F(t)]/dt$, where $F(t)$ is the complex envelope of the input. Of course, any given discriminator or rectifier circuit must be analyzed to determine how nearly accurate these descriptions of its action are.

If we integrate eq. (3.14) over $-\infty < t < \infty$ and recognize that for quasiharmonic signals the integrals of the terms proportional to $\cos 2\Omega t$ and $\sin 2\Omega t$ will be much smaller than the others, we get in place of eq. (1.1)

$$E = \tfrac{1}{2}\int_{-\infty}^{\infty} |F(t)|^2\, dt = \int_{-\infty}^{\infty} |f(\omega)|^2/4\pi \tag{3.15}$$

for what we have called the energy of the signal.

4. NARROWBAND FILTERS

Quasiharmonic signals are often transformed by means of filters that attenuate components of all frequencies except those in the neighborhood of the input carrier frequency. The analysis of these pass filters illustrates the simplification brought about by the concept of quasiharmonicity. We deal here with linear narrowband pass filters that least attenuate components whose frequencies lie in a range of width W about some high frequency Ω, with W much smaller than Ω. It is convenient to write the transfer function $Y(\omega)$ of such a filter in the form

$$Y(\omega) = y(\omega-\Omega)+y^*(-\omega-\Omega), \tag{4.1}$$

where the complex function $y(\omega)$ differs significantly from zero only over a narrow range of frequencies about $\omega = 0$. Equation (4.1) satisfies the condition of symmetry $Y(-\omega) = Y^*(\omega)$, which is a consequence of the reality of the impulse response $K(\tau)$. If a linear narrowband pass filter consists of lumped circuit elements, the poles of its transfer function $Y(\omega)$ lie in the neighborhood of $\omega = +\Omega$ and $\omega = -\Omega$. We can then make the decomposition of eq. (4.1) from the partial-fraction expansion, eq. (2.9), by taking the terms with poles near $\omega = +\Omega$ into $y(\omega-\Omega)$, leaving the remainder for the term $y^*(-\omega-\Omega)$.

Using eqs. (2.3) and (4.1) we can write the impulse response $K(\tau)$ of the narrowband filter as

$$\begin{aligned} K(\tau) &= \int_{-\infty}^{\infty} [y(\omega-\Omega)+y^*(-\omega-\Omega)]e^{i\omega\tau}\, d\omega/2\pi \\ &= \int_{-\infty}^{\infty} y(\omega)e^{i(\omega+\Omega)\tau}\, d\omega/2\pi + \int_{-\infty}^{\infty} y^*(\omega)e^{-i(\omega+\Omega)\tau}\, d\omega/2\pi = 2\,\mathrm{Rl}\, k(\tau)e^{i\Omega\tau}, \end{aligned} \tag{4.2}$$

where

$$k(\tau) = \int_{-\infty}^{\infty} y(\omega) e^{i\omega\tau} \, d\omega / 2\pi. \tag{4.3}$$

If $y(\omega)$ is significant only over a range of frequencies of width W, the function $k(\tau)$ changes appreciably in a range of values of τ of the order of $1/W$. By analogy with the concept of the envelope of a narrowband signal, we can consider $k(\tau)$ as one-half the complex envelope of the impulse response $K(\tau)$ of the narrowband filter. When such a filter is excited by a sharp impulse, it "rings", and its output oscillates with frequency Ω; this output decays with time in a manner described by the envelope $2k(\tau)$.

We shall now show that an equation like eq. (2.1) describes how the envelope function $k(\tau)$ transforms the complex envelope of the input signal to produce that of the output signal. Let the input and output signals of the narrowband filter be, respectively,

$$s_i(t) = \text{Rl } F_i(t) e^{i\Omega t}, \quad s_o(t) = \text{Rl } F_o(t) e^{i\Omega t}; \tag{4.4}$$

these are connected by eq. (2.1). Substituting from eqs. (4.4) and (4.2) we get

$$\begin{aligned} s_o(t) &= \tfrac{1}{2} \int_0^{\infty} K(\tau) \, F_i(t-\tau) \, e^{i\Omega(t-\tau)} \, d\tau + \text{c.c.} \\ &= \tfrac{1}{2} \, e^{i\Omega t} \int_0^{\infty} k(\tau) \, F_i(t-\tau) \, d\tau + \text{c.c.} \\ &\quad + \tfrac{1}{2} \, e^{i\Omega t} \int_0^{\infty} k^*(\tau) \, F_i(t-\tau) e^{-2i\Omega\tau} \, d\tau + \text{c.c.}, \end{aligned}$$

where "c.c." stands for the complex conjugate of the term preceding it. In the narrowband approximation we can neglect the second pair of terms, for their integrands vary so much more rapidly than those of the first pair that their values are relatively small. Comparing the remaining terms with eq. (4.4) we see that we can write

$$F_o(t) \doteq \int_0^{\infty} k(\tau) \, F_i(t-\tau) \, d\tau. \tag{4.5}$$

Hence we can find the complex envelope of the output signal in terms of that of the input signal by means of the simpler response function $k(\tau)$, which does not contain the oscillations of the impulse response $K(\tau)$. We shall call $k(\tau)$, defined by eqs. (4.2) or (4.3), the *complex impulse response* of the narrowband filter.

This representation of the output of a narrowband filter whose input is a quasiharmonic signal can be derived in another way. If the spectra of input and output are $S_i(\omega)$ and $S_o(\omega)$, respectively,

$$S_o(\omega) = Y(\omega)\, S_i(\omega),$$

and if we write the spectra as in eq. (3.10) and use eq. (4.1) for $Y(\omega)$, we find

$$\begin{aligned}
&\tfrac{1}{2}[f_o(\omega-\Omega)+f_o^*(-\omega-\Omega)] \\
&= [y(\omega-\Omega)+y^*(-\omega-\Omega)]\,[\tfrac{1}{2}f_i(\omega-\Omega)+\tfrac{1}{2}f_i^*(-\omega-\Omega)] \\
&= \tfrac{1}{2}y(\omega-\Omega)\, f_i(\omega-\Omega)+\tfrac{1}{2}y^*(-\omega-\Omega) f_i^*(-\omega-\Omega) \\
&\quad +\tfrac{1}{2}y^*(-\omega-\Omega)\, f_i(\omega-\Omega)+\tfrac{1}{2}y(\omega-\Omega)\, f_i^*(-\omega-\Omega).
\end{aligned}$$

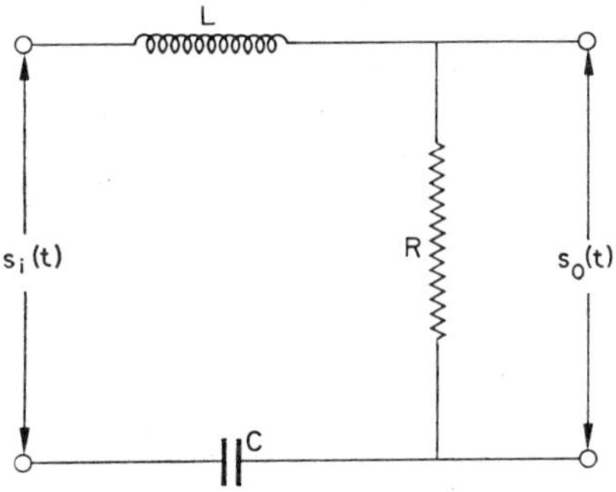

FIG. I.6. A simply resonant circuit.

With narrowband signals and filters the last two terms are much smaller than the first two, and we can write approximately

$$f_o(\omega-\Omega) \cong y(\omega-\Omega)\, f_i(\omega-\Omega) \quad \text{or} \quad f_o(\omega) \cong y(\omega)\, f_i(\omega),$$

from which eq. (4.5) follows by the convolution theorem (Appendix A, eqs. (A.7), (A.8)). By comparing the terms we dropped with those we retained, we see that the relative error we committed is of the order of magnitude of $|y(2\Omega)|/|y(0)|$ or $|f_i(2\Omega)|/|f_i(0)|$, whichever is the greater.

Let us illustrate these results for a filter consisting of a simply resonant circuit (Fig. I.6). If the input and output are measured across the terminals shown, the transfer function is

$$Y(\omega) = R\left[R+i\left(\omega L-\frac{1}{\omega C}\right)\right]^{-1} = \frac{2i\mu\omega}{\omega_0^2+2i\mu\omega-\omega^2}, \tag{4.6}$$

$$\mu = R/2L, \quad \omega_0^2 = 1/LC.$$

The poles of $Y(\omega)$ are at $\omega = i\mu+\nu$ and $\omega = i\mu-\nu$, $\nu^2 = \omega_0^2-\mu^2$. For a narrowband, or "high-Q", filter, $\mu \ll \omega_0$; and we can take the pass frequency as $\Omega = \nu$, which is close to the resonant frequency ω_0. Then it is easy to show that $y(\omega)$ satisfies eq. (4.1) when it is defined by

$$y(\omega) = \frac{\mu(\mu - i\nu)}{\nu(\omega - i\mu)} \cong (1 + i\omega/\mu)^{-1}. \tag{4.7}$$

By eq. (4.3) the complex impulse response has the simple form

$$\begin{aligned} k(\tau) &= \frac{\mu}{\nu}(\nu + i\mu)e^{-\mu\tau} \cong \mu e^{-\mu\tau}, \quad \tau > 0, \\ k(\tau) &= 0, \quad \tau < 0. \end{aligned} \tag{4.8}$$

For an input consisting of a carrier of frequency near Ω or ω_0, with a slowly varying modulation, it is much easier to calculate the modulation of the output by means of eqs. (4.8) and (4.5) than to use the usual methods embodied in formulas like eq. (4.1), for which $K(\tau)$ is a somewhat more complicated function.

5. THE UNCERTAINTY RELATION

In this section we shall present definitions for the duration and the bandwidth of a quasiharmonic signal and discuss the relations between them that are common to nearly all such signals. It is to be expected from dimensional considerations that among all signals of a given type, those with larger bandwidths have proportionally smaller time durations, so that the product of these measures is a constant. We shall see how this bandwidth-duration product depends on the form of the signals themselves.

Let the complex envelope of the signal $s(t)$ be $F(t)$, defined as in Section 3. If the Fourier transform of the envelope $F(t)$ is $f(\omega)$, we can define the mean frequency deviation $\bar{\omega}$ and the mean-square frequency deviation $\overline{\omega^2}$ by the formulas

$$\bar{\omega} = \int \omega\,|f(\omega)|^2\,d\omega \Big/ \int |f(\omega)|^2\,d\omega, \tag{5.1}$$

$$\overline{\omega^2} = \int \omega^2 |f(\omega)|^2\,d\omega \Big/ \int |f(\omega)|^2\,d\omega. \tag{5.2}$$

(The limits of all integrals in this section are $-\infty$ and $+\infty$, and the integrands are assumed to vanish sufficiently rapidly at these limits for the integrals to exist.) The root-mean-square (r.m.s.) frequency deviation or signal bandwidth $\Delta\omega$ is then defined by the equation

$$\Delta\omega^2 = \overline{\omega^2} - \bar{\omega}^2 = \overline{(\omega - \bar{\omega})^2}. \tag{5.3}$$

Using the convolution theorem for Fourier transforms, or applying the analytical methods of Appendix A, we can write the above definitions as

$$\bar{\omega} = -i \int F^*(t)F'(t)\,dt \Big/ \int |F(t)|^2\,dt, \tag{5.1a}$$

$$\overline{\omega^2} = \int |F'(t)|^2\,dt \Big/ \int |F(t)|^2\,dt, \tag{5.2a}$$

the prime denoting differentiation with respect to the argument of a function. By increasing the defined carrier frequency by $\bar{\omega}$, replacing $F(t)$ by $F(t)e^{-i\bar{\omega}t}$, we can produce a new complex envelope with zero mean frequency deviation; it is often convenient to do so.

Analogously we can define the mean and mean-square signal times by

$$\bar{t} = \int t\,|F(t)|^2\,dt \Big/ \int |F(t)|^2\,dt = i \int f^*(\omega)f'(\omega)\,d\omega \Big/ \int |f(\omega)|^2\,d\omega, \tag{5.4}$$

$$\overline{t^2} = \int t^2\,|F(t)|^2\,dt \Big/ \int |F(t)|^2\,dt = \int |f'(\omega)|^2\,d\omega \Big/ \int |f(\omega)|^2\,d\omega, \tag{5.5}$$

and the r.m.s. duration Δt of the signal is given by

$$\Delta t^2 = \overline{t^2} - \bar{t}^2 = \overline{(t-\bar{t})^2}. \tag{5.6}$$

We can make $\bar{t} = 0$ by properly picking the origin of the time scale.

Another useful quantity for describing the signal is $\overline{\omega t}$, defined by the equation

$$\begin{aligned} \overline{\omega t} &= -i/2 - i \int tF^*(t)\,F'(t)\,dt \Big/ \int |F(t)|^2\,dt \\ &= i/2 + i \int \omega f^*(\omega) f'(\omega)\,d\omega \Big/ \int |f(\omega)|^2\,d\omega. \end{aligned} \tag{5.7}$$

By taking the complex conjugate of the first part of this equation and integrating by parts, using the fact that $F(t)$ vanishes for $t = \pm\infty$, one can show that $\overline{\omega t}$ is real. We shall see that the quantity $(\overline{\omega t} - \bar{\omega}\bar{t})$ measures the amount of frequency modulation of the signal.

A clearer picture of the meaning of these quantities can be gained by introducing the representation, eq. (3.7), of $F(t)$ through its amplitude and phase: $F(t) = M(t)e^{i\phi(t)}$, $M(t) = |F(t)|$. If for simplicity we choose the origins of time and frequency so that $\bar{t} = 0$, $\bar{\omega} = 0$, and if we pick the amplitude of the signal so that

$$2E = \int |F(t)|^2\,dt = \int |f(\omega)|^2\,d\omega/2\pi = 1,$$

we get

$$\overline{t^2} = \int t^2[M(t)]^2\,dt, \tag{5.8}$$

$$\overline{\omega t} = \int t\phi'(t)\,[M(t)]^2\,dt, \tag{5.9}$$

$$\overline{\omega^2} = \int [M'(t)]^2\,dt + \int [\phi'(t)]^2\,[M(t)]^2\,dt. \tag{5.10}$$

Here we see how $\overline{\omega t}$ measures the amount of frequency modulation in the signal pulse; it is roughly the change in signal phase in a time of the order of the r.m.s. duration Δt, provided the carrier frequency Ω has been picked so as to remove any linear term $\overline{\omega t}$ in the phase; and it vanishes for a purely amplitude-modulated signal. The squared bandwidth, $\overline{\omega^2}$ here, is seen to be made up of a contribution from the changing of the amplitude modulation of the pulse (the first term of eq. (5.10)) and a part that is in effect the mean-square frequency modulation (the second term of eq. (5.10)).

Using Schwarz's inequality† we get

$$\left|\int tF^*(t)\,F'(t)\,dt\right|^2 \leqslant \int t^2\,|F(t)|^2\,dt \cdot \int |F'(t)|^2\,dt. \tag{5.11}$$

Substituting from eqs. (5.2), (5.5), and (5.7), and using the fact that $\overline{\omega t}$ is real, we find $\overline{\omega t}^2 + \frac{1}{4} \leqslant \overline{\omega^2}\cdot\overline{t^2}$, or

$$\overline{\omega^2}\cdot\overline{t^2} - \overline{\omega t}^2 \geqslant \tfrac{1}{4}, \qquad \bar{\omega} = 0, \quad \bar{t} = 0. \tag{5.12}$$

This equation implies that $\Delta\omega\cdot\Delta t \geqslant \frac{1}{2}$, which is known as the "uncertainty relation", a term borrowed from quantum mechanics, where it was first exploited. It implies that if one tries to make a pulse signal very narrow in time by decreasing Δt, the result will be a proportional increase in the bandwidth $\Delta\omega$.

The equality sign in eq. (5.12) can be shown to hold for Gaussian signals, which may be frequency modulated. Their complex envelopes are of the form

$$F(t) = Ae^{-Ct^2/2}, \qquad \text{Rl } C > 0, \tag{5.13}$$

for which the frequency modulation is $\phi'(t) = -t \text{ Im } C$. For such a pulse $\bar{\omega} = 0, \bar{t} = 0$, and

$$\overline{t^2} = 1/(2 \text{ Rl } C), \quad \overline{\omega t} = -\frac{\text{Im } C}{2 \text{ Rl } C}, \quad \overline{\omega^2} = \frac{|C|^2}{2 \text{ Rl } C}. \tag{5.14}$$

For further discussion of uncertainty relations, see the articles by Gabor (1946) and Kay and Silverman (1957).

The significance of the more detailed form, eq. (5.12), of the uncertainty relation can be appreciated in the following way. If we plot the ellipse given by the equation

$$\overline{\omega^2}\,\tau^2 - 2\overline{\omega t}\,w\tau + \overline{t^2}w^2 = 1 \qquad (\bar{\omega} = 0, \ \bar{t} = 0), \tag{5.15}$$

† Schwarz's inequality will be frequently used. For discrete variables it reads $\left(\sum_n a_n b_n\right)^2 \leq \sum_n a_n^2 \sum_n b_n^2$. For continuous complex functions $f(t)$ and $g(t)$, it takes the form

$$\left|\int_a^b f(t)\,g(t)\,dt\right|^2 \leq \int_a^b |f(t)|^2\,dt \cdot \int_a^b |g(t)|^2\,dt.$$

Equality of the two sides of the former expression occurs when the a_n stand in the same ratios to each other as the b_n; in the latter expression, the two sides are equal when $f(t)$ and $g(t)$ are proportional. See R. Courant and D. Hilbert, *Methoden der mathematischen Physik*, vol. 1, p. 2, p. 40, Springer, Berlin (1931). English translation, vol. 1, p. 2, p. 49, Interscience, New York (1953).

we obtain a figure like that in Fig. I.7, which gives the dimensions and the intercepts of the ellipse. We may call this figure an "uncertainty ellipse"; its area is

$$A = \pi[\overline{\omega^2}\cdot\overline{t^2}-\overline{\omega t}^2]^{-\frac{1}{2}} \leqslant 2\pi. \tag{5.16}$$

The area takes its largest value of 2π for the Gaussian pulse of eq. (5.13); for other types of signal it is smaller than 2π. For the Gaussian pulse the effect of a change in the amount of frequency modulation is to rotate or shear the ellipse with respect to the τ- and w-axes without changing its area.

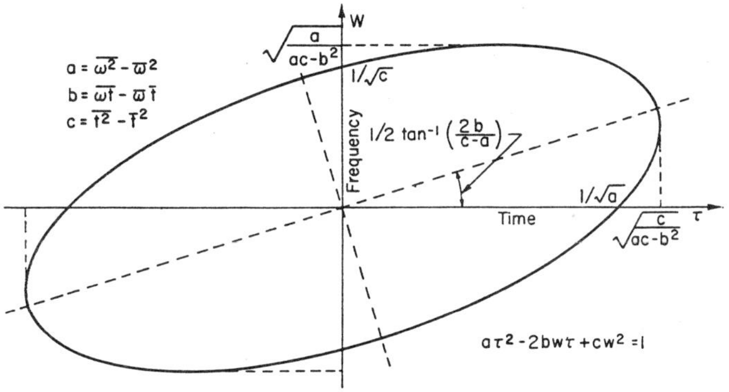

FIG. I.7. The uncertainty ellipse.

We shall now indicate that this is roughly true in general. If we substitute eqs. (5.8–10) into eq. (5.12) we get

$$\begin{aligned}\overline{\omega^2}\cdot\overline{t^2}-\overline{\omega t}^2 &= \int [M'(t)]^2\,dt\cdot\int t^2[M(t)]^2\,dt \\ &+\iint t_1\phi'(t_2)\,[t_1\phi'(t_2)-t_2\phi'(t_1)]\,[M(t_1)]^2\,[M(t_2)]^2\,dt_1\,dt_2 \geqslant \tfrac{1}{4}.\end{aligned} \tag{5.17}$$

One can show by Schwarz's inequality that the double integral involving $\phi'(t)$ is always positive, so that the effect of frequency modulation is always to decrease the area A of the uncertainty ellipse. However, if the phase modulation is of the form $\phi(t) = a+bt^2$ (the linear term is missing because we took $\overline{\omega} = 0$), the double integral vanishes. Hence the phase modulation must increase faster than the second power of the time, and the frequency modulation faster than the first power, if the area A of the uncertainty ellipse is to be altered. In most cases the change in area due to a frequency modulation is small, and the principal effect of frequency modulation is a rigid rotation of the ellipse. The uncertainty ellipse will arise later in our discussions of the resolution of signals and the measurement of signal parameters.

The temporal and spectral contents of the signal $s(t) = \mathrm{Rl}\, F(t)e^{i\Omega t}$ can b displayed simultaneously by means of the function

$$g(\tau, w) = \int_{-\infty}^{\infty} \psi^*(t;\ \tau, w)\, F(t)\, dt, \tag{5.18}$$

where

$$\psi(t;\tau, w) = (2\pi\,\sigma^2)^{-\frac{1}{4}} \exp\left[-\frac{(t-\tau)^2}{4\sigma^2} + iwt - \tfrac{1}{2}iw\tau\right] \tag{5.19}$$

is a Gaussian signal like that in eq. (5.13), but centered at $\bar{t} = \tau$ and $\bar{\omega} = w$ The relation in eq. (5.18) can be inverted,

$$F(t) = \int_{-\infty}^{\infty} \int_{-\infty}^{\infty} g(\tau, w)\, \psi(t;\tau, w)\, d\tau\, dw/2\pi. \tag{5.20}$$

This expression represents the complex envelope $F(t)$ as a superpositio of Gaussian signals of r.m.s. duration $\Delta t = \sigma$ and r.m.s. bandwidth $\Delta\omega =$ $1/2\sigma$. Gabor (1946) showed how a signal can be decomposed approxi mately into a discrete sum of such Gaussian "elementary signals". Hi method corresponds to replacing the double integral in eq. (5.20) by double summation,

$$F(t) \cong \sum_{m=-\infty}^{\infty} \sum_{n=-\infty}^{\infty} g_{mn}\psi(t;\, m\sigma, n/2\sigma). \tag{5.21}$$

The elementary signals are now separated in time by σ and in frequency b $1/2\,\sigma$. As the elementary signals $\psi(t;\, m\sigma, n/2\sigma)$ are not orthogonal, there i no simple way to calculate the coefficients g_{mn}.

The representation of $F(t)$ by eq. (5.20), on the other hand, is exact, an the expansion function $g(\tau, w)$ can be calculated from eq. (5.18). The func tion $g(\tau, w)$ is centered at $\tau = \bar{t}$, $w = \bar{\omega}$, where $\bar{t}$ is the mean epoch and $\bar{\omega}$ the mean frequency of the signal $F(t)$, as defined by eqs. (5.4) and (5.1)

$$\begin{aligned} \int_{-\infty}^{\infty} \int_{-\infty}^{\infty} \tau\, |g(\tau, w)|^2\, d\tau\, dw/2\pi &= \bar{t}, \\ \int_{-\infty}^{\infty} \int_{-\infty}^{\infty} w\, |g(\tau, w)|^2\, d\tau\, dw/2\pi &= \bar{\omega}, \end{aligned} \tag{5.22}$$

where we have chosen the same normalization for $F(t)$ as before, $2E = 1$ If for simplicity we again choose the origins of time and frequency so tha for the signal envelope $F(t)$, $\bar{t} = 0$, $\bar{\omega} = 0$, we obtain the following secon ıoments of the function $|g(\tau, w)|^2$,

$$\int_{-\infty}^{\infty}\int_{-\infty}^{\infty} \tau^2 |g(\tau, w)|^2 \, d\tau \, dw/2\pi = \overline{t^2}+\sigma^2,$$

$$\int_{-\infty}^{\infty}\int_{-\infty}^{\infty} \tau w |g(\tau, w)|^2 \, d\tau \, dw/2\pi = \overline{\omega t}, \qquad (5.23)$$

$$\int_{-\infty}^{\infty}\int_{-\infty}^{\infty} w^2 |g(\tau, w)|^2 \, d\tau \, dw/2\pi = \overline{\omega^2}+(4\sigma^2)^{-1}.$$

hus if $\overline{t^2} \gg \sigma^2$ and $\overline{\omega^2} \gg (4\sigma^2)^{-1}$, the function $|g(\tau, w)|^2$ for a purely mplitude-modulated signal occupies a part of the (τ, w)-plane whose xtent is roughly measured by the r.m.s. widths in time and frequency of ıe signal $s(t)$. If the signal contains frequency modulation, the contours of $(\tau, w)|^2$ lie aslant with respect to the time and frequency axes.

6. THE SYNTHESIS OF FILTERS†

The design of a filter to meet given specifications is known as "synthesis", ı contrast to "analysis", which determines the behavior of the filter once has been defined. The most common method of specifying a filter to be 'nthesized is to give the amplitude or the phase of its transfer function (ω); the two are not independent. The first step in synthesis, called the approximation problem", is to find a rational function $Y'(\omega)$ with poles the region $\mathrm{Im}\,\omega > 0$ that meets the specifications within prescribed toler-ıces. The second step, the "realization problem", is to find an arrange-ent of resistors, inductors, and capacitors to form as simple a network possible having the transfer function $Y'(\omega)$. Both of these steps have een treated extensively in the literature, and we need not go into them here. text on the subject is Guillemin's (1957).

In the detection systems to be derived in this work it is the impulse sponse $K(\tau)$ of the filter that is specified, rather than any part of the ansfer function $Y(\omega)$. The problem then is to find a rational function $'(\omega)$ whose transform

$$K'(\tau) = \int_{-\infty}^{\infty} Y'(\omega)\, e^{i\omega\tau} \, d\omega/2\pi \qquad (6.1)$$

pproximates $K(\tau)$ as closely as possible in some sense. The criterion may

† This section can be omitted on first reading.

be that some averaged square deviation E be a minimum:

$$E = \int_0^\infty w(\tau)\,|K'(\tau)-K(\tau)|^2\,d\tau, \tag{6.2}$$

where $w(\tau)$ is a suitable positive weighting function. Once $Y'(\omega)$ is deter mined, the filter can be realized by standard methods. It is not usuall sufficient to pick $Y'(\omega)$ as a good approximation to the transform $Y(\omega)$ o $K(\tau)$ by the methods used for this problem in the frequency domain, fo the resulting impulse response $K'(\tau)$ may be an undesirable approximatio to the given $K(\tau)$.

Since $Y'(\omega)$ for a filter composed of lumped circuit elements must be o the form of eq. (2.9), the resulting approximate impulse response will b

$$K'(\tau) = \sum_{k=1}^{N} A_k f_k(\tau),$$
$$f_k(\tau) = ie^{i\omega_k\tau}, \quad \operatorname{Im}\omega_k > 0, \tag{6.3}$$

with suitable modifications if there are multiple poles. The criterion tha the error E of eq. (6.2) be minimized leads to the set of linear simultaneou equations for the coefficients A_k:

$$\sum_{n=1}^{N} c_{mn}A_n = B_m, \quad 1 \leqslant m \leqslant N,$$
$$c_{mn} = \int_0^\infty w(t)\,f_m^*(t)\,f_n(t)\,dt, \tag{6.4}$$
$$B_m = \int_0^\infty w(t)\,f_m^*(t)\,K(t)\,dt.$$

The principal difficulty with this method is to choose the location of th poles ω_k to yield a good fit to $K(\tau)$ with a given number of terms (Kautz 1954). Little is known about how to accomplish this so that the resultin filter will be simple and economical to construct.

The method of Wiener and Lee (Lee, 1932) is a special form of this pro cedure in which the resulting approximate transfer function has a singl multiple pole at $\omega = ia$, a real. For a weighting function $w(\tau) = 1$ in eq (6.2), the desired impulse response $K(\tau)$ is expanded in a series of Laguerr functions:

$$K(\tau) \sim K'(\tau) = \sum_{k=0}^{N-1} b_k\lambda_k(2a\tau) = e^{-a\tau}\sum_{k=0}^{N-1} b_k L_k(2a\tau), \tag{6.5}$$

where $\lambda_k(x) = e^{-x/2}L_k(x)$ is a Laguerre function and $L_k(x)$ is a Laguerr polynomial. These polynomials are defined by the equation

$$L_k(x) = \frac{e^x}{k!}\frac{d^k}{dx^k}(x^k e^{-x}). \tag{6.6}$$

Since the Laguerre functions are orthonormal over the semi-infinite interval, the coefficients b_k are simply given by the formula

$$b_k = 2a \int_0^\infty K(\tau)\, \lambda_k(2a\tau)\, d\tau, \tag{6.7}$$

and the resulting minimum error is

$$E_{\min} = \int_0^\infty |K(\tau)|^2\, d\tau - \sum_{k=0}^{N-1} |b_k|^2. \tag{6.8}$$

The Fourier transform of the Laguerre function $\lambda_k(2at)$ is

$$\int_0^\infty \lambda_k(2at)\, e^{-i\omega t}\, dt = \frac{(i\omega - a)^k}{(i\omega + a)^{k+1}}, \tag{6.9}$$

so that $Y'(\omega)$ will be a rational function of ω as required. Tables of Laguerre functions and many useful formulas for them have been given in an article by Head and Wilson (1956).

In this method there is still one parameter, namely a, to be chosen before using eq. (6.7). It can be determined by computing $E_{\min}$ by eq. (6.8) for a number of values of a and picking the one that yields the smallest value. This is often laborious, however. Head and Wilson (1956) give a rough rule for choosing a, and since $E_{\min}$ does not vary rapidly with a, its choice is not critical. If N terms of the series are used, a is usually of the order of $2N/\Delta t$, where Δt is the duration of the function $K(\tau)$ to be approximated. In Fig. I.8 we show a rectangular pulse and the approximation to it found by taking $N = 11$ and $aT = 34$.

A second method of approximately synthesizing a filter for a prescribed impulse response $K(\tau)$ uses a broadband delay line that is tapped at uniformly spaced intervals. The ith tap, let us say, corresponds to a delay of τ_i seconds and has an impulse response $L(\tau)$. When a sharp impulse $\delta(t)$ is applied to the input, the signal from the ith tap will be $L(t-\tau_i)$. It is weighted by an amount $k_i = K(\tau_i)$ in an attenuator or broadband amplifier; there is one such device connected to each tap. Then the impulse response of the combination will be

$$K'(\tau) = \sum_{i=0}^{N} k_i L(\tau - \tau_i) = \sum_{i=0}^{N} K(\tau_i)\, L(\tau - \tau_i).$$

The width of the impulse response of each tap should be of the order of the difference $\tau_{i+1}-\tau_i$ in delay between two adjacent taps. By spacing the taps closely enough and making sure that they and the delay line have large enough bandwidths, the impulse response $K(\tau)$ can be approximated as accurately as desired.

The filters resulting from either of these methods may be cumbersome and expensive. Guillemin (1957) and Yengst (1964) devote a chapter to the synthesis of filters for prescribed impulse response and discuss methods that in many cases provide acceptable approximations in an economical manner.

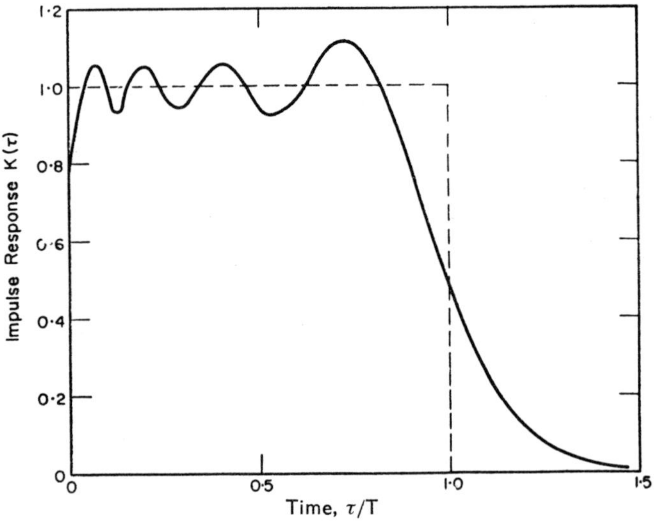

FIG. I.8. An approximation to a rectangular pulse.

To synthesize a narrowband pass filter, given the complex impulse response $k(\tau)$ of eq. (4.3), one first finds a rational function $y'(\omega)$ whose poles lie in the region Im $\omega > 0$ and whose transform $k'(\tau)$ is an adequate approximation to $k(\tau)$. Then the transfer function $Y'(\omega)$ of the filter is determined from eq. (4.1), where Ω is the specified pass frequency. The filter is constructed on the basis of this transfer function $Y'(\omega)$ by standard methods. Alternatively, tapped delay lines designed to operate in the spectral region of the carrier frequency Ω can be used in the manner just described.

PROBLEMS

1. Consider a simple integrating filter with impulse response

$$K(\tau) = 1, \quad 0 < \tau < T_1; \qquad K(\tau) = 0, \quad \tau < 0, \quad \tau > T_1.$$

Find and sketch the responses to these inputs: (a) a square pulse of height A and duration T greater than T_1; (b) an exponential signal $s(t) = Ae^{-t/D}$ starting at $t = 0$.

2. Let the impulse response of a filter be

$$K(\tau) = 1 - \frac{\tau}{T_1}, \qquad 0 < \tau < T_1,$$

and 0 elsewhere. Find and sketch the response to a square pulse of duration $T > T_1$.

3. Let $s_i(t)$ and $s_o(t)$ be the input and output signals of a stationary linear filter. Show that if the filter is stable and the input has finite energy, the output has finite energy. That is, given that

$$\int_{-\infty}^{\infty} |s_i(t)|^2 \, dt < \infty$$

show that

$$\int_{-\infty}^{\infty} |s_o(t)|^2 \, dt < \infty.$$

Hint. Use Parseval's theorem, Appendix, eq. (A.9).

4. Show that

$$\int_{-\infty}^{\infty} \int_{-\infty}^{\infty} k(s_1)\, k^*(s_2)\, F(s_2 - s_1) \exp[-i\omega(s_2 - s_1)]\, ds_1\, ds_2$$

$$= \int_{-\infty}^{\infty} |y(v-\omega)|^2 f(v)\, dv/2\pi,$$

where

$$k(s) = \int_{-\infty}^{\infty} y(u)\, e^{ius}\, du/2\pi, \quad F(s) = \int_{-\infty}^{\infty} f(v)\, e^{ivs}\, dv/2\pi.$$

5. For a narrowband signal with complex envelope

$$F(t) = te^{-(a-ib)t}, \quad 0 < t < \infty; \qquad F(t) = 0, \quad t < 0,$$

find $\bar{t}$, $\bar{\omega}$, $\overline{t^2}$, $\overline{\omega t}$, $\overline{\omega^2}$, $\Delta\omega$, Δt, $\overline{\omega t} - \bar{\omega}\bar{t}$ as defined in Section 5.

6. Derive eqs. (5.14), (5.22), (5.23).

7. The following expression can be considered as an approximate representation of a rectangular pulse with a finite rise time,

$$F(t) = (2\pi\sigma^2)^{-\frac{1}{2}} \int_{t-T}^{t+T} \exp(-u^2/2\sigma^2)\, du,$$

when $T \gg \sigma$. Work out approximately the value of the bandwidth-duration product $\Delta\omega \cdot \Delta t$ for $T \gg \sigma$.

8. Calculate the spectrum of the elementary signal $\psi(t; \tau, w)$ in eq. (5.19). Show that the spectrum $f(\omega)$ of the signal envelope $F(t)$ can be represented by a formula like eq. (5.18) in terms of the spectrum of $\psi(t; \tau, w)$.

9. Calculate the function $|g(\tau, w)|^2$ of eq. (5.18) for a signal with a linearly increasing frequency and the complex envelope $F(t) = \exp(ikt^2)$. Discuss the form of the result.

10. Work out the impulse response $K(\tau)$ of the simply resonant circuit in Fig. I.6 without making the narrowband approximation.

11. Let a rectangular narrowband signal like that of eq. (3.1) be impressed on the simply resonant circuit of Fig. I.6. Calculate the complex envelope of the output by means of eq. (4.5). Take the carrier frequency of the signal different from the resonant frequency of the filter by an amount that is arbitrary but of the order of the bandwidth of the filter.

BIBLIOGRAPHY (I)

Papers

1932 LEE, Y. W., "Synthesis of Electric Networks by Means of the Fourier Transform of Laguerre's Functions", *J. Math. Phys.* **11,** 83–113.

1946 GABOR, D., "Theory of Communication", J.I.E.E. **93** (III), 429–57.

1949 AIGRAIN, P. R. and WILLIAMS, E. M., "Design of Optimum Transient Response Amplifiers", *Proc. I.R.E.* **37,** 873–9 (Aug.).

BUNIMOVICH, V. I., "The Fluctuation Process as a Vibration with Random Amplitude and Phase", *J. Tech. Phys. U.S.S.R.* **19,** 1231–59 (Nov.).

1953 ZADEH, L. A., "Optimum Non-linear Filters", *J. Appl. Phys.* **24,** 396–404 (Apr.).

1954 BA HLI, F., "A General Method for Time-Domain Network Synthesis", *Trans. I.R.E.* **CT-1,** no. 3, 21–28 (Sept.).

CHAKRABARTY, N. B., "Synthesis of a Network for a Prescribed Time Function", *Ind. J. Phys.* **28,** 473–84 (Oct.).

KAUTZ, W. H., "Transient Synthesis in the Time Domain", *Trans. I.R.E.* **CT-1,** no. 3, 29–39 (Sept.).

1956 HEAD, J. W. and WILSON, W. P., "Laguerre Functions: Tables and Properties", *Proc. I.E.E.* **103C,** 428–40 (June).

McDONALD, J. R. and BRACHMAN, M. K., "Linear-system Integral Transform Relations", *Rev. Mod. Phys.* **28,** 393–422 (Oct.).

1957 KAY, I. and SILVERMAN, R. A., "On the Uncertainty Relation for Real Signals", *Information and Control* **1,** 64–75 (Sept.).

Books about Radar

1947–53 M.I.T. Radiation Laboratory Series, 28 vols., McGraw-Hill Book Co., New York, N.Y.

1949 Bell Telephone Laboratories Staff, *Radar: Systems and Components,* D. Van Nostrand, New York, N.Y.

1954 BOWEN, E. G., ed., *A Textbook of Radar,* Cambridge University Press, Cambridge, England.

1961 POVEJSIL, D. J., RAVEN, R. S. and WATERMAN, P., *Airborne Radar,* D. Van Nostrand Co., Inc., Princeton, N.J.

1962 SKOLNIK, M. I., *Introduction to Radar Systems,* McGraw-Hill Book Co., New York, N.Y.

1963 BOULDING, R. S. H., *Principles and Practice of Radar,* Geo. Newnes, Ltd., London, England (7th ed.).

1964 BARTON, D. K., *Radar System Analysis,* Prentice-Hall, Inc., Englewood Cliffs, N.J.

Other Books

1942 GARDNER, M. F. and BARNES, J. L., *Transients in Linear Systems,* John Wiley & Sons, Inc., New York, N.Y.

1951 SNEDDON, I. N., *Fourier Transforms*, McGraw-Hill Book Co., New York, N.Y.
TRANTER, C. J., *Integral Transforms in Mathematical Physics*, Methuen & Co., London, England.
1953 BLACK, H. S., *Modulation Theory*, D. Van Nostrand Co., Inc., Princeton, N.J.
GUILLEMIN, E. A., *Introductory Circuit Theory*, John Wiley & Sons, Inc., New York, N.Y.
1957 GUILLEMIN, E. A., *Synthesis of Passive Networks*, John Wiley & Sons, Inc., New York, N.Y.
1959 SCHWARTZ, M. S., *Information Transmission, Modulation, and Noise*, McGraw-Hill Book Co., New York, N.Y.
1963 GUILLEMIN, E. A., *Theory of Linear Physical Systems*, John Wiley & Sons, Inc., New York, N.Y.
1964 CARLIN, H. J. and GIORDANO, A. B., *Network Theory*, Prentice-Hall, Inc., Englewood Cliffs, N.J.
DOWNING, J. J., *Modulation Systems and Noise*, Prentice-Hall, Inc., Englewood Cliffs, N.J.
YENGST, W. C., *Procedures of Modern Network Synthesis*, Macmillan Co., New York, N.Y.
1966 SCHWARTZ, M., BENNETT, W. R. and STEIN, S., *Communication Systems and Techniques*, McGraw-Hill Book Co., New York, N.Y.

II

NOISE

1. STOCHASTIC PROCESSES AND THEIR DISTRIBUTIONS

(a) *The Probability Density Functions of a Process*

When radar and communication signals appear in a receiver, their detection is made uncertain by the simultaneous presence of random fluctuations, or "noise". If one were able to predict these variable noise voltages and currents exactly, they could be subtracted out and a clear decision about the presence or absence of the signal could be made. Such prediction is impossible, however, for the noise is created by the chaotic thermal motions of the ions and electrons of which the receiver, the antenna, and the surroundings are composed. The most one can do is to describe the noise fluctuations in terms of probability distributions and to use this statistical information to design a receiver that attains the maximum rate of successful detections in a long series of trials. In the present chapter we shall discuss the statistical description of noise; the next chapter will introduce various criteria of success and failure in statistical situations and indicate the reasoning to be followed in seeking optimum receiver designs.

When the voltage at a point in a receiver, say at the grid of the first amplifier tube, is recorded as a function of time, the record displays a most irregular appearance, and there seems to be no way of calculating or predicting its values. If the voltages at the corresponding points in a number of similar receivers under the same ambient conditions are simultaneously recorded, they differ in detail from receiver to receiver, but certain gross or average properties of the records are nearly the same. By studying a large number of such records and determining the relative frequencies with which values occur in various ranges, the behavior of the fluctuating voltages could be described statistically. Such descriptions are expressed in the language of the theory of probability, and it is by means of that theory that logical conclusions are drawn from them. In this chapter we shall apply probability to the analysis of noise fluctuations.

A function of time like the record of the fluctuating voltage just mentioned is called a *time series*, and a collection of time series like those measured in a large number of identical receivers under similar conditions is known as an *ensemble*. A random function whose values are described only by means of a set of probability distributions referred to such an ensemble often goes under the name of *stochastic process*. A particular member of the ensemble is called a *realization* of the stochastic process.

If measurements are taken continuously in time, one is dealing with a *continuous* stochastic process. Often data are measured only at a succession of points of time, yielding a *discrete* stochastic process, an example of which is the set of hourly or daily observations of the temperature at a weather station. We shall treat mainly the continuous processes, but many of the concepts we shall meet can be applied to discrete processes as well.

If a member of the ensemble of time series is chosen at random, the probability that its value x at an instant t lies between x' and $x'+dx$ is

$$\Pr\{x' < x < x'+dx\} = p_1(x', t)\,dx,$$

where $p_1(x, t)$ is the probability density function of the variable x. By this we mean, in terms of our example, that if the voltages are measured at the same point in a large number of identical receivers, the fraction of values lying in such an interval is $p_1(x, t)$ times the length dx of the interval, provided dx is small enough. Often the function $p_1(x, t)$ will be independent of the time t at which the measurements are made and will be written as $p_1(x)$. The probability density function (p.d.f.) $p_1(x, t)$ is a basic part of the statistical description of a stochastic process, but by itself it is insufficient, for it tells us nothing about how values of x measured at one time are related to those measured at other times.

The values of the time series $x(t)$ measured at a succession of times $t_1, t_2, \ldots, t_n$ will be labeled $x_1 = x(t_1), x_2 = x(t_2), \ldots, x_n = x(t_n)$. The joint probability density function $p_n(x_1, t_1; x_2, t_2; \ldots; x_n, t_n)$ is defined by the statement that the probability that the inequalities

$$x_1' < x_1 < x_1'+dx_1, \quad x_2' < x_2 < x_2'+dx_2, \quad \ldots, \quad x_n' < x_n < x_n'+dx_n$$

hold is equal to $p_n(x_1', t_1; x_2', t_2; \ldots; x_n', t_n)\,dx_1\,dx_2 \ldots dx_n$. A complete description of the continuous stochastic process $x(t)$ must be capable of providing the p.d.f.s p_n for all possible choices of the n times $t_1, t_2, \ldots, t_n$ and for all positive integers n. All these density functions are normalized so that

$$\int_{-\infty}^{\infty} \cdots \int_{-\infty}^{\infty} p_n(x_1, t_1; x_2, t_2; \ldots; x_n, t_n)\,dx_1\,dx_2 \ldots dx_n = 1 \qquad (1.1)$$

in accordance with the definition of probability. In addition, they must be consistent, so that p.d.f.s of lower orders can be obtained by integrating over the ranges of surplus variables. For instance,

$$p_3(x_1, t_1; x_2, t_2; x_3, t_3) = \int_{-\infty}^{\infty} p_4(x_1, t_1; x_2, t_2; x_3, t_3; x_4, t_4)\, dx_4. \tag{1.2}$$

Any n values or "samples" of the process $x(t)$ for which the expression

$$p_n(x_1, t_1; x_2, t_2; \ldots; x_n, t_n) = p_1(x_1, t_1)\, p_1(x_2, t_2) \ldots p_1(x_n, t_n) \tag{1.3}$$

holds are said to be *statistically independent*.†

The joint density functions p_n are operationally defined in terms of the relative frequencies of occurrence of various combinations of values of $x(t)$ at the n times in question, but it is obviously impossible to determine a complete set of p.d.f.s in this way. Instead, a theory of the process is constructed by applying the laws of physics to the situation and calling upon such disciplines as statistical mechanics and thermodynamics to provide hypothetical distributions. From this theory of the stochastic process, certain observable average quantities are calculated and compared with experimental results. When the situation is too complicated for such analysis, as in economics and meteorology, simple statistical models of the process are proposed; these furnish probability density functions containing a few unknown parameters, whose values are estimated from available data. From the density functions certain other quantities of interest are derived and, if possible, compared with the results of further observations. Fortunately, there is an extensive physical theory available to treat the electrical noise processes encountered in signal detection; some of this physical background will be presented in Section 5. First we must discuss some further concepts that will be useful in analyzing these stochastic processes.

(b) *Expected Values*

As long as a receiver is maintained at constant temperature and is connected to a motionless antenna with no signals impinging on it, the statistical description of the noise in the receiver will be independent of any origin of time. That is, the joint p.d.f.s p_n will depend only on the intervals t_2-t_1, t_3-t_1, $\ldots$, t_n-t_1 between measurements, and not on the times

† In eq. (1.3) the functions $p_1(x_1, t_1)$ and $p_1(x_2, t_2)$ may have different forms; the second may not necessarily be obtained from the first by replacing x_1 and t_1 by x_2 and t_2. In this book probability density functions are identified chiefly by their *arguments*. For this reason we write $p(x)\, dx = p(f)\, df$ when $f = f(x)$ is a function of x, although $p(f)$ and $p(x)$ have different forms. The alternative is a swarm of subscripts and superscripts about each density function, and that we prefer to avoid.

$t_1, t_2, \ldots, t_n$ themselves. Such stochastic processes are said to be *stationary*. Unless otherwise stated, we shall assume that the time series studied possess this property of time invariance or stationarity.

If a long record of a single realization of a stationary time series is examined, its general properties seem in most cases much the same in any one part as in any other. A large number of sections cut from a single member of the ensemble should, one believes, themselves constitute an ensemble with the same statistical properties. This attitude is reasonable if the variable measured is associated with a mechanical system like a gas or with an electrical one like a network, and if in the course of time this system passes through or near all states consistent with the external conditions imposed by the experimenter. In particular, averages performed over a long sample of a single realization of the process should equal those taken over all members of the ensemble at a single point of time. Stochastic processes with this property are said to be *ergodic*.

For example, the mean or expected value of a stationary time series is defined by the equation

$$\mathbf{E}(x) = \bar{x} = \int_{-\infty}^{\infty} x p_1(x)\, dx, \tag{1.4}$$

where $p_1(x)$ is the p.d.f. of a single sample. This mean value x is independent of time. On the other hand, one can define a time average $\bar{x}^t$ by the formula

$$\bar{x}^t = \lim_{T\to\infty} \frac{1}{T} \int_{T_1}^{T_1+T} x(t)\, dt. \tag{1.5}$$

Because of the stationarity, this time average is independent of the time T_1 at which averaging begins. If in addition the stochastic process $x(t)$ is ergodic, $\bar{x}^t = \bar{x}$. The same is true for expected values of other functions of x.

It is easy to think of stochastic processes that are not ergodic. A simple example is the ensemble of constant signals $x(t) \equiv a$, with the value of a falling anywhere between -1 and $+1$ with uniform probability. The ensemble average $\mathbf{E}[x(t)]$ vanishes, yet the time average $\bar{x}^t$ equals the value of a for whichever member of the ensemble happened to be chosen. Whenever the values of $x(t)$ or any of its parameters may become trapped in one of a number of different regions from which there is no escape, the process will not be ergodic. In this work, however, it will be assumed that all the fluctuation processes are ergodic. The validity of such an assumption rests on the success of the theory in which it is made, for although it conforms with our intuitions, explicit experimental verification is impossible. The assumption is essential in any problem in which statistical parameters are to be estimated from a single experimental realization of a process.

Various expected values characterizing stochastic processes will now be mentioned. One such, the mean, was defined above. The mean-square value is similarly given by

$$\mathbf{E}(x^2) = \overline{x^2} = \int_{-\infty}^{\infty} x^2 p_1(x)\, dx = \lim_{T\to\infty} \frac{1}{T} \int_{T_1}^{T_1+T} [x(t)]^2\, dt. \tag{1.6}$$

If $x(t)$ is a voltage across a resistance R, the average power dissipated there is $\overline{x^2}/R$. From this quantity we derive the mean-square deviation or *variance* of the random variable x,

$$\text{Var } x = \overline{x^2} - \bar{x}^2 = \overline{(x-\bar{x})^2}, \tag{1.7}$$

where the bar represents either an ensemble or a time average. The square-root of the variance, or the root-mean-square (r.m.s.) deviation, measures the order of magnitude of the fluctuations about the mean $\bar{x}$ at any chosen point of time.

Information about how the values of $x(t)$ at one time are related to those at other times is given by the *autocovariance*, defined by

$$\{x(t_1), x(t_2)\} = \overline{(x_1-\bar{x}_1)(x_2-\bar{x}_2)} = \phi(t_1, t_2)$$
$$= \int_{-\infty}^{\infty}\int_{-\infty}^{\infty} x_1 x_2\, p_2(x_1, t_1; x_2, t_2)\, dx_1\, dx_2 - \overline{x(t_1)}\cdot\overline{x(t_2)}. \tag{1.8}$$

For a stationary time series this autocovariance depends only on the time difference $\tau = t_2 - t_1$ and becomes the autocovariance function $\phi(\tau)$, which can also be defined by the time average

$$\phi(\tau) = \{x(t), x(t+\tau)\} = \lim_{T\to\infty} \frac{1}{T} \int_{T_1}^{T_1+T} x(t)\, x(t+\tau)\, dt - \bar{x}^2. \tag{1.9}$$

For this function the relations

$$\phi(0) = \text{Var } x, \quad \phi(-\tau) = \phi(\tau), \quad |\phi(\tau)| \leqslant \phi(0) \tag{1.10}$$

hold. In general the autocovariance function $\phi(\tau)$ approaches zero as τ increases, for values of $x(t)$ measured a long time apart tend to be statistically independent. Often $\phi(\tau)$ is a bell-shaped function with a single peak at $\tau = 0$, and the value of τ for which $\phi(\tau)$ takes on, say, half its peak value can be called the *correlation time* T_{cor} of the stochastic process. It roughly specifies the length of the interval beyond which values of the process are nearly independent random variables.

To be distinguished from the autocovariance function is the *correlation function* of a process. With stationarity and ergodicity it is defined by

$$\psi(t_1 - t_2) = \mathbf{E}[x(t_1)\, x(t_2)] = \int_{-\infty}^{\infty} \int_{-\infty}^{\infty} x_1 x_2 p_2(x_1, t_1; x_2, t_2)\, dx_1\, dx_2$$

$$= \lim_{T \to \infty} \frac{1}{T} \int_{T_1}^{T_1+T} x(t)\, x(t+\tau)\, dt. \tag{1.11}$$

It differs from the autocovariance function only by the square of the mean value, which is sometimes zero. The autocovariance function is the more significant, the correlation function the more directly measurable.

Given two ensembles of stationary time series $x_1(t)$ and $x_2(t)$, we can define their covariance function $\phi_{12}(\tau)$ by the equation

$$\phi_{12}(\tau) = \{x_1(t), x_2(t+\tau)\} = \lim_{T \to \infty} \frac{1}{T} \int_{T_1}^{T_1+T} x_1(t)\, x_2(t+\tau)\, dt - \bar{x}_1 \cdot \bar{x}_2. \tag{1.12}$$

This covariance indicates how the values of one time series are related to those of another. It is often useful in exploring the possibility of causal relations between two empirical time series.

(c) *The Measurement of Expected Values*

The definition of the mean value of a stationary process as a time average suggests measuring it by averaging or "integrating" the process in a low-pass filter. The simplest such filter is a resistor and a capacitor in series, with the process applied across both and a voltmeter connected across the capacitor. If the impulse response of the filter is $K(\tau)$, its output will be

$$y(t) = \int_0^{\infty} K(\tau)\, x(t-\tau)\, d\tau. \tag{1.13}$$

Since the expected value of a sum of random variables equals the sum of their expected values, the expected value of an integral such as this equals the integral of the expected value of the integrand, provided that the integral exists. Hence the mean value of the output of the integrating filter will be

$$\mathbf{E}[y(t)] = \int_0^{\infty} K(\tau)\, \mathbf{E}[x(t-\tau)]\, d\tau = \mathbf{E}(x) \int_0^{\infty} K(\tau)\, d\tau, \tag{1.14}$$

which is directly proportional to $\mathbf{E}(x)$.

The output of the filter will fluctuate about its mean value $\mathbf{E}[y(t)]$, but if the integration time of the filter is much longer than the correlation time T_{cor} of the process, the fluctuations will be small. Equivalently, the product $\Delta\omega \cdot T_{\text{cor}}$ must be much smaller than 1, where $\Delta\omega$ is the bandwidth of the integrating filter. It sometimes suffices to apply the process $x(t)$ directly to a very sluggish galvanometer and average the fluctuations of the meter by eye. If the mean-square value $\mathbf{E}(x^2)$ is desired, the process $x(t)$ can be squared by a rectifier before being fed to the integrating filter and the meter. In this way the average power of a noise process can be measured.

The correlation function of a stationary process is measured by a device known as a *correlator*, in which the input $x(t)$ is delayed by a time τ and multiplied by the undelayed input to form the product $x(t)x(t-\tau)$. This product is in turn applied to a low-pass integrating filter with impulse response $K(s)$, and the output of the filter,

$$y(t) = \int_0^\infty K(s)\, x(t-s)\, x(t-\tau-s)\, ds, \tag{1.15}$$

is fed to a meter. The expected value of this output is proportional to the correlation function $\psi(\tau)$,

$$\mathbf{E}[y(t)] = \int_0^\infty K(s)\, \mathbf{E}[x(t-s)\, x(t-\tau-s)]\, ds = \psi(\tau) \int_0^\infty K(s)\, ds. \tag{1.16}$$

The fluctuations of the meter about this expected value will again be small if the integration time of the filter is much longer than the correlation time of the process $x(t)$. By adjusting the delay τ to a number of values and reading the meter for each, the correlation function $\psi(\tau)$ can be plotted against τ. The autocovariance function $\phi(\tau)$ is obtained by subtracting the square $\bar{x}^2$ of the mean value.

The delays may be introduced by tapping a transmission line or an equivalent chain of filters; at audio frequencies the input may be recorded on a moving magnetic tape and read out again by an adjustable pickup head. Voltages $x_1 = x(t)$ and $x_2 = x(t-\tau)$ can be multiplied by passing their sum x_1+x_2 and their difference x_1-x_2 through separate quadratic rectifiers and subtracting the outputs. Correlators such as these have been used in encephalography to analyze the fluctuating waves of voltage in the brain.

2. THE SPECTRAL DENSITY

a) *Fourier Analysis of a Random Process*

In calculating the response of a linear system to a given input, it is often convenient to regard the input as the sum of a number of sinusoidal oscillations of the form $\cos(\omega_n t + \alpha_n)$ or $\exp i\omega_n t$. For periodic inputs one uses a Fourier series whose component frequencies are $\omega_n = 2\pi n/T$ rad/sec, where n is an integer and T is the period. In the first chapter we represented pulsed signals by means of the Fourier integral. Now we wish to do something similar for the fluctuating quantities $x(t)$ that we have called "time series", using a method developed by Rice (1944). Clearly such a representation will hold only in some average sense.

We consider a long section of a stationary time series stretching from $t = 0$ to $t = T$, and we imagine it periodically repeated. We can make a Fourier analysis of this realization of $x(t)$, writing it as

$$x(t) = \sum_{n=0}^{\infty} (a_n \cos \omega_n t + b_n \sin \omega_n t), \qquad \omega_n = 2\pi n/T, \tag{2.1}$$

or we can use the mathematically more convenient exponential form

$$x(t) = \sum_{n=-\infty}^{\infty} c_n \exp(i\omega_n t). \tag{2.2}$$

The complex coefficients c_n are given by the integrals

$$c_n = \frac{1}{T}\int_0^T x(t) \exp(-i\omega_n t)\, dt, \tag{2.3}$$

from which we can determine the a_n's and the b_n's,

$$\begin{aligned} c_n &= \tfrac{1}{2}(a_n - ib_n), \qquad n > 0, \\ &= \tfrac{1}{2}(a_{-n} + ib_{-n}), \qquad n < 0, \\ c_0 &= a_0. \end{aligned} \tag{2.4}$$

When as usual $x(t)$ is real, the coefficients for positive and negative indices are related by the equation $c_{-n} = c_n^*$.

If we took another member of the ensemble and computed the associated Fourier coefficients, we should obtain some other set of values of a_n and b_n; for these are random variables, whose values depend on the particular realization chosen and whose statistical distributions can be derived from the set of the p.d.f.s p_n for the stochastic process $x(t)$. In particular we car calculate their mean values and their variances.

The mean values of all the coefficients of the Fourier series are seen fron eq. (2.3) to vanish, except for $c_0 = a_0$, for which $\mathbf{E}(a_0) = \mathbf{E}[x(t)]$. Fo simplicity we may as well take the mean value $\mathbf{E}(x)$ equal to zero.

We now investigate how the coefficients a_n and b_n are related to eacl other by working out their covariances, which are most easily calculatec from the expected values of the products $c_n c_m^*$ and $c_n c_m$. For instance,

$$\begin{aligned}\mathbf{E}(c_n c_m^*) &= T^{-2} \int_0^T \int_0^T \mathbf{E}[x(t_1)\, x(t_2)] \exp(i\omega_m t_1 - i\omega_n t_2)\, dt_1\, dt_2 \\ &= T^{-2} \int_0^T \int_0^T \phi(t_1 - t_2) \exp(i\omega_m t_1 - i\omega_n t_2)\, dt_1\, dt_2.\end{aligned} \tag{2.5}$$

By a series of transformations given in Appendix C, we find for $n \neq n$

$$\begin{aligned}\mathbf{E}(c_n c_m^*) = \frac{4}{T} \int_0^T \phi(\tau) \cos\left[\frac{1}{2}(\omega_n + \omega_m)\tau\right] \cdot \\ \frac{\sin\left[\frac{1}{2}(\omega_n - \omega_m)(T - \tau)\right]}{(\omega_n - \omega_m)T} \exp\left[\frac{1}{2} i(\omega_m - \omega_n)T\right] d\tau,\end{aligned} \tag{2.6}$$

and for $m = n$,

$$\mathbf{E}(|c_n|^2) = \frac{2}{T} \int_0^T \phi(\tau) \left(1 - \frac{\tau}{T}\right) \cos \omega_n \tau\, d\tau. \tag{2.7}$$

We are interested in the behavior of these averages when the length T o the realization is very great, and it suffices to bound the one given in eq (2.6),

$$|\mathbf{E}(c_n c_m^*)| \leq \frac{4}{|\omega_m - \omega_n|\, T^2} \int_0^T |\phi(\tau)|\, d\tau. \tag{2.8}$$

If, as usual, $|\phi(\tau)|$ is integrable over the infinite range,

$$\lim_{T \to \infty} T\, |\mathbf{E}(c_n c_m^*)| = 0, \quad m \neq n. \tag{2.9}$$

In this and the following limits the frequencies ω_n and ω_m stay fixed as increases without bound. By replacing m by $-m$ and using $c_{-m}^* = c_m$, w find

$$\lim_{T \to \infty} T\, |\mathbf{E}(c_n c_m)| = 0, \quad m \neq -n. \tag{2.10}$$

ogether with eq. (2.4) these results imply

$$\lim_{T\to\infty} TE(a_n a_m) = \lim_{T\to\infty} TE(b_n b_m) = 0, \qquad n \neq m \tag{2.11}$$

nd for all n and m,

$$\lim_{T\to\infty} TE(a_n b_m) = 0. \tag{2.12}$$

From eq. (2.7), on the other hand, provided that

$$\int_0^\infty \tau\phi(\tau) \cos \omega_n\tau \, d\tau$$

s finite,

$$\lim_{T\to\infty} TE(|c_n|^2) = 2\int_0^\infty \phi(\tau) \cos \omega_n\tau \, d\tau = \int_{-\infty}^\infty \phi(\tau) \exp(-i\omega_n\tau) \, d\tau \tag{2.13}$$

nd

$$\lim_{T\to\infty} TE(a_n^2) = \lim_{T\to\infty} TE(b_n^2) = 2\int_{-\infty}^\infty \phi(\tau) \exp(-i\omega_n\tau) \, d\tau. \tag{2.14}$$

Taken together, these results indicate that when the length T of the rea-zation increases without bound, with the frequencies ω_n and ω_m kept fixed, he random variables $a_n T^{\frac{1}{2}}$ and $b_n T^{\frac{1}{2}}$ associated with those frequencies ecome uncorrelated, but they retain finite variances. The sine and cosine aves that by eq. (2.1) make up the random process $x(t)$ are in the limit f infinite T uncorrelated.

If we think of $x(t)$ in eq. (2.1) as the voltage across a resistor of 1 ohm, e power dissipated in the resistor by the spectral components of fre-uency ω_n is $\frac{1}{2}(a_n^2+b_n^2)$, and the average of this power over all members of e ensemble is, in the limit of large T,

$$\frac{1}{2}\,\overline{(a_n^2}+\overline{b_n^2)} \to \frac{2}{T}\int_{-\infty}^\infty \phi(\tau) \cos \omega_n\tau \, d\tau = [\Phi(\omega_n)+\Phi(-\omega_n)]\,\delta\omega/2\pi, \tag{2.15}$$

here $\delta\omega = 2\pi/T$ is the spacing between the frequencies ω_n.

Here we have defined a new function

$$\Phi(\omega) = \int_{-\infty}^\infty \phi(\tau) \cos \omega\tau \, d\tau = \int_{-\infty}^\infty \phi(\tau)e^{-i\omega\tau} \, d\tau, \tag{2.16}$$

hich is called the *power spectrum* or the *spectral density* of the stochastic rocess. By the Fourier inversion formula the autocovariance function is

$$\phi(\tau) = \int_{-\infty}^\infty \Phi(\omega)e^{i\omega\tau} \, d\omega/2\pi, \tag{2.17}$$

and in particular the variance is

$$\text{Var}\, x = \phi(0) = \int_{-\infty}^{\infty} \Phi(\omega)\, d\omega/2\pi. \tag{2.18}$$

If $\mathbf{E}[x(t)] = 0$, eqs. (2.15) and (2.18) express the total average power i the process $x(t)$ as the sum of the average powers in the spectral compc nents. Half the power at a given frequency is assigned to the positive fre quency, half to the negative frequency. This has been done to remov extraneous factors of 2 from the Fourier transforms of eqs. (2.16) an (2.17). Some writers assign all the power to the positive frequencies, an their formulas differ from ours by factors of 2.

When T is large enough, any frequency ω will be close to at least one c the frequencies ω_n, and on the basis of eqs. (2.13) and (2.3) we can asse that the spectral density $\Phi(\omega)$, defined by

$$\Phi(\omega) = \lim_{T \to \infty} \frac{1}{T} \mathbf{E} \left| \int_0^T x(t) e^{-i\omega t}\, dt \right|^2, \tag{2.19}$$

is—as in eq. (2.16)—equal to the Fourier transform of the autocovarianc function $\phi(\tau)$. This relationship is known as the Wiener–Khinchin theoren and it is of fundamental importance to the theory of stochastic processe More rigorous statements and proofs of the theorem are available in th literature (Doob, 1953).

A word about mathematical rigor is in order here. Since we have sai nothing about the integrability of the time series $x(t)$, we are not assure that any of the integrals in eq. (2.3) exist, nor even that the usual Rieman definition of an integral is applicable. There is also the question of th validity of certain limiting processes and exchanges of order of integratio that have been made. Since sharp discontinuities and infinities are neve observed in nature, we feel certain that our results are valid for the physic random processes of interest here. However, for a consistent, logical mathe matical theory such matters must be considered, and this is done in suc treatments of stochastic processes as are to be found in the books of Lév (1948), Doob (1953), and Blanc-Lapierre and Fortet (1953). By caref analysis one can determine the precise conditions under which the resul of this and the other sections are valid. We rely on physical intuition t justify the mathematical methods being used.

It was stated in the beginning that the spectral decomposition, eq. (2.1 of a stochastic process should be useful in determining how the process transformed by a linear filter. If we imagine long samples of the input $x($

and the output $y(t)$ periodically repeated, we can write them as

$$x(t) = \sum_{n=-\infty}^{\infty} c_n \exp(i\omega_n t), \quad y(t) = \sum_{n=-\infty}^{\infty} C_n \exp(i\omega_n t), \quad \omega_n = 2\pi n/T.$$

If the transfer function of the filter is $Y(\omega)$, the coefficients of these Fourier series are related by the formula

$$C_n = Y(\omega_n)c_n.$$

Hence $|C_n|^2 = |Y(\omega_n)|^2 |c_n|^2$, and since in the limit of large T the expected values of these squared coefficients are proportional to the spectral densities $\Phi_i(\omega_n)$ and $\Phi_o(\omega_n)$ of the input and output, respectively, we find

$$\Phi_o(\omega) = |Y(\omega)|^2 \Phi_i(\omega). \tag{2.20}$$

This equation must hold at all frequencies ω because the frequencies ω_n of the Fourier components become very close in the limit of large T. The spectral density of the output of a linear filter is, therefore, equal to the product of the spectral density of the input and the absolute square of the filter transfer function.

This formula can also be derived by using the relation between the spectral density and the autocovariance, eq. (2.17). From eq. (2.1) of Chapter I,

$$y(t) = \int_0^{\infty} K(s)x(t-s)\, ds,$$

where $K(s)$ is the impulse response of the filter. Letting $\phi_i(\tau)$ and $\phi_o(\tau)$ be the autocovariances of the input and the output, respectively, we find

$$\begin{aligned}\phi_o(\tau) = \mathbf{E}[y(t)y(t+\tau)] &= \int_0^{\infty}\int_0^{\infty} K(s_1)\, K(s_2)\mathbf{E}[x(t-s_1)x(t+\tau-s_2)]\, ds_1\, ds_2 \\ &= \int_0^{\infty}\int_0^{\infty}\int_{-\infty}^{\infty} K(s_1)K(s_2)\Phi(\omega) \exp[i\omega(s_1-s_2+\tau)]\, ds_1\, ds_2\, d\omega/2\pi \\ &= \int_{-\infty}^{\infty} Y(\omega)Y^*(\omega)\Phi(\omega)e^{i\omega\tau}\, d\omega/2\pi\end{aligned}$$

when we use the connection, eq. (I, 2.3), between the impulse response $K(\tau)$ and the transfer function $Y(\omega)$ of the filter. Eq. (2.20) follows immediately by a Fourier transformation.

(b) *Measuring the Spectral Density*

In eq. (2.19) the expected value **E** refers to an ensemble average, that is to an average over a large number of independent realizations of $x(t)$, each of length T much greater than T_{cor}. It might be thought that becaus the time series is ergodic, the relation in eq. (2.19) should hold without the symbol **E**, but this is untrue. Indeed, although one can show that for large T the random variable

$$F(\omega, T) = \frac{1}{T}\left|\int_0^T x(t)e^{-i\omega t}\,dt\right|^2$$

has a mean value $\mathbf{E}[F(\omega, T)]$ close to $\Phi(\omega)$, its variance is $[\Phi(\omega)]^2$ in the limit $T \to \infty$.† The probability density function of this variable does not narrow down about its mean value as T increases, and one cannot expect to obtain an accurate estimate of the spectral density $\Phi(\omega)$ by analyzing a single realization of a stochastic process in this way.

The spectral density is often used in the empirical study of time series, such as those in economics (prices, income, production) and oceanography (heights and lengths of ocean waves). Knowledge of the principal frequencies in such random processes is useful in devising causal explanations of the observed phenomena. What we have just said indicates that it will be difficult to determine the spectral density when only a single realization is at hand. The problems involved in empirical estimates of spectral densities are discussed at length by Grenander (1951), Wold (1954), Bartlett (1955), Grenander and Rosenblatt (1957), Blackman and Tukey (1958), Blackman (1965), and Kendall and Stuart (1966).

We shall not delve into these matters here, except to remark that one must give up the hope for an unbiased estimate of the spectrum at a single frequency ω and accept instead an average over a range of frequencies in the vicinity of ω. The estimates are mostly of the form

$$\begin{aligned} F_{\mathrm{av}}(\omega, T) &= \int_{-\infty}^{\infty} W(u)F(\omega-u, T)\,du \\ &= \frac{1}{T}\int_{-\infty}^{\infty} W(u)\left|\int_0^T x(t)e^{-i(\omega-u)t}\,dt\right|^2 du, \end{aligned} \tag{2.21}$$

or discrete counterparts obtained by replacing the integration by a summation over values of $x(t)$ measured at discrete times. Here $W(\omega)$ is a weighting function with a peak at $\omega = 0$ and a width of the order of W. When T is very large,

$$\mathbf{E}\,F_{\mathrm{av}}(\omega, T) \to \int_{-\infty}^{\infty} W(u)\Phi(\omega-u)\,du,$$

† This statement is strictly true only for the Gaussian processes to be defined in Section 4. For other processes it is approximate.

and Var $F_{av}(\omega, T)$ is of the order of $(WT)^{-1} |\Phi(\omega)|^2$. This estimate $F_{av}(\omega, T)$ is said to be "consistent" because values in the vicinity of the mean become more and more probable as the length T increases and becomes much greater than W^{-1}.

If $x(t)$ is a random voltage or current, its spectral density can be measured by means of a spectrum analyzer. In the simplest form of this instrument, the process $x(t)$ is fed through a narrowband pass filter whose pass frequency Ω is adjustable. The output $v(t)$ of this filter is a quasiharmonic function of time with a carrier frequency Ω even though the spectral density of the input $x(t)$ may be much broader than the transfer function of the filter. The output $v(t)$ is squared by a quadratic rectifier and applied to a low-pass integrating filter and a meter. The reading of the meter will be nearly proportional, on the average, to the spectral density $\Phi(\Omega)$ of the input at frequency Ω, as we shall now demonstrate.

The expected value $Z(\Omega)$ of the output of the integrating filter is, as in eq. (1.14), proportional to the expected value of its input,

$$Z(\Omega) = \tfrac{1}{2}B\mathrm{E}[v(t)]^2,$$

B a constant characteristic of the instrument. The input passband will be narrow enough, we assume, to reject d=c, and $\mathrm{E}[v(t)] = 0$. Hence,

$$Z(\Omega) = \tfrac{1}{2}B \operatorname{Var} v(t) = \tfrac{1}{2}B \int_{-\infty}^{\infty} \Phi_v(\omega)\, d\omega/2\pi,$$

where $\Phi_v(\omega)$ is the spectral density of the output of the pass filter. According to eq. (2.20), this spectral density is

$$\Phi_v(\omega) = \Phi(\omega)\,|Y(\omega)|^2,$$

where $Y(\omega)$, the transfer function of the input filter, can be written as in eq. (I, 4.1),

$$Y(\omega) = y(\omega-\Omega)+y^*(-\omega-\Omega),$$

in terms of the narrowband transfer function $y(\omega)$. When we form $|Y(\omega)|^2$, cross-products will be negligible because the passband is assumed to have a width $\Delta\omega$ much less than Ω. Thus we shall obtain for the expected value of the meter reading

$$\begin{aligned} Z(\Omega) &= \tfrac{1}{2}B \int_{-\infty}^{\infty} \Phi(\omega)\,[\,|y(\omega-\Omega)|^2+|y^*(-\omega-\Omega)|^2]\, d\omega/2\pi \\ &= B \int_{-\infty}^{\infty} |y(\omega-\Omega)|^2 \Phi(\omega)\, d\omega/2\pi, \end{aligned} \tag{2.22}$$

in which we have used $\Phi(\omega) = \Phi(-\omega)$. If the narrowband transfer function $y(\omega)$ is so narrow that over the range of frequencies about $\omega = 0$

where it is significant, $\Phi(\omega)$ is nearly constant, the mean integrated output $Z(\Omega)$ will be approximately

$$Z(\Omega) \cong B\Phi(\Omega) \int_{-\infty}^{\infty} |y(\omega)|^2 \, d\omega/2\pi.$$

In order for the meter indicator to fluctuate relatively little about the mean value $Z(\Omega)$, the integration time T_i of the low-pass filter after the rectifier must be much longer than the reciprocal of the bandwidth $\Delta\omega$ of the process $v(t)$, which bandwidth is the same as that of the narrowband input filter. An analysis leading to this conclusion has been presented by Davenport, Johnson, and Middleton (1952).

We see by comparing eqs. (2.21) and (2.22) that the spectrum analyzer provides an estimate of the spectral density similar to the mathematical one given as $F_{av}(\omega, T)$ in eq. (2.21). The transfer function $y(\omega)$ of the input filter corresponds to the weighting function $W(\omega)$, and the integration time T_i of the circuits following the rectifier corresponds to the length T of the sample analyzed. In order for the r.m.s. fluctuations of the meter to be reduced to a small fraction of the mean output, the bandwidth T_i^{-1} of the output circuits must be much smaller than that of the input narrowband pass filter, $\Delta\omega T_i \gg 1$.

The spectrum analyzer provides an operational definition of the spectral density in terms of the average response of a narrowband filter of arbitrary pass frequency to a stochastic process fed into it. One simply has to conceive of a limiting process in which the bandwidth of that filter vanishes. This operational viewpoint may clarify the more abstruse mathematical definition of the spectral density.

In a practical spectrum analyzer the pass frequency Ω of the narrowband filter must be tuneable over the region of frequencies in which the spectral density is to be measured. As in a superheterodyne receiver, the input can be multiplied in a mixer with a sinusoidal voltage generated by a local oscillator of variable frequency. The mixer selects from the product the components having frequencies equal to the difference—or the sum—of the frequencies of its two inputs, and these components are fed to a narrowband filter of fixed pass frequency. By tuning the local oscillator the frequency range of interest can be scanned. Other spectrum analyzers use a bank of parallel narrowband filters, each resonant at a different frequency. For audio inputs these filters may be vibrating reeds, the amplitudes of whose responses can be measured by the eye.

3. TWO VARIETIES OF NOISE

(a) *Random Impulses*

Measurement alone cannot establish the collection of probability density functions needed for a complete description of a stochastic process. The expected values, the first-order distribution, and the autocovariance function are usually the only statistical parameters of a process that are practically measurable, and even these can be determined only over limited ranges. As we mentioned earlier, one must have recourse to a model of the process for guidance in setting up a hypothetical class of probability distributions, whose parameters can then be evaluated from what measurements are available. In this section we shall describe a useful model of random noise.

Noise will be viewed as a succession of identical pulses that occur at a uniform average rate of ν per second, but at random instants of time. The amplitudes of the pulses are also random variables, and it is assumed that amplitudes and times of occurrence—or "epochs"—are statistically independent. The process can be described by the equation

$$x(t) = \sum_{k=-\infty}^{\infty} a_k f(t-t_k), \tag{3.1}$$

in which the function $f(t)$ specifying the shape of each pulse is taken with the normalization

$$\int_{-\infty}^{\infty} [f(t)]^2 \, dt = 1. \tag{3.2}$$

For simplicity we shall assume that the expected amplitude is zero, $\mathbf{E}(a_k) = 0$, and that all the amplitudes are distributed according to the same p.d.f. In an interval of duration T there is an average number νT of epochs t_k. The mean value $\mathbf{E}[x(t)]$ of the process is 0.

It is to be expected that the spectral density of this process will be related to the spectrum of the pulse shape $f(t)$, and to verify this we first calculate the autocovariance function of the process. The amplitudes a_k and the epochs t_k being independent, we can average over their distributions separately; and it is convenient to treat the former with an ensemble average, the latter with a time average. We express the autocovariance function as

$$\begin{aligned}\phi(\tau) &= \mathbf{E}[x(t)\, x(t+\tau)] \\ &= \lim_{T\to\infty} \frac{1}{2T} \sum_k \sum_m \mathbf{E}(a_k a_m) \int_{-T}^{T} f(t-t_k)\, f(t+\tau-t_m)\, dt.\end{aligned} \tag{3.3}$$

Because the amplitudes a_k are independent of each other and hence uncorrelated,

$$\mathbf{E}(a_k a_m) = \alpha^2 \delta_{km} = \begin{cases} \alpha^2, & k = m \\ 0, & k \neq m \end{cases}$$

where α is the r.m.s. amplitude and δ_{km} the Kronecker delta. Hence the autocovariance function is

$$\phi(\tau) = \alpha^2 \lim_{T \to \infty} \frac{1}{2T} \sum_k \int_{-T}^{T} f(t-t_k) f(t+\tau-t_k)\, dt. \tag{3.4}$$

When the interval $(-T, T)$ is very long, it will contain about $2\nu T$ pulses; and because of the limited duration of a pulse, only a negligible number of these will overlap the ends of the interval. For the majority of the epochs t_k, the integral in eq. (3.4) is equal to $\int_{-\infty}^{\infty} f(t) f(t+\tau)\, dt$; and the longer the interval, the more accurate are these approximations. In this way we obtain

$$\begin{aligned} \phi(\tau) &= \alpha^2 \lim_{T \to \infty} \frac{1}{2T} 2\nu T \int_{-\infty}^{\infty} f(t) f(t+\tau)\, dt \\ &= \nu\alpha^2 \int_{-\infty}^{\infty} f(t) f(t+\tau)\, dt. \end{aligned} \tag{3.5}$$

As the power P of the random process is given by

$$P = \phi(0) = \nu\alpha^2 \int_{-\infty}^{\infty} [f(t)]^2\, dt = \nu\alpha^2, \tag{3.6}$$

we can write the autocovariance function as

$$\phi(\tau) = P \int_{-\infty}^{\infty} f(t) f(t+\tau)\, dt. \tag{3.7}$$

The spectral density $\Phi(\omega)$ of the stochastic process is calculated by taking the Fourier transform of the autocovariance function in eq. (3.7). In terms of the spectrum

$$F(\omega) = \int_{-\infty}^{\infty} f(t)\, e^{-i\omega t}\, dt$$

of an individual pulse, it is simply

$$\Phi(\omega) = P\,|F(\omega)|^2. \tag{3.8}$$

Thus noise of a given spectral density $\Phi(\omega)$ can be thought of as consisting of pulses with random amplitudes and epochs, the spectrum of each pulse being proportional to $|\Phi(\omega)|^{\frac{1}{2}}e^{i\gamma(\omega)}$, where $\gamma(\omega)$ is an arbitrary phase. Without further investigation one cannot assert that the noise really is made up of such pulses, but it is often helpful to picture it in this way.

If, for instance, such noise is passed through a linear filter with a transfer function $Y(\omega)$, the spectrum of each pulse leaving the filter is proportional to $Y(\omega)F(\omega)$, and the spectral density of the stochastic process at the output is equal to $P\,|F(\omega)|^2\,|Y(\omega)|^2 = |Y(\omega)|^2\Phi(\omega)$, in agreement with eq. (2.20).

This model provides an apt description of a kind of noise that sometimes interferes with radar reception and is called "clutter". It consists of reflections of each transmitted pulse from a large number of randomly distributed scatterers such as raindrops in the air or wavelets on the surface of the sea. The current from a vacuum tube has a component of a similar kind, for each time an electron crosses from cathode to plate, a pulse is induced in the external circuit. The electrons are emitted at random times, but the amplitudes of the pulses may not be random because each electron carries a fixed charge. The analysis just given can be modified to take this lack of complete randomness into account, and the same result is obtained for the spectral density (Rice, 1944). The mean value of the current will not vanish, but will be given by

$$\mathbf{E}[x(t)] = va \int_{-\infty}^{\infty} f(t)\,dt, \tag{3.9}$$

where $a \equiv a_m$ is the fixed amplitude of each pulse.

By making appropriate assumptions about the probability distributions of the amplitudes a_k and the epochs t_k, the probability density functions of the process $x(t)$ can be calculated. This problem has been extensively treated by Middleton (1960, sections 11.2, 11.3), and we shall not enter into it here. In Section 4 we shall discuss the kind of stochastic process that arises when the rate v becomes very large and the mean-square amplitude α becomes very small, so that the process consists of a dense succession of infinitesimal pulses.

(b) *White Noise*

If the pulses making up the noise described in part (a) are very steep and narrow, their spectra are very broad, and little variation of the spectral density will be observed over a wide range of frequency. Most physical systems respond only to frequencies within a limited region, and if the spectral density of the noise input to such a system is nearly constant over that region, the system will behave in effect as though the spectral density of the noise were the same everywhere,

$$\Phi(\omega) \equiv N/2. \tag{3.10}$$

Once the random impulses applied to the system reach a certain degree of sharpness, making them much sharper and higher does not appreciably alter the output of the system, which takes its own time about responding. In the limit of zero width and infinite height the impulses making up the noise become delta-functions, and the autocovariance of the noise, which is the Fourier transform of eq. (3.10), is also a delta function,

$$\phi(\tau) = (N/2)\delta(\tau) = \mathbf{E}[x(t)\,x(t+\tau)] - [\mathbf{E}(x)]^2. \tag{3.11}$$

Such noise is called *white* noise.

The quantity N appearing in eqs. (3.10) and (3.11) is called the *unilateral* spectral density of the noise. If the noise is passed through a filter whose transfer function is

$$\begin{aligned} Y(\omega) &= 1, \quad \Omega - \pi\Delta f < |\omega| < \Omega + \pi\Delta f, \\ &= 0 \text{ elsewhere,} \end{aligned} \tag{3.12}$$

and whose bandwidth is $\Delta\omega = 2\pi\Delta f$, the variance of the output will equal $N\Delta f$.

The infinite power that eq. (3.11) seems to imply is illusory. Any apparatus used to measure the power in the process $x(t)$ would respond only over a finite band of frequencies and would yield a finite result. According to eq. (3.11) samples of the process $x(t)$ at times t and $t+\tau$ arbitrarily close together are uncorrelated. In practice the smallness of the interval between two samples is limited by the response time—or equivalently, by the bandwidth—of the measuring apparatus.

When white noise is applied to a linear filter whose transfer function is $Y(\omega)$, the spectral density $\Phi_o(\omega)$ of the output is, by eq. (2.20),

$$\Phi_o(\omega) = (N/2)\,|Y(\omega)|^2. \tag{3.13}$$

This output can be considered as made up of a dense succession of pulses of random amplitudes and epochs, each of which is proportional to the impulse response $K(\tau)$ of the filter. If the filter is composed of lumped circuit elements, $Y(\omega)$ and $\Phi_o(\omega)$ will be rational functions of frequency, and the pulses will be combinations of exponentials or exponentially damped sinusoids.

If, on the other hand, the spectral density of a noise process is a rational function of the frequency, the noise can be thought of as having been generated by passing white noise through a linear filter made of resistors, inductors, and capacitors. It is merely necessary to factor the spectral density into two parts, $\Psi(\omega)$ and $\Psi^*(\omega)$,

$$\Phi(\omega) = \Psi(\omega)\, \Psi^*(\omega) \tag{3.14}$$

in such a way that all the poles of $\Psi(\omega)$ lie above the Rl ω-axis and all the poles of $\Psi^*(\omega)$ lie below the Rl ω-axis. The transfer function of the filter is then proportional to $\Psi(\omega)$, and when the input to the filter is white noise, its output is noise with a spectral density proportional to $\Phi(\omega)$. Noise that can in this way be considered to have arisen from white noise passed through a filter with lumped components might be called "leucogenic" noise.† We shall see in Section 5 that networks of lumped elements themselves generate such noise.

Such factorization of rational spectral densities often helps in solving problems involving leucogenic noise. If the poles of the spectral density are im_j and $-im_j$, and the zeros are ih_j and $-ih_j$, the spectral density has the form

$$\Phi(\omega) = C \prod_{j=1}^{M'} (\omega^2+h_j^2) \prod_{k=1}^{M''} (\omega^2+m_k^2)^{-1}, \tag{3.15}$$

where C is a positive constant. The most useful factorization expresses the transfer function of the equivalent filter as

$$\Psi(\omega) = C^{\frac{1}{2}} \prod_{j=1}^{M'} (\omega-ih_j) \prod_{k=1}^{M''} (\omega-im_k)^{-1} \tag{3.16}$$

with Rl $h_j > 0$, Rl $m_j > 0$. By thus dividing the zeros as well as the poles of $\Phi(\omega)$, a "minimum-phase" filter is obtained. The filter whose transfer function is $[\Psi(\omega)]^{-1}$ is also physically realizable, and if noise of spectral density $\Phi(\omega)$ is passed through this filter, the output is white noise. Such an inverse filter is called a "whitening filter".

Indeed, problems in the prediction and filtering of both stationary and non-stationary stochastic processes, and in the design of servomechanisms for the optimum control of such processes, are appreciably simplified by regarding the processes as generated by the action of linear systems on one or more independent white-noise processes. By properly augmenting the set of random variables and making suitable additional assumptions about the hypothetical white-noise processes involved, one can treat the processes to be predicted or controlled as components of a special class of stochastic processes known as Markov processes.

Whether M random variables $\xi_1(t)$, $\xi_2(t)$, . . ., $\xi_M(t)$ are the components of a vector Markov process $\boldsymbol{\xi}(t)$ depends on the joint conditional p.d.f. $p(\boldsymbol{\xi}, t \,|\, \boldsymbol{\xi}_1, t_1 |; \boldsymbol{\xi}_2, t_2; \ldots \boldsymbol{\xi}_k, t_k)$ of their values at time t, given the results

† Gk. λευκός = white, γένος = lineage, family, descent.

$\xi_1 = \xi(t_1)$, $\xi_2 = \xi(t_2)$, ..., $\xi_k = \xi(t_k)$ of observations of the variables at an arbitrary number k of instants $t_k < t_{k-1} < \ldots < t_2 < t_1$ in the past. For a vector Markov process that joint conditional p.d.f. is a function only of ξ and the most recent observations ξ_1. This means that the future statistical properties of an ensemble of such processes depend only on the presently observed values, and not on the past history of the processes. The rapidly fluctuating white-noise processes that generate the Markov processes in the linear systems destroy all influence of the past other than what is embodied in the present states of the systems, that is, in the current values of the M components $\xi_1, \xi_2, \ldots, \xi_M$ of the process $\xi(t)$. For an introduction to Markov processes and their use in problems of prediction and control, we refer the reader to papers by Chandrasekhar (1943), Wang and Uhlenbeck (1945), and Kalman and Bucy (1961).

4. GAUSSIAN STOCHASTIC PROCESSES

(a) *The Probability Density Functions*

Returning to the model of random noise described in part (a) of Section 3, let us imagine that the amplitudes of the pulses are made very small, but their rate ν is increased proportionally, with the average power P of the stochastic process remaining the same. The value of $x(t)$ at any instant of time then becomes the sum of a very large number of independent random variables, the contributions of each of the many pulses with epochs t_k near t. It is shown in books on probability that in the limit $m \to \infty$ the sum of m independent random variables is distributed with the Gaussian p.d.f.

$$p_1(x) = (2\pi\sigma^2)^{-\frac{1}{2}} \exp\,[-(x-\bar{x})^2/2\sigma^2], \tag{4.1}$$

where $\bar{x} = \mathbf{E}(x)$ and $\sigma^2 = \operatorname{Var} x$. This assertion, known as the Central Limit Theorem, holds under very broad conditions on the component random variables. The p.d.f. in eq. (4.1), therefore, must govern the values of our random process $x(t)$.

Furthermore, if this process $x(t)$ is observed at n times $t_1, t_2, \ldots, t_n$, the joint p.d.f. of its values $x(t_1) = x_1$, $x(t_2) = x_2$, ..., $x(t_n) = x_n$ is also Gaussian, by which we mean that it is the exponential function of a quadratic form in the n variables $x_1, x_2, \ldots, x_n$,

$$p_n(x_1, t_1; x_2, t_2; \ldots; x_n, t_n) = M_n \exp\left[-\tfrac{1}{2} \sum_{j=1}^{n} \sum_{k=1}^{n} \mu_{jk}(x_j-\bar{x}_j)(x_k-\bar{x}_k)\right]. \tag{4.2}$$

Here $\bar{x}_j = \mathbf{E}[x(t_j)]$, and the numbers μ_{jk} are the elements of a symmetrical, positive-definite matrix $\boldsymbol{\mu}$. The normalization constant M_n has such a value that the multiple integral in eq. (1.1) equals 1,

$$M_n = (2\pi)^{-n/2}\,|\det \boldsymbol{\mu}|^{\frac{1}{2}}, \tag{4.3}$$

where det $\boldsymbol{\mu}$ is the determinant of the matrix $\boldsymbol{\mu}$. A process $x(t)$ all of whose probability density functions have the form of eq. (4.2) is called a *Gaussian* stochastic process.

Why the joint p.d.f.s of our impulsive noise process must also have the Gaussian form of eq. (4.2) in the limit $\nu \to \infty$ can be understood in the following way. An arbitrary linear combination

$$y = \sum_{k=1}^{n} b_k x(t_k) = \sum_{k=1}^{n} b_k x_k$$

of a finite number of samples of the process

$$x(t) = \sum_{=-\infty}^{\infty} a_j f(t-t_j)$$

will itself be the sum of an infinitely large number of independent random variables when the rate ν of the pulses is allowed to pass to infinity as just described. The p.d.f. of y must then be Gaussian as in eq. (4.1), although with a mean $\bar{y}$ and a variance Var y depending on the coefficients b_k. It is not hard to show that such an arbitrary linear combination of random variables $x_1, x_2, \ldots, x_n$ is Gaussian if and only if the joint p.d.f.s of the variables have the Gaussian form of eq. (4.2). The proof involves the characteristic functions of the variables, whose properties are reviewed in Appendix B.

The matrix $\boldsymbol{\mu}$ in eq. (4.2) is the inverse $\boldsymbol{\mu} = \boldsymbol{\phi}^{-1}$ of the matrix $\boldsymbol{\phi} = ||\phi_{ij}||$ of the covariances of the random variables $x_1, x_2, \ldots, x_n$,

$$\phi_{ij} = \mathbf{E}[x(t_i)\, x(t_j)] - \bar{x}_i \bar{x}_j. \tag{4.4}$$

The coefficients μ_{ij} of the quadratic form can be obtained by inverting the matrix $\boldsymbol{\phi}$, which amounts to solving the n^2 linear simultaneous equations

$$\sum_{j=1}^{n} \mu_{ij}\phi_{jk} = \delta_{ik} = \begin{cases} 1, & i = k, \\ 0, & i \neq k, \end{cases} \qquad i, k = 1, 2, \ldots, n. \tag{4.5}$$

Stated otherwise,

$$\mu_{jk} = \text{cof } \phi_{jk}/\det \boldsymbol{\phi} \tag{4.6}$$

where det $\boldsymbol{\phi}$ is the determinant of the covariance matrix and cof ϕ_{jk} is the cofactor of the (jk) element of that matrix. In terms of $\boldsymbol{\phi}$, the normalization constant in eq. (4.2) is

$$M_n = (2\pi)^{-n/2}\,|\det \boldsymbol{\phi}|^{-\frac{1}{2}}. \tag{4.7}$$

Thus to calculate the joint p.d.f.s of a Gaussian stochastic process $x(t)$ one needs only the expected value $\mathbf{E}[x(t)]$ and the covariance function

$$\phi(t, s) = \{x(t), x(s)\}$$

of the process. One seldom knows more about a stochastic process than this.

We shall mostly be concerned with Gaussian processes that are stationary in all respects but one; the expected value $\mathbf{E}[x(t)]$ may not be constant. The covariance matrix $\boldsymbol{\phi}$ has the form

$$\boldsymbol{\phi} = ||\phi_{ij}|| = ||\phi(t_i - t_j)||,$$

but the expected values $\bar{x}_j = \mathbf{E}[x(t_j)]$ appearing in eq. (4.2) may not be equal. Such a process is usually the sum of a stationary Gaussian process of mean zero, the "noise", and a known function of time, the "signal".

(b) *Some Properties of Gaussian Noise*

(i) *Its maximum disorder.* In information theory the disorder of n random variables $x_1, x_2, \ldots, x_n$, or one's average ignorance of their values, is measured by the entropy integral

$$I[p] = -\int_{-\infty}^{\infty} \ldots \int_{-\infty}^{\infty} p_n(x_1, \ldots, x_n) \ln p_n(x_1, \ldots, x_n)\, dx_1 \ldots dx_n \quad (4.8)$$

(Shannon and Weaver, 1949). If the values of $x_1, x_2, \ldots, x_n$ are known exactly, $I[p] = -\infty$. It can be shown that for given values of the means $\bar{x}_1, \bar{x}_2, \ldots, \bar{x}_n$ and the covariances ϕ_{ij} (i and $j = 1, 2, \ldots, n$), this disorder or ignorance is greatest when the joint p.d.f. $p_n(x_1, x_2, \ldots, x_n)$ is the Gaussian p.d.f. in eq. (4.2). In this sense, one is making the fewest possible assumptions about a stochastic process in describing it as Gaussian. Any other set of joint p.d.f.s would imply that something more was known or assumed about how samples of the process $x(t)$ are distributed than what is contained in its expected value $\mathbf{E}[x(t)]$ and its covariance function $\phi(t, s)$.

As we shall indicate in the next section, many natural stochastic processes, particularly those causing the electrical noise of concern to detection theory, can be regarded as the sum of a large number of small, random integrants, and it is appropriate to treat them as Gaussian processes. We have already mentioned the current in a diode as such a phenomenon. Furthermore, it is often possible to invoke statistical mechanics and the entropy principle to verify that the distributions of noise processes are Gaussian; and in many cases these distributions have been amply confirmed experimentally.

(ii) *The moments and characteristic functions.* With the joint p.d.f.s depending only on the mean values and covariances of the process, all expected values of products of Gaussian random variables as well will depend only on those quantities. If for simplicity we take a process with mean value zero, we find that the expected value of a product of an odd number of the variables vanishes,

$$\mathbf{E}(x_1 x_2 \ldots x_{2k+1}) = 0, \quad k \text{ any integer.}$$

For any four Gaussian variables

$$\mathbf{E}(x_1 x_2 x_3 x_4) = \phi_{12}\phi_{34} + \phi_{13}\phi_{24} + \phi_{14}\phi_{23}. \tag{4.9}$$

The expected value of a product of any even number $2k$ of Gaussian variables is a similar sum of terms, $(2k)!\, 2^{-k}(k!)^{-1}$ in all, with one term for each way the $2k$ variables can be arranged in pairs. Each term contains k factors ϕ_{ij} whose indices are correspondingly paired. From these, formulas holding for Gaussian variables whose mean values do not vanish can be derived.

The characteristic function (ch.f.) of a number of samples of a Gaussian process has, like the p.d.f., an exponential form. As described in Appendix B, the ch.f. of the n variables $x_1, x_2, \ldots, x_n$ is the n-dimensional Fourier transform of their joint p.d.f. For samples of a Gaussian process it turns out to be

$$\begin{aligned}\mathbf{E}\exp(iu_1x_1 + iu_2x_2 + \ldots + iu_nx_n) \\ = \int_{-\infty}^{\infty} \ldots \int_{-\infty}^{\infty} \exp\left(i\sum_{j=1}^{n} u_j x_j\right) p_n(x_1, x_2, \ldots, x_n)\, dx_1\, dx_2 \ldots dx_n \\ = \exp\left(i\sum_{j=1}^{n} u_j \bar{x}_j - \tfrac{1}{2}\sum_{j=1}^{n}\sum_{k=1}^{n} \phi_{jk} u_j u_k\right).\end{aligned} \tag{4.10}$$

The quadratic form here involves the covariance matrix $\boldsymbol{\phi}$ in much the same way as the joint p.d.f. involves the inverse matrix $\boldsymbol{\mu}$.

The ch.f. can be used to verify that the joint p.d.f.s in eq. (4.2) are consistent in the sense of eq. (1.2). Integrating a joint p.d.f. over the entire range of a variable x_j is equivalent to setting the corresponding Fourier variable u_j in the ch.f. equal to 0. When any of the u_j's in eq. (4.10) are set equal to 0, the ch.f. of the reduced set of variables results.

As described in Appendix B, the ch.f. can be used to work out the p.d.f. of a sum of random variables. If they are described by a joint Gaussian p.d.f., the exponential form of the ch.f. given by eq. (4.10) is preserved in this calculation. Therefore, the p.d.f. of any linear combination of Gaussian random variables, dependent or not, is also Gaussian. Since an integral can be considered as the limit of a sum, the probability density function of any integral involving a Gaussian random function linearly is also of Gaussian form. By eq. (I, 2.1), which defines the output of a linear filter in terms of its impulse response and its input, these statements imply that if the input to a linear filter is a Gaussian stochastic process, the output is one also. The expected value of the output is found by substituting the expected value of the input into the defining equation (I, 2.1). The autocovariance of the output is the Fourier transform of $|Y(\omega)|^2\Phi_i(\omega)$, where $Y(\omega)$ is the transfer function of the filter and $\Phi_i(\omega)$ is the spectral density of the input. These two functions, the mean value and the autocovariance, suffice to determine the joint p.d.f.s of the output of the filter, as in eq. (4.2).

(iii) *The second-order density function.* The first-order p.d.f. of a Gaussian process is given in eq. (4.1). Let us examine the second-order p.d.f., and for simplicity let us assume that the process is stationary and has mean value 0. Then eq. (4.2) becomes

$$p_2(x_1, t_1; x_2, t_2) = \frac{1}{2\pi\sigma^2\sqrt{1-r^2}} \exp\left(-\frac{x_1^2-2rx_1x_2+x_2^2}{2\sigma^2(1-r^2)}\right), \quad (4.11)$$

$$\sigma^2 = \phi(0) = \text{Var } x, \quad r = \phi(t_2-t_1)/\phi(0).$$

This is the *bivariate normal* density function, and r is the coefficient of correlation, $-1 < r < 1$. (If $r = 1$, $x_2 = x_1$; if $r = -1$, $x_2 = -x_1$.)

The conditional p.d.f. of x_2, given x_1, is obtained by dividing eq. (4.11) by eq. (4.1),

$$p(x_2, t_2 | x_1, t_1) = [2\pi\sigma^2(1-r^2)]^{-\frac{1}{2}} \exp\left(-\frac{(x_2-rx_1)^2}{2\sigma^2(1-r^2)}\right). \quad (4.12)$$

The conditional expected value of $x(t_2)$ is

$$\mathbf{E}(x_2, t_2 | x_1, t_1) = rx_1 = x_1\phi(t_2-t_1)/\phi(0). \quad (4.13)$$

It indicates that after observing the process $x(t)$ take the value x_1 at time t_1, we believe that the most likely value for the process to have at time t_2 is equal to rx_1. This value decays to 0 in proportion to the autocovariance function $\phi(t_2-t_1)$.

The variance of x_2, conditioned on observation of the value x_1 at time t_1, is

$$\text{Var}(x_2, t_2 | x_1, t_1) = \sigma^2(1-r^2) = \phi(0) - \frac{[\phi(t_2-t_1)]^2}{\phi(0)}. \quad (4.14)$$

When t_2 follows closely upon t_1, this variance is small, and we expect $x(t_2)$ to lie near its conditional expected value rx_1. As t_2 recedes into the future, the conditional variance in eq. (4.14) approaches the variance $\sigma^2 = \phi(0)$, and our uncertainty about the value $x(t_2)$ is as great as if we had not observed the process at all.

(iv) *Gaussian white noise.* The white noise treated in part (b) of Section 3 is considered to be Gaussian if the output of an arbitrary linear filter to which it is applied is a Gaussian random process of mean zero and spectral density

$$\Phi_o(\omega) = \frac{N}{2} \, |Y(\omega)|^2,$$

where $Y(\omega)$ is the transfer function of the filter and N is the unilateral spectral density of the input process. Samples of white Gaussian noise taken by an instrument having a bandwidth $\Delta\omega = W$ will be Gaussian random variables with the p.d.f.

$$p_1(x) = (2\pi N_0)^{-\frac{1}{2}} \exp(-x^2/2N_0), \qquad (4.15)$$
$$N_0 = NW/2\pi,$$

and the joint p.d.f. of samples $x_1, x_2, \ldots, x_n$ at times $t_1, t_2, \ldots, t_n$ separated by intervals much longer than $2\pi/W$ will be statistically independent,

$$p_n(x_1, t_1; x_2, t_2; \ldots; x_n, t_n) = \prod_{k=1}^{n} p_1(x_k) = (2\pi N_0)^{-n/2} \exp\left(-\frac{1}{2N_0} \sum_{k=1}^{n} x_k^2\right). \qquad (4.16)$$

In treating the detection of signals in the presence of this kind of noise, we shall imagine sampling the random processes by an instrument whose bandwidth is much greater than that of any of the signals involved. We can then apply eq. (4.16) to the values of the noise at times $t_1, t_2, \ldots, t_n$ that are arbitrarily close.

Whenever successive measurements are made of a physical process, something occurs in each measurement that is unrelated to what happened in any of the previous ones. A component of the outcome of each measurement will therefore be independent of all earlier and later results, no matter how close together in time the measurements are made. As a consequence, the outcomes will always contain a random element that resembles white noise.

The enormous number of molecules composing a macroscopic measuring instrument will, if nothing else does, contribute such a random element to the outcomes of the measurements. Their effect will be the sum of a large number of small, independent random variables, and the resulting random part of the outcomes can be represented as white Gaussian noise. In the next section we shall describe in some detail how the molecular constitution of matter entails such noise processes in electrical circuits.

5. THE PHYSICS OF NOISE

(a) *The Nyquist Law*

The simplest source of electrical noise is a resistor. The ions and electrons that compose it are forever vibrating and moving about in a completely haphazard way, and the energy of their chaotic motions is what we

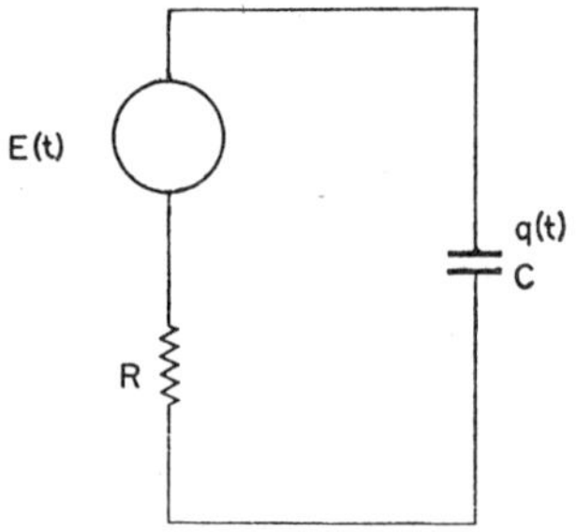

FIG. II.1. An RC circuit in thermal equilibrium.

call "heat". In the course of these microscopic jigglings and jostlings small electrical dipoles form and vanish throughout the resistor and cause a fluctuating voltage to appear between its terminals. Because the ions and electrons change their positions so quickly, the fluctuations of the voltage across the resistor are extremely rapid and can be thought of as a dense succession of sharp positive and negative pulses. We have learned that the spectral density of such a stochastic process is nearly constant over a broad range of frequencies.

If the resistor is connected to a capacitor, as shown in Fig. II.1, the fluctuating voltage $E(t)$ that it generates will make charges move at random from one plate of the capacitor to the other. The instantaneous net charge $q(t)$ on the capacitor will obey a linear differential equation of the first order,

$$R\frac{dq}{dt}+\frac{q}{C}=E(t), \tag{5.1}$$

where R is the resistance and C the capacitance in the circuit.

The charge $q(t)$ cannot change so rapidly as the voltage $E(t)$, for its variations are limited by the natural response time RC of the circuit, as is shown by the solution of eq. (5.1),

$$q(t) = \frac{1}{R}\int_0^\infty e^{-s/RC}\,E(t-s)\,ds. \tag{5.2}$$

This formula indicates that the charge $q(t)$ and the voltage $E(t)$ are related like the output and the input of a filter whose impulse response is $R^{-1}e^{-\tau/RC}$ and whose transfer function is

$$Y_{E,Q}(\omega) = C(1+iRC\omega)^{-1}. \tag{5.3}$$

If the spectral density of the voltage $E(t)$ is $\Phi_E(\omega)$, the fluctuations of the charge $q(t)$ have a spectral density given by eq. (2.20) as

$$\Phi_Q(\omega) = \Phi_E(\omega)\,|Y_{E,Q}(\omega)|^2 = C^2\Phi_E(\omega)/(1+R^2C^2\omega^2). \tag{5.4}$$

For any ordinary resistor and capacitor the factor $|Y_{E,Q}(\omega)|^2$ differs significantly from 0 only in a range of frequencies over which the spectral density $\Phi_E(\omega)$ is nearly constant. This is equivalent to saying that during an interval equal to the response time RC, the voltage $E(t)$ fluctuates a great many times. Hence we can evaluate the mean-square charge on the capacitor by integrating eq. (5.4) under the assumption that $\Phi_E(\omega)$ is constant, $\Phi_E(\omega) \equiv \Phi_E$,

$$\mathbf{E}(q^2) = \overline{q^2} = \int_{-\infty}^{\infty} \Phi_Q(\omega)\,d\omega/2\pi = (C/2R)\,\Phi_E. \tag{5.5}$$

The average energy stored in the capacitor is then

$$\bar{E} = \overline{q^2}/2C = \Phi_E/4R. \tag{5.6}$$

The system made up of the resistor and the capacitor possesses a vast number of degrees of freedom. One degree is associated with the charge on the capacitor, the rest with the positions and velocities of the particles in the resistor. The fluctuations of the charge manifest the thermal variations of the dynamical variables specifying the configuration of the system "resistor + capacitor". Statistical mechanics tells us that when such a system is in thermal equilibrium at absolute temperature T, its thermal energy is so distributed among the degrees of freedom that each takes on an average amount equal to $kT/2$, where $k = 1.38 \cdot 10^{-16}$ erg/deg is Boltzmann's constant. This is the Law of Equipartition of Energy.

For this reason we can assign to the average energy $\overline{E}$ stored in the capacitor the value $kT/2$, and by eq. (5.6) the spectral density of the fluctuating voltage $E(t)$ is

$$\Phi_E(\omega) = 2kTR. \tag{5.7}$$

The voltage generated by the resistor is a form of white noise with unilateral spectral density $N = 4kTR$. H. Nyquist (1928) derived this formula by arguments from thermodynamics and statistical mechanics, and it has become known as the Nyquist Law. An outline of the proof and additional discussion are given by Lawson and Uhlenbeck (1950). Nyquist's work was prompted by the experiments of the physicist J. B. Johnson (1928), for whom this kind of noise has been named "Johnson noise".

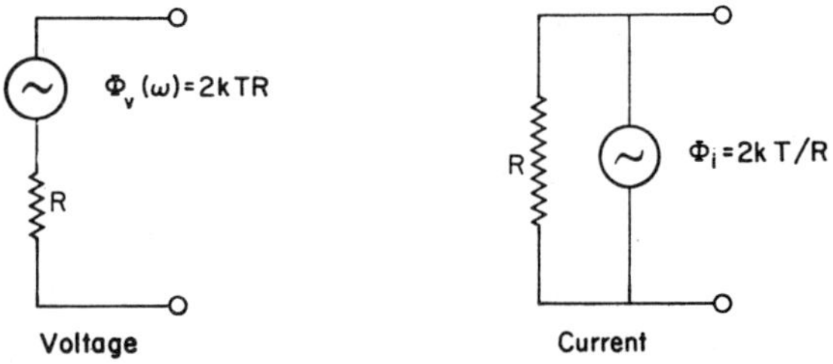

FIG. II.2. Equivalent noise generators for a resistor at absolute temperature T.

There are two equivalent statements of the Nyquist Law, illustrated by Fig. II.2. The first asserts that a resistor behaves as though there were connected in series with it a generator of a fluctuating voltage of spectral density $\Phi_E(\omega) = 2kTR$. The second views the resistor as having in parallel with itself a generator of a random current whose spectral density is

$$\Phi_I(\omega) = 2kT/R. \tag{5.8}$$

It must be remembered that in our definition of the spectral density half the power is in the negative frequencies and half in the positive frequencies, for we prefer bilateral spectral densities to the unilateral ones sometimes meant in expressions of the Nyquist Law. The dimensions of each side of eq. (5.7) are volts$^2\cdot$sec when R is in ohms and kT in joules (1 joule $= 10^7$ ergs); thus what is often called the "power spectrum" does not have the usual dimensions of power (joules/sec).

The spectral density given in eq. (5.7) cannot be maintained at extremely high frequencies. In the first place, capacitance between the terminals of the resistor shorts out the fluctuations of very high frequency and causes the function $\Phi_E(\omega)$ to fall to zero. Even if the capacitance were not present, quantum-mechanical effects at still higher frequencies would cause the spectral density ultimately to vanish. When only these quantum-mechanical effects are taken into account, the formula in eq. (5.7) is modified by what is known as the "Planck factor",

$$\Phi_E(\omega) = 2kTR\eta(|\omega|),$$

$$\eta(\omega) = \frac{\hbar\omega}{kT}(e^{\hbar\omega/kT}-1)^{-1}, \tag{5.9}$$

where $\hbar = h/2\pi = 1.05 \cdot 10^{-27}$erg·sec is Planck's constant. The Planck factor is approximately equal to 1 when ω is much smaller than $kT/\hbar$, but it drops off to 0 as ω increases. For a temperature of 20°C = 293°K, $\hbar\omega/kT = 1$ for a frequency of $\omega/2\pi = kT/h = 6.1 \cdot 10^{12}$ Hertz. As this is much higher than any frequencies with which we shall be concerned, we shall henceforth omit the Planck factor.

The noise voltage measured between any pair of terminals of a complex network is made up of contributions from all the resistors in the network. To compute the spectral density of this voltage, one places in series with each resistor R_j a generator of a fluctuating voltage V_j with a spectral density given by eq. (5.7),

$$\Phi_{v_j}(\omega) = 2kTR_j;$$

the noise voltages of separate generators are statistically independent. The voltage across the output terminals due to each of these generators is calculated by ordinary circuit theory. If the voltage across the output terminals is $E_j e^{i\omega t}$ when there is a voltage $V_j e^{i\omega t}$ in series with the jth resistor, we can define a transfer function $Y_j(\omega)$ by

$$E_j = V_j Y_j(\omega).$$

Then by eq. (2.20) the spectral density of the noise output is

$$\Phi_o(\omega) = 2kT\sum_j R_j\,|Y_j(\omega)|^2. \tag{5.10}$$

It is simpler, however, to calculate the noise voltage across a pair of output terminals of a network by replacing the network with its equivalent impedance $Z_e(\omega)$ measured between the terminals. The equivalent impedance $Z_e(\omega)$ is easily determined by the methods of circuit theory. The noise behavior of the network as far as any external circuits are concerned is the same as though there were a generator in series with this equivalent impedance, the spectral density of whose output voltage is

$$\Phi_v(\omega) = 2kT\,\mathrm{Rl}\,Z_e(\omega). \tag{5.11}$$

If the resistors of a network have different temperatures, eq. (5.10) must be replaced by the formula

$$\Phi_o(\omega) = 2k \sum_j T_j R_j \,|\, Y_j(\omega)\,|^2,$$

where T_j is the absolute temperature of the jth resistor. This extended form of the Nyquist Law has also been verified experimentally—see Van der Ziel (1954). The concept of equivalent impedance, as in eq. (5.11), cannot be used for noise calculations unless the entire network is at the same temperature.

(b) *Noise in a Simply Resonant Circuit*

Consider for example the network of Fig. II.3. What is the spectral density of the noise voltage E measured across the capacitor? The equi-

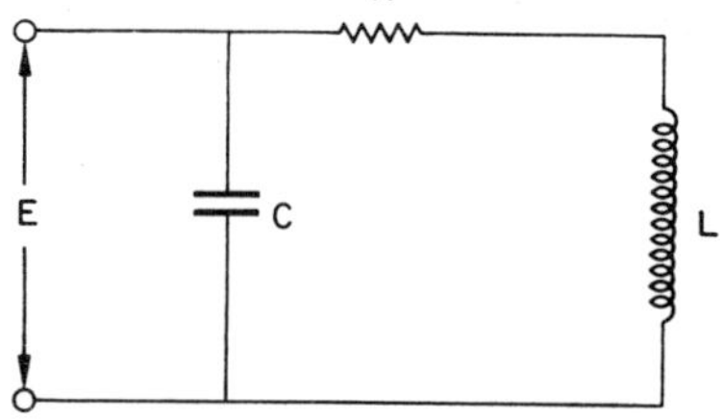

FIG. II.3. A simply resonant circuit.

valent impedance between the terminals shown is

$$Z_e = \frac{R+i\omega L}{i\omega C\left[R+i\left(\omega L-\dfrac{1}{\omega C}\right)\right]}.$$

From eq. (5.11) the spectral density of the voltage E must be

$$\Phi_E(\omega) = 2kT\,\mathrm{Rl}\,Z_e^{2} = \frac{2kTR}{\omega^2 C^2\left[R^2+\left(\omega L-\dfrac{1}{\omega C}\right)^2\right]}.$$

Another way to obtain this formula is to insert a generator of voltage V in series with the resistor R, and to set the spectral density of V equal to $\Phi_V(\omega) = 2kTR$. The transfer function from V to E at any frequency ω is

$$Y(\omega) = E/V = I/i\omega CV = (i\omega C)^{-1}\left[R+i\left(\omega L-\frac{1}{\omega C}\right)\right]^{-1},$$

where $I = V[R+i(\omega L-1/\omega C)]^{-1}$ is the current in the circuit. Then we can use eq. (5.10) to find the spectral density of the voltage E,

$$\Phi_E(\omega) = |Y(\omega)|^2 \Phi_V(\omega) = \frac{2kTR}{\omega^2 C^2 \left[R^2 + \left(\omega L - \frac{1}{\omega C}\right)^2\right]}.$$

Thus both methods yield the same result, though the former is often the simpler one for analyzing complex circuits.

The mean-square voltage across the capacitor in the circuit of Fig. II.3 is found by integrating the spectral density,

$$\overline{E^2} = \int_{-\infty}^{\infty} \Phi_E(\omega)\, d\omega/2\pi = kT/C,$$

and the average energy stored in the capacitor is $C\overline{E^2}/2 = kT/2$. One can similarly derive the spectral density of the current I and integrate it to show that the average energy in the magnetic field of the inductance is $L\overline{I^2}/2 = kT/2$. Here again is an illustration of the Law of Equipartition of Energy. For an analysis of the fluctuations of a general network from this standpoint, see the article by Wang and Uhlenbeck (1945). The currents and charges in each mesh of a network made up of resistors, inductors, and capacitors are represented in the most general case by the components of a $2n$-dimensional Gaussian Markov process, where n is the number of meshes in the network.

A quantum-mechanical treatment of the fluctuations in linear dissipative systems has been given by Callen and Welton (1951). Such a system has a large number of closely spaced energy levels, among which the energy in thermal equilibrium is distributed according to the Boltzmann law. A generalized impedance $Z(\omega)$ is defined for the system in such a way that the power dissipated in it by a sinusoidally varying applied "force" $V_0 \cos \omega t$ is given by

$$V_0^2 \operatorname{Rl} Z(\omega)/2\,|Z(\omega)|^2.$$

In thermal equilibrium the system behaves as though it contained a generator of a fluctuating generalized force whose spectral density is $2kT \operatorname{Rl} Z(\omega)\eta(|\omega|)$. Applied to an electrical network this theory yields the Nyquist formula, eq. (5.7) or, more generally, eq. (5.11). It can be used in other problems as well. The spectral density of the random forces causing the Brownian motion of a particle suspended in a viscous liquid can be calculated in terms of the power loss when the particle is deliberately oscillated by an externally applied force, and the Planck radiation law can be derived from the nature of the drag of the electromagnetic field on an oscillating charge. The theory in this way reveals the fundamental identity of diverse thermal fluctuations.

(c) *Transfer of Noise Power*

It is instructive to make an accounting of the fluctuating currents and voltages in a simple network like that of Fig. II.4, which consists of two impedances Z_1 and Z_2 in series. Each of these may itself be a complex network of resistors, inductors, and capacitors. In order to deal only with

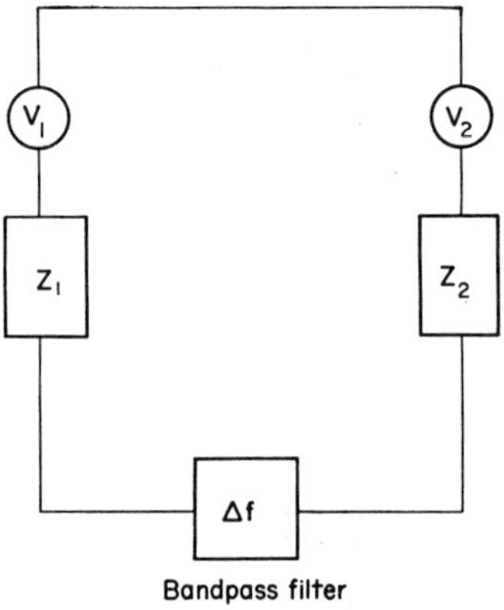

FIG. II.4. Network for analysis of noise power transfer.

spectral components of frequencies in the vicinity of a single frequency ω', a hypothetical bandpass filter of bandwidth $\Delta\omega = 2\pi\Delta f$ rad/sec has been inserted. This filter attenuates all components except those with frequencies between $\omega' - \pi\Delta f$ and $\omega' + \pi\Delta f$ and between $-\omega' - \pi\Delta f$ and $-\omega' + \pi\Delta f$, which are passed unchanged. When this circuit is in thermal equilibrium at temperature T, there is a fluctuating current present that one can imagine is produced by two generators, one associated with impedance Z_1 and having a mean-square output voltage

$$\overline{v_1^2} = 4kT(\mathrm{Rl}\, Z_1)\,\Delta f,$$

the other associated with Z_2 and having a mean-square output voltage

$$\overline{v_2^2} = 4kT(\mathrm{Rl}\, Z_2)\,\Delta f.$$

The current in the circuit due to the thermal fluctuations in impedance Z_1 is $I_1 = v_1/(Z_1 + Z_2)$; that due to the fluctuations in Z_2 is $I_2 = v_2/(Z_1 + Z_2)$. These currents are statistically independent.

The average power dissipated in a network is found by taking the real part of the product E^*I, where E is the r.m.s. vector voltage across the terminals of the network and I is the r.m.s. vector current flowing in at one terminal and out at the other.† Thus the power dissipated in impedance Z_2 due to the fluctuating voltage v_1 of the first impedance is

$$P_{12} = \mathrm{Rl}\left(\frac{v_1^* Z_2^*}{Z_1^*+Z_2^*}\cdot\frac{v_1}{Z_1+Z_2}\right) = \frac{\overline{v_1^2}\,\mathrm{Rl}\,Z_2}{|Z_1+Z_2|^2}$$
$$= \frac{4kT(\mathrm{Rl}\,Z_1)(\mathrm{Rl}\,Z_2)\,\Delta f}{|Z_1+Z_2|^2} = P_{21}.$$

Here P_{21} is the power dissipated in impedance Z_1 due to the noise voltage v_2; in thermal equilibrium it must equal P_{12}, as is evident from the symmetry of the above expression. The fluctuation power in Z_1 due to v_1 is similarly

$$P_{11} = \frac{\overline{v_1^2}\,\mathrm{Rl}\,Z_1}{|Z_1+Z_2|^2} = \frac{4kT(\mathrm{Rl}\,Z_1)^2\,\Delta f}{|Z_1+Z_2|^2},$$

and that in Z_2 due to v_2 is

$$P_{22} = \frac{4kT(\mathrm{Rl}\,Z_2)^2\,\Delta f}{|Z_1+Z_2|^2}.$$

The total fluctuation power in the range of frequencies passed by the filter is then given by

$$P = P_{11}+P_{12}+P_{21}+P_{22} = \frac{4kT\,|\mathrm{Rl}\,(Z_1+Z_2)|^2\,\Delta f}{|Z_1+Z_2|^2}.$$

With the bandpass filter removed, the total power associated with the fluctuations in the circuit is found by integrating this expression over the range $0 < \omega' < \infty$.

The power P_{12} transferred from impedance Z_1 to impedance Z_2 is a maximum when $Z_1 = Z_2^*$; the impedances are then said to be "matched"‡ Under these circumstances $Z_1+Z_2 = 2\mathrm{Rl}\,Z_1 = 2\mathrm{Rl}\,Z_2$, and

$$P_{12} = P_{21} = kT\,\Delta f.$$

It is said that $kT\Delta f$ is the maximum available noise power from the impedance Z_1 in the frequency ranges $\pm\omega'-\pi\Delta f < \omega < \pm\omega'+\pi\Delta f$. This state-

† See, for instance, Kerchner, R. M. and Corcoran, G. F., *Alternating-Current Circuits*, 2nd ed., p. 87, Wiley, New York (1943).
‡ *Ibid.*, p. 124.

ment is analogous to the assertion that the maximum power available from a generator is $E^2/4(\mathrm{Rl}\, Z)$, where E is the r.m.s. voltage generated and Z is the internal impedance of the generator; the maximum power transfer takes place when the generator and its load are matched in the above sense. The concept of maximum available noise power is useful in studying the random fluctuations of linear devices like antennas and transmission lines that can be assigned impedances, yet are not made up of resistors and other circuit elements.

(d) *Other Sources of Noise*

For instance, a radar antenna exhibits a fluctuating noise voltage across its output terminals. To see why this is so, consider the antenna and its surroundings to be enclosed in a large insulating box, so that they are in thermal equilibrium. Let there be an impedance Z_a^* matching the radiation impedance Z_a of the antenna connected across its terminals. (The real part of $Z_a(\omega)$ is the radiation resistance, which represents the power lost by radiation when the antenna is excited by an alternating voltage of frequency ω.) Since this impedance is matched to the antenna, it supplies the antenna with $kT\Delta f$ watts of power in a frequency band of width $\Delta\omega = 2\pi\Delta f$. Because at thermal equilibrium the same amount of power must be supplied by the antenna, the available power at the terminals of the antenna must be $kT\Delta f$ in this range. Thus the antenna can be regarded as a generator of a fluctuating voltage of spectral density $\Phi_a(\omega) = 2kT\, \mathrm{Rl}\, Z_a$; the internal impedance of the generator is Z_a, the equivalent impedance of the antenna.

In practice it is found that the spectral density of the noise voltage at the antenna terminals is a function of the direction of the antenna, and certain portions of the sky act as sources of large amounts of so-called "cosmic noise". The engineer accounts for this variation by assigning an effective temperature T_{eff} to the antenna surroundings, so that the spectral density of the received voltage is $2kT_{\mathrm{eff}}\, \mathrm{Rl}\, Z_a$; this effective temperature is in general a function of the frequency. A study of effective antenna noise temperatures is reported in Lawson and Uhlenbeck (1950). The antenna noise is due to thermal motions in the surroundings toward which the antenna is directed; the chaotically vibrating ions and electrons create random fluctuations in the electromagnetic field, which in turn excite the antenna. Certain astronomical bodies have high effective noise temperatures because of the ionization and turbulence of the matter composing them, and the cosmic noise provides a new way of studying physical conditions in the stars and nebulae.

The vacuum tubes, transistors, and diodes in a radar receiver are themselves sources of noise because of the random nature of the physical processes like electron emission by which they operate. For instance, a theorem due to Schottky states that the spectral density of the fluctuations in the current I through a vacuum-tube diode is

$$\Phi_I(\omega) = eI, \tag{5.12}$$

where e = electronic charge = $1.60 \cdot 10^{-19}$ coulombs. This formula describes the spectral density up to frequencies determined by effects like the transit time of the electrons and the interelectrode capacitances; at still higher frequencies the spectral density drops to zero. In more complicated tubes such as triodes and pentodes there are other effects enhancing the noise output. "Partition noise" is due to the random selection of grids by the electrons impinging on them. Other noise is caused by random secondary emission of electrons from the electrodes of the vacuum tube. In radar receivers the principal sources of noise are the input resistor of the first amplifier stage and the crystal mixer. For a detailed discussion of the noise in receivers, methods of measuring it, and design of low-noise circuits, we refer the reader to texts such as those of Lawson and Uhlenbeck (1950) and Van der Ziel (1954).

6. NARROWBAND NOISE

(a) *The Spectral Density*

In Sections 3 and 4 of Chapter I we discussed narrowband signals and filters, whose spectra and transfer functions differ significantly from zero only in frequency bands about some high carrier frequency Ω and about its image $-\Omega$; the widths of the bands are small compared with Ω. Similarly we can envision random noise whose spectral density is largely confined to such limited ranges of frequency. We call this type "narrowband noise". It is convenient to write its spectral density as

$$\Phi(\omega) = \tilde{\Phi}(\omega - \Omega) + \tilde{\Phi}(-\omega - \Omega), \tag{6.1}$$

where $\tilde{\Phi}(\omega)$ is a real, positive function of ω that is significantly large only near $\omega = 0$.

The autocovariance function of this narrowband noise is found by substituting eq. (6.1) into the Fourier transformation formula, eq. (2.17),

$$\begin{aligned} \phi(\tau) &= \int_{-\infty}^{\infty} [\tilde{\Phi}(\omega - \Omega) + \tilde{\Phi}(-\omega - \Omega)]\, e^{i\omega\tau}\, d\omega/2\pi \\ &= \int_{-\infty}^{\infty} \tilde{\Phi}(\omega)\, [e^{i(\omega+\Omega)\tau} + e^{-i(\omega+\Omega)\tau}]\, d\omega/2\pi = \text{Rl}\, \tilde{\phi}(\tau)\, e^{i\Omega\tau}, \end{aligned} \tag{6.2}$$

where the complex function $\tilde{\phi}(\tau)$ is defined by

$$\begin{aligned} \tilde{\phi}(\tau) &= 2 \int_{-\infty}^{\infty} \tilde{\Phi}(\omega)\, e^{i\omega\tau}\, d\omega/2\pi; \\ \tilde{\Phi}(\omega) &= \tfrac{1}{2} \int_{-\infty}^{\infty} \tilde{\phi}(\tau)\, e^{-i\omega\tau}\, d\tau. \end{aligned} \tag{6.3}$$

Because $\tilde{\Phi}(\omega)$ is real, $\tilde{\phi}(-\tau) = \tilde{\phi}^*(\tau)$, the $*$ denoting the complex conjugate. The function $\tilde{\phi}(\tau)$ is real only if the narrowband part $\tilde{\Phi}(\omega)$ of the spectral density is symmetrical about $\omega = 0$. As $|\tilde{\phi}(\tau)| \leqslant \tilde{\phi}(0)$, the absolute value $|\tilde{\phi}(\tau)|$ is a function with a peak at $\tau = 0$. This function decreases nearly to zero for values of τ of the order of the reciprocal of the width of $\tilde{\Phi}(\omega)$. For narrowband noise the autocovariance function $\phi(\tau)$ exhibits many oscillations of "frequency" Ω as τ varies, and the related function $\tilde{\phi}(\tau)$ is the complex envelope of these oscillations. We shall call $\tilde{\phi}(\tau)$ the "complex autocovariance function" of the narrowband noise, and $\tilde{\Phi}(\omega)$ will be called the "narrowband spectral density".

When noise of spectral density $\Phi_i(\omega)$ passes into a narrowband filter whose transfer function $Y(\omega)$ is given by eq. (I, 4.1),

$$Y(\omega) = y(\omega-\Omega)+y^*(-\omega-\Omega),$$

the spectral density of the output is, according to eq. (2.20),

$$\begin{aligned} \Phi_o(\omega) &= \Phi_i(\omega)\, |y(\omega-\Omega)+y^*(-\omega-\Omega)|^2 \\ &\cong \Phi_i(\omega)\, [|y(\omega-\Omega)|^2+|y(-\omega-\Omega)|^2], \end{aligned} \tag{6.4}$$

since for narrowband filters the cross-product $\text{Rl}\, y(\omega-\Omega)\, y^*(-\omega-\Omega)$ is much smaller than the other terms. If the spectral density of the input is much wider than the transfer function of the filter, we can replace $\Phi_i(\omega)$ by its value at $+\Omega$ or $-\Omega$, and by comparison with eq. (6.1) we find

$$\tilde{\Phi}_o(\omega) \cong \Phi_i(\Omega)\, |y(\omega)|^2 \tag{6.5}$$

for the narrowband spectral density of the output at all frequencies ω where this function is of significant magnitude. If, on the other hand, the input noise is narrowband, with a spectral density like that in eq. (6.1), we find

$$\tilde{\Phi}_o(\omega) = \tilde{\Phi}_i(\omega)\, |y(\omega)|^2 \tag{6.6}$$

by discarding all the terms of eq. (6.4) that are small in this approximation. Thus we can use the narrowband spectral density and transfer function in much the same way as the original functions $\Phi(\omega)$ and $Y(\omega)$.

(b) *The Complex Envelope*

So far our work with narrowband noise has been mainly formal. To expand the theory it is desirable to define a complex envelope of the noise itself and, if possible, connect the statistical properties of the envelope with the functions $\tilde{\phi}(\tau)$ and $\tilde{\Phi}(\omega)$. We should like such a definition of the complex envelope $V(t)$ of narrowband noise $v(t)$ that

$$v(t) = \text{Rl}\, V(t)\, e^{i\Omega t} = X(t) \cos \Omega t - Y(t) \sin \Omega t, \qquad V(t) = X(t) + iY(t), \tag{6.7}$$

where $X(t)$ and $Y(t)$ are the quadrature components of the noise. We could then treat narrowband signals and noise in the same way.

For this purpose we use the representation of the noise voltage $v(t)$ given in eq. (2.2), breaking it into its positive- and negative-frequency components,

$$\begin{aligned} v(t) &= v_+(t) + v_-(t), \\ v_+(t) &= \tfrac{1}{2}c_0 + \sum_{n=1}^{\infty} c_n \exp(i\omega_n t), \\ v_-(t) &= \tfrac{1}{2}c_0 + \sum_{n=-\infty}^{-1} c_n \exp(i\omega_n t), \\ \omega_n &= 2\pi n/T, \end{aligned} \tag{6.8}$$

where T is the length of a long sample of the noise, which is assumed to be periodically repeated. Later we shall let T increase without limit.

Since $c_{-n} = c_n^*$, $v_-(t) = v_+^*(t)$ and $v(t) = 2\,\text{Rl}\, v_+(t)$. For narrowband noise only those coefficients c_n corresponding to frequencies $\omega_n = 2\pi n/T$ in the neighborhood of the carrier frequency Ω are significant. In the limit $T \to \infty$ their mean-square values are given for positive n by eqs. (2.13), (2.16), and (6.1),

$$\lim_{T\to\infty} T\text{E}(|c_n|^2) = \Phi(\omega_n) \cong \tilde{\Phi}(\omega_n - \Omega) \tag{6.9}$$

when the frequency ω_n is near Ω. If we then define the complex envelope by

$$V(t) = 2v_+(t)\, e^{-i\Omega t} = c_0\, e^{-i\Omega t} + 2 \sum_{n=1}^{\infty} c_n \exp i(\omega_n - \Omega)\, t, \tag{6.10}$$

we can disregard all the terms except those with ω_n near Ω, and $V(t)$ will be a slowly varying function of time. Since the r.m.s. values of the coefficients

c_n are significant only for a range of values of ω_n determined by the width of the narrowband spectral density $\tilde{\Phi}(\omega)$, changes in $V(t)$ will occur in times of the order of the reciprocal of that width. Within such times there will be a large number of oscillations of the carrier $\cos \Omega t$, and the function $V(t)$ possesses the desired properties of a complex envelope.

Another way of seeing that narrowband noise can be represented as in eq. (6.7) is to think of it as made up of pulses occurring at random times and having random amplitudes, as in the model described in part (a) of Section 3. The spectral density will then have the form given in eq. (6.1) if the pulses are narrowband signals and can be written as

$$s(t) = \text{Rl}\, F(t)\, e^{i\Omega t},$$

for if $f(\omega)$ is the spectrum of the complex envelope $F(t)$, the spectral density will be given by eqs. (3.8), (I, 3.10) as

$$\begin{aligned}\Phi(\omega) &= \tfrac{1}{4}P\,|f(\omega-\Omega)+f^*(-\omega-\Omega)|^2 \\ &= \tfrac{1}{4}P\,|f(\omega-\Omega)|^2+\tfrac{1}{4}P\,|f(-\omega-\Omega)|^2,\end{aligned}$$

the cross-product terms being negligible. The process itself will now as in eq. (3.1) be given by

$$v(t) = \text{Rl}\, e^{i\Omega t} \sum_{n=-\infty}^{\infty} a_n\, F(t-t_n) \exp(-i\Omega t_n),$$

which corresponds to a quasiharmonic function with the complex envelope

$$V(t) = \sum_{n=-\infty}^{\infty} a_n \exp(-i\phi_n)\, F(t-t_n).$$

Because the times t_n are random, the phases $\phi_n = \Omega t_n$ are also random; and when they are reduced "modulo 2π" to the interval $(0, 2\pi)$, the phases are uniformly distributed within it.

Let us now determine the covariances of the quadrature components $X(t)$ and $Y(t)$ of the complex envelope $V(t)$ of such a narrowband random process. We form the autocovariance function of the process $v(t)$ as follows. From eq. (6.7),

$$v(t_j) = \tfrac{1}{2}V(t_j) \exp(i\Omega t_j)+\tfrac{1}{2}V^*(t_j) \exp(-i\Omega t_j), \qquad j = 1, 2.$$

Multiplying and averaging, we get

$$\begin{aligned}\mathbf{E}[v(t_1)\, v(t_2)] &= \phi(t_1-t_2) \\ &= \tfrac{1}{2}\tilde{\phi}(t_1-t_2) \exp[i\Omega(t_1-t_2)]+\tfrac{1}{2}\tilde{\phi}^*(t_1-t_2) \exp[-i\Omega(t_1-t_2)] \\ &= \tfrac{1}{4}\mathbf{E}[V(t_1)\, V(t_2)] \exp i\Omega(t_1+t_2)+\text{c.c.} \\ &\quad +\tfrac{1}{4}\mathbf{E}[V(t_1)\, V^*(t_2)] \exp i\Omega(t_1-t_2)+\text{c.c.}\end{aligned}$$

Therefore

$$\begin{aligned} \mathbf{E}[V(t_1)\, V^*(t_2)] &= 2\tilde{\phi}(t_1-t_2), \\ \mathbf{E}[V(t_1)\, V(t_2)] &= 0. \end{aligned} \tag{6.11}$$

These two formulas will be useful in our future work. From them one can easily show that the covariances of the quadrature components $X(t)$ and $Y(t)$ of the narrowband noise are given by

$$\begin{aligned} \mathbf{E}[X(t_1)\, X(t_2)] &= \mathbf{E}[Y(t_1)\, Y(t_2)] = \text{Rl}\, \tilde{\phi}(t_1-t_2), \\ \mathbf{E}[Y(t_1)\, X(t_2)] &= -\mathbf{E}[X(t_1)\, Y(t_2)] = \text{Im}\, \tilde{\phi}(t_1-t_2). \end{aligned} \tag{6.12}$$

These equations relate the covariances of the quadrature components of the narrowband noise to its complex autocovariance function $\tilde{\phi}(\tau)$, which is itself the "envelope" of the original autocovariance function $\phi(\tau)$ of the process $v(t)$.

As a quasiharmonic function, the process $v(t)$ must have an amplitude modulation $|V(t)|$ and a phase modulation arg $V(t)$ of the same kind as described in Section 3 of Chapter I. From the statistics of $v(t)$ one can determine the probability distributions of the outputs of rectifiers, discriminators, and other devices whose inputs are narrowband signals and noise. The statistical properties of the envelope of narrowband noise have been treated by Rice (1944), Bunimovich (1949), Arens (1957), Dugundji (1958), and Reed (1962). When the noise is both narrowband and Gaussian, its joint p.d.f.s can be put into an especially simple form that facilitates calculations. It will be developed in the next section.

(c) *The Circular Gaussian Process*

If the noise $v(t)$ has a Gaussian distribution, so also do the real and imaginary parts of the coefficients c_n of eq. (6.10), since they are connected with $v(t)$ by a linear relation, eq. (2.3). Therefore the components $X(t)$ and $Y(t)$ of the complex envelope $V(t)$ are Gaussian stochastic processes, for they consist of linear combinations of Gaussian random variables. The joint p.d.f. of $x = X(t)$ and $y = Y(t)$, for instance, is

$$\begin{aligned} p(x, y) &= (2\pi\sigma^2)^{-1} \exp\,[-(x^2+y^2)/2\sigma^2], \\ \sigma^2 &= \phi(0) = \tilde{\phi}(0). \end{aligned} \tag{6.13}$$

Because of the circular symmetry of this joint p.d.f., a complex Gaussian process $V(t) = X(t)+iY(t)$ is sometimes called a "circular process". If the spectral density is symmetrical about the carrier frequency, $\tilde{\Phi}(\omega) = \tilde{\Phi}(-\omega)$, the two quadrature components are statistically independent.

More generally, it is said that the M complex numbers $z_m = x_m + iy_m$ are drawn from a circular Gaussian distribution if their real and imaginary parts are Gaussian random variables with the following means and covariances,

$$\begin{aligned} \mathbf{E}(x_m+iy_m) &= \zeta_m, \\ \{x_m, x_n\} = \{y_m, y_n\} &= \phi_{x,\,mn} = \mathrm{Rl}\,\phi_{mn}, \\ \{y_m, x_n\} = -\{x_m, y_n\} &= \phi_{y,\,mn} = \mathrm{Im}\,\phi_{mn}, \end{aligned} \tag{6.14}$$

where $\phi_{mn} = \phi_{x,\,mn} + i\phi_{y,\,mn}$ is an element of the complex covariance matrix $\boldsymbol{\phi} = \boldsymbol{\phi}_x + i\boldsymbol{\phi}_y$, which is Hermitian,

$$\phi^*_{mn} = \phi_{nm}.$$

By comparing these covariances with those in eq. (6.12) we see that the complex envelope of the narrowband Gaussian random process just described is a stationary form of a circular process. By introducing the means ζ_m we can account for a narrowband signal that might be present in the midst of this kind of noise.

The joint p.d.f. of the $2M$ random variables $x_1, x_2, \ldots, x_M, y_1, y_2, \ldots, y_M$ can be written most concisely as

$$\begin{aligned} p_{2M}(x_1, \ldots, x_M, y_1, \ldots, y_M) &= \tilde{p}_M(z_1, \ldots, z_M) \\ &= (2\pi)^{-M}\,|\det \boldsymbol{\phi}|^{-1} \exp\left[-\tfrac{1}{2}\sum_{m=1}^{M}\sum_{n=1}^{M} \mu_{mn}(z^*_m-\zeta^*_m)(z_n-\zeta_n)\right], \end{aligned} \tag{6.15}$$

where μ_{mn} are the elements of the matrix $\boldsymbol{\mu}$ inverse to $\boldsymbol{\phi}$,

$$\sum_{n=1}^{M} \mu_{mn}\phi_{np} = \delta_{mp}, \quad m, p = 1, 2, \ldots, M. \tag{6.16}$$

The μ_{mn}'s are also complex numbers, and $\boldsymbol{\mu}$ is Hermitian, $\mu^*_{mn} = \mu_{nm}$. Later we shall find this form convenient in dealing with narrowband Gaussian random processes. It is derived in Appendix D from the usual form represented by eq. (4.2). Here $\tilde{p}_M(z_1, \ldots, z_M)$ is *not* a joint probability density function of the variables $z_1, z_2, \ldots, z_M$ in the ordinary sense.

The joint characteristic function of the variables $x_1, x_2, \ldots, x_M, y_1, y_2, \ldots, y_M$ can be written in a similarly concise form. It is the $2M$-dimensional Fourier transform of the joint p.d.f. in eq. (6.15), and as shown in Appendix D it can be expressed as

$$\begin{aligned} h(u_{x1}, \ldots, u_{xM}, u_{y1}, \ldots, u_{yM}) \\ &= \tilde{h}(w_1, \ldots, w_M; w_1^*, \ldots, w_M^*) \\ &= \mathbf{E} \exp \left[i \sum_{n=1}^{M} (u_{xn}x_n + u_{yn}y_n) \right] \\ &= \exp \left(\tfrac{1}{2} i \sum_{n=1}^{M} (w_n^* \zeta_n + w_n \zeta_n^*) - \tfrac{1}{2} \sum_{m=1}^{M} \sum_{n=1}^{M} \phi_{mn} w_m^* w_n \right) \end{aligned} \tag{6.17}$$

with $w_n = u_{xn} + iu_{yn}$.

By writing

$$\begin{aligned} \tilde{h}(w_1, \ldots, w_M; w_1^*, \ldots, w_M^*) \\ &= \mathbf{E} \exp \left[\tfrac{1}{2} i \sum_{n=1}^{M} (w_n^* z_n + w_n z_n^*) \right] \end{aligned} \tag{6.18}$$

and regarding w_n and w_n^* as mathematically distinct variables, one can derive the covariances of the samples of a circular Gaussian process by differentiating eq. (6.17). Thus if we take $\zeta_n = 0$ for simplicity, we find

$$\{z_m, z_n^*\} = \mathbf{E}(z_m z_n^*) = -4 \frac{\partial^2 \tilde{h}}{\partial w_m^* \, \partial w_n} = 2\phi_{mn} \tag{6.19}$$

as in eq. (6.11), and

$$\begin{aligned} \mathbf{E}(z_1^* z_2^* z_3 z_4) &= 16 \frac{\partial^4 \tilde{h}}{\partial w_1 \, \partial w_2 \, \partial w_3^* \, \partial w_4^*} \\ &= 4(\phi_{31}\phi_{42} + \phi_{32}\phi_{41}), \end{aligned} \tag{6.20}$$

the derivatives being evaluated at $w_m = w_m^* = 0$. Formulas for moments of higher order have been given by Reed (1962). Again with $\zeta_m = 0$, the expected value of a product vanishes unless the numbers of starred and unstarred factors are equal.

Ordinary white noise cannot be expressed directly in terms of quadrature components, for its spectral density occupies much too wide a range of frequencies. However, in problems concerned with the detection of narrowband signals in white noise it would be convenient to represent the input noise in this way. To this end one can assume that the signals and the noise have passed through a filter whose passband includes the spectrum of the signals, but is much wider. Usually it will be possible to treat this new filter as narrowband. It can have little effect on signal detectability, however, for it cuts out only noise components with frequencies far from those of the signal, affecting the signal hardly at all. Then one can expediently write the white noise $n(t)$ as

$$n(t) = \text{Rl}\, N(t)e^{i\Omega t}, \quad N(t) = x(t)+iy(t), \tag{6.21}$$

with

$$\begin{aligned} &\overline{x(t_1)x(t_2)} = \overline{y(t_1)y(t_2)} = N\,\delta(t_1-t_2), \\ &\overline{x(t_1)y(t_2)} = 0, \\ &\overline{N(t_1)N^*(t_2)} = 2N\,\delta(t_1-t_2), \\ &\overline{N(t_1)N(t_2)} = 0, \\ &\tilde{\Phi}(\omega) = N/2, \quad \tilde{\phi}(\tau) = N\,\delta(\tau). \end{aligned} \tag{6.22}$$

These relations are consistent with the definition in eq. (6.3), as well as with eqs. (6.5) and (6.6), in which both $\Phi_i(\omega)$ and $\tilde{\Phi}_i(\omega)$ can be set equal to $N/2$. There is no formal difficulty in regarding white noise as narrow-band noise whose spectral density is constant over a range of frequencies—usually those of a quasiharmonic signal—of interest in many detection problems, and a considerable simplification often follows from this viewpoint.

PROBLEMS

1. The random variables $x_1, x_2, \ldots$ are statistically independent and uniformly distributed over the interval $(-\frac{1}{2}, \frac{1}{2})$. Find the probability density functions of $y_2 = x_1+x_2$, $y_3 = x_1+x_2+x_3$. Observe that the p.d.f. of y_3 already somewhat resembles a Gaussian density function. The p.d.f. of $y_4 = x_1+x_2+x_3+x_4$ will look even more Gaussian.

2. Find the variance of the output of the integrating filter used as in Section 1, part (c) to measure the mean value of a stochastic process $x(t)$. Evaluate it for $K(\tau) = 1/T$ $0 < \tau < T$, $K(\tau) = 0, \tau < 0, \tau > T$; and for an input process of autocovariance $\phi(\tau) = \sigma^2 e^{-\mu|\tau|}$. What are the spectral densities of the input process $x(t)$ and the output process $y(t)$ of this filter?

3. A Gaussian random process $x(t)$ has mean 0 and autocovariance $\phi(\tau)$. The variance of the process is estimated by forming the quantity

$$Z = \frac{1}{T}\int_0^T [x(t)]^2\, dt.$$

Find the expected value of Z and show that

$$\text{Var}\, Z = 4T^{-2}\int_0^T (T-s)\,[\phi(s)]^2\, ds.$$

4. Let a stochastic process $x(t)$ consist of a succession of square pulses of duration T. They occur at random times t_k with a rate ν pulses per second and with statistically independent random amplitudes a_k, $\mathbf{E}(a_k) = 0$. Find the spectral density and the autocovariance of the process. If the process is passed through a simple integrating filter with impulse response $K(\tau) = 1/S$, $0 < \tau < S$, $K(\tau) = 0$, $\tau < 0$, $\tau > S$, what is the spectral density of the output?

5. For the circuit shown in Fig. II. 1, which is in thermal equilibrium at absolute temperature T, what is the spectral density of the fluctuating voltage $E(t)$ measured between the terminals?

6. Prove that in the simply resonant circuit discussed in part (b) of Section 5 the mean energy in the inductance is

$$\tfrac{1}{2}L\overline{I^2} = kT/2$$

by integrating over the spectral density of the current $I(t)$.

7. In the circuit in Fig. II. 3, let $e_1(t)$ be the voltage across the capacitor C and $e_2(t)$ be the voltage across the inductor L. Find the covariance $\mathbf{E}[e_1(t)e_2(t)]$ when the circuit is in thermal equilibrium.

8. Let the input $x(t)$ to a linear stationary filter be white noise; call the output $y(t)$. Show that the covariance function $\mathbf{E}[x(t)y(t+\tau)]$ between the input and the output is proportional to the impulse response of the filter.

9. Let $\tilde{\phi}(\tau)$ be the complex autocovariance function of a narrowband Gaussian random process of mean value 0. In terms of $\tilde{\phi}(\tau)$ find the autocovariance function of the output of a quadratic rectifier to which $x(t)$ is applied. The rectifier forms $[x(t)]^2$ and completely attenuates the components of twice the carrier frequency.

10. Let the autocovariance function of a mean-zero stationary process $x(t)$ be $\phi(\tau)$. Show that the autocovariance function of the derivative $\dot{x}(t) = dx/dt$ is $-d^2\phi(\tau)/d\tau^2$ and that $x(t)$ and $\dot{x}(t)$ when measured at the same instant are uncorrelated. For $x(t)$ Gaussian write down the joint p.d.f. of x and $\dot{x}$.

11. Show that in general the autocovariance of a stationary stochastic process is given by

$$\phi(t_1-t_2) = \mathbf{E}[x_1\mathbf{E}(x_2 \mid x_1)]$$

where $x(t_i) = x_i$, $i = 1, 2$, and $\mathbf{E}(x_2 \mid x_1)$ is the conditional expected value of x_2 given x_1. Compare with eq. (4.13).

12. A stochastic process with mean zero and spectral density $\Phi(\omega)$ is passed separately through two parallel filters with transfer functions $Y_1(\omega)$ and $Y_2(\omega)$, whose outputs are $y_1(t)$ and $y_2(t)$, respectively. Express the covariance $\mathbf{E}[y_1(t)y_2(t-\tau)]$ in terms of $Y_1(\omega)$, $Y_2(\omega)$, and $\Phi(\omega)$, and discuss the correlation between components of the same stochastic process lying in disjoint spectral bands.

BIBLIOGRAPHY (II)

Papers

1928 JOHNSON, J. B., "Thermal Agitation of Electricity in Conductors", *Phys. Rev.* **32,** 97–109 (July).

NYQUIST, H., "Thermal Agitation of Electric Charge in Conductors", *Phys. Rev.* **32,** 110–13 (July).

1943 CHANDRASEKHAR, S., "Stochastic Problems in Physics and Astronomy", *Rev. Mod. Phys.* **15,** 1–89 (Jan.) (reprinted in Wax, 1954).

1944 RICE, S. O., "The Mathematical Analysis of Random Noise", *Bell Sys. Tech. J.* **23,** 282–332 (July); **24,** 46–156 (Jan. 1945) (reprinted in Wax, 1954).

1945 WANG, M. C. and UHLENBECK, G. E., "On the Theory of the Brownian Motion (II)", *Rev. Mod. Phys.* **17,** 323–42 (Apr., July) (reprinted in Wax, 1954).

1949 BUNIMOVICH, V. I., "The Fluctuation Process as a Vibration with Random Amplitude and Phase", *J. Tech. Phys. U.S.S.R.* **19,** 1231–59 (Nov.).

1951 CALLEN, H. B. and WELTON, T. A., "Irreversibility and Generalized Noise", *Phys. Rev.* **83,** 34–40 (July 1).

GRENANDER, U., "On Empirical Spectral Analysis of Stochastic Processes", *Arkiv för Mat.* **1,** 503–31 (no. 35).

1952 DAVENPORT, W. B., JOHNSON, R. A. and MIDDLETON, D., "Statistical Errors in

Measurements on Random Time Functions", *J. Appl. Phys.* **23,** 377–88 (Apr.).

1957 ARENS, R., "Complex Processes for Envelopes of Normal Noise", *Trans. I.R.E.* **IT–3,** 204–7 (Sept.).

1958 BLACKMAN, R. B. and TUKEY, J. W., "The Measurement of Power Spectra from the Point of View of Communications Engineering", *Bell Sys. Tech. J.* **37,** 185–282 (Jan.), 485–569 (Mar.).

DUGUNDJI, J., "Envelopes and Pre-Envelopes of Real Waveforms", *Trans. I.R.E.* **IT–4,** 53–57 (Mar.).

1961 KALMAN, R. E. and BUCY, R. S., "New Results in Linear Filtering and Prediction Theory", *Trans. A.S.M.E., J. of Basic Engrg.* **83D,** 95–108 (Mar.).

1962 REED, I. S., "On a Moment Theorem for Complex Gaussian Processes", *Trans. I.R.E.* **IT–8,** 194–5 (Apr.).

1965 JENKINS, G. M., "A Survey of Spectral Analysis", *Appl. Statistics* **14,** 2–32 (no. 1).

Books

1946 CRAMÉR, H., *Mathematical Methods of Statistics*, Princeton University Press, Princeton, N.J.

1948 LÉVY, P., *Processus Stochastiques et Mouvement Brownien*, Gauthier-Villars, Paris.

1949 SHANNON, C. E. and WEAVER, W., *The Mathematical Theory of Communication*, University of Illinois Press, Urbana, Ill.

1950 LAWSON, J. L. and UHLENBECK, G. E., *Threshold Signals*, McGraw-Hill Book Co., New York, N.Y.

1953 BLANC-LAPIERRE, A. and FORTET, R., *Théorie des Fonctions Aléatoires*, Masson et Cie., Paris.

DOOB, J. L., *Stochastic Processes*, John Wiley & Sons, Inc., New York, N.Y.

1954 VAN DER ZIEL, A., *Noise*, Prentice-Hall, Inc., Englewood Cliffs, N.J.

WAX, N., *Selected Papers on Noise and Stochastic Processes*, Dover Publications, Inc., New York, N.Y.

WOLD, H., *A Study in the Analysis of Stationary Time Series*, Almqvist & Wiksell, Stockholm (2nd ed.).

1955 BARTLETT, M. S., *Stochastic Processes*, Cambridge University Press, Cambridge, England.

1957 GRENANDER, U. and ROSENBLATT, M., *Statistical Analysis of Stationary Time Series*, John Wiley & Sons, Inc., New York, N.Y.

1958 DAVENPORT, W. B. and ROOT, W. L., *An Introduction to the Theory of Random Signals and Noise*, McGraw-Hill Book Co., New York, N.Y.

LANDAU, L. and LIFSHITZ, E., *Statistical Physics*, E. and R. F. Peierls, trans., Addison-Wesley Publishing Co., Reading, Mass.

WIENER, N., *Nonlinear Problems in Random Theory*, John Wiley & Sons, Inc., New York, N.Y.

1960 BENNETT, W. R., *Electrical Noise*, McGraw-Hill Book Co., New York, N.Y.

MIDDLETON, D., *An Introduction to Statistical Communication Theory*, McGraw-Hill Book Co., New York, N.Y.

PARZEN, E., *Modern Probability Theory and Its Applications*, John Wiley & Sons, Inc., New York, N.Y.

1962 GNEDENKO, B. V., *The Theory of Probability*, B. D. Seckler, trans., Chelsea Publishing Co., New York, N.Y.

PARZEN, E., *Stochastic Processes*, Holden-Day, Inc., San Francisco, Calif.

1963 HARMON, W., *Principles of the Statistical Theory of Communication*, McGraw-Hill Book Co., New York, N.Y.

Stratonovich, R., *Topics in the Theory of Random Noise*, R. A. Silverman, trans., Gordon & Breach, New York, N.Y.

1965 Blackman, R. B., *Linear Data-Smoothing and Prediction in Theory and Practice*, Addison-Wesley Publishing Co., Reading, Mass.

Fry, T. C., *Probability and Its Engineering Uses*, D. Van Nostrand Co., Princeton, N.J. (2nd ed.).

Papoulis, A., *Probability, Random Variables, and Stochastic Processes*, McGraw-Hill Book Co., New York, N.Y.

1966 Kendall, M. G. and Stuart, A., *The Advanced Theory of Statistics*, vol. 3, ch. 49, 'Spectrum Theory', pp. 454–71, Hafner Publishing Co., New York, N.Y.

III
HYPOTHESIS TESTING

1. SIGNAL DETECTION AND STATISTICS

The voltage at the input terminals of a radar or communications receiver is always fluctuating in a random manner because of the chaotic thermal motions of the surroundings. Any signals that are present—echoes from a distant target or information-bearing communication signals—are added to this noisy background; and if the strength of the signals is small, they are difficult to distinguish from the noise. The task of an observer is to decide whether signals of some specified type are present in the total input voltage received during a certain interval of time. No matter what procedure he uses to make these decisions, there is always a chance that he may be wrong, declaring a signal is present when there is none, or vice versa. He seeks a way of handling the receiver input so that the decisions are made with the greatest possible success in a series of observations. His strategy will depend not only on the nature of the signals to be detected and on the character of the noise that corrupts them, but also on his definition of success.

At first we shall deal with the simplest type of detection problem. If the signal $s(t)$ is present, it appears at a precisely known time, and its shape and amplitude are known in detail. The receiver input voltage $v(t)$ is observed over an interval of time that would contain the signal. The observer must then choose between two possible situations: (H_0) there is no signal, and the input consists of noise alone, $v(t) = n(t)$; or (H_1) the signal is present, and $v(t) = s(t)+n(t)$. These two statements are called *hypotheses*, and the observer must pick the one that he believes is the better description of reality. The decision is uncertain because the form of the noise voltage $n(t)$ cannot be predicted in advance; at most one possesses a statistical description of the noise as a stochastic process. This detection problem might arise in the following way. Once every hour a certain action is to be performed if the signal $s(t)$ is received; otherwise the action is omitted. If the commanding signal is transmitted, this is done at a fixed time during the hour, and the same signal is always sent. The observer carries out the designated action each time he chooses hypothesis H_1. Since mistakenly omitting or performing the action may be costly, he needs a way of processing the input voltage $v(t)$ so as to minimize losses due to incorrect decisions.

Because of the stochastic nature of the noise, we are confronted here with a problem in the testing of statistical hypotheses, and the present chapter will introduce the theory of such testing, which is based on the theory of probability. In the next chapter the theory will be applied to this simplest of detection problems, after which more complicated situations will be analyzed. The theory of hypothesis testing may be said to have begun with the work of Thomas Bayes (1763) on "inverse" or conditional probability. Tests that minimize the chance of error were proposed by Neyman and Pearson (1933). The notions of cost and risk were introduced by Wald (1939), who can be credited with much of the recent development of the theory along the lines of the theory of games. Some of these ideas were applied to radar detection by Siegert and others at the M.I.T. Radiation Laboratory during World War II (Lawson and Uhlenbeck, 1950).

Communication receivers based on conditional probability were recommended by Kotel'nikov in a dissertation written in the U.S.S.R. in 1947, published there in 1956, and translated into English in 1959. In the meantime Woodward and Davies (1952) and Woodward (1953) suggested applying conditional probability to signal detection. The analysis of signal detection in terms of statistical decision theory was developed by Middleton (1953) while the design of receivers on the basis of the likelihood ratio was being advanced by a group at the University of Michigan (Peterson, Birdsall, and Fox, 1954). Since then many problems in the detection of signals and the measurement of signal parameters have been studied in the light of the theory of statistical decisions.

In pursuing this subject the reader should keep in mind that mathematics is a form of reasoning; by itself it tells us nothing about the world. Science describes our observations of the world in terms of laws, hypotheses, and theories, whose purpose is to encompass a wide range of phenomena in the simplest possible form. Mathematics is used to derive the logical consequences of a proposed theory, and these are tested by experiment to determine whether they too are a satisfactory description of some aspect of nature. If the theory fails to describe the results of such an experiment, its validity is placed in doubt and modifications are sought.

Statistics is mathematical reasoning about empirical data; its principal tool is the theory of probability. Its purpose is often to produce a simple description or condensation of a mass of data, in order to ease the task of the mind in comprehending the data and fitting them into what is already known about the phenomenon studied. This condensation may be expressed in terms of quantities like means, variances, and confidence limits. The simplification is made on the basis of certain conventional assumptions, such as that certain variations or "errors" in the data can be described by a normal probability distribution—assumptions that have worked well in practice and can often be justified by simpler ones about the causes of errors, but that must be remembered in interpreting the results of a statistical analysis. Such an analysis is often followed by human decisions and actions—lots of manufactured goods are accepted or rejected, missiles are fired to attack suspected radar targets, and so forth—and much of the newest development of statistical decision theory has been concerned with adapting the statistical procedure to the decisions and actions that follow it, aiming usually to minimize the average total costs incurred.

In radar and communications the data to be interpreted are the sequence of voltages measured at the terminals of an antenna. The errors in the data are introduced largely by the noise, for which we possess a good physical theory, couched in the language of probability. The observer must take certain actions on the basis of his interpretation of these input voltages; the task of the statistical theory of signal detection is to find a way to process these data that enables him to decide on a course of action with maximum efficiency. The various decision criteria discussed in this chapter formalize the concepts of efficiency and long-run success, and by exploiting the analogy between the observer's task and the statistical testing of hypotheses, optimum detectors can be designed.

2. TESTING OF SIMPLE HYPOTHESES BY A SINGLE MEASUREMENT

(a) *An Introductory Example*

To introduce the concepts of the statistical theory of hypothesis testing, we shall imagine that an observer measures a single quantity x and chooses on the basis of the outcome of the measurement one of two hypotheses H_0 and H_1 as being the better description of the experimental situation. If the value of x always turned out to be a_0 when hypothesis H_0 is true, and a_1 when H_1 applies, there would be no problem. But on account of errors in the measurement or as a result of some factors not understood, the outcome is a random variable that must be described statistically, by giving its probability density functions $p_0(x)$ and $p_1(x)$ under hypotheses H_0 and H_1 respectively. If both these p.d.f.s are completely given and depend on no unknown parameters, the hypotheses are called "simple".

The observer must adopt a strategy that assigns a definite choice of one hypothesis or the other to each possible outcome of the measurement. The strategy can be considered a division of the range of values of x into two regions R_0 and R_1, such that the observer chooses hypothesis H_0 when the outcome x lies in region R_0 and hypothesis H_1 when x lies in R_1. The problem is to determine these regions to ensure the greatest long-run success in many repetitions of the experiment.

As a definite but fanciful example, suppose that a weatherman is to decide each day between two hypotheses H_0, "It will rain tomorrow", and H_1, "It will be fair tomorrow". The decision is to be based on a single quantity, the average rate of change x of the barometric pressure during the past 24 hours. From records compiled over many years the probability density function $p_0(x)$, describing the distribution of the rates x on days preceding rainy days, and the p.d.f. $p_1(x)$, describing the distribution of x on days preceding fair ones, are computed. For instance, the rate x may be Gaussian or normally distributed, with means a_0 or a_1 and variance σ^2:

$$p_k(x) = (2\pi\sigma^2)^{-\frac{1}{2}} \exp [-(x-a_k)^2/2\sigma^2], \qquad k = 0, 1, \tag{2.1}$$

where $a_0 < 0 < a_1$. These density functions are sketched in Fig. III.1. The first p.d.f. implies that on days before rainy days the barometer tends to fall with an average rate $|a_0|$, but the rate is not always the same, being

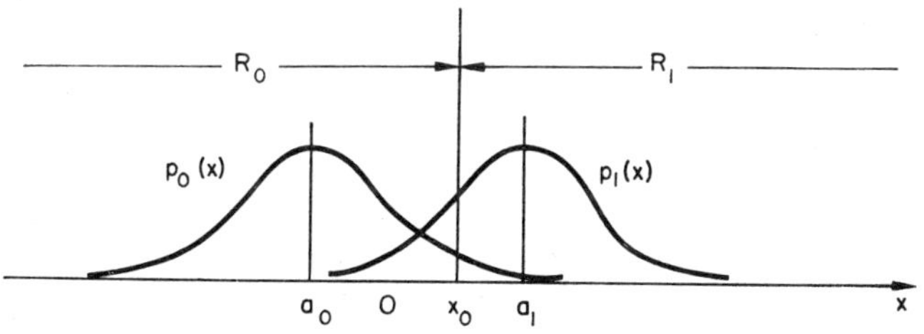

FIG. III.1. Probability density functions under hypotheses H_0 and H_1.

sometimes higher and sometimes lower for reasons the weatherman may not understand in detail. Similarly the second implies that before a fair day the barometer usually rises, with an average rate a_1. Besides these probability density functions for the rate x, the records also provide the fractions ζ of rainy days and $(1-\zeta)$ of fair days during some long period in the past. We may call ζ the *prior probability* of a rainy day and $(1-\zeta)$ the prior probability of a fair one.

Using the above information, how shall the weatherman determine his strategy? The structure of the p.d.f.s indicates that a simple dichotomy of the range of values of x will be sufficient, letting the region R_0 of values leading to the choice of hypothesis H_0 be given by $x < x_0$, while R_1 is made up of the values $x > x_0$. But no matter where the observer sets his point of division x_0, he will occasionally make a wrong decision. In fact the probability Q_0 of choosing hypothesis H_1 when H_0 is true, a so-called "error of the first kind", is

$$Q_0 = \int_{x_0}^{\infty} p_0(x)\, dx; \tag{2.2}$$

it is represented by the area under the curve of $p_0(x)$ to the right of x_0 (Fig. III.1). The probability of choosing H_0 when H_1 is true, an "error of the second kind", is

$$Q_1 = \int_{-\infty}^{x_0} p_1(x)\, dx. \tag{2.3}$$

The value of x_0 that the observer uses will depend on how much these mistakes cost him. To make the situation more definite, we can imagine that the weatherman is fined a certain amount for each type of mistake; for an error of the first kind he is charged an amount C_0 and for one of the second kind C_1. The product C_0Q_0 is called the *risk* associated with hypothesis H_0; it is made up in this problem solely of the average fine the weatherman incurs for incorrectly predicting fair weather. Similarly the product C_1Q_1 is the risk associated with hypothesis H_1. The average risk per decision is

$$\begin{aligned} \bar{C}(x_0) &= \zeta C_0 Q_0 + (1-\zeta) C_1 Q_1 \\ &= \zeta C_0 \int_{x_0}^{\infty} p_0(x)\, dx + (1-\zeta) C_1 \int_{-\infty}^{x_0} p_1(x)\, dx. \end{aligned} \tag{2.4}$$

When the weatherman makes his predictions in the manner described above, his total fine will be nearly $n\bar{C}(x_0)$ in a large number n of daily forecasts, provided the given statistical description of the weather continues to be valid.

The observer naturally picks that value of x_0 that minimizes his average risk $\bar{C}(x_0)$. To find this point of dichotomy, differentiate eq. (2.4) with respect to x_0 and set the derivative equal to zero. The result is

$$\frac{p_1(x_0)}{p_0(x_0)} = \frac{\zeta C_0}{(1-\zeta) C_1} = \Lambda_0, \tag{2.5}$$

minimizing ave risk per decision

vhich for the distributions of eq. (2.1) yields

$$x_0 = (a_0+a_1)/2+\frac{\sigma^2}{a_1-a_0}\ln\frac{\zeta C_0}{(1-\zeta)C_1}. \tag{2.6}$$

f $\zeta = 1-\zeta = \frac{1}{2}$ and $C_0 = C_1$, this gives $x_0 = (a_0+a_1)/2$, the average of he two rates of change of barometric pressure. However, if the weather-nan's fine C_0 for predicting fair weather when it rains is high enough hat $\zeta C_0 > (1-\zeta)C_1$, he will pick x_0 somewhat larger than the average ate in order to cut down his losses. When the point x_0 has been chosen y eqs. (2.5) or (2.6), it can be substituted back into eq. (2.4) to determine he minimum average risk $\bar{C}_{min}$. The weatherman may compare $\bar{C}_{min}$ with is salary to decide whether it is worth his while to retain his position.

b) *The Bayes Criterion*

The rule that the decision strategy be picked to minimize the average isk is known as the "Bayes criterion"; it is a natural one for an observer vho must make a large number of decisions under similar circumstances. efore it can be applied, the costs attendant on each type of error must be scertained, and the prior probabilities of the two hypotheses must be nown. As in the example above, the prior probability ζ of hypothesis I_0† may be the relative frequency with which H_0 was true in the past, the navoidable assumption being made that this frequency will hold in the uture. Otherwise, ζ may be computed from a physical theory of the phe-omenon being observed (in part (a), the weather). Such a theory will at ome point use an assumption about the distribution of certain random, npredictable effects, and it must be possible in principle to check this ssumption by comparing the calculated value of the prior probability ζ ith the actual relative frequency of hypothesis H_0 over a long series of bservations. The concept of prior probability used in the derivation of e Bayes strategy demands this possibility of a large number of observa-ons or trials.

In general one can list the costs of each type of decision as elements of cost matrix **C**:

$$\mathbf{C} = \begin{bmatrix} C_{00} & C_{01} \\ C_{10} & C_{11} \end{bmatrix}, \tag{2.7}$$

here C_{ij} is the cost of choosing hypothesis H_i when actually H_j is true $, j = 0, 1)$. The relative cost of an error of the first kind is $C_{10}-C_{00}$,

† By "the probability of hypothesis H_0" we mean "the probability of the event ypothesis H_0 is true'".

of an error of the second kind $C_{01}-C_{11}$; both are positive. In the abov example the cost matrix takes the form

$$\mathbf{C} = \begin{bmatrix} 0 & C_1 \\ C_0 & 0 \end{bmatrix}.$$

The costs depend on the action taken after each decision and on the con sequences of this action.

Let hypothesis H_0 be chosen whenever the outcome x of the measure ment lies in the region R_0, and let H_1 be chosen when x lies in R_1. If th prior probabilities of hypotheses H_0 and H_1 are ζ and $(1-\zeta)$ respectively the average risk per decision is

$$\begin{aligned}\bar{C} = \zeta &\left[C_{00} \int_{R_0} p_0(x)\, dx + C_{10} \int_{R_1} p_0(x)\, dx\right] \\ &+ (1-\zeta)\left[C_{01} \int_{R_0} p_1(x)\, dx + C_{11} \int_{R_1} p_1(x)\, dx\right].\end{aligned} \tag{2.8}$$

The terms in the brackets are the risks connected with the two hypotheses and they are weighted according to the relative frequency with which eac hypothesis occurs. It will be shown immediately that the average risk $\bar{C}$ is a minimum when the regions R_0 and R_1 are defined as follows. For eac observation x compute the quantity

$$\Lambda(x) = p_1(x)/p_0(x); \tag{2.9}$$

this is called the *likelihood ratio*. The region R_0 consists of values of x fo which $\Lambda(x) < \Lambda_0$, and R_1 of values of x for which $\Lambda(x) > \Lambda_0$, where th critical value Λ_0 is given by

$$\Lambda_0 = \frac{\zeta(C_{10}-C_{00})}{(1-\zeta)(C_{01}-C_{11})}. \tag{2.10}$$

This strategy is known as the "Bayes solution" of the decision problem As we shall see later, the Bayes solution can be expressed in terms of th likelihood ratio even when the decision is based on measurements of mor than one variable. The minimum value $\bar{C}_{\min}$ is called the "Bayes risk"

To prove that this strategy yields minimum average risk, we compute th average risk $\bar{C}'$ when some other strategy, represented by the regions R and R_1', is used. We denote the set of values of x common to the region R_0' and R_1 by r_1, and the set of those common to R_0 and R_1' by r_2; in th notation of set theory, $r_1 = R_0' \cap R_1$ and $r_2 = R_0 \cap R_1'$. The difference c the average risks is then

$$\begin{aligned}
\bar{C}'-\bar{C}_{\min} &= \zeta(C_{10}-C_{00})\left[\int_{r_2} p_0(x)\,dx-\int_{r_1} p_0(x)\,dx\right] \\
&\quad -(1-\zeta)(C_{01}-C_{11})\left[\int_{r_2} p_1(x)\,dx-\int_{r_1} p_1(x)\,dx\right] \\
&= (1-\zeta)(C_{01}-C_{11})\left\{\int_{r_2}[\Lambda_0 p_0(x)-p_1(x)]\,dx\right. \\
&\quad \left.+\int_{r_1}[p_1(x)-\Lambda_0 p_0(x)]\,dx\right\}.
\end{aligned} \tag{2.11}$$

In the region of intersection r_1, $p_1(x) > \Lambda_0 p_0(x)$; in r_2, $p_1(x) < \Lambda_0 p_0(x)$, where Λ_0 is given by eq. (2.10). Hence the right side of eq. (2.11) is positive and $\bar{C}' > \bar{C}_{\min}$, which was to be proved.

The Bayes solution can be described in another way. The conditional probability of hypothesis H_0, given that the value x has been obtained in the measurement, is

$$p(H_0 \mid x) = \zeta p_0(x)/p(x) \tag{2.12a}$$

and the conditional probability of H_1 is

$$p(H_1 \mid x) = (1-\zeta)\, p_1(x)/p(x), \tag{2.12b}$$

where $p(x) = \zeta p_0(x)+(1-\zeta)p_1(x)$ is the total probability density function of the outcome x in all trials. The "conditional risk" attending a decision in favor of hypothesis H_0 is defined by

$$C(H_0 \mid x) = C_{00}p(H_0 \mid x)+C_{01}p(H_1 \mid x);$$

the conditional risk of choosing H_1 is

$$C(H_1 \mid x) = C_{10}p(H_0 \mid x)+C_{11}p(H_1 \mid x).$$

The observer chooses that hypothesis for which the conditional risk, given the outcome x of the measurement, is the smaller. Using eqs. (2.12a, b) the reader can show that this prescription is equivalent to the one given above. The conditional risk $C(H_0 \mid x)$ would be the average cost per decision if hypothesis H_0 were picked in all cases in which the outcome of the measurement lies in a small region in the neighborhood of the value x.

If the relative costs of the two kinds of error are equal,

$$C_{10}-C_{00} = C_{01}-C_{11},$$

the hypothesis is chosen whose conditional probability is the greater. These conditional probabilities, $p(H_0 \mid x)$ and $p(H_1 \mid x)$, are sometimes called "inverse" probabilities, or the *posterior* probabilities of the two hypotheses. The idea of basing decisions on posterior probabilities is credited to the Rev. Thomas Bayes (1763). In detection theory Middleton (1953) labeled it the criterion of the "ideal observer". When the hypothesis with the greater posterior probability is always selected, the total probability of error

$$P_e = \zeta Q_0 + (1-\zeta)Q_1$$

is minimized. As this criterion is a special form of the Bayes criterion, we need not mention it specifically in the sequel.

(c) *The Minimax Criterion*

It may happen that the observer is unable to estimate the prior probabilities ζ and $(1-\zeta)$ of the two hypotheses H_0 and H_1. For instance, H_1 may never have occurred naturally in the past at all—though it could have been created artificially in order to measure the p.d.f. $p_1(x)$—and hence there is no information about the relative frequency with which it can be expected to occur in the future. With the value of ζ unknown the Bayes solution cannot be found. It has been suggested that the criterion of minimum average risk then be replaced by the so-called "minimax criterion", which is motivated by an analogy to the theory of games. It directs the observer to use the Bayes strategy appropriate for that value of ζ for which the Bayes risk is a maximum. An extensive treatment of the application of game theory to statistical testing of hypotheses has been given by Blackwell and Girshick (1954).

Use of the minimax criterion is often justified by the following argument. Nature, or some other adversary, and the observer are considered opponents in a two-person, zero-sum game. At each play of the game Nature picks one of the two hypotheses H_0 and H_1 or, what is the same thing, one of the two p.d.f.s $p_0(x)$ and $p_1(x)$. A value of a random variable x is somehow generated by a chance mechanism so that its p.d.f. is the one chosen by Nature; on the basis of this value of x the observer tries to guess which hypothesis Nature selected. The cost matrix $\mathbf{C}$ of eq. (2.7) represents the "payoff" at the end of the game. If the observer guesses H_1 when Nature has picked H_0, he must pay her an amount C_{10}, and so forth. Nature has at her disposal the relative frequencies ζ and $(1-\zeta)$ with which she can pick the two hypotheses; the observer can work out any way he likes to make his choice. Each tries to attain the maximum gain, or minimum loss, averaged over a large number of plays.

If the observer knew the value of ζ Nature is using, he would employ the Bayes solution appropriate to that value of ζ, whereupon his loss would be the Bayes risk $\bar{C}_{\min}(\zeta)$, a graph of which as a function of ζ looks somewhat like the one in Fig. III.2. If the observer uses the Bayes solution for a prior probability $\zeta = \zeta_1$, and if nature uses some other value ζ, the

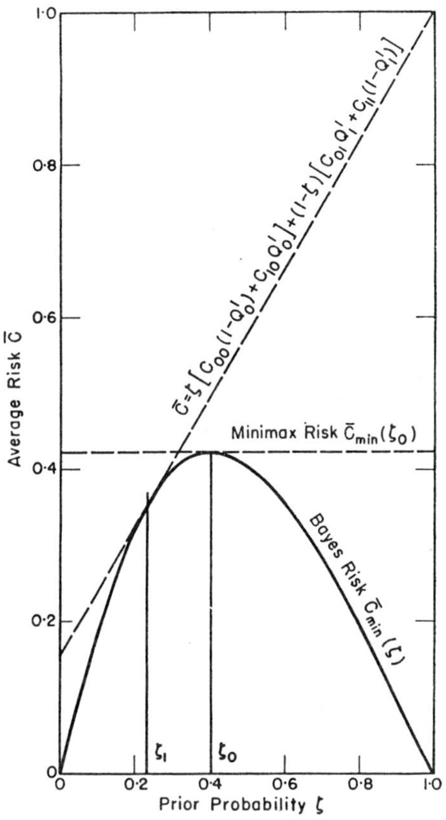

FIG. III.2. The Bayes and minimax risks.

average loss to the observer will be given by a straight line tangent to the curve $\bar{C}_{\min}(\zeta)$ at $\zeta = \zeta_1$. The equation of this line is†

$$\begin{aligned} \bar{C} &= \zeta[C_{00}(1-Q_0')+C_{10}Q_0']+(1-\zeta)\,[C_{01}Q_1'+C_{11}(1-Q_1')], \\ Q_0' &= Q_0(\zeta_1), \quad Q_1' = Q_1(\zeta_1). \end{aligned} \tag{2.13}$$

† Any point on this line, for $\zeta \neq \zeta_1$, represents the average risk for a possible strategy, namely the strategy using decision regions appropriate to a prior probability ζ_1. Since the Bayes strategy yields the minimum average risk, the curve $\bar{C}_{\min}(\zeta)$ must lie below the straight line for all $\zeta \neq \zeta_1$.

This loss could be quite large—certainly larger than necessary. But if the observer uses the Bayes solution for the value $\zeta = \zeta_0$ at which the Bayes risk $\bar{C}_{\min}(\zeta)$ is a maximum, the straight line is horizontal; and he is sure that no matter what relative frequency ζ Nature actually picks, his loss will not exceed $\bar{C}_{\min}(\zeta_0)$. Nature, on the other hand, is led to use just the relative frequency ζ_0; for if she picked any other, and if the observer happened to set up the Bayes strategy for a value of ζ near hers, her average gain would be smaller than the amount $\bar{C}_{\min}(\zeta_0)$ that she might otherwise attain. The Bayes strategy for $\zeta = \zeta_0$ is called the "minimax strategy" and $\bar{C}_{\min}(\zeta_0)$ the "minimax risk".

The curve of Fig. III.2 has been plotted for the example of the weatherman in section (a), using the values $a_0 = -1$, $a_1 = +1$, $\sigma = 2$, $C_0 = 2$, and $C_1 = 1$. By eq. (2.6) the Bayes criterion directs the observer to predict rain (choose H_0) whenever $x < x_0 = 2 \ln [2\zeta/(1-\zeta)]$. The probabilities of error are found from eqs. (2.1–3) to be

$$Q_0(x_0) = \operatorname{erfc} [(x_0 - a_0)/\sigma],$$
$$Q_1(x_0) = 1 - \operatorname{erfc} [(x_0 - a_1)/\sigma]$$

where erfc x is the error-function integral

$$\operatorname{erfc} x = (2\pi)^{-\frac{1}{2}} \int_x^\infty \exp(-t^2/2)\, dt, \qquad (2.14)$$
$$\operatorname{erfc}(-\infty) = 1.$$

The Bayes risk is then

$$\bar{C}_{\min} = \zeta C_0 Q_0(x_0) + (1-\zeta) C_1 Q_1(x_0).$$

Its maximum occurs for $\zeta = 0.40$, for which $x_0 = 0.60$; and the minimax risk is $\bar{C}_{\min}(\zeta_0) = 0.42$. Of course, the assumption that Nature picks the frequency of rainy days to maximize the weatherman's losses is absurd, but in a case like this the observer can usually estimate the prior probability ζ from past experience and need not use the minimax criterion. The minimax solution is useful, nevertheless, in characterizing a decision problem in a manner that is independent of the evaluation of prior probabilities.

The straight line specified by $\bar{C}(\zeta)$ of eq. (2.13) intercepts the vertical lines $\zeta = 0$ and $\zeta = 1$, as in Fig. III.2, at the risks

$$c_0 = C_{00}(1-Q_0) + C_{10} Q_0,$$
$$c_1 = C_{01} Q_1 + C_{11}(1-Q_1)$$

of the two hypotheses. For the minimax solution the straight line is horizontal and the two risks are equal, $c_0 = c_1$. This condition provides an equation for the point of dichotomy x_0; in our example the equation is simply

$$C_0Q_0(x_0) = C_1Q_1(x_0).$$

The resulting risk $c_0 = c_1$ is the minimax risk.

(d) *The Neyman–Pearson Criterion*

In many situations not only the prior probabilities but also the costs are difficult to estimate or perhaps even to define. This is especially true in signal-detection problems in radar, where it is hard to judge the cost of failing to detect a target, and where the prior probability of a signal may not even be a meaningful concept. When hypothesis H_1 is true extremely rarely, the principal factor in the total average cost is the fraction Q_0 of trials in which H_1 is incorrectly chosen and an error of the first kind is made, whereupon some costly action is taken in vain. In a radar detection system, for instance, such a "false alarm" may lead to firing an expensive missile to attack a nonexistent target.

Under such circumstances it is appropriate for the observer to determine a value of the probability Q_0 that he can afford, and to seek a decision strategy that attains this value and at the same time yields the minimum possible probability Q_1 of making an error of the second kind. This strategy is said to fulfil the "Neyman–Pearson criterion". It corresponds in radar to maximizing the probability of detecting a target for a given false-alarm probability. In the theory of hypothesis testing Q_0 is called the "size" of the test and often denoted by α. The maximum attainable value of $(1-Q_1)$ is called the "power" of the test and denoted by β.

To apply this criterion when the decision is based on the outcome of a single measurement of some quantity x, the likelihood ratio of eq. (2.9) is computed as a function of x. It is compared with some fixed value Λ_0, and hypothesis H_0 is chosen if $\Lambda(x) < \Lambda_0$, H_1 if $\Lambda(x) > \Lambda_0$. Under hypothesis H_0 this likelihood ratio, which is also a random variable, has a probability density function $P_0(\Lambda)$; it is related to the known p.d.f. $p_0(x)$ by the relation

$$P_0(\Lambda)\, d\Lambda = p_0(x)\, dx \quad \text{for} \quad \Lambda(x) = p_1(x)/p_0(x).$$

The probability Q_0 of an error of the first kind is then

$$Q_0 = \int_{\Lambda_0}^{\infty} P_0(\Lambda)\, d\Lambda. \tag{2.15}$$

The value of Λ_0 is chosen so that Q_0 takes on the preassigned value. The probability of an error of the second kind is then determined by

$$Q_1 = \int_0^{\Lambda_0} P_1(\Lambda)\, d\Lambda, \tag{2.16}$$

where $P_1(\Lambda)$ is the p.d.f. of Λ under hypothesis H_1. In many problems the likelihood ratio is a monotone function of x, as in the example of part (a), and the application of the Neyman–Pearson criterion is almost trivial, for there is no minimization involved. When the decision is based on the outcome of a number of measurements, however, this is not so, as we shall see in the next section.

In the following chapters we shall deal mainly with the Neyman–Pearson criterion, for it seems to be the most appropriate one in signal detection problems. We lose nothing by this, however, for the Neyman–Pearson solution contains all the information needed to apply the Bayes and the minimax criteria. Even when many measurements are used, as we shall see, all three criteria require computation of a likelihood ratio of the same form. It is only the value of the quantity Λ_0 with which the ratio is compared that depends on the criterion. This value can be obtained from the results of the application of the Neyman–Pearson criterion.

These results are best presented in the form of a curve of the power $Q_d = 1-Q_1$ of the test versus the size Q_0. (In detection problems $Q_d = 1-Q_1$ is called the "detection probability", and Q_0 is known as the "false-alarm probability".) This curve is often called the "operating characteristic" of the test. It depends only on the p.d.f.s of the measured quantities under the two hypotheses, and not on any costs or prior probabilities. In Fig. III.3 the operating characteristic for the example of part (a) is drawn; it was computed by using the equations and values given in part (c).

The slope of the operating characteristic at any point is the critical value Λ_0 of the likelihood ratio,

$$dQ_d/dQ_0 = \Lambda_0; \tag{2.17}$$

this can be proved immediately by differentiating eqs. (2.15) and and (2.16) and using the relation $\Lambda = P_0(\Lambda)/P_1(\Lambda) = p_1(x)/p_0(x)$ (Peterson, Birdsall, and Fox, 1954). It also follows from the fact that the straight line of eq. (2.13) is tangent to the curve of the Bayes risk $\bar{C}_{\min}(\zeta)$ (Fig. III.2). In using the Bayes criterion one computes the value of Λ_0 by eq. (2.10) in terms of the known costs and prior probabilities. One then finds a point on the operating characteristic where the slope equals this value of Λ_0. This can easily be done by drawing a line having the proper slope and moving a straight-edge so that it remains parallel to this line, until the straight-edge becomes tangent to the operating characteristic. The point of tangency gives the values of Q_0 and $Q_d = 1-Q_1$ for the Bayes strategy. The Bayes risk

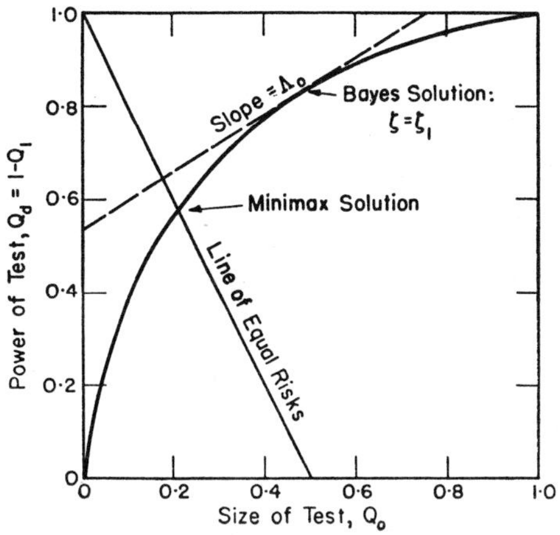

FIG. III.3. The operating characteristic for a statistical test.

can then be calculated from eq. (2.8). The dashed line in Fig. III.3 represents the solution corresponding to the value $\zeta = \zeta_1$ of the prior probability marked on Fig. III.2. ($\zeta_1 = 0.23$, $\Lambda_0 = e^{-\frac{1}{2}}$, $x_0 = -1$.)

To find the minimax solution one uses the fact that the risks are equal:

$$C_{00}(1-Q_0)+C_{10}Q_0 = C_{01}(1-Q_d)+C_{11}Q_d. \tag{2.18}$$

This is the equation of a straight line in the (Q_d, Q_0)-plane; it is labeled the "line of equal risks" in Fig. III. 3. (This line has been drawn by using the values given in part (c).) It intersects the operating characteristic at the minimax values of the probabilities Q_0 and Q_d. The slope of the operating characteristic at this point gives the value of Λ_0, from which the prior probability ζ_0 can be computed by using eq. (2.10). The minimax risk $\bar{C}_{\min}(\zeta_0)$ is the value of each side of eq. (2.18).

The reader can easily verify that if the costs C_{ij} satisfy either of the inequalities

$$C_{11} < C_{01} < C_{00} < C_{10} \quad \text{(or)} \quad C_{00} < C_{10} < C_{11} < C_{01},$$

the line of equal risks will not intersect the operating characteristic at all in the only region, $0 < (Q_0, Q_d) < 1$, where it is meaningful. There is then no minimax solution in the usual sense; instead the best strategy for Nature is to pick $\zeta = 1$ when the first inequality holds and $\zeta = 0$ when the second holds. (Nature is said to adopt a "pure" strategy.) The first inequality implies that the observer's losses will always be greater when hypothesis H_0 is true than when H_1 is true, no matter which strategy he uses to make his decisions. His adoption of the minimax criterion then forces him to conclude that hypothesis H_0 will always be true. When his costs are ordered according to the second inequality, he is similarly led to believe that hypothesis H_1 will always occur.

3. TESTING OF SIMPLE HYPOTHESES BY MULTIPLE MEASUREMENTS

(a) *The Likelihood Ratio*

The theory developed in the last section can readily be extended to the more usual case in which the choice between two hypotheses H_0 and H_1 is based on the outcomes of more than one measurement. Let the quantities measured be $x_1, x_2, \ldots, x_n$; these may represent successive measurements of the same physical parameter, the simultaneous measurement of n different parameters, or any combination of these possibilities. It is known that these quantities are described by the joint probability density functions $p_0(\mathbf{x}) = p_0(x_1, x_2, \ldots, x_n)$ and $p_1(\mathbf{x}) = p_1(x_1, x_2, \ldots, x_n)$ under hypotheses H_0 and H_1 respectively. Indeed, one can view the test as a choice of one of these p.d.f.s as the better description of the results of an experiment, the word "better" being defined in terms of one of the decision criteria introduced earlier. If the p.d.f.s $p_0(\mathbf{x})$ and $p_1(\mathbf{x})$ contain no unknown parameters, the corresponding hypotheses are termed "simple"; we restrict ourselves to this case for the time being.

For purposes of visualization it is convenient to represent the set of n outcomes of an experiment as a point in an n-dimensional Cartesian space with coordinates $\mathbf{x} = (x_1, x_2, \ldots, x_n)$. The decision strategy can be expressed as a division of this space into two regions R_0 and R_1 such that the observer chooses hypothesis H_0 when the outcome-point $\mathbf{x}$ lies in R_0, and H_1 when it lies in R_1. The regions are separated by a surface D known as the "decision surface". The strategy could also be described by a set of inequalities on the n variables x_i, $1 \leq i \leq n$, but the geometrical representation is less cumbersome. In Fig. III.4 the decision regions are illustrated for an experiment involving two measurements. The location of the decision surface D is to be determined by the particular criterion used.

If the observer can evaluate a cost matrix $\mathbf{C}$ (eq. (2.7)) that specifies the costs attending each possible decision under the two hypotheses, and if he knows the prior probabilities ζ of hypothesis H_0 and $(1-\zeta)$ of H_1, he is in a position to apply the Bayes criterion of minimum average risk. As in eq. (2.8) the average risk per decision is

$$\bar{C} = \zeta \left[C_{00} \int_{R_0} p_0(\mathbf{x})\, d^n\mathbf{x} + C_{10} \int_{R_1} p_0(\mathbf{x})\, d^n\mathbf{x} \right] + (1-\zeta) \left[C_{01} \int_{R_0} p_1(\mathbf{x})\, d^n\mathbf{x} + C_{11} \int_{R_1} p_1(\mathbf{x})\, d^n\mathbf{x} \right], \tag{3.1}$$

where $d^n\mathbf{x} = dx_1\, dx_2 \ldots dx_n$ is the volume element in the n-dimensional space of the outcome $\mathbf{x}$. The first integral in eq. (3.1) is the probability when hypothesis H_0 is true that the experimental results can be represented

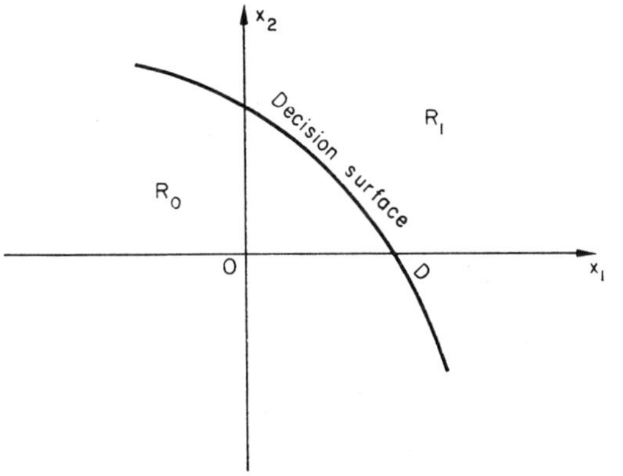

FIG. III. 4. Decision regions for two data.

by a point in region R_0, whereupon the observer makes the correct choice of hypothesis H_0. This integral is multiplied with the cost C_{00} of that decision. The two terms in the first bracket make up the risk associated with hypothesis H_0; the risk is multiplied by the prior probability (or relative frequency) ζ that that hypothesis is true.

The Bayes criterion requires the decision surface D to be picked so that the average risk, eq. (3.1), is a minimum. By the method used for a single measurement (eq. (2.11)) it can be proved that this criterion is satisfied when the observer computes the likelihood ratio

$$\Lambda(\mathbf{x}) = \frac{p_1(\mathbf{x})}{p_0(\mathbf{x})} \tag{3.2}$$

for the given set $\mathbf{x}$ of outcomes of the experiment, compares it with the quantity Λ_0 of eq. (2.10), and decides in favor of hypothesis H_0 or H_1

according as $\Lambda(\mathbf{x}) < \Lambda_0$ or $\Lambda(\mathbf{x}) > \Lambda_0$, respectively. Thus the equation of the decision surface D is $\Lambda(\mathbf{x}) = \Lambda_0$; the region R_0 consists of those points $\mathbf{x}$ for which $\Lambda(\mathbf{x}) < \Lambda_0$, R_1 of those for which $\Lambda(\mathbf{x}) > \Lambda_0$. The minimum average risk $\bar{C}_{\min}$ is given by eq. (3.1) when these Bayes decision regions are used. Again the Bayes strategy can be defined as the choice of that hypothesis yielding the smaller conditional risk; conditional probabilities and risks of the two hypotheses are given by the equations of Section 2, part (b), if one replaces the single outcome x by the set $\mathbf{x}$.

When the cost matrix $\mathbf{C}$ is given, but the prior probabilities are unknown, it may be appropriate to use the minimax criterion. For each value of the prior probability ζ the minimum average risk $\bar{C}_{\min}(\zeta)$ can be computed for the Bayes solution given above. The minimax strategy is then the Bayes strategy for that value $\zeta = \zeta_0$ for which $\bar{C}_{\min}(\zeta)$ attains its largest value; the minimax risk is equal to this maximum value $\bar{C}_{\min}(\zeta_0)$.

With each point $\mathbf{x}$ in the space representing the outcome of an experiment there is associated a value of the likelihood ratio $\Lambda(\mathbf{x})$ determined by eq. (3.2). The quantity $\Lambda(\mathbf{x})$ is a random variable with probability density functions $P_0(\Lambda)$ and $P_1(\Lambda)$ under hypotheses H_0 and H_1 respectively. To compute these p.d.f.s one can proceed in the following way. Let $R(\lambda)$ be the region in the n-dimensional space for which the likelihood ratio $\Lambda(\mathbf{x}) = p_1(\mathbf{x})/p_0(\mathbf{x})$ is less than λ. Under hypothesis H_0 the probability that the set $\mathbf{x}$ of outcomes lies in $R(\lambda)$ is

$$\Pr\{\mathbf{x} \in R(\lambda) \mid H_0\} = \int_{R(\lambda)} p_0(\mathbf{x})\, d^n\mathbf{x} = \int_0^{\lambda} P_0(\Lambda)\, d\Lambda.$$

This function of λ is the cumulative distribution of the likelihood ratio; by differentiating it with respect to λ one obtains the p.d.f. $P_0(\lambda)$ sought. A similar procedure using $\Pr\{x \in R(\lambda) \mid H_1\}$ yields $P_1(\lambda)$. In terms of these probability density functions the probabilities Q_0 and Q_1 of errors of the first and second kinds are, respectively,

$$\begin{aligned} Q_0 &= \int_{R_1} p_0(\mathbf{x})\, d^n\mathbf{x} = \int_{\Lambda_0}^{\infty} P_0(\Lambda)\, d\Lambda, \\ Q_1 &= \int_{R_0} p_1(\mathbf{x})\, d^n\mathbf{x} = \int_0^{\Lambda_0} P_1(\Lambda)\, d\Lambda. \end{aligned} \tag{3.3}$$

The risks c_0 and c_1 associated with hypotheses H_0 and H_1, respectively, can now be written down in terms of these probabilities:

$$\begin{aligned} c_0 &= C_{00}(1-Q_0)+C_{10}Q_0, \\ c_1 &= C_{01}Q_1+C_{11}(1-Q_1). \end{aligned} \tag{3.4}$$

Again the minimax strategy is characterized by the equality of these risks, $c_0 = c_1$, a condition that leads, through eqs. (3.3) and (3.4), to an equation for the value of Λ_0 with which the likelihood ratio must be compared in the decision process. The common value of these risks is then the minimax risk $\bar{C}_{\min}(\zeta_0)$.

The Neyman–Pearson criterion requires one to pick the location of the decision surface D to minimize the probability Q_1 of an error of the second kind, when the probability Q_0 of an error of the first kind is held fixed. This criterion is appropriate in situations when an estimate of the prior probabilities of the hypotheses is not available, and the costs attending the various decisions are not accurately known. The observer somehow decides on a value of the probability Q_0 that he can afford. The larger this probability is, the larger is the probability $(1-Q_1)$ of correctly identifying an occurrence of hypothesis H_1.

To find the optimum position for the decision surface D under this criterion, we can use the technique of Lagrangian multipliers, forming the linear combination

$$\Gamma(D) = Q_1(D)+\lambda Q_0(D) = \int_{R_0} p_1(\mathbf{x})\, d^n\mathbf{x}+\lambda \int_{R_1} p_0(\mathbf{x})\, d^n\mathbf{x}. \tag{3.5}$$

The decision surface D can now be varied until this linear combination attains a minimum; the resulting position of the surface will be a function of the multiplier λ. If we compare eqs. (3.5) and (3.1), we see that they are identical for a cost matrix $\mathbf{C} = \begin{bmatrix} 0 & 2 \\ 2\lambda & 0 \end{bmatrix}$ and prior probabilities $\zeta = 1-\zeta = \frac{1}{2}$. Then by eqs. (3.2) and (2.10) we find that the equation of the surface D that minimizes $\Gamma(D)$ is

$$\frac{p_1(\mathbf{x})}{p_0(\mathbf{x})} = \Lambda(\mathbf{x}) = \lambda. \tag{3.6}$$

The optimum decision surface is thus one of a family of surfaces generated by varying λ in eq. (3.6). That value of λ is chosen for which the probability

$$Q_0 = \int_{\lambda}^{\infty} P_0(\Lambda)\, d\Lambda$$

equals the preassigned value; we denote it by $\lambda = \Lambda_0$. The Neyman–Pearson criterion thus leads us to a strategy in which the likelihood ratio, eq. (3.2), is compared with a fixed constant Λ_0; hypothesis H_0 is chosen if $\Lambda(\mathbf{x}) < \Lambda_0$, H_1 if $\Lambda(\mathbf{x}) > \Lambda_0$. From a plot of the power $Q_d = 1-Q_1$ of the test versus the probability Q_0 of an error of the first kind—the "operating characteristic" of the test—the Bayes and minimax solutions can be obtained as discussed in Section 2, part (d).

Here is an independent derivation of the decision rule for the Neyman–Pearson criterion. The false-alarm probability, whose value is preassigned, is

$$Q_0 = \int_{R_1} p_0(\mathbf{x}) \, d^n\mathbf{x}, \tag{3.7}$$

and the probability of detection is

$$\begin{aligned} Q_d &= \int_{R_1} \Lambda(\mathbf{x}) \, p_0(\mathbf{x}) \, d^n\mathbf{x}, \\ \Lambda(\mathbf{x}) &= p_1(\mathbf{x})/p_0(\mathbf{x}). \end{aligned} \tag{3.8}$$

Here both $\Lambda(\mathbf{x})$ and $p_0(\mathbf{x})$ are positive. To make Q_d as large as possible, for a fixed value of Q_0, points $\mathbf{x}$ with large values of $\Lambda(\mathbf{x})$ should be assigned to region R_1, and points with small values of $\Lambda(\mathbf{x})$ should be assigned to region R_0. Suppose that these regions are separated by a surface D given by the equation $\Lambda(\mathbf{x}) = \Lambda_0$, with Λ_0 chosen so that the integral in eq. (3.7) equals the preassigned false-alarm probability. Transferring points from R_1 to R_0 or vice versa by altering the decision surface D, even while maintaining eq. (3.7), will replace larger values of $\Lambda(\mathbf{x})$ in the integrand of eq. (3.8) by smaller values, and it can only decrease the probability Q_d of detection. The original position of the surface D must therefore be optimum.

The choice between hypotheses H_0 and H_1 can be based not only on the likelihood ratio $\Lambda(\mathbf{x})$, but also on any monotone function $G = G(\Lambda(\mathbf{x}))$ of the likelihood ratio. Without loss of generality we suppose this to be an increasing function of Λ. If G exceeds a certain "decision level" G_0, hypothesis H_1 is chosen; if not, H_0 is chosen. Under the Neyman–Pearson criterion the value of G_0 is picked so that the false-alarm probability

$$Q_0 = \int_{G_0}^{\infty} p_0(G) \, dG \tag{3.9}$$

takes on the preassigned value, where $p_0(G)$ is the p.d.f. of G under hypothesis H_0. The probability of detection is then

$$Q_d = \int_{G_0}^{\infty} p_1(G) \, dG, \tag{3.10}$$

with $p_1(G)$ the p.d.f. of G under H_1.

The quantity G is a function of the measurements $\mathbf{x} = (x_1, x_2, \ldots, x_n)$ and, like the likelihood ratio $\Lambda(\mathbf{x})$, it embodies all the information in them that contributes toward making the decision in the best possible way under our three criteria. A quantity that replaces and summarizes the data $\mathbf{x}$ in this way is called a *statistic;* the likelihood ratio itself is a statistic. If instead of measuring the n x_i's individually one can measure a statistic G depending on them only through the likelihood ratio, one can make the decision with the same efficacy. A likelihood ratio can be formed with the statistic G as well,

$$\Lambda(G) = p_1(G)/p_0(G), \tag{3.11}$$

and under the Bayes criterion the level G_0 with which the statistic G is to be compared is given by the equation

$$\Lambda(G_0) = p_1(G_0)/p_0(G_0) = \Lambda_0 = \frac{\zeta(C_{10}-C_{00})}{(1-\zeta)(C_{01}-C_{11})}. \tag{3.12}$$

The points on the operating characteristic (Fig. III.3) are indexed by the values of G_0 or Λ_0, and the parametric equations of that curve are

$$Q_d = Q_d(G_0), \quad Q_0 = Q_0(G_0),$$

with these functions of G_0 given by eqs. (3.9) and (3.10). In this framework eq. (3.12) reiterates that the slope of the operating characteristic is equal to the likelihood ratio. For the minimax criterion the value of the decision level G_0 can be found by solving the equation of equal risks, eq. (2.18), with Q_d and Q_0 expressed as functions of G_0. The solution can be determined graphically as described at the end of Section 2.

The statistic most commonly used is proportional to the logarithm of the likelihood ratio,

$$g = \ln\,[p_1(\mathbf{x})/p_0(\mathbf{x})]. \tag{3.13}$$

When the p.d.f.s are jointly Gaussian, this statistic takes a particularly simple form. When data are taken in statistically independent batches, whatever their joint p.d.f.s, the logarithm of the likelihood ratio equals the sum of this statistic for each batch. The value of g for the batch comprises all the relevant information in the batch and can be measured in its stead.

(b) *Some Examples*

As a simple example of the use of these methods, suppose that the quantities $x_1, x_2, \ldots, x_n$ are statistically independent and have Gaussian distributions with variance σ^2. Let the expected value of each be a_0 under hypothesis H_0 and a_1 under H_1. Their joint probability density functions are then

$$p_k(\mathbf{x}) = (2\pi\sigma^2)^{-n/2} \exp\left[-\sum_{i=1}^{n} (x_i-a_k)^2/2\sigma^2\right], \qquad k = 0, 1. \tag{3.14}$$

The likelihood ratio is now

$$\Lambda(\mathbf{x}) = p_1(\mathbf{x})/p_0(\mathbf{x}) = \exp\left[\frac{(a_1-a_0)}{\sigma^2}\sum_{i=1}^{n} x_i - \frac{n(a_1^2-a_0^2)}{2\sigma^2}\right].$$

The observer will choose hypothesis H_0 when $\Lambda(\mathbf{x}) < \Lambda_0$, where the value of Λ_0 depends on the decision criterion used. Since the exponential function is monotone, the decision can just as well be based on the value of

$$X = \sum_{i=1}^{n} x_i/n,$$

the so-called "sample mean" of the observations, which is to be compared with the quantity M given by

$$M = (a_0+a_1)/2 + \frac{\sigma^2 \ln \Lambda_0}{n(a_1-a_0)}.$$

Hypothesis H_0 is chosen when $X < M$, H_1 when $X > M$ $(a_1 > a_0)$. If the Bayes criterion is being used, M depends on the costs and prior probabilities through Λ_0, which is given by eq. (2.10). In this problem the decision surface D is the plane

$$\sum_{i=1}^{n} x_i = nM.$$

The sample mean X is thus a statistic in the sense just explained. It is a Gaussian random variable because it is a linear combination of Gaussian random variables. Its mean or expected values under hypotheses H_0 and H_1 are a_0 and a_1 respectively, and its variance is σ^2/n. Hence the probabilities of errors of the first and second kinds are

$$Q_0 = \operatorname{erfc}\left(\frac{M-a_0}{\sigma/\sqrt{n}}\right), \quad Q_1 = 1-\operatorname{erfc}\left(\frac{M-a_1}{\sigma/\sqrt{n}}\right),$$

where again erfc x is the error-function integral. To use the Neyman–Pearson criterion the observer chooses the value of M so that the probability Q_0 of an error of the first kind takes on the preassigned value.

As a second example, suppose the observer must decide which of two sources of Gaussian random noise is present, the one having a mean-square voltage N_0, the other N_1. The mean value of the noise voltage is zero in both cases. He measures the voltage at n times far enough apart that the results $x_1, x_2, \ldots, x_n$ are statistically independent. The two hypotheses between which he must choose are (H_0) "The mean-square value of the voltage is N_0", and (H_1) "The mean-square value of the voltage is N_1". The joint p.d.f.s of the set of n measured voltages are given by

$$p_k(\mathbf{x}) = (2\pi N_k)^{-n/2} \exp\left[-\sum_{i=1}^{n} x_i^2/2N_k\right], \qquad k = 0, 1. \tag{3.15}$$

The likelihood ratio for these measurements is

$$\Lambda(\mathbf{x}) = (N_0/N_1)^{\frac{n}{2}} \exp\left[-\sum_{i=1}^{n} x_i^2\left(\frac{1}{2N_1}-\frac{1}{2N_0}\right)\right]. \tag{3.16}$$

The observer computes this likelihood ratio for the outcome of his experiment and compares it with a fixed quantity Λ_0. If $\Lambda(\mathbf{x}) < \Lambda_0$ he decides that the mean-square voltage of the noise source was N_0. If $N_0 < N_1$ the decision surface D is an n-dimensional hypersphere of radius r_0 given by $\Lambda(\mathbf{x}) = \Lambda_0$, or

$$r_0^2 = \frac{2N_0N_1}{N_1-N_0} \ln\left[\Lambda_0(N_1/N_0)^{\frac{n}{2}}\right],$$

and the regions R_0 and R_1 are respectively the interior and exterior of this hypersphere. Hence, to make his choice the observer needs merely to compute the sum of squares

$$S = \sum_{i=1}^{n} x_i^2;$$

if $S < r_0^2$ he chooses hypothesis H_0, otherwise H_1.

To compute the probabilities of error one needs the p.d.f.s of the sum S. They can be calculated by the technique described earlier for finding the p.d.f.s of the likelihood ratio. Under hypothesis H_0 the probability that $0 < S < s$ is

$$\Pr\{0 < S < s \mid H_0\} = \int_0^s P_0(S)\, dS$$

$$= (2\pi N_0)^{-n/2} \int_{\Sigma}\!\!\ldots\!\int \exp\left[-(x_1^2+\ldots x_n^2)/2N_0\right],\; dx_1\ldots dx_n,$$

where the volume Σ is the n-dimensional hypersphere whose boundary surface is given by the equation $x_1^2+x_2^2+\ldots x_n^2 = s$. The volume integral can be evaluated using the formula for the surface "area" of such a sphere. If we let the radius vector to a point within the sphere have length r,

$x_1^2+x_2^2+\ldots x_n^2 = r^2$, the volume of a spherical shell of thickness dr is†

$$dV = \frac{2\pi^{\frac{n}{2}}}{\Gamma(n/2)} r^{n-1}\, dr,$$

where $\Gamma(x)$ is the gamma-function. (For positive integral values of x, $\Gamma(x) = (x-1)!$. For half-integral values one can use the formulas $\Gamma(\frac{1}{2}) = \sqrt{\pi}$, $\Gamma(x+1) = x\Gamma(x)$. Thus $\Gamma(\frac{3}{2}) = \frac{1}{2}\sqrt{\pi}$, $\Gamma(\frac{5}{2}) = (3\cdot 1/2\cdot 2)\sqrt{\pi}$, and so forth.) Substituting in the above integral we obtain

$$\int_0^s P_0(S)\, dS = \frac{2}{(2N_0)^{\frac{n}{2}}\Gamma(n/2)} \int_0^{\sqrt{s}} e^{-r^2/2N_0}\, r^{n-1}\, dr.$$

Differentiating with respect to s and setting $s = S$ we get the p.d.f.

$$P_0(S) = \frac{S^{\frac{n}{2}-1} e^{-S/2N_0}}{(2N_0)^{\frac{n}{2}}\Gamma(n/2)}. \tag{3.17}$$

For $N_0 = 1$ this is the χ^2-distribution for n degrees of freedom (Hald, 1952, ch. 10). Extensive tables of the percentage points of this distribution are available (Fisher and Yates, 1953), from which one can compute the error probabilities Q_0 and Q_1. Alternatively, one can use tables of the incomplete gamma-function (Pearson, 1934).

(c) *Discrete Data*

We now mention briefly the treatment of data that can take on only discrete values under both hypotheses, although such data seldom appear in ordinary signal detection problems. The probability densities in such cases can be thought of as concentrated in delta-function spikes at discrete points $\mathbf{x}$ of the n-dimensional space of the observations $x_1, x_2, \ldots, x_n$. The strength of each delta-function is proportional to the probability that the associated set of values of the x_i's occurs under the given hypothesis. The likelihood ratio $\Lambda(\mathbf{x})$ becomes the ratio of the *probabilities* $P_1(\mathbf{x})$ and $P_0(\mathbf{x})$, under the two hypotheses, that the experiment selects the point $\mathbf{x}$,

$$\Lambda(\mathbf{x}) = P_1(\mathbf{x})/P_0(\mathbf{x}).$$

With a Neyman–Pearson criterion, hypothesis H_1 is chosen when the ratio $P_1(\mathbf{x})/P_0(\mathbf{x})$ exceeds a threshold Λ_0 whose value is so chosen that the

† Edwards, J., *A Treatise on the Integral Calculus*, Chelsea (1954), chap. 25.

size of the test,

$$Q_0 = \sum_{\mathbf{x} \in R_1} P_0(\mathbf{x}), \tag{3.18}$$

takes on the preassigned value, R_1 again being the region in the space of $\mathbf{x}$ in which hypothesis H_1 is chosen. It may not be possible to achieve an arbitrary value of Q_0 exactly, for assigning a borderline point to region R_0 may make the right-hand side of eq. (3.18) too small, and assigning it to R_1 may make the sum too large. This dilemma is sometimes resolved by tossing a properly biased coin whenever the experiment selects such a borderline point, so that sometimes H_0, sometimes H_1 is chosen with the correct probability to make the size of the test exactly the value desired. This procedure is known as "randomization".

In this chapter we have confined ourselves to decisions between simple hypotheses, for which the p.d.f.s of the data contain no unknown parameters. When unknown parameters appear in the distributions, the hypotheses are called "composite". In Chapter V we shall treat the problem of deciding between a simple and a composite hypothesis. Most of the difficulties of decision theory arise when one or both hypotheses are composite, and we shall present only an introduction to this aspect. A thorough account is to be found in Lehmann (1959). For some of the philosophical background of decision theory we cite the books by Luce and Raiffa (1957) and Savage (1954, 1962). Wald's fundamental papers have been collected in a single volume (Wald, 1957).

PROBLEMS

1. Prove the statement on p. 83 that the average risk is minimized by choosing the hypothesis for which the conditional risk is the smaller.

2. Derive the conditions that the line of equal risks does not intersect the operating characteristic in the region $0 < Q_0 < 1$, $0 < Q_d < 1$, and show that they lead to the inequalities on p. 89.

3. Find the Bayes test to choose between the hypotheses H_0 and H_1, whose prior probabilities are $\frac{5}{8}$ and $\frac{3}{8}$ respectively, when under H_0 the datum x has the p.d.f.

$$p_0(x) = (2/\pi)^{\frac{1}{2}} e^{-x^2/2},$$

and under H_1 it has the p.d.f.

$$p_1(x) = e^{-x},$$

x being always positive. Let the relative costs of the two kinds of errors be equal. Find the minimum average probability of error.

4. The random variables x and y are Gaussian with mean value 0 and variance 1. Their covariance $\{x, y\}$ may be 0 or some known positive value $r > 0$. Show that the best choice between these possibilities on the basis of a measurement of x and y depends on where the point (x, y) lies with respect to a certain hyperbola in the (x, y)-plane.

5. A sequence of N independent measurements is taken of a Poisson-distributed variable x whose mean is m_0 under hypothesis H_0, m_1 under hypothesis H_1. (The Poisson distribution with mean m assigns a probability $P(x) = m^x e^{-m}/x!$ to the positive integer x and probability 0 to all non-integral values of x.) On what combination of the measurements should a Bayes test be based, and with what decision level should its outcome be compared, for given prior probabilities $(\zeta, 1-\zeta)$ and a given cost matrix **C**?

6. A random variable x is distributed according to a Cauchy distribution,

$$p(x) = \frac{m}{\pi(m^2+x^2)} \cdot$$

The parameter m can take on either of two values m_0 and m_1, $m_0 < m_1$. Design a statistical test to decide on the basis of a single measurement of x between the two hypotheses H_0 $(m = m_0)$ and H_1 $(m = m_1)$. Use the Neyman–Pearson criterion. For this test calculate the power $Q_d = 1-Q_1$ as a function of the size Q_0.

7. Under hypotheses H_0 and H_1 a random variable has the following probability density functions,

$$\begin{aligned} p_0(x) &= 1-|x|, \quad |x| < 1, & p_1(x) &= (2-|x|)/4, \quad |x| < 2, \\ &= 0, \quad |x| > 1. & &= 0, \quad |x| > 2. \end{aligned}$$

Choosing H_0 when H_1 is true costs twice as much as choosing H_1 when H_0 is true. Correct choices cost nothing. Find the minimax strategy for deciding between the two hypotheses.

8. A choice is to be made between hypotheses H_0 and H_1 on the basis of a single measurement of a quantity x. Under hypothesis H_0, $x = n$; under H_1, $x = s+n$. Here both s and n are positive random variables with the p.d.f.s

$$p(n) = be^{-bn}, \quad p(s) = ce^{-cs}, \quad c > b.$$

Calculate the p.d.f.s of x under H_0 and H_1. Find the decision level on x to yield a given false-alarm probability Q_0, and calculate the probability Q_d of correctly choosing hypothesis H_1.

9. For the logarithm g of the likelihood ratio, as defined by eq. (3.13), $e^g = p_1(g)/p_0(g)$. Define the moment generating functions of g under hypotheses H_0 and H_1 by

$$f_j(s) = \mathbf{E}(e^{gs} \mid H_j), \quad j = 0, 1.$$

Show that $f_1(s) = f_0(s+1)$. Determine $f_0(s)$ for the logarithms of the likelihood ratios in the two examples in part (b) of Section 3.

BIBLIOGRAPHY (III)

Papers

1763 BAYES, T., "An Essay Toward Solving a Problem in the Doctrine of Chances", *Phil. Trans. Roy. Soc.* **53**, 370–418. Reprinted in *Biometrika* **45**, 293–315 (1958).

1933 NEYMAN, J. and PEARSON, E., "The Testing of Statistical Hypotheses in Relation to Probability *a priori*", *Proc. Camb. Phil. Soc.* **29**, no. 4, 492–510.

NEYMAN, J. and PEARSON, E., "On the Problem of the Most Efficient Tests of Statistical Hypotheses", *Phil. Trans. Roy. Soc.* A **231**, no. 9, 289–337.

1939 WALD, A., "Contributions to the Theory of Statistical Estimation and Testing of Hypotheses", *Ann. Math. Stat.* **10**, 299–326.

1952 WOODWARD, P. M. and DAVIES, I. L., "Information Theory and Inverse Probability in Telecommunication", *Proc. I.E.E.* **99** (III), 37–51 (Mar.).

1953 MIDDLETON, D., "Statistical Criteria for the Detection of Pulsed Carriers in Noise", *J. Appl. Phys.* **24**, 371–8, 379–91 (Apr.).

1954 PETERSON, W. W., BIRDSALL, T. G. and FOX, W. C., "The Theory of Signal Detectability", *Trans. I.R.E.* **PGIT-4,** 171–212 (Sept.).

Books

1934 PEARSON, K., *Tables of the Incomplete Γ-Function*, Cambridge University Press, Cambridge.

1946 CRAMÉR, H., *Mathematical Methods of Statistics*, Princeton University Press, Princeton, N.J.

1950 LAWSON, J. L. and UHLENBECK, G. E., *Threshold Signals*, McGraw-Hill Book Co., New York, N.Y.

WALD, A., *Statistical Decision Functions*, John Wiley & Sons, Inc., New York, N.Y.

1952 HALD, A., *Statistical Theory with Engineering Applications*, John Wiley & Sons, Inc., New York, N.Y.

1953 FISHER, R. and YATES, F., *Statistical Tables for Biological, Agricultural, and Medical Research*, Oliver & Boyd, Edinburgh.

WOODWARD, P. M., *Probability and Information Theory with Applications to Radar*, McGraw-Hill Book Co., New York, N.Y. (2nd ed., 1965).

1954 BLACKWELL, D. and GIRSHICK, M. A., *Theory of Games and Statistical Decisions*, John Wiley & Sons, Inc., New York, N.Y.

SAVAGE, L. J., *The Foundations of Statistics*, John Wiley & Sons, Inc., New York, N.Y.

1957 LUCE, R. D. and RAIFFA, H., *Games and Decisions*, John Wiley & Sons, Inc., New York, N.Y.

WALD, A., *Selected Papers in Probability and Statistics*, Stanford University Press, Stanford, Calif.

1959 CHERNOFF, H. and MOSES, L. E., *Elementary Decision Theory*, John Wiley & Sons, Inc., New York, N.Y.

KOTEL'NIKOV, V. A., *The Theory of Optimum Noise Immunity*, R. A. Silverman trans., McGraw-Hill Book Co., New York, N.Y.

LEHMANN, E., *Testing of Statistical Hypotheses*, John Wiley & Sons, Inc., New York, N.Y.

1962 SAVAGE, L. J., *The Foundations of Statistical Inference*, John Wiley & Sons, Inc., New York, N.Y.

1963 FREEMAN, H., *Introduction to Statistical Inference*, Addison-Wesley Publishing Co., Inc., Reading, Mass.

1964 FISHBURN, P. C., *Decision and Value Theory*, John Wiley & Sons, Inc., New York, N.Y.

IV

DETECTION OF A KNOWN SIGNAL

1. DETECTION IN WHITE GAUSSIAN NOISE

(a) *The Likelihood Ratio*

With the theory of statistical tests introduced in the previous chapter we can now attack the simplest signal-detection problem, in which a signal $s(t)$ of specified form and amplitude may arrive at a definite time and be superimposed on Gaussian noise $n(t)$. The input $v(t)$, which may be the voltage between the terminals of a receiving antenna, is measured during a period of time $0 < t < T$, the observation interval. On the basis of this input an observer must choose one of two hypotheses, (H_0) there is no signal present, and the input consists only of Gaussian noise of mean zero, $v(t) = n(t)$; or (H_1) the input is the sum of the expected signal and noise, $v(t) = s(t)+n(t)$. He has adopted some criterion by which to evaluate his success in a large number of decisions of this kind; as discussed in Chapter III, this criterion will influence his way of treating the data.

For example, the signal might be a rectangular pulse of duration $T' < T$,

$$s(t) = A, \quad 0 \leqslant t_1 < t < t_1+T' \leqslant T,$$

$$s(t) = 0, \quad t < t_1, \quad t > t_1+T'.$$

It occurs at a definite time within the observation interval. A communication system might be using such pulses to convey a message that has been translated into a binary code with symbols "0" and "1". Every T seconds a pulse is or is not sent, depending on whether the current message symbol is a "1" or a "0". At the end of each interval of T seconds the observer decides which of the symbols was transmitted. Because of the noise he will occasionally err, and his aim may be to minimize the probability of doing so, judging errors in the two symbols equally expensive. His decision criterion is then the Bayes, with equal relative costs, $C_{10}-C_{00} = C_{01}-C_{11}$, provided he knows the relative frequencies ζ and $(1-\zeta)$ with which the transmitter sends the symbols "0" and "1".

We shall assume first that the noise $n(t)$ is of the white Gaussian kind described at the end of Section 4, Chapter II. The unilateral spectral density of the noise is N; its dimensions are $V^2 \cdot$ sec when $s(t)$ and $n(t)$ are stated in volts.

The decision strategies derived in the previous chapter involved only a finite number of measurements. Let us begin, therefore, by supposing that the observer chooses between the two hypotheses on the basis of the voltages $v_k = v(t_k)$ measured at n uniformly spaced instants t_k during the observation interval,

$$t_k = k\,\Delta t = kT/n, \quad k = 1, 2, \ldots, n.$$

These voltages are described by the joint probability density functions $p_0(\mathbf{v}) = p_0(v_1, v_2, \ldots, v_n)$ and $p_1(\mathbf{v}) = p_1(v_1, v_2, \ldots, v_n)$ under the hypotheses H_0 and H_1, respectively. We learned in Chapter III that the observer's decision is best made on the basis of the likelihood ratio

$$\Lambda(\mathbf{v}) = \Lambda(v_1, v_2, \ldots, v_n) = p_1(\mathbf{v})/p_0(\mathbf{v}). \tag{1.1}$$

Its value for the data at hand is compared with a fixed decision level Λ_0; if $\Lambda(\mathbf{v}) < \Lambda_0$ the observer decides that there is no signal present (hypothesis H_0). The level Λ_0 is governed by the decision criterion preferred—Bayes, minimax, or Neyman–Pearson.

The measurements of the voltage $v(t)$ at times t_k are, we assume, made by an instrument of such a large bandwidth that however small the intervals Δt between them, their outcomes have statistically independent noise components. Under hypothesis H_0 their joint p.d.f. is then, as in eq. (4.16) of Chapter II,

$$p_0(\mathbf{v}) = (2\pi N_0)^{-n/2} \exp\left(-\sum_{k=1}^{n} v_k^2/2N_0\right),$$

$$N_0 = NW/2\pi. \tag{1.2}$$

We shall find that the bandwidth W of the measuring instrument does not appear in our final results.

When the signal is present, the part of the voltage v_k due to the noise is $v_k - s_k$, with $s_k = s(t_k)$ a sample of the signal. Under hypothesis H_1 the joint p.d.f. of the data is therefore given by eq. (1.2) with v_k replaced by $v_k - s_k$,

$$p_1(\mathbf{v}) = (2\pi N_0)^{-n/2} \exp\left[-\sum_{k=1}^{n} (v_k - s_k)^2/2N_0\right]. \tag{1.3}$$

In other words, when the signal is present, the data v_k are independent Gaussian random variables with mean values s_k and variances N_0. This decision problem is similar to the first example of Chapter III, Section 3, part (b).

The likelihood ratio, eq. (1.1), now becomes

$$\Lambda(\mathbf{v}) = \exp\left[\sum_{k=1}^{n} (2s_k v_k - s_k^2)/2N_0\right].$$

The observer chooses hypothesis H_0 if $\Lambda(\mathbf{v}) < \Lambda_0$ or, because of the monotone character of the exponential function, if

$$\Delta t \sum_{k=1}^{n} s_k v_k < \tfrac{1}{2} \Delta t \sum_{k=1}^{n} s_k^2 + N_0 \Delta t \ln \Lambda_0.$$

Hence he can base his decision on the value of the quantity

$$G_n = \Delta t \sum_{k=1}^{n} s(t_k)\, v(t_k), \tag{1.4}$$

comparing it with some fixed amount G_{n0} determined by the criterion. In the n-dimensional Cartesian space with coordinates v_k, the decision surface D is a hyperplane

$$\sum_{k=1}^{n} s_k v_k = \text{constant},$$

which is perpendicular to the vector with components s_k.

Since the noise has been assumed to be white, the intervals Δt can be made much smaller than the duration of the signal, and the number n of samples can be very large. In the limit $n \to \infty$ the quantity G_n of eq. (1.4) becomes

$$G = \int_0^T s(t)\, v(t)\, dt. \tag{1.5}$$

The observer may as well use the statistic G of eq. (1.5) if he can, and we shall see in the next section how it can be generated by passing the input $v(t)$ through the proper kind of linear filter. The decision system is then said to "cross-correlate" the input $v(t)$ with the expected signal $s(t)$, whence the name "correlation detector".

The statistic G is to be compared with some fixed critical value G_0, which we call the "decision level". If $G < G_0$ the observer decides for hypothesis H_0, "no signal present"; if $G > G_0$ he chooses H_1, "signal present". The value of G_0 is determined according to one of the criteria of Chapter III. The statistic G is a random variable, described by one of the two p.d.f.s $p_0(G)$ and $p_1(G)$, according to whether a signal is absent or present. If $G > G_0$ when there is no signal, an error of the first kind, or "false alarm", is incurred. The "false-alarm probability" Q_0 is

$$Q_0 = \int_{G_0}^{\infty} p_0(G)\, dG. \tag{1.6}$$

If on the other hand $G < G_0$ when there is a signal present, an error of the second kind, sometimes called a "false dismissal", is made; its probability is Q_1. If the signal is correctly declared to be present ($G > G_0$ under hypothesis H_1), it is said to have been *detected*; the probability $Q_d = 1-Q_1$ of this event, known as the "probability of detection", is

$$Q_d = \int_{G_0}^{\infty} p_1(G)\, dG. \tag{1.7}$$

We now seek the probability density functions of the statistic G.

Since G of eq. (1.5) is the result of a linear operation on the Gaussian random variable $v(t)$, it too is a Gaussian variable. Under hypothesis H_0 its mean value is $\overline{G} = 0$ because $\overline{n(t)} = 0$; under H_1 at any point of time the mean of the input $v(t)$ is $\overline{v(t)} = s(t)$, since signal and noise are simply additive. Therefore, the mean value of the statistic G is

$$\mathbf{E}[G \mid H_1] = \int_0^T [s(t)]^2\, dt = E. \tag{1.8}$$

The variance of G is the same under both hypotheses; it is given by

$$\begin{aligned} \operatorname{Var} G &= \int_0^T \int_0^T s(t_1)\, s(t_2)\, \overline{n(t_1)\, n(t_2)}\, dt_1\, dt_2 \\ &= \frac{N}{2} \int_0^T \int_0^T s(t_1)\, s(t_2)\, \delta(t_1 - t_2)\, dt_1\, dt_2 \\ &= \frac{N}{2} \int_0^T [s(t)]^2\, dt = NE/2, \end{aligned} \tag{1.9}$$

where we have used the delta-function form of the autocovariance function of white noise, eq. (3.11) of Chapter II. The quantity E is the energy dissipated during the observation interval in a resistor of 1 ohm, if the signal $s(t)$ is the voltage across that resistor.

The probability density functions of the statistic G can now be written down from eq. (4.1) of Chapter II. They are

$$\begin{aligned} p_0(G) &= (\pi NE)^{-\frac{1}{2}} \exp(-G^2/NE), \\ p_1(G) &= (\pi NE)^{-\frac{1}{2}} \exp[-(G-E)^2/NE]. \end{aligned} \tag{1.10}$$

The false-alarm probability is then

$$Q_0 = \text{erfc}\, x, \quad x = G_0 \sqrt{2/NE}, \tag{1.11}$$

and the detection probability is

$$Q_d = \text{erfc}\,(x-d) \tag{1.12}$$

where erfc x is again the error-function integral, eq. (III, 2.14). The quantity

$$d = \sqrt{2E/N} \tag{1.13}$$

is called the *signal-to-noise ratio*.

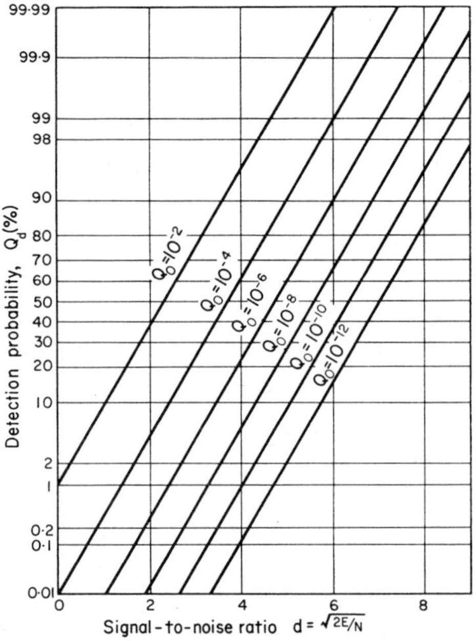

FIG. IV.1. Probability of detection: completely known signal.

When the Neyman–Pearson criterion is used, the value of the false-alarm probability Q_0 is fixed in advance, usually on the basis of the relative number of errors of the first kind the observer can afford. The decision level G_0 is then determined from eq. (1.11), and the resulting probability of detection is given by eq. (1.12) as a function of the signal-to-noise ratio d. In Fig. IV.1 the probability of detection Q_d has been plotted against the signal-to-noise ratio d for a number of values of the false-alarm probability Q_0. The pair of eqs. (1.11) and (1.12) represents in parametric form the operating characteristics of the test or the detection system; a number of these are shown in Fig. IV.2 for various values of the signal-to-noise ratio *d*.

In terms of the statistic *G* the likelihood ratio is, from eq. (1.10),

$$\begin{aligned} \Lambda[v(t)] &= p_1(G)/p_0(G) = \exp\,[(2G-E)/N] \\ &= \exp\left[\frac{2}{N}\int_0^T s(t)\,v(t)\,dt - \frac{1}{N}\int_0^T [s(t)]^2\,dt\right]. \end{aligned} \tag{1.14}$$

We write this as $\Lambda[v(t)]$ to indicate that all the information in the input $v(t)$ has been utilized.

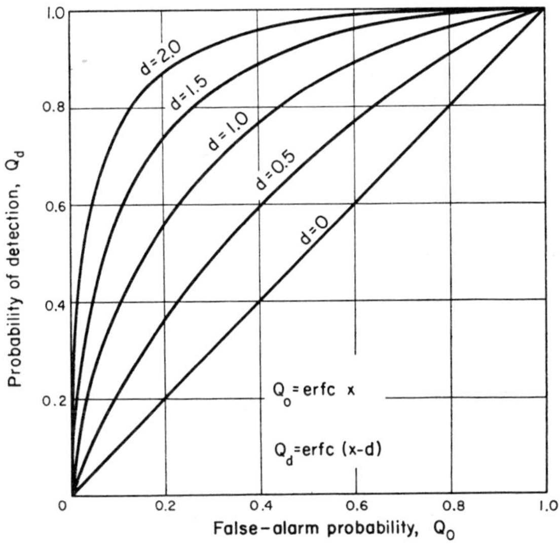

FIG. IV.2. Receiver operating characteristics: completely known signal.

In applying the Bayes criterion, the statistic *G* is compared with a decision level G_0 given by eq. (III, 3.12), which with eq. (1.14) becomes

$$G_0 = \tfrac{1}{2}E + \tfrac{1}{2}N \ln \Lambda_0,$$

where Λ_0 involves the costs and prior probabilities as in eq. (III, 2.10). If the prior probabilities of the two hypotheses are unknown, the observer may wish to use the minimax criterion. By equating the risks of the two hypotheses, an equation, eq. (III, 2.18), is obtained for the decision level G_0. It can be solved graphically as described in Chapter III, Section 2, part (d), once the operating characteristic for the specified signal-to-noise ratio has been plotted.

It is often convenient to describe the effectiveness of a detection system by quoting the signal-to-noise ratio of the "minimum detectable signal", that is, the value of $d = \sqrt{2E/N}$ required to attain a certain probability Q_d of detection for a given false-alarm probability Q_0. For instance, if the values chosen are $Q_0 = 10^{-10}$ and $Q_d = 0.90$, we obtain from Fig. IV.1 the ratio $d = \sqrt{2E/N} = 7.6$.

(b) *The Meaning of the Signal-to-Noise Ratio*

To understand better what the signal-to-noise ratio d governing the probability of detection really means, we shall examine a simple receiver in which the voltage $v(t)$ is measured across a load of impedance $Z_L = R_L + iX_L$, which is connected to the terminals of an antenna of impedance $Z_a = R_a + iX_a$. The equivalent circuit is shown in Fig. IV.3. The noise voltage $n(t)$ across the load is not necessarily white, and we assign it a spectral density $\Phi(\omega)$.

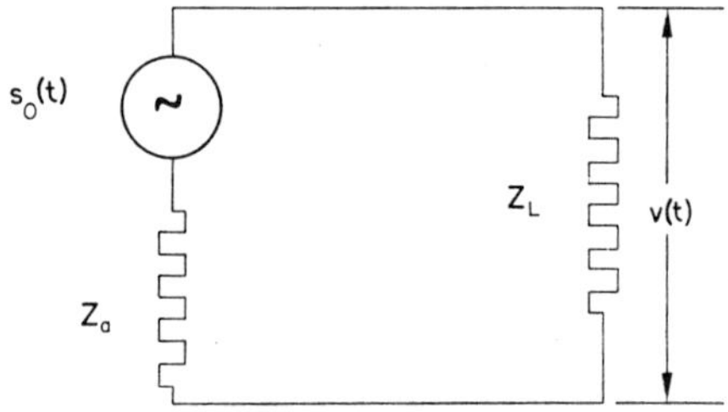

FIG. IV.3. The equivalent circuit for the input to a receiver.

The detection of a signal in Gaussian noise that is not white will be treated in Section 3. There it will be shown that the false-alarm and detection probabilities are still given by eqs. (1.11) and (1.12), but with an effective signal-to-noise ratio d that cannot exceed an upper bound d_∞ defined by the equation

$$d_\infty^2 = \int_{-\infty}^{\infty} \frac{|S(\omega)|^2}{\Phi(\omega)} \frac{d\omega}{2\pi}, \tag{1.15}$$

where $S(\omega)$ is the spectrum of the signal voltage across the load. This upper limit d_∞ is approached when the observation interval is much longer than the duration of the signal and the response time of the input circuit. When

$\Phi(\omega) = N/2$, as for white noise of unilateral spectral density N, d_∞ from eq. (1.15) is equal to the value of d given by eq. (1.13).

The antenna can be represented as a generator in series with its equivalent impedance Z_a, as shown in Fig. IV.3. When the electromagnetic waves carrying the signal to be detected pass the antenna, the equivalent generator produces an output voltage that we shall call $s_0(t)$. If the Fourier transform of this signal is $S_0(\omega)$, the signal appearing across the load has the spectrum

$$S(\omega) = \frac{Z_L}{Z_L+Z_a} S_0(\omega). \tag{1.16}$$

When the effective absolute temperature of the surroundings of the antenna is T_0, the antenna seems to have in series with its equivalent impedance a generator of a random voltage with spectral density $\Phi_0(\omega) = 2kT_0 \, \mathrm{Rl}\, Z_a = 2kT_0R_a$, where k is Boltzmann's constant. The load, at absolute temperature T_L, similarly generates a random voltage of spectral density $\Phi_L(\omega) = 2kT_L \, \mathrm{Rl}\, Z_L = 2kT_LR_L$. The net spectral density of the noise voltage $n(t)$ observed between the terminals of the load is

$$\begin{aligned} \Phi(\omega) &= [\Phi_0(\omega)+\Phi_L(\omega)] \left| \frac{Z_L}{Z_L+Z_a} \right|^2 \\ &= 2k(T_0R_a+T_LR_L) \left| \frac{Z_L}{Z_L+Z_a} \right|^2, \end{aligned} \tag{1.17}$$

for the outputs of the two random generators are statistically independent. The maximum signal-to-noise ratio in eq. (1.15) is thus given by

$$\begin{aligned} d_\infty^2 &= \int_{-\infty}^{\infty} [2k(T_0R_a+T_LR_L)]^{-1} \, |S_0(\omega)|^2 \, d\omega/2\pi \\ &= [2k(T_0R_a+T_LR_L)]^{-1} \int_{-\infty}^{\infty} [s_0(t)]^2 \, dt, \end{aligned} \tag{1.18}$$

if we make the reasonable assumption that the radiation resistance R_a of the antenna and the resistance R_L of the load are constant over the spectrum of the signal.

The integral in this expression must be proportional to the energy density in the electromagnetic field of the signal as it passes the antenna, and that energy density is conveniently measured by the energy ε that would be absorbed from the signal field if the antenna were matched to the load. To match the antenna, the load is given an impedance $Z_L = Z_a^* = R_a - iX_a$, and the absorbed energy is what is then dissipated in the load, namely

$$\varepsilon = \mathrm{Rl} \int_{-\infty}^{\infty} \frac{|S(\omega)|^2}{Z_L} \frac{d\omega}{2\pi} = \mathrm{Rl} \int_{-\infty}^{\infty} \frac{Z_L^* |S_0(\omega)|^2}{|Z_L + Z_a|^2} \frac{d\omega}{2\pi}$$

$$= \frac{1}{4R_a} \int_{-\infty}^{\infty} [s_0(t)]^2 \, dt, \tag{1.19}$$

with the same assumption as before about the frequency dependence of R_a and R_L. In terms of this energy ε the effective signal-to-noise ratio d governing the probability of detection cannot exceed an upper limit given by the inequality

$$d \leqslant \left[\frac{2\varepsilon R_a}{k(T_0 R_a + T_L R_L)} \right]^{\frac{1}{2}} < \sqrt{\frac{2\varepsilon}{kT_0}}. \tag{1.20}$$

The maximum possible value of d, $\sqrt{2\varepsilon/kT_0}$, is approached as the bandwidth of the input circuit is made very great, the observation time is made very long, and the temperature of the load is reduced toward absolute zero.

The energy ε absorbed by a matched load is equal to $\mathcal{E}A_r$, where $\mathcal{E}$ is the total energy in the electromagnetic field of the signal passing through a unit area normal to the direction of propagation, and A_r is the effective area of the antenna for waves moving in that direction. In terms of the gain Γ of the antenna in that same direction, $A_r = \Gamma\lambda^2/4\pi$, where λ is the wavelength of the signal radiation. If the dimensions of a plane antenna are much greater than a wavelength, as shown by antenna theory (Silver, 1949), the maximum value of the effective area A_r is equal to the geometrical area of the antenna. The energy ε is then simply the total energy in the signal field that passes through an area equal to that of the antenna and perpendicular to the direction of propagation. In this sense we can call ε the signal energy intercepted by the antenna, and eq. (1.20) informs us that at best the signal-to-noise ratio d equals the square root of twice the intercepted signal energy divided by kT_0. As we learned in Chapter 2, this quantity kT_0 is the noise power per unit of frequency available from the surroundings, whose effective absolute temperature is T_0. Thus in the example at the end of part (a), the minimum detectable signal must furnish a total energy ε of at least $29kT_0$ during the observation interval. (For $T_0 = 23°\mathrm{C} = 290°\mathrm{K}$, $kT_0 = 4 \cdot 10^{-14}$ ergs.)

The signal dealt with here was assumed to be completely known in amplitude, form, and time of arrival. In radar practice, as often in communications, signal parameters may be known only within wide ranges, with a consequent decrease in the probability of detection or increase in the energy of the minimum detectable signal. Strategies for detecting more vaguely known signals will be discussed in a later chapter.

In a practical receiver the input from the antenna must be amplified before it can be processed to form the statistic G and the comparison with the decision level G_0 can be made. The signal and the input noise are amplified together, and the amplifiers themselves add noise generated through the shot effect and other random mechanisms.

How an amplifier affects the signal-to-noise ratio is often measured by the "noise figure" F, $F \geqslant 1$, in terms of which the signal-to-noise ratio d_{out} at the output of the amplifier is given by $d_{out} = d_{in}F^{-\frac{1}{2}}$, where d_{in} is the signal-to-noise ratio at the input. In specifying the noise figure it is conventional to have the antenna or a signal generator matched to the load, with both at a standard temperature T_s of 290°K. Then by eq. (1.20), in which the left-hand sign "$\leqslant$" can be replaced by "$=$" when R_a and R_L are equal and independent of frequency,

$$d_{in} = (\varepsilon/kT_s)^{\frac{1}{2}}, \quad d_{out} = (\varepsilon\gamma/kT_sF\gamma)^{\frac{1}{2}} = (\varepsilon/kT_sF)^{\frac{1}{2}},$$

where γ is the power gain of the amplifier. At both input and output, d^2 is the ratio of the available signal energy—ε or $\varepsilon\gamma$—to the available noise power per unit of frequency at temperature T_s—kT_s or $kT_sF\gamma$. An ideal amplifier would have a noise figure of 1, and the signal-to-noise ratio at its output would equal that at its input.

It is shown in texts on radio and radar that for two networks in cascade having noise figures F_1 and F_2 and power gains γ_1 and γ_2, in that order, the noise figure of the combination is given by

$$F = F_1 + (F_2 - 1)/\gamma_1.$$

Hence, if the first amplifier has such a large gain that $\gamma_1 \gg F_2 - 1$, its noise figure effectively determines that of the combination. Extension to a chain of many amplifiers is immediate. For further discussion of these matters, see Davenport and Root (1958, ch. 10) and Haus and Adler (1958).

2. THE MATCHED FILTER

In the last section we found that the decision about the presence of a signal $s(t)$ in white Gaussian noise should be based on the quantity

$$G = \int_0^T s(t)\,v(t)\,dt,$$

where $v(t)$ is the input voltage over the observation interval $0 < t < T$. It would be useful to be able to generate the statistic G by filtering the input. Since G is the result of a linear operation on $v(t)$, the filter should be linear.

An appropriate linear filter for this purpose is one with an impulse response

$$\begin{aligned} K(\tau) &= s(T-\tau), \quad 0 < \tau < T \\ &= 0, \quad \tau < 0, \quad \tau > T. \end{aligned} \tag{2.1}$$

When the input of this filter is $v(t)$, the output is

$$y(t) = \int_0^T s(T-\tau)\,v(t-\tau)\,d\tau = \int_0^T s(u)\,v(u+t-T)\,du, \tag{2.2}$$

by eq. (2.1) of Chapter I. At time T the output is

$$y(T) = \int_0^T s(u)\,v(u)\,du = G. \tag{2.3}$$

Therefore, if the input $v(t)$ is passed through a linear filter having the impulse response of eq. (2.1), the output at the end of the observation interval is the statistic G needed. This output is compared with some fixed decision level G_0, and if $G = y(T) > G_0$ an alarm can be made to indicate the decision that a signal $s(t)$ was present in the observation interval. The filter of eq. (2.1) is said to be *matched* to the signal $s(t)$. The concept of the matched filter was proposed by North (1943) and applied to this decision problem by Peterson, Birdsall, and Fox (1954).

For example, let the signal be a triangular pulse of the form

$$s(t) = t, \quad 0 < t < T_1; \qquad s(t) = 0, \quad t < 0, \quad t > T_1.$$

It is illustrated in Fig. IV.4. If the observation interval is $(0, T)$, with $T \geqslant T_1$, the impulse response of the matched filter is

$$\begin{aligned} K(\tau) &= T-\tau, \quad T-T_1 < \tau < T, \\ &= 0, \quad \tau < T-T_1, \quad \tau > T. \end{aligned}$$

hen the output of the filter when only the signal $s(t)$ is applied is

$$\begin{aligned} y_s(t) &= 0, \quad t < T-T_1, \\ &= \tfrac{1}{2}[T_1^2-(T-t)^2], \quad T-T_1 < t < T+T_1, \\ &= 0, \quad t > T+T_1. \end{aligned}$$

his output is illustrated in Fig. IV.4. It reaches a maximum at $t = T$, ie time at which the decision is made. With such a pulse of limited duration here is no point to making the length T of the observation interval greater ian T_1.

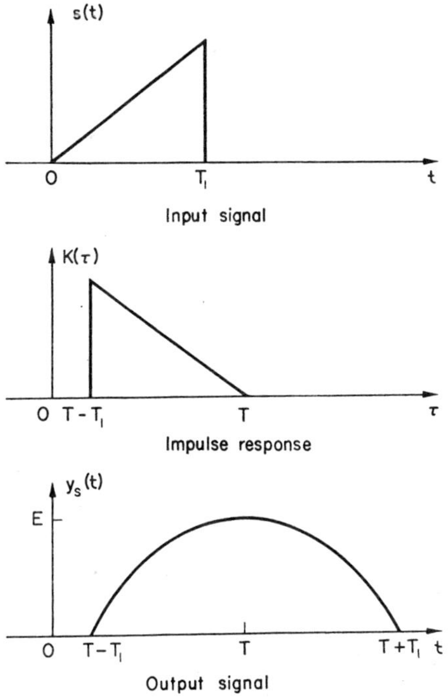

FIG. IV.4. The matched filter for a triangular signal.

Among all linear filters to which the signal $s(t)$ starting at $t = 0$ might e applied in addition to stationary white noise $n(t)$, the matched filter ields the largest signal-to-noise ratio at time $t = T$ (North, 1943; Van leck and Middleton, 1946). From a filter of impulse response $K(\tau)$ the gnal part of the output at time T is

$$y_s(T) = \int_0^T K(\tau)\, s(T-\tau)\, d\tau, \tag{2.4}$$

when $s(t) = 0$ for $t < 0$. The output due to the noise is, at any time t

$$y_n(t) = \int_0^\infty K(\tau)\, n(t-\tau)\, d\tau. \tag{2.5}$$

Its variance is, with $\mathbf{E}n(t) = 0$,

$$\operatorname{Var} y_n(t) = \frac{N}{2} \int_0^\infty [K(\tau)]^2\, d\tau, \tag{2.6}$$

which can be derived in the same way as eq. (1.9). Now using Schwarz' inequality (see the footnote on p. 20) we get from eq. (2.4)

$$[y_s(T)]^2 \leqslant \int_0^T [K(\tau)]^2\, d\tau \cdot \int_0^T [s(T-t)]^2\, dt,$$

with equality when and only when $K(\tau) = s(T-\tau)$, $0 < \tau < T$. Since

$$\int_0^T [K(\tau)]^2\, d\tau \leqslant \int_0^\infty [K(\tau)]^2\, d\tau,$$

we obtain from eq. (2.6),

$$[y_s(T)]^2/\operatorname{Var} y_n(t) \leqslant \frac{2}{N} \int_0^T [s(T-t)]^2\, dt = 2E/N = d^2.$$

The signal-to-noise ratio at the end of the observation interval will therefore always be less than d, unless the impulse response of the filter is the one given in eq. (2.1). It also follows from Schwarz's inequality that among all signals $f(t)$ for which

$$\int_0^T [f(t)]^2\, dt = E,$$

the part of the filter output at time $t = T$ due to the signal alone is largest for the signal $f(t) = s(t)$. These two properties show that the term "matched" is appropriate for the filter whose impulse response is given by eq. (2.1).

If the signal is confined to the observation interval, the transfer function of the matched filter is proportional to the complex conjugate of the spectrum of the signal,

$$S(\omega) = \int_0^T s(t) e^{-i\omega t}\, dt,$$

or by eq. (I, 2.3),

$$Y(\omega) = \int_0^\infty K(\tau)e^{-i\omega\tau}\,d\tau = \int_0^T s(T-\tau)e^{-i\omega\tau}\,d\tau$$
$$= \int_0^T s(u)e^{-i\omega(T-u)}\,du = e^{-i\omega T}S^*(\omega).$$

The factor $e^{-i\omega T}$ corresponds to a delay of T seconds in the response of the filter.

Sometimes the signal will not have vanished by the end of the observation interval. Consider an exponential pulse arriving at $t = 0$, $s(t) = Ae^{-\alpha t}$, $\alpha > 0$. If the input is observed during an interval $(0, T)$, the decision about the presence of a signal being made at time T, the matched filter must have an impulse response given by

$$K(\tau) = Ae^{-\alpha(T-\tau)}, \quad 0 < \tau < T,$$
$$= 0, \quad \tau > T.$$

The signal-to-noise ratio at $t = T$ is d, given by

$$d^2 = \frac{2}{N}\int_0^T [s(t)]^2\,dt = \frac{2A^2}{2N}\,\frac{1-e^{-2\alpha T}}{\alpha}.$$

As the length of the observation interval increases, so does d and hence also the probability of detection Q_d for a given probability Q_0 of a false alarm. However, to benefit from this the observer must accept a longer delay before making his decision.

To construct the matched filter one can use the methods discussed in Chapter I, Section 6 for synthesizing a filter with prescribed transient response. In order to attain the maximum signal-to-noise ratio at time $t = T$ for an input consisting of the given signal and white noise, the mean-square error criterion of eq. (I, 6.2) should be used with a constant weighting function. Figure I.8 illustrates an approximation obtained in that way for the impulse response of a filter to be matched to a rectangular pulse. The subject of matched filters has been extensively reviewed by Turin (1960).

3. DETECTION IN COLORED NOISE

(a) *The Likelihood Ratio*

Again we treat the problem of deciding between two hypotheses: (H_0) the input $v(t)$ contains only noise, $v(t) = n(t)$, and (H_1) it contains both noise and a known signal, $v(t) = s(t)+n(t)$. The input is observed over an interval $(0, T)$, at the end of which the choice is to be made. The noise $n(t)$ is Gaussian and has a zero mean value, but it is no longer assumed to be white and stationary. Instead we permit the noise to be nonstationary and require only that it have a positive-definite autocovariance function

$$\mathbf{E}[n(t)n(s)] = \phi(t, s).$$

If the noise should be stationary, its autocovariance will have the familiar form $\phi(t, s) = \phi(t-s)$, and it will possess a spectral density

$$\Phi(\omega) = \int_{-\infty}^{\infty} \phi(\tau)e^{-i\omega\tau}\, d\tau. \tag{3.1}$$

Such noise is sometimes called "colored" to distinguish it from white noise, whose spectral density is constant and whose autocovariance is a Dirac delta-function.

The decision is to be based on a likelihood ratio between two probability density functions of a set of measurements of the input $v(t)$. The most direct way of reaching the ultimate decision statistic is to suppose the measurements to be made at a set of $n+1$ times t_k spaced uniformly throughout the observation interval,

$$t_k = k\,\Delta t, \quad t_0 = 0, \quad t_n = n\,\Delta t = T, \quad k = 0, 1, \ldots, n.$$

Let the values of the input at these instants be $v(t_k) = v_k$, and put $s(t_k) = s_k$. The joint p.d.f. of the data $\{v_k\}$ is Gaussian with the covariances

$$\{v_j, v_k\} = \phi(t_j, t_k) = \phi_{jk}$$

under both hypotheses. The mean values of the data are

$$\mathbf{E}(v_k \mid H_0) = 0, \quad \mathbf{E}(v_k \mid H_1) = s_k.$$

Their joint p.d.f.s under hypotheses H_0 and H_1 are hence, by eq. (II, 4.2),

$$\begin{aligned} p_0(\mathbf{v}) &= M_{n+1} \exp\left[-\tfrac{1}{2}\sum_{j=0}^{n}\sum_{k=0}^{n} \mu_{jk}v_jv_k\right], \\ p_1(\mathbf{v}) &= M_{n+1} \exp\left[-\tfrac{1}{2}\sum_{j=0}^{n}\sum_{k=0}^{n} \mu_{jk}(v_j-s_j)(v_k-s_k)\right], \end{aligned} \tag{3.2}$$

where $\mathbf{v} = (v_0, v_1, \ldots, v_n)$ and M_{n+1} is given by eq. (II, 4.3). The μ_{jk} are the elements of a matrix that is the inverse of the matrix $\|\phi_{jk}\|$,

$$\sum_{j=0}^{n} \mu_{ij}\phi_{jk} = \delta_{ik}, \qquad i, k = 0, 1, \ldots, n. \tag{3.3}$$

The likelihood ratio is the quotient of these two p.d.f.s,

$$\Lambda(\mathbf{v}) = \exp\left[\sum_{j=0}^{n} \sum_{k=0}^{n} \mu_{kj}(s_j v_k - \tfrac{1}{2} s_j s_k)\right], \tag{3.4}$$

and to decide between the two hypotheses the observer compares the value of $\Lambda(\mathbf{v})$ for his data with a fixed decision level Λ_0, which depends on his criterion of success. He decides that there is no signal present if $\Lambda(\mathbf{v}) < \Lambda_0$. Again because the exponential function is monotone, the observer can instead base his decision on the value of the statistic

$$\begin{aligned} G_n &= \sum_{j=0}^{n} \sum_{k=0}^{n} \mu_{kj} s_j v_k = \sum_{k=0}^{n} q_k v_k, \\ q_k &= \sum_{j=0}^{n} \mu_{kj} s_j. \end{aligned} \tag{3.5}$$

We have introduced the numbers q_k, which are the solutions of the $n+1$ simultaneous linear equations

$$\sum_{j=0}^{n} \phi(t_k, t_j) q_j = s(t_k), \qquad 0 \leq k \leq n. \tag{3.6}$$

Again we are going to let the number of data increase beyond all bounds by dividing the interval of observation into finer and finer subintervals Δt. This passage to the limit $n = \infty$ can instructively be considered from the standpoint of the Bayes criterion. Compare the Bayes strategy B_n for deciding between hypotheses H_0 and H_1 on the basis of $n+1$ data v_0, $v_1, \ldots, v_n$, collected at times separated by Δt, with the Bayes strategy B_{2n} based on $2n+1$ data $v_0', v_1', \ldots, v_{2n}'$ taken at times separated by $\Delta t/2$. Then $v_{2k}' = v_k$ for all k, and the strategy B_n is the same as a strategy for handling the $2n+1$ data $v_0', v_1', \ldots, v_{2n}'$ that simply disregards every other datum. This strategy B_n cannot achieve an average cost lower than the cost C_{2n} of the strategy B_{2n}, which uses all $2n+1$ of the data. The Bayes cost C_n of a detection procedure using $n+1$ uniformly spaced data must, therefore, be a nonincreasing function of n, at least when n is a power of 2.

On the other hand, the Bayes cost can never be less than the average cost of making the decision without error, which in the notation of Chapter 3 is equal to $\zeta C_{00}+(1-\zeta)C_{11}$. The sequence of Bayes costs C_n must therefore have a lower limit approached as n increases without bound. It may turn out that this lower limit is equal to $\zeta C_{00}+(1-\zeta)C_{11}$, an eventuality that is called the "singular case" of perfect detection.

To facilitate our formal passage to the limit, we introduce a function $q(t)$ defined by

$$q(t) = [q_k+(q_{k+1}-q_k)(t-t_k)/\Delta t](\Delta t)^{-1}, \qquad t_k < t < t_{k+1}.$$

Then $q_k = q(t_k)\,\Delta t$. This function will depend on n, but only weakly when n is very large. If we substitute for q_k in eqs. (3.5) and (3.6) and pass to the limit $n \to \infty$, $\Delta t \to 0$, the summations will become integrations, and the detection statistic G_n will become

$$G = \int_0^T q(t)v(t)\,dt, \tag{3.7}$$

where $q(t)$ is now the solution of the integral equation

$$s(t) = \int_0^T \phi(t, u)q(u)\,du, \qquad 0 < t < T. \tag{3.8}$$

This is a "Fredholm integral equation of the first kind"; its kernel is the autocovariance function of the noise. It is the statistic G that is to be compared with a decision level G_0 in deciding whether a signal is present.

The expected values of G under the two hypotheses are

$$\mathbf{E}(G \mid H_0) = 0, \quad \mathbf{E}(G \mid H_1) = \int_0^T q(t)s(t)\,dt = d^2, \tag{3.9}$$

and its variance is the same under both hypotheses,

$$\begin{aligned} \text{Var } G &= \int_0^T \int_0^T q(t_1)q(t_2)\mathbf{E}[n(t_1)n(t_2)]\,dt_1\,dt_2 \\ &= \int_0^T \int_0^T q(t_1)q(t_2)\phi(t_1, t_2)\,dt_1\,dt_2 \\ &= \int_0^T q(t_1)\,s(t_1)\,dt_1 = d^2, \end{aligned} \tag{3.10}$$

in the reduction of which we have used the integral equation (3.8). The quantity d given by

$$d^2 = \int_0^T s(t)q(t)\,dt \tag{3.11}$$

we shall call the signal-to-noise ratio for detection in colored noise. When the noise is white and has a unilateral spectral density N, the kernel of the integral equation (3.8) is $\phi(t, s) = (N/2)\delta(t-s)$, its solution is $q(t) = 2s(t)/N$, and $d = \sqrt{2E/N}$, where E is the energy of the signal as defined in eq. (1.8).

The p.d.f.s of the statistic G under the two hypotheses are

$$p_0(G) = (2\pi d^2)^{-\frac{1}{2}} \exp(-G^2/2d^2),$$
$$p_1(G) = (2\pi d^2)^{-\frac{1}{2}} \exp[-(G-d^2)^2/2d^2], \tag{3.12}$$

and its likelihood ratio is

$$\Lambda[v(t)] = \Lambda(G) = \exp(G - \tfrac{1}{2}d^2)$$
$$= \exp\left[\int_0^T q(t)v(t)\,dt - \tfrac{1}{2}\int_0^T s(t)q(t)\,dt\right]. \tag{3.13}$$

When the noise is white, this reduces to eq. (1.14). It represents the limiting form of the likelihood ratio in eq. (3.4), and as the entire input $v(t)$ is now being utilized in the best possible way, we write this likelihood ratio as $\Lambda[v(t)]$. By having the likelihood ratio $\Lambda[v(t)]$ in the forms given by eqs. (1.14) and (3.13), we can avoid in more complicated problems the necessity of sampling the input and carrying out a limiting process.

The false-alarm and detection probabilities are, from eq. (3.12),

$$Q_0 = \Pr\{G > G_0 \mid H_0\} = \operatorname{erfc}(G_0/d),$$
$$Q_d = \Pr\{G > G_0 \mid H_1\} = 1 - \operatorname{erfc}(d - G_0/d), \tag{3.14}$$

where G_0 is the decision level with which the statistic G is compared, and erfc x is the error-function integral, eq. (III, 2.14). The detection probability is again as plotted in Fig. IV.1, and the operating characteristics are as in Fig. IV.2, with the signal-to-noise ratio d as defined by eq. (3.11).

The method we used to calculate the likelihood ratio, by sampling $v(t)$ at $n+1$ times and passing to the limit $n \to \infty$, is mathematically questionable. A more legitimate procedure, due to Grenander (1950) and to be presented in the next section, leads to the same result. Questionable also is the existence of a solution $q(t)$ of the integral equation (3.8), which is needed in order to specify the detection statistic G. In some cases delta-functions and their derivatives are required to express the solution; in others even these unusual functions may not suffice.

Our conclusion that

$$G = \int_0^T q(t)v(t)\,dt,$$

when it exists, is the optimum statistic is lent further credibility by the observation that the input $v(t)$ can be divided into two parts,

$$v(t) = v_1(t)+v_2(t), \tag{3.15}$$

of which $v_1(t)$ depends on the input only through G, and $v_2(t)$ is independent both of $v_1(t)$ and of the hypothesis (Kailath, 1967). The part $v_2(t)$ is, therefore, irrelevant to the decision between H_0 and H_1, which can be based entirely on $v_1(t)$, that is, on G. These two parts are

$$v_1(t) = d^{-2}\,Gs(t), \qquad v_2(t) = v(t)-v_1(t). \tag{3.16}$$

Since $\mathbf{E}[v_1(t) \mid H_1] = s(t)$,

$$\mathbf{E}[v_2(t) \mid H_0] = \mathbf{E}[v_2(t) \mid H_1] = 0.$$

As $v_2(t)$ depends linearly on the input $v(t)$, it too is a Gaussian process; and its autocovariance, like that of $v(t)$, is the same under both hypotheses. The array of p.d.f.s of the process $v_2(t)$ is therefore the same under both H_0 and H_1. To prove that $v_2(t)$ and $v_1(t)$ are independent, we need only to show that G and $v_2(t)$ are uncorrelated for all times t in $(0, T)$. Under hypothesis H_0 we evaluate

$$\mathbf{E}[Gv_2(t)] = \mathbf{E}[Gv(t)]-\mathbf{E}[Gv_1(t)].$$

Now

$$\mathbf{E}[Gv(t)] = \int_0^T q(s)\mathbf{E}[v(s)v(t) \mid H_0]\,ds$$

$$= \int_0^T q(s)\phi(t, s)\,ds = s(t),$$

and

$$\mathbf{E}[Gv_1(t)] = d^{-2}\,s(t)\mathbf{E}(G^2 \mid H_0) = s(t),$$

by eq. (3.10). Hence, $\mathbf{E}[Gv_2(t) \mid H_0] = 0$. The proof that G and $v_2(t)$ are uncorrelated under hypothesis H_1 follows the same lines. As both G and $v_2(t)$ are Gaussian random variables, their lack of correlation implies their statistical independence.

If in forming the likelihood ratio we had decomposed the input $v(t)$ as in eq. (3.15), each p.d.f. could have been factored into a part involving only G and a part involving $v_2(t)$. The second part would have canceled out of the quotient of the p.d.f.s, being the same under both H_0 and H_1, and the likelihood ratio would have been left depending on the input $v(t)$ only through the statistic G, as in eq. (3.13).

The detectability of the signal depends, as indicated by eq. (3.14), on the quantity

$$d^2 = \int_0^T s(t)q(t)\,dt,$$

and if this is finite, false alarms and missed signals are always probable. If on the other hand this integral diverges, the detection problem is "singular", and a system can in principle be designed to detect the signal $s(t)$ with a pair of probabilities Q_0, $1-Q_d$ as small as desired. Whether detection will be perfect in this way can in general not be predicted without solving the integral equation (3.8) for $q(t)$.

When the noise is stationary, the question of singularity is somewhat simpler. Let $s_\infty(t)$ be a signal that coincides with $s(t)$ in the interval $(0, T)$ and is quadratically integrable over the infinite interval $(-\infty, \infty)$. The probability of detecting $s_\infty(t)$ by observations over the infinite interval $(-\infty, \infty)$ must, for a given false-alarm probability, be at least as great as that of detecting $s(t)$ by observations over $(0, T)$, for discarding the input $v(t)$ outside $(0, T)$ can only reduce the probability of detecting $s_\infty(t)$. Therefore d^2 of eq. (3.11) is less than

$$d_\infty^2 = \int_{-\infty}^{\infty} s_\infty(t)q_\infty(t)\,dt, \tag{3.17}$$

where $q_\infty(t)$ is the solution of the integral equation

$$s_\infty(t) = \int_{-\infty}^{\infty} \phi(t-s)q_\infty(s)\,ds, \tag{3.18}$$

the noise being stationary. Equation (3.18) can be solved by Fourier transforms, as shown in Appendix A, and

$$d_\infty^2 = \int_{-\infty}^{\infty} \frac{|S_\infty(\omega)|^2}{\Phi(\omega)} \frac{d\omega}{2\pi} \tag{3.19}$$

where $\Phi(\omega)$ is the spectral density of the noise, eq. (3.1), and $S_\infty(\omega)$ is the spectrum of the extended signal $s_\infty(t)$. If $d_\infty^2 < \infty$, then $d^2 < \infty$ and detection of $s(t)$ in $(0, T)$ cannot be singular (Kailath, 1966a). When, as is most usual, any white noise at all is present in the input $v(t)$, all that is required for d_∞^2 to be finite and the detection to be imperfect is that the signal $s(t)$ have a finite energy, $\int_{-\infty}^{\infty} [s(t)]^2\,dt < \infty$.

We have touched on these questions of existence and singularity only lightly. Numerous papers have been written on the subject, and the reader who wishes to pursue it further may consult those listed in the bibliography of this chapter. As a guide to their vocabulary, we mention that "equivalence" of the probability measures associated with $v(t)$ under the two hypotheses means that detection is imperfect; "perpendicularity" of the measures means that it is perfect and that the singular case is at hand. What we have called the likelihood ratio $\Lambda[v(t)]$ is often termed the "Radon–Nikodym derivative" of one measure with respect to the other. Before delving into this literature, however, the reader should peruse our Section 4 on the Karhunen–Loève expansion.

(b) *The Matched Filter for Colored Noise*

The detection statistic G of eq. (3.7) can be generated by passing the input $v(t)$ through a filter whose impulse response is

$$\begin{aligned} K(\tau) &= q(T-\tau), \quad 0 < \tau < T, \\ &= 0, \quad \tau < 0, \quad \tau > T. \end{aligned} \tag{3.20}$$

The output of the filter at time $t = T$ is equal to G and can be compared with a decision level G_0 to decide whether a signal is present. Such a filter can be termed the "matched filter" for this detection problem.

Let the input $v(t) = s(t)+n(t)$ be applied to an arbitrary linear filter of impulse response $K(\tau)$, starting at time $t = 0$. Let the part of the output $y(t)$ due to the signal be $y_s(t)$, the part due to the noise $y_n(t)$. The signal-to-noise ratio at time $t = T$ can be defined by

$$d^2 = [y_s(T)]^2/\mathbf{E}[y_n(T)]^2. \tag{3.21}$$

In terms of the autocovariance function $\phi(t, s)$ of the noise, d^2 is given by

$$d^2 = \frac{\left| \int_0^T K(u)s(T-u)\,du \right|^2}{\int_0^T \int_0^T K(s_1)K(s_2)\phi(T-s_1, T-s_2)\,ds_1\,ds_2}. \tag{3.22}$$

It is not hard to show that the impulse response of the filter for which this signal-to-noise ratio is a maximum is the solution of the integral equation

$$s(t) = \int_0^T K(T-u)\phi(t, u)\,du, \quad 0 < t < T. \tag{3.23}$$

By comparing this equation with eq. (3.8) we see that the solution is $K(\tau) = q(T-\tau)$, $0 < \tau < T$. The filter that maximizes the signal-to-noise ratio must, therefore, have the same impulse response as the matched filter over the interval $0 < \tau < T$.

If the noise is stationary, and if the interval $(0, T)$ is long enough to include substantially all of the signal $s(t)$, the integral equation (3.23) can be solved by Fourier transforms to yield the impulse response $Y(\omega)$ of the filter that maximizes the output signal-to-noise ratio at time $t = T$,

$$Y(\omega) = e^{-i\omega T} S^*(\omega)/\Phi(\omega), \tag{3.24}$$

where $S(\omega)$ is the spectrum of the signal and $\Phi(\omega)$ is the spectral density of the noise (Dwork, 1950). This is the transfer function of the matched filter for detecting the signal $s(t)$ in noise of spectral density $\Phi(\omega)$ when the observation interval is much longer than the duration of the signal or the correlation time of the noise. The output signal-to-noise ratio then becomes equal to d_∞ as defined by eq. (3.19). This is the maximum possible value of the signal-to-noise ratio d (Turin, 1960).

If the spectral density of the noise can be factored as $\Phi(\omega) = \Psi(\omega)\Psi^*(\omega)$, where the function $\Psi(\omega)$ contains all the poles and zeros of $\Phi(\omega)$ lying above the real axis in the ω-plane, the transfer function $Y(\omega)$ in eq. (3.24) can be expressed as

$$Y(\omega) = Y_1(\omega)Y_2(\omega)$$

with

$$Y_1(\omega) = 1/\Psi(\omega), \quad Y_2(\omega) = e^{-i\omega T} S^*(\omega)/\Psi^*(\omega), \tag{3.25}$$

and the matched filtering can be carried out in two stages, as shown in Fig. IV.5.

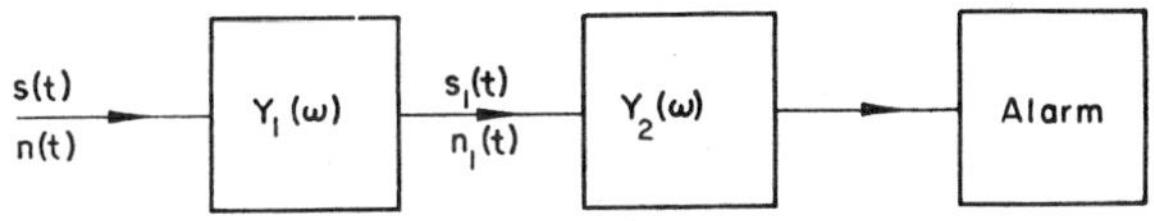

FIG. IV.5. The matched filter for a long observation interval: $Y_1(\omega)Y_2(\omega) = e^{-i\omega T}S^*(\omega)/\Phi(\omega)$.

At the output of the first filter, the spectral density of the noise is constant, $\Phi_1(\omega) = \Phi(\omega)\,|\,Y_1(\omega)\,|^2 = 1$; the noise $n_1(t)$ at that point is white. For this reason the filter whose transfer function is $Y_1(\omega) = 1/\Psi(\omega)$ is called a "whitening filter" (Bode and Shannon, 1950). The spectrum of the signal at that point, $s_1(t)$, is

$$S_1(\omega) = S(\omega)Y_1(\omega) = S(\omega)/\Psi(\omega).$$

The task of the second filter is to facilitate the detection of a known signal,

$s_1(t)$, in white noise, and eq. (3.25) shows that it has indeed the proper transfer function. A system such as this can be realized only approximately, and even so only by accepting a long delay T, but it serves to exemplify the results of our mathematical analysis.

4. THE KARHUNEN–LOÈVE EXPANSION

(a) *The Orthonormal Functions*

The likelihood ratio for detecting a signal in colored Gaussian noise was worked out in the previous section by imagining that the input $v(t)$ is sampled at uniformly spaced instants of time, after which the number of data was made to increase to infinity and the spacing of the sampling points to vanish. Some of the mathematical difficulties of that procedure can be avoided by the approach taken by Grenander (1950). The input $v(t)$ is expanded in a series of orthonormal functions, and the decision is based on a finite number of the coefficients in the expansion, the number being later allowed to pass to infinity. Such expansions, proposed by Loève (1945, 1946) and Karhunen (1947), go under the name of "Karhunen–Loève expansions", and they are met so frequently in communication theory that we shall introduce them here in the context of the detection problem. Their first application to this subject was made by Kac and Siegert (1947) in analyzing the filtered output of a quadratic rectifier whose input is colored Gaussian noise. Further discussion of their use in detection can be found in Kelly, Reed, and Root (1960) and in Selin (1965).

In the method we used in Section 3 for obtaining the likelihood ratio, the samples of the input, taken at times separated by Δt, were correlated. It is simpler to use a set of quantities v_k that are uncorrelated, but can be generated by linear operations on the input $v(t)$. These quantities will be the coefficients of an expansion of the input in a particular kind of Fourier series.

The input $v(t)$ is written in the form

$$v(t) = \sum_k v_k f_k(t), \tag{4.1}$$

in which the real functions $f_k(t)$ form an orthonormal set with respect to the interval $(0, T)$. This means that they satisfy the equations

$$\int_0^T f_m(t) f_k(t)\, dt = \delta_{mk} = \begin{cases} 1, & m = k, \\ 0, & m \neq k, \end{cases} \tag{4.2}$$

for all values of the indices. Because of these relationships the coefficients v_k can be calculated from

$$v_k = \int_0^T f_k(t)v(t)\,dt, \tag{4.3}$$

and they are linearly related to the input $v(t)$. Any one of them, say v_k, could be generated by passing the input through a filter matched to a signal of the form $f_k(t)$, $0 < t < T$. According to our discussion in Section 2, the output of this matched filter at the end of the observation interval would be the value of v_k for the given input. We recall that in Chapter II, Section 2 we used an expansion like eq. (4.1) to describe a sample of noise. The orthonormal functions there were $T^{-\frac{1}{2}} \exp (i\omega_n t)$, $\omega_n = 2\pi n/T$, for all integers n. As we shall see, however, it is sometimes convenient to adopt a different set of orthonormal functions.

The choice between the two hypotheses H_0 and H_1 will be made on the basis of the values of a finite number n of these coefficients v_k; later we shall let n increase without limit. As stated above, the analysis is simplified if the coefficients are uncorrelated random variables. From eq. (4.3) their covariances are given by the equation

$$\begin{aligned}\{v_k, v_m\} &= \int_0^T \int_0^T f_k(t_1)f_m(t_2)\,\overline{n(t_1)n(t_2)}\,dt_1\,dt_2 \\ &= \int_0^T \int_0^T f_k(t_1)f_m(t_2)\phi(t_1, t_2)\,dt_1\,dt_2,\end{aligned} \tag{4.4}$$

where $\phi(t, s)$ is the autocovariance of the noise. Our goal will be achieved if we can find a set of orthonormal functions $\{f_k(t)\}$ such that this expression vanishes whenever k and m are different. This will be so if the following relation holds for each function $f_m(t)$:

$$\int_0^T \phi(t, s)f_m(s)\,ds = \lambda_m f_m(t), \qquad 0 < t < T, \tag{4.5}$$

where the constants λ_m have yet to be determined. If we substitute eq. (4.5) into the autocovariance, eq. (4.4), and use the orthonormality relation we find

$$\{v_k, v_m\} = \lambda_m\,\delta_{km}\,. \tag{4.6}$$

The coefficients v_k are then uncorrelated, and their variances are the numbers λ_k. We must prove, of course, that the solutions of eq. (4.5), which is called *a homogeneous integral equation*, satisfy the orthonormality relation (4.2). This will be done in the next section, where we shall study some of the properties of integral equations.

(b) *Integral Equations*

In a homogeneous integral equation of the form

$$\lambda f(t) = \int_0^T \phi(t, s) f(s)\, ds, \qquad 0 < t < T, \tag{4.7}$$

the function $\phi(t, s)$ of two variables is known as the *kernel*; in the application to signal detection the kernel is the autocovariance function of the noise. Here we allow the kernel to be complex, but we require of it the symmetry property

$$\phi(t, s) = \phi^*(s, t), \tag{4.8}$$

where the asterisk denotes the complex conjugate. It is then possible that λ and $f(t)$ are complex. Most of the integral equations occurring in signal detection theory can be put into such a form that their kernels obey eq. (4.8). The kernel is then said to be *Hermitian*; if it is also real, it is simply called *symmetrical.*

Solutions of eq. (4.7) exist only for certain values of the parameter λ; these special values are called *eigenvalues*, and the associated solutions are called *eigenfunctions*. (Sometimes these are called "proper" values and functions.) The equation for any eigenfunction is then

$$\lambda_k f_k(t) = \int_0^T \phi(t, s) f_k(s)\, ds, \qquad 0 < t < T. \tag{4.9}$$

The theory of these integral equations is described in a number of texts: Lovitt (1924), Courant and Hilbert (1931), Hilbert (1953), and Morse and Feshbach (1953), to name a few. The theory is similar to that of linear operators, which act on vectors in a so-called "Hilbert space" of an infinite number of dimensions; these vectors correspond to functions defined over the interval $0 < t < T$. Multiplication of a function of s by $\phi(t, s)\, ds$ and integration over $0 < s < T$ to yield a new function make up a particular type of linear operation. A linear operator rotates and stretches the vectors on which it acts in such a way that the transformed sum of two vectors is the sum of the transformed vectors, and so on. An integral like

$$\int_0^T f^*(t)\, g(t)\, dt$$

corresponds to the scalar product of the vectors representing the functions $f(t)$ and $g(t)$.

First we shall prove that the eigenfunctions of eq. (4.7) possess an orthonormality property like that of eq. (4.2). To do so we multiply both sides of eq. (4.9) by $f_m^*(t)\,dt$ and integrate:

$$\lambda_k \int_0^T f_m^*(t) f_k(t)\,dt = \int_0^T \int_0^T f_m^*(t)\phi(t, s) f_k(s)\,dt\,ds.$$

Taking the complex conjugate of eq. (4.9) and writing it for the mth eigenfunction, we get

$$\lambda_m^* f_m^*(s) = \int_0^T \phi^*(s, t) f_m^*(t)\,dt = \int_0^T f_m^*(t)\,\phi(t, s)\,dt,$$

on account of the Hermitian character of the kernel, eq. (4.8). If we multiply both sides of this equation by $f_k(s)\,ds$ and integrate, it becomes

$$\lambda_m^* \int_0^T f_m^*(s) f_k(s)\,ds = \int_0^T \int_0^T f_m^*(t)\phi(t, s) f_k(s)\,ds\,dt.$$

Subtracting from the above equation, we find

$$(\lambda_k - \lambda_m^*) \int_0^T f_m^*(t) f_k(t)\,dt = 0.$$

In most problems the eigenvalues λ_k are all different. Then for $k \neq m$ we must have

$$\int_0^T f_m^*(t) f_k(t)\,dt = 0, \qquad k \neq m.$$

On the other hand, for $m = k$ the integral is positive, so that $\lambda_k - \lambda_k^* = 0$. Therefore all the eigenvalues λ_k are *real*. From the form of eq. (4.9) we see that an eigenfunction is determined only up to an arbitrary multiplying constant, which can be chosen so that the integral of the absolute square of the function equals 1. Then for all indices

$$\int_0^T f_m^*(t) f_k(t)\,dt = \delta_{mk}, \tag{4.10}$$

and the eigenfunctions form an orthonormal set. In the vector-space analogy the eigenfunctions $f_k(t)$ correspond to a mutually orthogonal set of vectors of unit length.

We shall further assume that the kernel $\phi(t, s)$ is *positive-definite*, which means that for any function $g(t)$ that is not identically zero

$$\int_0^T \int_0^T g^*(t)\phi(t, s) g(s)\,dt\,ds > 0. \tag{4.11}$$

Since the expected value of a random variable that is never negative cannot itself be negative,

$$\mathbf{E}\left|\int_0^T g(t)n(t)\,dt\right|^2 = \int_0^T\int_0^T g^*(t)g(s)\mathbf{E}[n(t)\,n(s)]\,dt\,ds$$
$$= \int_0^T\int_0^T g^*(t)\phi(t, s)\,g(s)dt\,ds \geqslant 0,$$

and an autocovariance function is at least *non-negative definite*. For the equality sign to pertain, the function $g(t)$ would have to be orthogonal to all possible realizations $n(t)$ of the noise, an unlikely occurrence; the autocovariances generally encountered in communication theory are positive-definite.

When the kernel $\phi(t, s)$ is positive-definite, its eigenvalues λ_k are all positive, for from eqs. (4.9) and (4.11) we obtain

$$\lambda_k \int_0^T |f_k(t)|^2\,dt = \lambda_k = \int_0^T\int_0^T f_k^*(t)\phi(t, s)f_k(s)\,dt\,ds > 0.$$

The linear operator changes the lengths of the orthogonal vectors corresponding to the eigenfunctions $f_k(t)$, but it does not rotate them. A positive-definite linear operator does not reverse the direction of any of these basic orthogonal vectors.

If the kernel $\phi(t, s)$ is real and symmetrical, the eigenfunctions must also be real, as one can show by taking the complex conjugate of eq. (4.9), for then both $f_k(t)$ and $f_k^*(t)$ are eigenfunctions of the kernel $\phi(t, s)$, and since we assume that there is no more than one eigenfunction for each eigenvalue, these functions must be identical. The arbitrary phase factor left undetermined by the normalization, eq. (4.2), is set equal to 1.

Let us assign the indices so that the eigenvalues appear in descending order, $\lambda_1 > \lambda_2 > \lambda_3 > \ldots > 0$, and let us assume that as in detection in stationary noise, the kernel is the real function $\phi(t-s)$. We can investigate the form of the eigenfunctions in the following rough manner. The kernel $\phi(t-s)$ tends to smooth any function on which it operates, acting somewhat like the impulse response of a linear filter, as can be seen by referring to eq. (2.2) of Chapter I. If the "input" to this filter is an eigenfunction $f_k(t)$, the "output" must have the same form. We know that the only signals that are not distorted by a linear filter are the sinusoids. Hence, we expect the eigenfunctions to have oscillatory forms, although only certain discrete "frequencies" of oscillation are permitted, in contrast to the behavior of an ordinary linear filter. If the function $\phi(\tau)$ is bell-shaped, the equivalent filter is of the low-pass type; and inputs of high "frequency" are attenuated more than those of low frequency. Therefore, we expect the eigenfunctions with small eigenvalues λ to exhibit a larger number of oscillations in $(0, T)$ than those with large eigenvalues. In Section 5 we shall calculate the eigenfunctions of a simple kernel, and we shall find them to have this oscillatory form.

Since the eigenfunctions $\{f_k(t)\}$ make up an orthonormal set, they can be used for Fourier expansions of functions that are well behaved in the interval $(0, T)$. Such a function $q(t)$ can be written

$$q(t) = \sum_k q_k f_k(t), \tag{4.12}$$

and the coefficients of the series are given by

$$q_k = \int_0^T f_k^*(t) q(t)\, dt \tag{4.13}$$

through the orthonormality relation, eq. (4.10). Such an expansion can be used to solve the Fredholm equation of the first kind that appeared in the previous section,

$$s(t) = \int_0^T \phi(t, s) q(s)\, ds, \qquad 0 < t < T. \tag{4.14}$$

We are given $s(t)$ and wish to find $q(t)$. If both functions are expanded into Fourier series like eq. (4.12), with coefficients s_k and q_k, and if these expansions are substituted into the equation, we find

$$\sum_k s_k f_k(t) = \sum_k q_k \int_0^T \phi(t, s) f_k(s)\, ds = \sum_k q_k \lambda_k f_k(t),$$

and $s_k = q_k \lambda_k$. The solution of eq. (4.14) can therefore be given, at least formally, by

$$q(t) = \sum_k s_k f_k(t)/\lambda_k. \tag{4.15}$$

Indeed, the kernel itself possesses such a Fourier expansion,

$$\phi(t, s) = \sum_k \lambda_k f_k(t) f_k^*(s), \tag{4.16}$$

which can be proved by substituting it into the integral equation (4.9) and using eq. (4.10).

For any two functions $r(t)$ and $s(t)$ having Fourier expansions like eq. (4.12), with coefficients r_k and s_k, respectively, there is the useful relation

$$\int_0^T s^*(t)\, r(t)\, dt = \sum_{k,m} s_k^* r_m \int_0^T f_k^*(t) f_m(t)\, dt = \sum_{k,m} s_k^* r_m \delta_{km} = \sum_k s_k^* r_k\,. \tag{4.17}$$

The coefficients s_k correspond to the components of the "vector" $s(t)$ along the orthogonal unit vectors $f_k(t)$ in the Hilbert space. Equation (4.17) is the formula for the scalar product of two such vectors in this space.

The solution of the integral equation (4.14) can sometimes be written as

$$q(t) = \int_0^T \psi(t, u) s(u)\, du, \tag{4.18}$$

where the "reciprocal kernel" $\psi(t, u)$ given by the expansion

$$\psi(t, u) = \sum_k f_k(t) f_k^*(u)/\lambda_k \tag{4.19}$$

is the solution of the integral equation

$$\int_0^T \phi(t, s)\psi(s, u)\, ds = \delta(t-u), \quad 0 < (t, u) < T. \tag{4.20}$$

Here we use the "closure relation"

$$\sum_k f_k(t) f_k^*(s) = \delta(t-s) \tag{4.21}$$

which is necessary for a Fourier series of the type of eq. (4.12) to be possible. For certain types of kernel $\phi(t, s)$ the inverse kernel $\psi(t, s)$ involves delta-functions and their derivatives; for others it is doubtful whether $\psi(t, s)$ can be expressed even in terms of such abnormal functions. Nevertheless, eq. (4.18) is useful as a formal expression of the solution $q(t)$ of eq. (4.15), which must depend in some linear way on the given function $s(t)$.

(c) *Derivation of the Test Statistic*

When applied to the integral equation (4.5), whose kernel $\phi(t, s)$ is the autocovariance function of the noise, the theory of the last part substantiates our expansion of the system input $v(t)$ in a Fourier series, eq. (4.2). The eigenfunctions of that integral equation are thereby shown to form an orthonormal set, so that the coefficients v_k of the expansion can be computed by eq. (4.3). These coefficients are then, according to eq. (4.6), uncorrelated, and their variances are the corresponding eigenvalues λ_k of the integral equation (4.5). Since the kernel $\phi(t, s)$ is positive-definite, the eigenvalues λ_k are all positive, as variances should be. We assume that the indices are assigned so that $\lambda_1 > \lambda_2 > \lambda_3 > \ldots > 0$, and that the eigenvalues are distinct. The eigenfunctions $f_k(t)$ are all real because the kernel $\phi(t, s)$ is real and symmetric.

Returning to the problem of making an optimum choice between the two hypotheses H_0 and H_1, we elect to base that choice on the values of the first n coefficients v_k, $1 \leq k \leq n$, of the expansion, eq. (4.1), of the given input. We noted in part (a) that these n values could be generated by a set of n filters in parallel—each matched to one of the $f_k(t)$—through which the input is passed. It is now necessary to determine the probability density functions of these n quantities under the two hypotheses. Because the coefficients v_k are formed by linear operations on the Gaussian stochastic process $v(t)$, they must be Gaussian random variables. They have already been shown to be uncorrelated; their variances are

$$\text{Var } v_k = \lambda_k .$$

Taking the expected value of both sides of eq. (4.3) under hypothesis H_0, when $v(t) = n(t)$, we find that the mean value of v_k is 0. Under hypothesis H_1, on the other hand, when $v(t) = s(t)+n(t)$,

$$\mathbf{E}[v_k \mid H_1] = \int_0^T f_k(t)\, s(t)\, dt = s_k, \tag{4.22}$$

where s_k is the coefficient of $f_k(t)$ in a Fourier expansion of the signal. From these results we can write down the joint p.d.f.s of the coefficients v_k,

$$\begin{aligned} p_0(\mathbf{v}) &= \prod_{k=1}^{n} (2\pi\lambda_k)^{-\frac{1}{2}} \exp\left(-\sum_{k=1}^{n} v_k^2/2\lambda_k\right), \\ p_1(\mathbf{v}) &= \prod_{k=1}^{n} (2\pi\lambda_k)^{-\frac{1}{2}} \exp\left[-\sum_{k=1}^{n} (v_k - s_k)^2/2\lambda_k\right]. \end{aligned} \tag{4.23}$$

By the considerations of Chapter III, the choice between the two hypotheses is to be made on the basis of the value of the likelihood ratio

$$\Lambda(\mathbf{v}) = \exp\left[\sum_{k=1}^{n} (2s_k v_k - s_k^2)/2\lambda_k\right], \tag{4.24}$$

which is to be compared with some fixed critical value Λ_0 that depends on the observer's criterion of success. He declares that there is no signal present if $\Lambda(\mathbf{v}) < \Lambda_0$ or, what is the same thing, if

$$G_n = \sum_{k=1}^{n} s_k v_k/\lambda_k < \ln \Lambda_0 + \sum_{k=1}^{n} s_k^2/2\lambda_k = G_{n0}. \tag{4.25}$$

In the n-dimensional Cartesian space with coordinates v_k the decision surface D is the plane

$$\sum_{k=1}^{n} s_k v_k/\lambda_k = \text{const.}$$

The larger n is, the more information is used about the input $v(t)$. Therefore, we are tempted to have the decision made on the basis of the limiting quantity

$$G = \sum_{k=1}^{\infty} s_k v_k/\lambda_k, \tag{4.26}$$

if this exists and can be conveniently generated. According to part (b) the quantities $q_k = s_k/\lambda_k$ are the Fourier coefficients of the solution $q(t)$ of the integral equations (4.14) or (3.8), and by means of the relation in eq. (4.17) we can write the statistic G as

$$G = \int_0^T q(t)\, v(t)\, dt. \tag{4.27}$$

This is the same as the detection statistic derived in Section 3.

If instead of passing to the limit of an infinite number of data v_k, we had used the statistic G_n of eq. (4.25), the false-alarm and detection probabilities would still be given as in eq. (3.14), but with the signal-to-noise ratio d replaced by a d_n given by the equation

$$d_n^2 = \sum_{k=1}^{n} s_k^2/\lambda_k, \tag{4.28}$$

with s_k as given by eq. (4.22). As n increases, so does d_n. If the series in eq. (4.28) does not converge when n goes to infinity, the signal-to-noise ratios d_n increase without bound; and for any false-alarm probability, however small, the probability of detection can be made as close to 1 as desired by taking n large enough. This is the singular case of perfect detection. When the series does converge, the limiting value of d_n^2 is equal to d^2 of eq. (3.11). In order for the solution $q(t)$ of eq. (3.8) to be quadratically integrable and to represent a signal of the usual kind, as

Grenander (1950) showed, the series

$$\sum_{k=1}^{n} s_k^2/\lambda_k^2$$

must converge, a more stringent requirement. As we shall see, the solution $q(t)$ often contains delta-functions and their derivatives and is not quadratically integrable.

5. SOLUTION OF THE INTEGRAL EQUATIONS

(a) *The Inhomogeneous Equation*

To determine the impulse response of the optimum filter for detection of a known signal $s(t)$ in stationary Gaussian noise of autocovariance function $\phi(\tau)$, one must solve an integral equation of the form

$$s(t) = \int_0^T \phi(t-u)\, q(u)\, du, \qquad 0 < t < T, \tag{5.1}$$

for the unknown function $q(t)$. Since this type of equation occurs frequently in the theory of linear prediction and filtering, as well as in detection theory, it is worth while to study methods of solving it. In the above form it is a "Fredholm integral equation of the first kind". A continuous solution $q(t)$ does not in general exist for continuous $s(t)$, unless the kernel $\phi(t-u)$ has some singularity or the range of integration is unbounded (Courant and Hilbert, 1931, vol. 1, p. 135). We shall see that for certain types of kernel a solution in closed form can be obtained, but it involves delta-functions and their derivatives. One's first thought is to treat eq. (5.1) numerically, replacing the integral by a summation and solving the resulting set of linear, simultaneous equations for the values of $q(t)$ at a finite set of points in the interval $0 < t < T$. However, a solution involving delta-function singularities can hardly be well approximated in this way.

The situation is more favorable when the noise contains a part that has a flat spectrum, that is, when the autocovariance of the noise is of the form

$$\phi(\tau) = \frac{N}{2}\,\delta(\tau) + \psi(\tau), \tag{5.2}$$

where $\psi(\tau)$ is continuous and integrable. Then eq. (5.1) becomes

$$s(t) = \frac{N}{2}\,q(t) + \int_0^T \psi(t-u)\, q(u)\, du, \qquad 0 < t < T; \tag{5.3}$$

this is a "Fredholm integral equation of the second kind", and a solution will generally exist unless $(-N/2)$ is an eigenvalue of the integral equation

$$\lambda f(t) = \int_0^T \psi(t-u) f(u)\, du$$

(Courant and Hilbert, 1931, vol. 1, ch. 3). Since $\psi(t-u)$ is in ordinary cases a positive-definite kernel, the integral equation cannot have a negative eigenvalue, and there is no trouble about the existence of a solution. If the amount of colored noise is small, a solution of eq. (5.3) can be obtained by iteration,

$$q(t) = \frac{2}{N}\left[s(t) - \frac{2}{N}\int_0^T \psi(t-u)\, s(u)\, du + \ldots\right]. \tag{5.4}$$

Otherwise one can calculate a solution numerically by replacing the integral by a summation and solving the resulting simultaneous equations for the values of $q(t)$ at a finite set of points in $(0, T)$. See Fox and Goodwin (1953) for a discussion of these numerical methods.

Stationary leucogenic noise furnishes a wide class of autocovariances $\phi(\tau)$ for which the integral equation (5.1) can be solved explicitly. As we said earlier, such noise can be generated by passing white noise through a linear filter composed of lumped circuit elements—resistors, capacitors, and inductors. Its spectral density $\Phi(\omega)$, proportional to $|Y(\omega)|^2$, where $Y(\omega)$ is the transfer function of the filter, is then a rational function of ω^2. The autocovariance itself is the sum of exponential functions of $|\tau|$, possibly multiplied by polynomials in $|\tau|$. Some or all of the exponents in the exponential functions may be complex, lending the autocovariance the appearance of a bilaterally damped sinusoid.

The spectral density of the noise can now be written in the form

$$\Phi(\omega) = \int_{-\infty}^{\infty} \phi(\tau)\, e^{-i\omega\tau}\, d\tau = N(\omega)/P(\omega), \tag{5.5}$$

where $N(\omega)$ and $P(\omega)$ are polynomials in ω with real coefficients, only even powers of ω appearing. Let the degree of $N(\omega)$ be $2m$, and let that of $P(\omega)$ be $2n$, with $m \leq n$. By finding the zeros of these polynomials, one can express the spectral density in the rational form

$$\Phi(\omega) = C \prod_{k=1}^{m} (\omega^2 + h_k^2) \prod_{j=1}^{n} (\omega^2 + m_j^2)^{-1}, \tag{5.6}$$

where C is a positive constant, and where the h_k's and the m_j's are taken with positive real parts. We assume that the m h_k's are distinct. If not, some of our equations have to be modified.

When the kernel $\phi(\tau)$ is a covariance of stationary leucogenic noise, the solution of the integral equation (5.1) must have the form

$$q(t) = q_0(t) + \sum_{j=0}^{n-m-1} [a_j \delta^{(j)}(t) + b_j \delta^{(j)}(t-T)] + \sum_{k=1}^{m} \{c_k \exp(-h_k t) + d_k \exp[-h_k(T-t)]\}, \tag{5.7}$$

where the a's, b's, c's, and d's are constants to be determined (Zadeh and Ragazzini, 1950). Here $\delta^{(j)}(t-w)$ is the jth derivative of the delta-function, defined by

$$\int_{-\infty}^{\infty} f(t)\,\delta^{(j)}(t-w)\,dt = (-1)^j \frac{d^j}{dt^j} f(t)\Big|_{t=w} = (-1)^j f^{(j)}(w), \tag{5.8}$$

and $q_0(t)$ is the solution of the integral equation with infinite limits,

$$s(t) = \int_{-\infty}^{\infty} \phi(t-u)\, q_0(u)\, du. \tag{5.9}$$

This equation can usually be solved by Fourier transforms,

$$q_0(t) = \int_{-\infty}^{\infty} Q_0(\omega)\, e^{i\omega t}\, d\omega/2\pi, \quad Q_0(\omega) = S(\omega)/\Phi(\omega), \tag{5.10}$$

where $S(\omega)$ is the spectrum of the signal $s(t)$. When $m = n$ the terms with the delta-functions do not appear in $q(t)$ of eq. (5.7); when $m = 0$ the exponential functions are absent.

The detection statistic G is obtained by substituting $q(t)$ into eq. (3.7),

$$G = \int_0^T q_0(t)\, v(t)\, dt + \sum_{j=0}^{n-m-1} (-1)^j [a_j v^{(j)}(0) + b_j v^{(j)}(T)] + \sum_{k=1}^{m} \int_0^T \{c_k \exp(-h_k t) + d_k \exp[-h_k(T-t)]\}\, v(t)\, dt. \tag{5.11}$$

The terms in the first summation require the input $v(t)$ to be differentiated at most n–m–1 times and sampled at $t = 0$ and $t = T$. The noise in the input can be differentiated as many as n–m–1 times because its spectral density $\Phi(\omega)$ decreases at infinity like $\omega^{-2(n-m)}$, and the variance

$$\text{Var}\, n^{(n-m-1)}(t) = \int_{-\infty}^{\infty} \omega^{2(n-m-1)}\Phi(\omega)\, d\omega/2\pi$$

of the (n–m–1)th derivative is finite. The remaining terms in eq. (5.11) can be generated by passing the input $v(t)$ through a filter matched to the signal

$$q_0(t) + \sum_{k=1}^{m} \{c_k \exp(-h_k t) + d_k \exp[-h_k(T-t)]\}$$

and sampling the output at the end of the observation interval. No singularities appear in the expression for the detection statistic G, even though the solution of the integral equation contains delta-functions and their derivatives.

The solution in eq. (5.7) involves $2n$ constants, n–m each of the a's and b's, and m each of the c's and d's. To find them one can substitute $q(t)$ from that equation into the integral equation (5.1). After the integration is carried out, one will be able to cancel $s(t)$, and there will remain $2n$ distinct functions of t, each multiplied by some linear combination of the unknown constants. (If the $2n$ poles of $\Phi(\omega)$ are distinct, these functions will be $\exp m_k t$ and $\exp(-m_k t)$, $k = 1, 2, \ldots, n$.) The coefficients of each of these functions must vanish in order for the integral equation to be satisfied, and one obtains in this way $2n$ linear equations that can be solved for the unknown constants.

As a simple example, let the autocovariance of the noise be

$$\phi(\tau) = \phi_0\, e^{-\mu|\tau|}. \tag{5.12}$$

The spectral density of the noise is then

$$\Phi(\omega) = 2\mu\phi_0(\mu^2+\omega^2)^{-1} \tag{5.13}$$

and $m = 0$, $n = 1$, $C = 2\mu\phi_0$, $m_1 = \mu$. The function $q_0(t)$ is now, by eq. (5.10),

$$q_0(t) = (2\mu\phi_0)^{-1} \int_{-\infty}^{\infty} (\omega^2+\mu^2)\, S(\omega)\, d\omega/2\pi = (2\mu\phi_0)^{-1}[\mu^2 s(t) - s''(t)],$$

where the primes indicate differentiation with respect to t. The solution of the integral equation will be

$$q(t) = (2\mu\phi_0)^{-1}[\mu^2 s(t) - s''(t)] + a_0\delta(t) + b_0\delta(t-T). \tag{5.14}$$

When this is substituted into the integral equation, one obtains

$$s(t) = \phi_0 \int_0^T e^{-\mu|t-u|} q(u)\, du = \phi_0[a_0 e^{-\mu t} + b_0 e^{\mu(t-T)}]$$

$$+(2\mu)^{-1} e^{-\mu t} \int_0^t e^{\mu u}[\mu^2 s(u) - s''(u)]\, du + (2\mu)^{-1} e^{\mu t} \int_t^T e^{-\mu u}[\mu^2 s(u) - s''(u)]\, du. \tag{5.15}$$

Integrating the terms containing $s''(u)$ twice by parts, one finally gets

$$\begin{aligned} s(t) = \phi_0[a_0 e^{-\mu t} + b_0 e^{\mu(t-T)}] - (2\mu)^{-1}\{e^{-\mu t}[\mu s(0) - s'(0)] \\ + e^{\mu(t-T)}[\mu s(T) + s'(T)] - 2\mu s(t)\}. \end{aligned} \tag{5.16}$$

In order for this equation to hold for all values of t in the interval $(0, T)$, the coefficients of $e^{\mu t}$ and $e^{-\mu t}$ must each vanish, and the coefficients a_0 and b_0 must be given by

$$\begin{aligned} a_0 &= [\mu s(0) - s'(0)]/2\mu\phi_0, \\ b_0 &= [\mu s(T) + s'(T)]/2\mu\phi_0. \end{aligned} \tag{5.17}$$

The detection statistic G now becomes

$$G = (2\mu\phi_0)^{-1}\left\{[\mu s(0) - s'(0)]\, v(0) + [\mu s(T) + s'(T)]\, v(T) + \int_0^T [\mu^2 s(t) - s''(t)]\, v(t)\, dt\right\}. \tag{5.18}$$

The signal-to-noise ratio d that determines the probability of detection is obtained by putting $s(t)$ for $v(t)$ in G, and after an integration by parts, one finds

$$d^2 = (2\phi_0)^{-1}\left\{[s(0)]^2 + [s(T)]^2 + \mu^{-1} \int_0^T \{\mu^2[s(t)]^2 + [s'(t)]^2\}\, dt\right\}. \tag{5.19}$$

If the rational spectral density $\Phi(\omega)$ is any more complicated than the one used in this example, the method of substituting $q(t)$ into the integral equation will be extremely tedious. Formal schemes requiring less labor have been developed, and one is described in Appendix E, which also provides references to other methods of solving the integral equation (5.1).

If $\phi(t, s)$ is the autocovariance of non-stationary leucogenic noise, the integral equation

$$s(t) = \int_0^T \phi(t, s)\, q(s)\, ds \tag{5.20}$$

can be solved by a natural extension of the method of this section; it is described by Miller and Zadeh (1956) and Laning and Battin (1956, § 8.5). Such a noise process is the solution of the differential equation

$$L_t n(t) = M_t w(t),$$

where $w(t)$ is a white-noise process of unit bilateral spectral density, and L_t and M_t are linear differential operators of the form

$$L_t f(t) = \sum_{j=0}^{n-1} l_j(t) \frac{d^j f}{dt^j}, \quad M_t f(t) = \sum_{k=0}^{m-1} m_k(t) \frac{d^k f}{dt^k}$$

with $m \leqslant n$. The covariance $\phi(t, s)$ is given by

$$\phi(t, s) = \int_{-\infty}^{\infty} \Gamma(t, x) \Gamma(s, x) \, dx, \tag{5.21}$$

where $\Gamma(t, x)$ is the solution of the equation

$$L_t \Gamma(t, x) = M_t \delta(t-x).$$

To solve the integral equation one must be able to invert the operator $M_t^* M_t$, that is, to solve the differential equation

$$M_t^* M_t g(t) = \delta(t-x),$$

where M_t^* is the operator adjoint to M_t. This inversion is seldom easy.

Kailath (1966b) has shown how to solve the integral equation (5.20) for a kernel of the form

$$\begin{aligned} \phi(t, s) &= f(t)\, g(s), \quad 0 \leqslant t \leqslant s \leqslant T, \\ &= f(s)\, g(t), \quad 0 \leqslant s \leqslant t \leqslant T, \end{aligned} \tag{5.22}$$

where $f(t)$ and $g(t)$ are continuous functions of t and their quotient $f(t)/g(t)$ is continuous and strictly increasing in the interval $0 \leqslant t \leqslant T$. Equations with similar kernels were treated by Shinbrot (1957). Kailath (1966b) has also solved the integral equation for a triangular kernel, $\phi(t, s) = 1-|t-s|$, $0 \leqslant |t-s| \leqslant 1$, $\phi(t, s) = 0$, $|t-s| > 1$, and for linear combinations of the triangular kernel and a kernel of the type of eq. (5.22).

(b) *The Homogeneous Equation*

When the kernel $\phi(t-s)$ of the homogeneous integral equation

$$\lambda f(t) = \int_0^T \phi(t-s) f(s) \, ds \tag{5.23}$$

is an autocovariance of noise with a rational spectral density, the process of solving it is much like the method of part (a). The solution will in general be a linear combination of exponential functions,

$$f(t) = \sum_{k=1}^{n} [g_k \exp p_k t + h_k \exp(-p_k t)]. \tag{5.24}$$

When this is substituted into eq. (5.23), it is found that the n numbers p_k must be solutions of the algebraic equation

$$N(-ip) - \lambda P(-ip) = 0, \quad p = \pm p_k, \quad k = 1, 2, \ldots, n, \tag{5.25}$$

where $N(\omega)$ and $P(\omega)$ are the polynomials in the numerator and denominator of the spectral density $\Phi(\omega)$.

At the same time, certain linear combinations of the functions $\exp m_k t$ and $\exp(-m_k t)$ appear, where im_k, $-im_k$, $k = 1, 2, \ldots, n$, are the $2n$ roots of the equation $P(\omega) = 0$. These combinations must vanish in order for the integral equation to be satisfied, and in this way one obtains $2n$ homogeneous linear equations for the coefficients g_k and h_k, $k = 1, 2, \ldots, n$. These linear equations have a solution only when the parameter λ is one of the eigenvalues of the integral equation, and the vanishing of the determinant of the coefficients of the $2n$ linear equations provides a transcendental equation for the eigenvalues. General formulas that abbreviate the work have been given by Youla (1957), and a similar method is described in Appendix E.

For the exponential kernel in eq. (5.12) we can use the solution in eq. (5.14) by putting $s(t) = \lambda f(t)$,

$$f(t) = \frac{\lambda}{2\mu\phi_0} \{[\mu f(0) - f'(0)]\,\delta(t) + [\mu f(T) + f'(T)]\,\delta(t-T) + \mu^2 f(t) - f''(t)\}.$$

It is clear from eq. (5.23) that the solution $f(t)$ cannot contain any delta-functions. The coefficients of $\delta(t)$ and $\delta(t-T)$ must therefore vanish, and we obtain the differential equation

$$\begin{aligned} f''(t) + \gamma^2 f(t) &= 0, \\ \gamma^2 &= 2\mu\phi_0\lambda^{-1} - \mu^2, \end{aligned} \tag{5.26}$$

with the boundary conditions

$$\begin{aligned} \mu f(0) - f'(0) &= 0, \\ \mu f(T) + f'(T) &= 0. \end{aligned}$$

The solution of the differential equation is

$$f(t) = A \cos \gamma t + B \sin \gamma t \tag{5.27}$$

and the boundary conditions give two equations for the coefficients A and B:

$$\mu A - \gamma B = 0,$$
$$\mu(A\cos\gamma T + B\sin\gamma T) + \gamma(B\cos\gamma T - A\sin\gamma T) = 0.$$

In order for a non-zero solution of these equations to exist, the determinant of the coefficients of A and B must vanish:

$$\begin{vmatrix} \mu & -\gamma \\ \mu\cos\gamma T - \gamma\sin\gamma T & \mu\sin\gamma T + \gamma\cos\gamma T \end{vmatrix} = 0.$$

This equation determines the values of γ and hence, from eq. (5.26), of the eigenvalues λ. If we number the eigenfunctions starting from $k = 0$, we obtain from the determinant the following sets of equations:

$$\begin{aligned} x_k \tan x_k &= \mu T/2, \qquad k \text{ even}, \\ x_k \cot x_k &= -\mu T/2, \quad k \text{ odd}, \\ x_k &= \gamma_k T/2, \quad k = 0, 1, 2, \ldots, \\ \lambda_k &= 2\mu\phi_0/(\gamma_k^2 + \mu^2). \end{aligned} \tag{5.28}$$

The first four eigenvalues of the integral equation are plotted versus the parameter μT in Fig. IV.6. It can be shown that for $\mu T \ll 1$,

$$\begin{aligned} \gamma_0 T &\cong \sqrt{2\mu T}, \qquad \lambda_0/\phi_0 T \doteq 1 - \frac{\mu T}{3} \\ \gamma_k T &\cong k\pi + \frac{2\mu T}{k\pi}, \qquad \lambda_k/\phi_0 T \doteq 2\mu T/k^2\pi^2, \end{aligned} \tag{5.29}$$

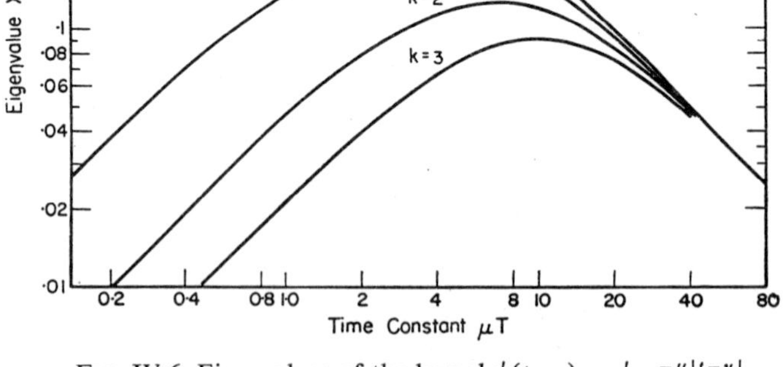

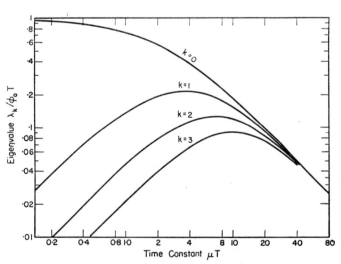

FIG. IV.6. Eigenvalues of the kernel $\phi(t-u) = \phi_0 e^{-\mu|t-u|}$.

and for $\mu T \gg \max\{1, k\pi\}$

$$\gamma_k T \sim (k+1)\pi \left(1 - \frac{2}{\mu T}\right), \quad \lambda_k/\phi_0 T \sim 2/\mu T. \tag{5.30}$$

The eigenfunctions $f_k(t)$ can be shown to be proportional to $\cos \gamma_k(t-T/2)$ for k even and to $\sin \gamma_k(t-T/2)$ for k odd. As we pointed out in Section 4, part (b), the number of oscillations of the eigenfunction in the interval $0 < t < T$ increases with the index k, as the eigenvalue λ_k decreases. The eigenfunction $f_k(t)$ in this problem has exactly k zeros in the interval $0 < t < T$.

If the kernel is not of the exponential type studied above, the exact solution of the homogeneous equation may be very difficult to determine. However, many approximation techniques have been developed for computing the eigenfunctions and eigenvalues of positive-definite linear operators, especially in connection with problems in quantum mechanics. Some methods and references to the literature on this subject are given in Morse and Feshbach (1953), ch. 9. We shall discuss only one, the Rayleigh–Ritz method, which is an especially simple way to compute the largest eigenvalue, which we shall call λ_0. For an integral equation like eq. (4.9) with a general positive-definite kernel $\phi(t, s)$, the method is based on the inequality

$$R = \frac{\int_0^T \int_0^T g^*(t)\, \phi(t, s)\, g(s)\, dt\, ds}{\int_0^T |g(t)|^2\, dt} \leq \lambda_0, \tag{5.31}$$

where $g(t)$ is any complex function of t. The equality holds when $g(t)$ is proportional to the first eigenfunction $f_0(t)$. To prove the inequality we write a Fourier expansion

$$g(t) = \sum_{k=0}^{\infty} g_k f_k(t)$$

in terms of the eigenfunctions of the integral equation (4.9). Then by the orthonormality relations, eq. (4.2),

$$R = \frac{\sum_{k=0}^{\infty} \lambda_k |g_k|^2}{\sum_{k=0}^{\infty} |g_k|^2}.$$

Arranging the eigenvalues so that $\lambda_0 > \lambda_1 > \lambda_2 > \lambda_3 > \ldots > 0$, we have

$$\sum_k \lambda_k |g_k|^2 \leq \lambda_0 \sum_k |g_k|^2,$$

since replacing each λ_k in the sum by λ_0 increases its value. Then $R \leqslant \lambda_0$ follows immediately. The equality holds when all g_k equal 0 except g_0, whereupon $g(t) = g_0 f_0(t)$.

As an illustration of the method we apply it to the homogeneous equation with kernel $\phi(t-s) = \phi_0 e^{-\mu|t-s|}$ studied above. A simple choice for $g(t)$ is a constant: $g(t) = 1$. Substituting into the inequality, eq. (5.31), we get

$$R = \frac{\phi_0}{T} \int_0^T \int_0^T e^{-\mu|t-s|}\, dt\, ds = 2\phi_0(\mu T - 1 + e^{-\mu T})/\mu^2 T < \lambda_0 .$$

If the reader will plot the quantity $R/\phi_0 T$ as a function of the parameter μT and compare the result with the graph of $\lambda_0/\phi_0 T$ in Fig. IV.6, he will verify that R is an extremely close approximation to λ_0 over the entire range of values of μT.

Improved approximations can be obtained by using for $g(t)$ a linear combination of a finite number of functions with arbitrary coefficients:

$$g(t) = \sum_{k=1}^{n} c_k h_k(t).$$

This is substituted into the expression for R, and the coefficients c_k are varied until R is a maximum. The result is a set of linear simultaneous equations for the c_k that can be written in the form

$$\sum_{k=1}^{n} (m_{jk} - \lambda h_{jk}) c_k = 0,$$

$$m_{jk} = \int_0^T \int_0^T h_j^*(t)\, \phi(t, s)\, h_k(s)\, dt\, ds,$$

$$h_{jk} = \int_0^T h_j^*(t)\, h_k(t)\, dt.$$

In order for these equations to have a solution other than $c_k \equiv 0$, the determinant of the coefficients must vanish:

$$\det (m_{jk} - \lambda h_{jk}) = 0.$$

This is an algebraic equation whose largest root is a good approximation to the largest eigenvalue λ_0 of the integral equation. If this root is substituted into the simultaneous equations, they can be solved for a set of coefficients c_k. The function

$$\sum_{k=1}^{n} c_k h_k(t)$$

is then an approximation to $bf_0(t)$, where b is a constant factor determined by the normalization condition, eq. (4.2).

The homogeneous integral equation (5.23) has been solved by Slepian and Pollak (1961) for a kernel that is the autocovariance of band-limited white noise,

$$\phi(\tau) = \frac{\sin W\tau}{\pi W\tau}.$$

The eigenfunctions are angular prolate spheroidal functions, and they have the unusual property of being orthogonal over both the finite interval $(0, T)$ and over the infinite interval $(-\infty, \infty)$. These solutions have provided the basis of an extensive treatment of the uncertainty relation for signals (Landau and Pollak, 1961, 1962).

PROBLEMS

In these problems the noise is Gaussian and the observation interval is $(0, T)$ unless otherwise stated.

1. Work out the optimum detector of a completely specified narrowband signal $s(t) = \text{Rl}\, F(t)e^{i\Omega t+i\psi}$ of carrier frequency Ω in the presence of stationary narrowband Gaussian noise of autocovariance $\phi(\tau) = \text{Rl}\, \tilde{\phi}(\tau)\, e^{i\Omega\tau}$. Show that the logarithm of the likelihood ratio is

$$\ln \Lambda[v(t)] = \text{Rl}\, e^{-i\psi} \int_0^T Q^*(t)\, V(t)\, dt - \tfrac{1}{2} \int_0^T Q^*(t)\, F(t)\, dt,$$

where $Q(t)$ is the solution of the integral equation

$$\int_0^T \tilde{\phi}(t-u)\, Q(u)\, du = F(t), \qquad 0 \leqslant t \leqslant T,$$

and the input to the system is $v(t) = \text{Rl}\, V(t)\, e^{i\Omega t}$.

Hint. Represent the noise as a circular Gaussian process as in Chapter II, Section 6.

2. Suppose that the signal in Problem 1 is to be detected in Gaussian noise whose spectral density is approximately constant over the significant part of the spectrum of the signal. Use the narrowband representation of white noise in Chapter II, Section 6, to show that the optimum detection statistic is

$$\ln \Lambda\, [v(t)] = \text{Rl}\, e^{-i\psi} \frac{1}{N} \int_0^T F^*(t)\, V(t)\, dt - \frac{1}{2N} \int_0^T |F(t)|^2\, dt,$$

where N is the unilateral spectral density of the noise over the frequency band of the signal.

3. (a) The optimum detector for a signal $s(t)$ in white Gaussian noise has been constructed, but the signal that appears at its input is not $s(t)$, but $s_1(t)$. Calculate the probability of detecting $s_1(t)$ and show how it depends on the integral

$$\int_0^T s(t)\, s_1(t)\, dt.$$

(b) Do the same for narrowband signals $s(t) = \text{Rl}\, F(t)e^{i\Omega t}$ and $s_1(t) = \text{Rl}\, F_1(t)e^{i\Omega t}$. Suppose that $F_1(t) = F(t)e^{i\theta}$, that is, that the phase is in error by an angle θ. How is the probability of detection affected? (c) If instead $F_1(t) = F(t-\tau)e^{iwt}$, it represents a signal that has arrived τ seconds late and with a carrier shifted by w from the frequency for which the detector was designed. Write down the counterpart of the above integral. For an infinite observation interval, this is the "ambiguity function", of importance in the theory of signal resolution.

4. The signal $s(t) = A(1-e^{-at})$ is to be detected in the presence of white Gaussian noise of unilateral spectral density N. Let the observation interval be $0 \leqslant t \leqslant T$. Find the impulse response of the proper matched filter, and work out the output of the matched filter as a function of time when the input is the signal $s(t)$.

5. A system is to be designed to decide which of two signals, $s_0(t)$ or $s_1(t)$, has been received in the presence of white Gaussian noise of unilateral spectral density N. Show that the system can base its decision on the correlation of the input with the difference of the signals. Relate the decision level on the optimum statistic to the critical value Λ_0 of the likelihood ratio.

6. In problem 5, find the probabilities Q_0 and Q_1 of each of the two kinds of errors. Show that for Q_0 fixed, the probability Q_1 depends on an "effective signal-to-noise ratio"

$$d = \sqrt{2(E_1+E_0-2R)/N}$$

where E_0 and E_1 are the energies of the two signals, and R is

$$R = \int_0^T s_0(t)\, s_1(t)\, dt.$$

7. Let λ_k be the kth eigenvalue of the integral equation

$$\lambda f(t) = \int_0^T \phi(t, u)\, f(u)\, du.$$

Prove that

$$\sum_{k=1}^{\infty} \lambda_k = \int_0^T \phi(t, t)\, dt, \qquad \sum_{k=1}^{\infty} \lambda_k^2 = \int_0^T\int_0^T \phi(t, u)\, \phi(u, t)\, dt\, du.$$

Hint. Use eq. (4.16).

8. The signal $s(t) = Ate^{-bt}$, $t > 0$, is received in the presence of noise of autocovariance $\phi(\tau) = \phi_0 e^{-\mu|\tau|}$. Show how the input should be processed by a matched filter and a delay line to decide whether the signal is present. Calculate the effective signal-to-noise ratio d, and state how the probability of detection depends on it.

Hint. Use the results of Section 5.

9. A signal $s(t)$ is to be detected in a mixture of white noise of unilateral spectral density N and correlated noise whose autocovariance is that given in problem 8. The spectral density of the noise is thus

$$\Phi(\omega) = \frac{N}{2} + \frac{2\mu\phi_0}{\omega^2+\mu^2}.$$

Show how to calculate the impulse response of the detection filter by the methods of Appendix E, or apply the technique described in Section 5. As an example take the signal as $s(t) = A(1-e^{-at})$ and work out the impulse response of the filter and the effective signal-to-noise ratio d.

BIBLIOGRAPHY (IV)

Papers

1943 NORTH, D. O., "An Analysis of the Factors which Determine Signal-Noise Discrimination in Pulsed Carrier Systems", RCA Laboratory Report PTR-6C; reprinted in *Proc. I.E.E.E.* **51,** 1016–27 (July 1963).

1945 LOÈVE, M., "Sur les Fonctions Aléatoires Stationnaires du Second Ordre", *Revue Sci.* **83,** 297–303.

1946 LOÈVE, M., "Fonctions Aléatoires du Second Ordre", *Revue Sci.* **84,** 195–206.

VAN VLECK, J. H. and MIDDLETON, D., "A Theoretical Comparison of the Visual, Aural, and Meter Reception of Pulsed Signals in the Presence of Noise", *J. Appl. Phys.* **17,** 940–71 (Nov.).

1947 KAC, M. and SIEGERT, A. J. F., "On the Theory of Noise in Radio Receivers with Square Law Detectors", *J. Appl. Phys.* **18,** 383–97 (Apr.).

KAC, M., and SIEGERT, A. J. F., "An Explicit Representation of a Stationary Gaussian Process", *Ann. Math. Stat.* **18,** no. 3, 438–42.

KARHUNEN, K., "Über linearen Methoden in der Wahrscheinlichkeitsrechnung", *Ann. Acad. Sci. Fennicae*, Ser. A. I. Math.–Physics, no. 37, 79 pp.

1948 SHANNON, C., "A Mathematical Theory of Communication", *Bell Sys. Tech. J.* **27,** 379–423 (July), 623–55 (Oct.).

1950 BODE, H. W. and SHANNON, C., "A Simplified Derivation of Linear Least-Square Smoothing and Prediction Theory", *Proc. I.R.E.* **38,** 417–25 (Apr.).

DWORK, B. M., "The Detection of a Pulse Superposed on Fluctuation Noise", *Proc. I.R.E.* **38,** 771–4 (July).

GRENANDER, U., "Stochastic Processes and Statistical Inference", *Arkiv för Mat.* **1,** no. 17, 195–277.

ZADEH, L. A. and RAGAZZINI, J. R., "An Extension of Wiener's Theory of Prediction", *J. Appl. Phys.* **21,** 645–55 (July).

1952 ZADEH, L. A. and RAGAZZINI, J. R., "Optimum Filters for the Detection of Signals in Noise", *Proc. I.R.E.* **40,** 1223–31 (Oct.).

1953 FOX, L. and GOODWIN, E. T., "The Numerical Solution of Non-singular, Linear Integral Equations", *Phil. Trans. Roy. Soc.* (A) **245,** 501–34 (Feb. 17).

1954 PETERSON, W. W., BIRDSALL, T. G. and FOX, W. C., "The Theory of Signal Detectability", *Trans. I.R.E.* **PGIT-4,** 171–212 (Sept.).

1956 MILLER, K. S. and ZADEH, L. A., "Solution of an Integral Equation Occurring in the Theories of Prediction and Detection", *Trans. I.R.E.* **IT-2,** no. 2, 72.

1957 SHINBROT, M., "A Generalization of a Method for the Solution of the Integral Equation Arising in Optimization of Time-Varying Linear Systems with Nonstationary Inputs", *Trans. I.R.E.* **IT-3,** 220–4 (Dec.).

YOULA, D., "The Solution of a Homogeneous Wiener–Hopf Integral Equation Occurring in the Expansion of Second-order Stationary Random Functions", *Trans. I.R.E.* **IT-3,** 187–93 (Sept.).

1958 HÁJEK, J., "A Property of Normal Distributions of any Stochastic Process", *Czech. Math. J.* **8** (83), 610–18. Translated in *American Mathematical Society Selected Translations in Mathematical Statistics and Probability*, **1,** 245–52 (1961).

HAUS, H. A. and ADLER, R. B., "Optimum Noise Performance of Linear Amplifiers", *Proc. I.R.E.* **46,** 1517–33 (Aug.).

1960 KELLY, E. J., REED, I. S. and ROOT, W. L., "The Detection of Radar Echoes in Noise", *J. Soc. Ind. Appl. Math.* **8,** (I) 309–41, (II) 481–507.

TURIN, G. L., "An Introduction to Matched Filters", *Trans. I.R.E.* **IT-6,** 311–29 (June).

1961 LANDAU, H. J. and POLLAK, H. O., "Prolate Spheroidal Wave Functions, Fourier Analysis and Uncertainty, II", *Bell Sys. Tech. J.* **40**, 65–84 (Jan.)
MARTEL, H. C. and MATHEWS, M. V., "Further Results on the Detectability of Known Signals in Gaussian Noise", *Bell Sys. Tech. J.* **40**, 423–51 (Mar.).
SLEPIAN, D. and POLLAK, H. O., "Prolate Spheroidal Wave Functions, Fourier Analysis and Uncertainty, I", *Bell Sys. Tech. J.* **40**, 43–63 (Jan.).
1962 HÁJEK, J., "On Linear Statistical Problems in Stochastic Processes", *Czech. Math. J.* **12** (87), 404–44.
LANDAU, H. J. and POLLAK, H. O., "Prolate Spheroidal Wave Functions, Fourier Analysis and Uncertainty, III", *Bell Sys. Tech. J.* **41**, 1295–1336 (July).
PARZEN, E., "Extraction and Detection Problems and Reproducing Kernel Hilbert Spaces", *J. Soc. Ind. Appl. Math.*, Series A on Control, **1**, no. 1, 35–62.
1963 CAPON, J., "Radon-Nikodym Derivatives of Stationary Gaussian Measures", *Ann. Math. Stat.* **35**, 517–31 (June).
PARZEN, E., "Probability Density Functionals and Reproducing Kernel Hilbert Spaces", *Proceedings of the Symposium on Time Series Analysis*, M. ROSENBLATT, ed., John Wiley & Sons, Inc., New York, N.Y., pp. 155–69.
ROOT, W. L., "Singular Gaussian Measures in Detection Theory", *ibid.*, pp 292–315.
YAGLOM, A. M., "On the Equivalence and Perpendicularity of Two Gaussian Probability Measures in Function Space", *ibid.*, pp. 327–46.
1965 CAPON, J., "Hilbert Space Methods for Detection Theory and Pattern Recognition", *Trans. I.E.E.E.* **IT-11**, 247–59 (Apr.).
KADOTA, T. T., "Optimum Reception of Binary Sure and Gaussian Signals", *Bell Sys. Tech. J.* **44**, 1621–58 (Oct.).
1966 KAILATH, T., (a) "Some Results on Singular Detection", *Info. & Control* **9**, 130–52 (Apr.).
KAILATH, T., (b) "Some Integral Equations with 'Nonrational' Kernels", *Trans I.E.E.E.* **IT-12**, 442–7 (Oct.).
1967 KAILATH, T., "A Projection Method for Signal Detection in Colored Gaussian Noise", *Trans. I.E.E.E.* **IT-13**, 441–7 (July).

Books

1924 LOVITT, W. V., *Linear Integral Equations*, McGraw-Hill Book Co., New York N.Y.
1931 COURANT, R. and HILBERT, D., *Methoden der mathematischen Physik*, J. Springer Verlag, Berlin. English translation: Interscience Publishers Inc., New York N.Y. (1953).
1949 SILVER, S., *Microwave Antenna Theory and Design*, M.I.T. Radiation Lab. Series no. 12, McGraw-Hill Book Co., New York, N.Y.
1953 HILBERT, D., *Grundzüge einer allgemeinen Theorie der linearen Integralgleichungen*, Chelsea Publishing Co., New York, N.Y.
MORSE, P. M. and FESHBACH, H., *Methods of Theoretical Physics*, McGraw-Hill Book Co., New York, N.Y.
1955 LOÈVE, M., *Probability Theory*, D. Van Nostrand, Inc., Princeton, N.J.
1956 LANING, J. H. and BATTIN, R. H., *Random Processes in Automatic Control*, McGraw-Hill Book Co., New York, N.Y.
1958 DAVENPORT, W. B. JR. and ROOT, W. L., *An Introduction to the Theory of Random Signals and Noise*, McGraw-Hill Book Co., New York, N.Y.
1960 MIDDLETON, D., *An Introduction to Statistical Communication Theory*, McGraw-Hill Book Co., New York, N.Y.
1965 MIDDLETON, D., *Topics in Communication Theory*, McGraw-Hill Book Co., New York, N.Y.

SELIN, I., *Detection Theory*, Princeton Univ. Press, Princeton, N.J.

WOZENCRAFT, J. M. and JACOBS, I. M., *Principles of Communication Engineering*, John Wiley & Sons, Inc., New York, N.Y.

1966 HANCOCK, J. C. and WINTZ, P. A., *Signal Detection Theory*, McGraw-Hill Book Co., New York, N.Y.

SCHWARTZ, M., BENNETT, W. R. and STEIN, S., *Communication Systems and Techniques*, McGraw-Hill Book Co., New York, N.Y.

V

DETECTION OF SIGNALS OF UNKNOWN PHASE

1. TESTING COMPOSITE HYPOTHESES

(a) *The Bayes Criterion*

In Chapter III we discussed strategies for choosing between two hypotheses on the basis of a fixed number of measurements. That decision problem was in essence to select which of two probability density functions (p.d.f.s), $p_0(\mathbf{x})$ or $p_1(\mathbf{x})$, is the more consistent with the observed values $\mathbf{x} = (x_1, x_2, \ldots, x_n)$ of n random variables; the choice is to be optimum under some criterion—Bayes, minimax, or Neyman–Pearson—corresponding to a definition of long-run success. It was assumed that the two p.d.f.s are known in all respects. In Chapter IV we applied this theory to the detection of a unique signal in Gaussian noise.

Signals to be detected, however, are only rarely unique; seldom is the form with which they appear at the receiver completely known. It is most commonly necessary to detect one of a class of signals specified by parameters taking values anywhere in more or less well-defined ranges. A narrowband radar echo, for example, has the form

$$s(t; A, t_0, \Omega) = A \text{ Rl } S(t-t_0) \exp i\Omega(t-t_0);$$

its amplitude is A, its time of arrival t_0, and its carrier frequency Ω. The amplitude depends on the size and reflectivity of the target, the arrival time on the range of the target, and the carrier frequency—through the Doppler effect—on the velocity of the target; none of these quantities may be known in advance with much precision. To be useful a radar system must be designed to detect echoes with a spectrum of values of A, t_0, and Ω.

In a communication system utilizing quasiharmonic signals it is only under the most carefully controlled circumstances that the amplitude A and the phase $\psi = -\Omega t_0$ of each signal are known by the receiver, and the carrier frequency too may sometimes vary. To treat the detection of such imperfectly specified signals the principles of the theory must be modified and augmented.

The two hypotheses between which the receiver must choose are now H_0, "only noise is present", and H_1, "one of a class of signals is present also". Hypothesis H_1 is said to be *composite;* hypothesis H_0 remains *simple.* If $\mathbf{x} = (x_1, x_2, \ldots, x_n)$ represents the set of data upon which the receiver is to base its decisions, the p.d.f. $p_1(\mathbf{x})$ under hypothesis H_1 depends on the parameters of the signal actually present. If there are m parameters, $\theta_1, \theta_2, \ldots, \theta_m$, we can represent them by a vector $\boldsymbol{\theta} = (\theta_1, \theta_2, \ldots, \theta_m)$ in an m-dimensional parameter space. We denote by $p_1(\mathbf{x}; \boldsymbol{\theta})$ the p.d.f. of the observations when a signal with parameters $\boldsymbol{\theta}$ is present. If the parameters $\boldsymbol{\theta}$ can be considered as random variables, $p_1(\mathbf{x}; \boldsymbol{\theta})$ is a conditional probability density function. For the radar echo in eq. (1.1) we might put $\theta_1 = A$, $\theta_2 = t_0$, $\theta_3 = \Omega$.

The task of the receiver is in effect one of deciding whether the values of $\mathbf{x}$ actually measured were drawn from a population described by the p.d.f. $p_0(\mathbf{x})$ (hypothesis H_0) or from one described by a p.d.f. $p_1(\mathbf{x}; \boldsymbol{\theta})$ for a set of parameters $\boldsymbol{\theta}$ lying somewhere in a given domain (hypothesis H_1). Again the decision strategy can be described as a division of the n-dimensional Cartesian space of the observations $\mathbf{x}$ into two regions R_0 and R_1. Hypothesis H_0 is chosen when the point whose coordinates are given by the observed values $\mathbf{x} = (x_1, x_2, \ldots, x_n)$ lies in region R_0, H_1 when it lies in R_1. The decision surface D dividing these regions is to be selected so that the statistical test is optimum in some sense.

Ideally, but rarely, all the prior probabilities and costs are well defined and the Bayes criterion is applicable, a situation treated by Wald (1950), whose theory was applied to signal detection by Middleton and Van Meter (1955). The observer knows not only the prior probabilities ζ and $(1-\zeta)$ with which hypotheses H_0 and H_1 respectively occur, but also a joint prior p.d.f. $z(\boldsymbol{\theta}) = z(\theta_1, \theta_2, \ldots, \theta_m)$ of the parameters $\boldsymbol{\theta}$, which describes their relative frequencies of occurrence when hypothesis H_1 is true. As for all joint p.d.f.s, its integral over the parameter space equals 1,

$$\int \ldots \int z(\boldsymbol{\theta}) d^m\boldsymbol{\theta} = 1, \quad d^m\boldsymbol{\theta} = d\theta_1\, d\theta_2 \ldots d\theta_m. \tag{1.1}$$

Besides all this, the observer knows the costs C_{00} and C_{10} of choosing hypotheses H_0 and H_1, respectively, when H_0 is true, and the costs C_{01} and C_{11} of choosing hypotheses H_0 and H_1 when H_1 is true. The costs C_{01} and C_{11} may now depend on the actual set of parameter values of $\boldsymbol{\theta}$ that has occurred, and we write these costs as $C_{01}(\boldsymbol{\theta})$ and $C_{11}(\boldsymbol{\theta})$ to exhibit this dependence.

The average risk per decision is now, as an evident modification of eq. (III, 3.1),

$$\bar{C} = \zeta\left[C_{00}\int_{R_0} p_0(\mathbf{x})\, d^n\mathbf{x} + C_{10}\int_{R_1} p_0(\mathbf{x})\, d^n\mathbf{x}\right]$$
$$+(1-\zeta)\left[\int_{R_0} d^n\mathbf{x}\int d^m\boldsymbol{\theta}\, z(\boldsymbol{\theta})\, C_{01}(\boldsymbol{\theta})\, p_1(\mathbf{x};\boldsymbol{\theta})\right.$$
$$\left.+\int_{R_1} d^n\mathbf{x}\int d^m\boldsymbol{\theta}\, z(\boldsymbol{\theta})\, C_{11}(\boldsymbol{\theta})\, p_1(\mathbf{x};\boldsymbol{\theta})\right], \tag{1.2}$$
$$d^n\mathbf{x} = dx_1 \dots dx_n, \quad d^m\boldsymbol{\theta} = d\theta_1 \dots d\theta_m,$$

where the integration $\int d^m\boldsymbol{\theta}$ is taken over the entire ranges—or the "space" —of the m parameters $\boldsymbol{\theta} = (\theta_1, \theta_2, \dots, \theta_m)$. The first bracket of eq. (1.2) is the risk associated with hypothesis H_0; the second is that associated with H_1. To satisfy the Bayes criterion of minimum average risk the decision surface D separating the regions R_0 and R_1 must be chosen to minimize $\bar{C}$. The analysis is the same as that used in Chapter III (eq. (2.11)) to derive the Bayes strategy for a choice between simple hypotheses; it shows that the decision surface D consists of those points $\mathbf{x}$ satisfying the equation

$$\zeta(C_{10}-C_{00})\, p_0(\mathbf{x}) = (1-\zeta)\int d^m\boldsymbol{\theta}\, z(\boldsymbol{\theta})\, [C_{01}(\boldsymbol{\theta})-C_{11}(\boldsymbol{\theta})]\, p_1(\mathbf{x};\boldsymbol{\theta}), \quad \mathbf{x}\in D. \tag{1.3}$$

Those points $\mathbf{x}$ for which the left-hand side of eq. (1.3) is larger than the right-hand side make up R_0; those for which it is smaller make up R_1. Hence, to choose between hypotheses H_0 and H_1 the observer calculates the cost-likelihood ratio

$$\Lambda_c = \frac{(1-\zeta)\int d^m\boldsymbol{\theta}\, z(\boldsymbol{\theta})\, [C_{01}(\boldsymbol{\theta})-C_{11}(\boldsymbol{\theta})]\, p_1(\mathbf{x};\boldsymbol{\theta})}{\zeta(C_{10}-C_{00})\, p_0(\mathbf{x})}$$

on the basis of his observations $\mathbf{x}$. He decides for hypothesis H_0 if $\Lambda_c < 1$ and for H_1 if $\Lambda_c > 1$.

If the costs C_{01} and C_{11} are independent of the values of the parameters, the Bayes criterion requires the observer to form the average likelihood ratio

$$\bar{\Lambda}(\mathbf{x}) = \int d^m\boldsymbol{\theta}\, z(\boldsymbol{\theta})\, p_1(\mathbf{x};\boldsymbol{\theta})/p_0(\mathbf{x}) = \int d^m\boldsymbol{\theta}\, z(\boldsymbol{\theta})\, \Lambda(\mathbf{x};\boldsymbol{\theta}),$$
$$\Lambda(\mathbf{x};\boldsymbol{\theta}) = p_1(\mathbf{x};\boldsymbol{\theta})/p_0(\mathbf{x}). \tag{1.4}$$

The average likelihood ratio $\bar{\Lambda}(\mathbf{x})$ is compared with the quantity

$$\Lambda_0 = \frac{\zeta(C_{10}-C_{00})}{(1-\zeta)(C_{01}-C_{11})}\,. \tag{1.5}$$

As before, hypothesis H_0 is chosen if $\bar{\Lambda}(\mathbf{x}) < \Lambda_0$, H_1 if $\bar{\Lambda}(\mathbf{x}) > \Lambda_0$.

The Bayes risk, which is the minimum value $\bar{C}_{\min}$ of eq. (1.2) obtained when the decision surface D is given by eq. (1.3), depends on the prior probability ζ and on the form of the p.d.f. $z(\theta)$. If these are unknown, but the costs are defined, one might apply the minimax criterion by seeking ζ and $z(\theta)$ so that $\bar{C}_{\min}$ is maximum, assuming for instance that some adversary is picking them so as to make the observer's minimum loss as large as possible. The form of the prior p.d.f. $z(\theta)$ that with the proper value of ζ maximizes the Bayes risk $\bar{C}_{\min}$ is called the "least favorable distribution" of the parameters θ. In some problems it can be found by inspection; in others it may be difficult to calculate. Once this p.d.f. $\tilde{z}(\theta)$ is known, the minimax value of ζ and the minimax risk can be found by the methods of Chapter III, Section 2. We shall return to the concept of the least favorable distribution in connection with the Neyman–Pearson criterion. For an extensive treatment of the Bayes criterion we refer the reader to the text by Blackwell and Girshick (1954).

If both hypotheses H_0 and H_1 are composite, two prior p.d.f.s of the parameters θ must be specified, $z_0(\theta)$ for their values under hypothesis H_0, $z_1(\theta)$ for their values under H_1. If the costs are independent of the true values of the parameters, the optimum decision under the Bayes criterion—as it is not hard to see—is made by comparing the average likelihood ratio

$$\bar{\Lambda}(\mathbf{x}) = \frac{\int d^m\theta \, z_1(\theta) \, p_1(\mathbf{x}; \theta)}{\int d^m\theta \, z_0(\theta) \, p_0(\mathbf{x}; \theta)} \tag{1.6}$$

with the decision level Λ_0 of eq. (1.5). Again unknown prior p.d.f.s $z_0(\theta)$ and $z_1(\theta)$ might be replaced by least favorable p.d.f.s $\tilde{z}_0(\theta)$ and $\tilde{z}_1(\theta)$ if these can be discovered.

Suppose that the receiver is to decide, on the basis of its input $v(t)$, which of two signals $s_1(t; \theta)$ and $s_2(t; \theta)$ has been added to the random noise to form $v(t)$. Let hypothesis H_i denote the presence of signal $s_i(t; \theta)$, $i = 1, 2$. Under hypothesis H_i the parameters of the signal have a prior p.d.f. $z_i(\theta)$. If samples of the input $v(t)$ are designated by the vector $\mathbf{x}$, the receiver bases its decision on the average likelihood ratio

$$\bar{\Lambda}(\mathbf{x}) = \frac{\int d^m\theta \, z_2(\theta) \, p_2(\mathbf{x}; \theta)}{\int d^m\theta \, z_1(\theta) \, p_1(\mathbf{x}; \theta)} \tag{1.7}$$

where $p_i(\mathbf{x}; \theta)$ is the joint p.d.f. under hypothesis H_i. The receiver decides that a signal $s_1(t; \theta)$ is present if $\bar{\Lambda}(\mathbf{x}) < \Lambda_0$. If we divide the numerator and the denominator by $p_0(\mathbf{x})$, the joint p.d.f. of the sample values when neither signal is present, we can pass to the limit of an infinite number of samples as in the previous chapter, and we can write the average likelihood ratio as

$$\bar{\Lambda}[v(t)] = \frac{\int d^m\theta\, z_2(\theta)\, \Lambda_2[v(t); \theta]}{\int d^m\theta\, z_1(\theta)\, \Lambda_1[v(t); \theta]}. \tag{1.8}$$

Here $\Lambda_i[v(t); \theta]$ is the likelihood ratio for detecting the signal $s_i(t; \theta)$ in the presence of noise. We learned in the previous chapter how to write down such a likelihood ratio for detection in Gaussian noise, and using it in eq. (1.8) avoids the process of sampling and passing to the limit each time.

(b) *The Neyman–Pearson Criterion*

The probability Q_0 of an error of the first kind, or false alarm, is

$$Q_0 = \int_{R_1} p_0(\mathbf{x})\, d^n\mathbf{x}, \tag{1.9}$$

where R_1 is the region of the observation space in which hypothesis H_1 is chosen. The probability Q_d of detection is now a function of the existing parameter values θ,

$$Q_d(\theta) = \int_{R_1} p_1(\mathbf{x}; \theta)\, d^n\mathbf{x}. \tag{1.10}$$

To satisfy the Neyman–Pearson criterion for a given set of parameter values θ, the decision surface D separating regions R_0 and R_1 must be chosen so that for a fixed value of Q_0 the probability Q_d is maximum.

In the simplest situation under the Neyman–Pearson criterion, the position of the surface D that maximizes $Q_d(\theta)$ for given Q_0 is independent of the parameter values θ. Then the same decision surface D is optimum for all values of θ and for all prior p.d.f.s of θ, and the strategy is said to be a "uniformly most powerful test" of hypothesis H_1 against H_0.

Here is an example of a uniformly most powerful test. Let the observations $\mathbf{x}$ be normally distributed, independent random variables with variance σ^2, and let their mean values be zero under hypothesis H_0 and $m > 0$ under H_1. Then the joint p.d.f.s are

$$p_0(\mathbf{x}) = (2\pi\sigma^2)^{-n/2} \exp\left(-\sum_{k=1}^{n} x_k^2/2\sigma^2\right),$$

$$p_1(\mathbf{x}; m) = (2\pi\sigma^2)^{-n/2} \exp\left[-\sum_{k=1}^{n} (x_k - m)^2/2\sigma^2\right].$$

Of the true mean all that is known is that it is positive. Now for any fixed positive value of m, our work in Chapter III, Section 2 showed that the optimum decision strategy is equivalent to comparing the sample mean

$$X = \sum_{k=1}^{n} x_n/n$$

with some fixed critical value M and picking hypothesis H_0 when $X < M$, H_1 when $X > M$. This critical value M is determined completely by the probability Q_0 of an error of the first kind, in particular by the equation

$$Q_0 = \int_M^\infty p_0(X)\, dX,$$

where $p_0(X)$ is a normal density function with mean zero and variance σ^2/n. The decision surface D is now the hyperplane

$$\sum_{k=1}^{n} x_k = nM,$$

and it is independent of the true mean m under hypothesis H_1. The test is therefore a uniformly most powerful one when only positive values of the true mean are possible; it can be used in ignorance of the actual value of m.

It is rather the exception than the rule for the decision surface D to be independent of the parameters $\boldsymbol{\theta}$. In most cases the same surface $D(\boldsymbol{\theta})$ will not be optimum for all values of $\boldsymbol{\theta}$, and a uniformly most powerful test does not exist. This is so, for instance, when the true mean m in the example can be either positive or negative. A possible compromise is to select some reasonable prior p.d.f. $z(\boldsymbol{\theta})$ of the parameter values and to try to maximize the average probability $\bar{Q}_d$ of detection,

$$\bar{Q}_d[z] = \int z(\boldsymbol{\theta})\, Q_d(\boldsymbol{\theta})\, d^m\boldsymbol{\theta} = \int_{R_1} d^n\mathbf{x} \int z(\boldsymbol{\theta})\, p_1(\mathbf{x}; \boldsymbol{\theta})\, d^m\boldsymbol{\theta}. \tag{1.11}$$

The observer then agrees to be satisfied with a strategy that performs well against an ensemble of possible values of the parameters $\boldsymbol{\theta}$ distributed according to this p.d.f. $z(\boldsymbol{\theta})$.

By our previous methods of analysis we can show that the strategy for which the average detection probability $\bar{Q}_d$ is maximum, for fixed false-alarm probability Q_0, is one in which the observer calculates the average likelihood ratio of eq. (1.4) with the preferred distribution $z(\boldsymbol{\theta})$. This ratio $\bar{\Lambda}(\mathbf{x})$ is compared with a fixed level Λ_0, and hypothesis H_0 is chosen if $\bar{\Lambda}(\mathbf{x}) < \Lambda_0$, H_1 if $\bar{\Lambda}(\mathbf{x}) > \Lambda_0$. The critical level Λ_0 is picked to yield the pre-assigned value of Q_0,

$$Q_0 = \int_{\Lambda_0}^\infty P_0(\bar{\Lambda})\, d\bar{\Lambda},$$

where $P_0(\bar{\Lambda})$ is the p.d.f. of $\bar{\Lambda}(\mathbf{x})$ under hypothesis H_0. The maximum average probability $\bar{Q}_d$ of detection is then

$$\bar{Q}_d = \iint_{\Lambda_0}^{\infty} z(\boldsymbol{\theta})\, P_1(\bar{\Lambda}; \boldsymbol{\theta})\, d\bar{\Lambda}\, d^m\boldsymbol{\theta},$$

where $P_1(\bar{\Lambda}; \boldsymbol{\theta})$ is the p.d.f. of $\bar{\Lambda}(\mathbf{x})$ under hypothesis H_1 when the parameter values are $\boldsymbol{\theta}$.

In particular, there may be one distribution $\tilde{z}(\boldsymbol{\theta})$ for which this maximum average value of the probability $\bar{Q}_d[z]$ of detection is the smallest possible; this is the least favorable distribution under the Neyman–Pearson criterion. It would seem to be wise in situations where the parameter values are unknown to use the Neyman–Pearson criterion in connection with this least favorable distribution, for as we shall indicate later, the detection probability cannot fall below this value $\bar{Q}_d[\tilde{z}]$ no matter what the true p.d.f. of the parameter values turns out to be in future trials. This procedure corresponds to using the minimax criterion, except that neither costs nor prior probabilities of the two hypotheses are involved.

To elucidate this problem, let us assume at first that the parameter set takes on only k discrete values $\boldsymbol{\theta}_1, \boldsymbol{\theta}_2, \ldots, \boldsymbol{\theta}_k$. In the signal detection problem, for instance, there may be k possible signals to be detected, only one of which could be present in a given trial; the observer is not concerned which of the signals it is. Let the prior probabilities of these parameter values or signals be $z_1, z_2, \ldots, z_k$, with

$$z_1 + z_2 + \ldots + z_k = 1. \tag{1.12}$$

The set of probabilities $\{z_j\}$ gives the relative frequencies of the various parameter values when hypothesis H_1 is true, that is, when there is some signal present. These values could be represented as a point in a k-dimensional space, and eq. (1.12) requires the point to lie on a particular hyperplane in that space.

When the jth signal is present, the joint p.d.f. of the observations $\mathbf{x}$ is abbreviated as

$$p_1(\mathbf{x}; \boldsymbol{\theta}_j) = p_j(\mathbf{x});$$

the joint p.d.f. of $\mathbf{x}$ under hypothesis H_0 is still $p_0(\mathbf{x})$. The average probability $\bar{Q}_d$ of detection is then

$$\bar{Q}_d[z_j] = \sum_{j=1}^{k} z_j \int_{R_1} p_j(\mathbf{x})\, d^n\mathbf{x}, \tag{1.13}$$

where R_1 is the region of the space of observations $\mathbf{x}$ in which hypothesis H_1 is chosen. The Neyman–Pearson criterion directs us to maximize the average probability $\bar{Q}_d$ for a fixed false-alarm probability Q_0 given by

$$Q_0 = \int_{R_1} p_0(\mathbf{x}) \, d^n\mathbf{x}. \tag{1.14}$$

The regions R_0 and R_1 are separated by the decision surface D whose position we must determine. In particular, we shall seek a set of prior probabilities $\{z_j\}$ and a decision surface D so that the maximum value of $\bar{Q}_d[z_j]$ is as small as possible.

The prior probabilities $\{z_j\}$ are restricted to the range (0, 1),

$$0 \leq z_j \leq 1, \quad j = 1, 2, \ldots, k;$$

the vector $\{z_j\}$ lies in the unit hypercube of the k-dimensional space of these vectors. This requirement further constrains the variational problem at hand. With each point $\{z_j\}$ of this unit hypercube there is associated a maximum value of $\bar{Q}_d[z_j]$, for a given value of Q_0, and this maximum detection probability may attain its smallest value on the boundary of the admissible region, that is, when some—or all but one—of the prior probabilities z_j are zero. The problem of determining such constrained stationary values is handled in the theory of linear programming and in game theory (Blackwell and Girshick, 1954). However, as long as the stationary value lies within the admissible region, the usual methods of the calculus of variations can be applied, and we shall assume at first that this is so.

To find the least favorable distribution $\{\tilde{z}_j\}$ we can use the technique of Lagrange multipliers. We seek a stationary value of eq. (1.13) under the constraints of eqs. (1.12) and (1.14). Hence, we try to find a value of the quantity

$$\Gamma = \sum_{j=1}^{k} z_j \int_{R_1} p_j(\mathbf{x}) \, d^n\mathbf{x} - \lambda \int_{R_1} p_0(\mathbf{x}) \, d^n\mathbf{x} + \mu \sum_{j=1}^{k} z_j \tag{1.15}$$

that is maximum for a variation in the decision surface D and minimum for a variation in the quantities $\{z_j\}$. These variations can now be made independently. The position of the surface D and the values of the z_j's for which the stationary value is attained are functions of the Lagrange multipliers λ and μ. The values of the multipliers are then chosen so that the constraints in eqs. (1.12) and (1.14) are satisfied.

First taking the z_j's as fixed, we vary the surface D until the quantity Γ is maximum. As in our analysis of Chapter III, Section 3, the maximum is attained when the decision surface D is one of a family of surfaces described by the equation

$$\Lambda(\mathbf{x}) = \sum_{j=1}^{k} z_j p_j(\mathbf{x}) / p_0(\mathbf{x}) = \lambda. \tag{1.16}$$

The value of the parameter λ is later chosen so that the false-alarm probability of eq. (1.14) equals the preassigned value. When the decision surface D is given by eq. (1.16), any small variation in it will produce a decrease in the quantity Γ that is of second order in the magnitude of the change in the position of the surface, as is usually the case with stationary values.

Assuming now that the regions R_0 and R_1 are separated by a surface D given by eq. (1.16), let us vary each z_j in eq. (1.15) so as to minimize the quantity Γ. This variation will cause a change in the surface D as well as in the z_j's appearing explicitly in eq. (1.15), but the effect on Γ of the variation of the surface D is of second order, and it is only the variation in the explicit z_j's that matters. In this way we obtain the set of k equations

$$\frac{\partial \Gamma}{\partial z_j} = \int_{R_1} p_j(\mathbf{x})\, d^n\mathbf{x} + \mu = 0, \qquad j = 1, 2, \ldots, k.$$

These equations state that for the set $\{z_j\}$ we are seeking, the Neyman–Pearson strategy yields a detection probability

$$Q_j = \int_{R_1} p_j(\mathbf{x})\, d^n\mathbf{x} \tag{1.17}$$

for the jth signal (or set of parameter values $\boldsymbol{\theta}_j$) that is the same for all signals, $Q_j \equiv -\mu$, $j = 1, 2, \ldots, k$. Along with eq. (1.16) and the constraints of eqs. (1.12) and (1.14), these equations suffice to determine the set $\{z_j\}$ of prior probabilities.

This solution must be checked to verify that each z_j lies between 0 and 1. If this is not so, there is no true stationary value of the quantity Γ within the admissible region of values of the z_j's, and one must seek a point on the boundary of that region where the maximum detection probability $\bar{Q}_d[z_j']$ takes on its smallest value. There is then a set of parameter values $\boldsymbol{\theta}_j$ for which the corresponding prior probabilities z_j vanish. For the remaining parameter sets, however, the detection probabilities Q_j are equal, since the variation $\partial\Gamma/\partial z_j$ can be made as before for these non-zero z_j's. In particular, the solution of the variational problem may indicate that there is one signal, say the ith, for which $z_i = 1$, $z_j = 0$, $j \neq i$. The detection probability Q_i for this signal is then smaller than for all the others, $Q_i < Q_j$, $j \neq i$. We shall soon present an example of this possibility.

The set of prior probabilities $\{\tilde{z}_j\}$ determined in this way is the least favorable distribution of the parameter values $\boldsymbol{\theta}_j$, whether the set $\{\tilde{z}_j\}$ lies within or on the boundary of the region of admissible values $0 \leqslant z_j \leqslant 1$.

For this least favorable distribution the detection probabilities satisfy the equations

$$Q_j = \bar{Q}_d[\tilde{z}_j] = \sum_{j=1}^{k} \tilde{z}_j Q_j, \quad \tilde{z}_j \neq 0, \tag{1.18}$$
$$Q_{j'} > \bar{Q}_d[\tilde{z}_j], \quad \tilde{z}_{j'} = 0, \quad j, j' = 1, 2, \ldots, k,$$

provided the decision surface D has been chosen according to eq. (1.16). The parameter λ is picked so that the false-alarm probability Q_0 of eq. (1.14) equals the preassigned value. The observer is then assured that his strategy yields the desired false-alarm probability and that the probability of detection will not fall below the common value $\bar{Q}_d[\tilde{z}_j]$ of eq. (1.18), no matter what the true set of relative frequencies of the signals (or parameter values θ_j) turns out to be in future trials.

(c) *Detection of Signals of Unknown Amplitudes*

As an example of the testing of composite hypotheses, let us study the problem of detecting k mutually exclusive signals $s_j(t)$ of the same form but of different amplitudes A_j,

$$s_j(t) = A_j f(t), \qquad j = 1, 2, \ldots, k.$$

At first we shall assume that the amplitudes are all positive. The noise is white and Gaussian, and the input $v(t)$ is observed over an interval $0 < t < T$. The observer must choose between two hypotheses, (H_0) noise alone is present, $v(t) = n(t)$, and (H_1) noise and one of the k possible signals is present, $v(t) = A_j f(t) + n(t)$. He does not know in advance which of the signals to expect. The observer is to use the Neyman–Pearson criterion with the least favorable distribution of prior probabilities z_j of the k signals.

In Chapter IV, Section 1, we found that the proper strategy for detecting one of these signals, say the jth, is to form the statistic

$$\int_0^T s_j(t)\, v(t)\, dt$$

for the input $v(t)$ and to compare the value of the statistic with some critical value or decision level determined by the preassigned false-alarm probability Q_0. A constant factor in this statistic is inessential, however, a change in it merely requiring a proportional change in the decision level. The decision could hence be as well based on the proportional statistic

$$g = \int_0^T f(t)\, v(t)\, dt, \tag{1.19}$$

and this statistic will be appropriate for any of the k signals. It is compared with a decision level g_0, and hypothesis H_0 is chosen if $g < g_0$, H_1 if $g > g_0$. The decision level g_0 is determined by the equation

$$Q_0 = \Pr\{g > g_0 \mid H_0\} = \int_{g_0}^{\infty} P_0(g)\, dg,$$

$$P_0(g) = (2\pi\sigma^2)^{-\frac{1}{2}} \exp(-g^2/2\sigma^2), \tag{1.20}$$

$$\sigma^2 = NF/2, \quad F = \int_0^T [f(t)]^2\, dt.$$

The detection probability of the jth signal is then

$$Q_j = \Pr\{g > g_0 \mid H_1, s(t) = A_j f(t)\} = \int_{g_0}^{\infty} P_j(g)\, dg,$$

$$P_j(g) = (2\pi\sigma^2)^{-\frac{1}{2}} \exp[-(g-A_jF)^2/2\sigma^2]. \tag{1.21}$$

The probability of detection is clearly smallest for the signal of smallest amplitude, $Q_j > Q_i$ if $A_j > A_i$, $j \neq i$. Hence, the least favorable distribution is

$$\tilde{z}_i = 1, \quad \tilde{z}_j = 0, \quad j \neq i, \quad A_i = \min_j A_j.$$

The worst possible situation for the observer is that in which it is always the weakest signal that is transmitted. In this example the solution of the variational problem of part (b) lies on the boundary of the admissible region of prior distributions $\{z_j\}$. An observer using the strategy just derived is assured that the detection probability will never be less than $Q_i = \min_j Q_j$, no matter with what relative frequencies the various signals are transmitted. The strategy itself is independent of any of the possible signal amplitudes, as long as they must be positive, and it therefore is a uniformly most powerful test.

The extension of the results of part (b) to the case of parameters $\boldsymbol{\theta}$ with a continuous range of values is fraught with some uncertainty, for the least favorable distribution $\tilde{z}(\boldsymbol{\theta})$ may not exist, at least not in a conventional sense. Consider the detection of a signal $s(t) = Af(t)$ in white, Gaussian noise, when the form $f(t)$ is given, but the amplitude A is not. If only positive values of A are permitted, the strategy just described as using the statistic g of eq. (1.19) is clearly optimum. Yet the smaller the amplitude A, the smaller the detection probability $Q_d(A) = \Pr\{g > g_0 \mid H_1, s(t) = Af(t)\}$. The minimum value of $Q_d(A)$ is attained only on the boundary ($A = 0$)

of the range $A > 0$ of possible amplitudes. In this case, fortunately, the strategy constitutes a uniformly most powerful test, and the non-existence of the least favorable distribution does not matter.

When the signal amplitudes A can be either positive or negative, a uniformly most powerful test no longer exists, for the optimum strategy for a signal of positive amplitude is not the same as for one of negative amplitude. Now conditions are least favorable when signals of each sign appear equally often, $\Pr\{A > 0\} = \Pr\{A < 0\}$. A strategy satisfying the Neyman–Pearson criterion is then to form the statistic g of eq. (1.19) and to choose hypothesis H_0 only when the absolute value $|g|$ is less than a new decision level g_1, which is determined by the equation

$$Q_0 = \Pr\{|g| > g_1 | H_0\} = 1 - \int_{-g_1}^{g_1} P_0(g)\, dg.$$

The probability of detecting a signal of amplitude A is

$$Q_d(A) = \Pr\{|g| > g_1 | H_1,\ s(t) = Af(t)\}.$$

It can be calculated as in eq. (1.21) if the limits of integration are properly altered, and it is found to be smaller than the probability of detecting signals whose amplitudes are known to be positive. The uncertainty in the sign of the signal decreases the probability of detecting it.

In general, we can expect the parameter space to be divided into two regions, which may or may not be simply connected. In the one region, which we label Θ, the least favorable p.d.f. $\tilde{z}(\boldsymbol{\theta})$ is positive and the detection probability is independent of $\boldsymbol{\theta}$,

$$\begin{aligned} \tilde{z}(\boldsymbol{\theta}) &> 0, \quad \boldsymbol{\theta} \in \Theta, \\ Q_d(\boldsymbol{\theta}) &= \int_{\Theta} \tilde{z}(\boldsymbol{\theta})\, Q_d(\boldsymbol{\theta})\, d^m\boldsymbol{\theta} = \bar{Q}_d[\tilde{z}]. \end{aligned} \tag{1.22}$$

In the complementary region Θ', the least favorable p.d.f. vanishes; and if we were really playing a game against a malevolent adversary, we should not expect him to send us signals with parameter values in this region. If such a signal does occur, its probability of detection will be greater than the uniform minimum value for region Θ,

$$\tilde{z}(\boldsymbol{\theta}) \equiv 0, \quad Q_d(\boldsymbol{\theta}) > \bar{Q}_d[\tilde{z}], \quad \boldsymbol{\theta} \in \Theta'.$$

These detection probabilities $Q_d(\boldsymbol{\theta})$ are achieved by a system that forms from the data $\mathbf{x}$ an average likelihood ratio

$$\begin{aligned} \bar{\Lambda}(\mathbf{x}) &= \int \tilde{z}(\boldsymbol{\theta})\, \Lambda(\mathbf{x}; \boldsymbol{\theta})\, d^m\boldsymbol{\theta}, \\ \Lambda(\mathbf{x}; \boldsymbol{\theta}) &= p_1(\mathbf{x}; \boldsymbol{\theta})/p_0(\mathbf{x}) \end{aligned} \tag{1.23}$$

and compares it with a decision level Λ_0 fixed by the preassigned false-alarm probability $Q_0 = \Pr\{\bar{\Lambda}(\mathbf{x}) > \Lambda_0 | H_0\}$. It is usually very difficult to compute the least favorable p.d.f. $\tilde{z}(\boldsymbol{\theta})$ if it cannot be discovered immediately through some symmetry or natural ordering of the parameters involved. In the next section we shall study the detection of a narrow-band signal depending on a single unknown parameter, the phase, for which a least favorable distribution exists and is easy to find.

(d) *Threshold Detection and Maximum-likelihood Detection*

In detecting a signal of unknown amplitude, conditions are least favorable when the amplitude is very small. The doctrine just presented leads us then to develop the likelihood ratio $\Lambda(\mathbf{x}; \boldsymbol{\theta})$ in a power series in the amplitude, say $\theta_1 = A$, and to use the first term of the resulting average likelihood ratio as the detection statistic. If we denote the remaining parameters $\theta_2, \theta_3, \ldots,$ by $\boldsymbol{\theta}'$ and assume them independent of the amplitude of the signal, we can write eq. (1.23) as

$$\begin{aligned}\bar{\Lambda}(\mathbf{x}) &= \int \tilde{z}(A, \boldsymbol{\theta}')\,[1 + A\Lambda_A(\mathbf{x}; 0, \boldsymbol{\theta}') + \tfrac{1}{2}A^2\Lambda_{AA}(\mathbf{x}; 0, \boldsymbol{\theta}') + \ldots]\, dA\, d^{m-1}\boldsymbol{\theta}' \\ &= 1 + \bar{A} \int \tilde{z}(\boldsymbol{\theta}')\, \Lambda_A(\mathbf{x}; 0, \boldsymbol{\theta}')\, d^{m-1}\boldsymbol{\theta}' \\ &\qquad + \tfrac{1}{2}\overline{A^2} \int \tilde{z}(\boldsymbol{\theta}')\, \Lambda_{AA}(\mathbf{x}; 0, \boldsymbol{\theta}')\, d^{m-1}\boldsymbol{\theta}' + \ldots,\end{aligned} \tag{1.24}$$

where

$$\Lambda_A(\mathbf{x}; A, \boldsymbol{\theta}') = \frac{\partial}{\partial A}\Lambda(\mathbf{x}; A, \boldsymbol{\theta}'),$$

$$\Lambda_{AA}(\mathbf{x}; A, \boldsymbol{\theta}') = \frac{\partial^2}{\partial A^2}\Lambda(\mathbf{x}; A, \boldsymbol{\theta}'),$$

and so on. This is known as a "threshold expansion", the word "threshold" referring to the limit of perception or detectability of the signal (Middleton, 1960, § 19.4; Rudnick, 1961).

The decision about the presence or absence of a signal is based on the "threshold statistic"

$$\int \tilde{z}(\boldsymbol{\theta}')\, \frac{\partial^k}{\partial A^k}\Lambda(\mathbf{x}; A, \boldsymbol{\theta}')\bigg|_{A=0} d^{m-1}\boldsymbol{\theta}'$$

with the smallest index k for which this quantity does not vanish. The derivative of the likelihood ratio is averaged over the least favorable distribution of the remaining parameters. The statistic g in eq. (1.19) is a threshold statistic, which in this simple case is uniformly most powerful.

The threshold expansion emphasizes the detection of the weakest signals, for it requires us to evaluate the likelihood ratio as though the signal were vanishingly small. We shall see later an example in which the threshold statistic requires an excessive signal-to-noise ratio to attain a satisfactory combination of false-alarm and detection probabilities, such as $Q_0 = 10^{-4}$, $Q_d = 0.90$. For such signal-to-noise ratios a superior detection system can sometimes be found by avoiding the stress placed on the weakest signals by the threshold statistic.

The dominant contribution to the average likelihood ratio

$$\bar{\Lambda}(\mathbf{x}) = \int z(\boldsymbol{\theta})\, \Lambda(\mathbf{x};\boldsymbol{\theta})\, d^m\boldsymbol{\theta}$$

at large signal-to-noise ratios comes from the region in the parameter space about the set of parameters $\tilde{\boldsymbol{\theta}}$ that maximizes the likelihood ratio $\Lambda(\mathbf{x};\boldsymbol{\theta})$. If the prior p.d.f. $z(\boldsymbol{\theta})$ is a slowly varying function of the parameters $\boldsymbol{\theta}$ in the neighborhood of $\tilde{\boldsymbol{\theta}}$—as will occur when the only advance knowledge of the signal parameters is that they lie somewhere in a broad region of the parameter space—the value of the average likelihood ratio depends only weakly on the prior p.d.f. It is then appropriate to base the decision on the maximum value of the likelihood ratio,

$$\max_{\boldsymbol{\theta}} \Lambda(\mathbf{x};\boldsymbol{\theta}) = \Lambda(\mathbf{x};\tilde{\boldsymbol{\theta}}),$$

by comparing it with a decision level determined by the false-alarm probability. The set $\tilde{\boldsymbol{\theta}}$ that maximizes the likelihood ratio $\Lambda(\mathbf{x};\boldsymbol{\theta})$ provides the "maximum-likelihood estimates" of the parameters $\boldsymbol{\theta}$. If both hypotheses are composite, the decision is based on the ratio

$$\max_{\boldsymbol{\theta}} p_1(\mathbf{x};\boldsymbol{\theta}) / \max_{\boldsymbol{\theta}} p_0(\mathbf{x};\boldsymbol{\theta}).$$

We shall describe the use of this "principle of maximum likelihood" in detection in Chapter IX, postponing it until after we have studied the estimation of signal parameters.

2. DETECTION OF A SIGNAL OF UNKNOWN PHASE

In radar the echo signals to be detected are usually narrowband pulses like those discussed in Chapter I, Section 3. A typical signal can be written in the form

$$s(t) = \text{Rl}\, F(t-t_0) \exp i\Omega(t-t_0), \tag{2.1}$$

where $F(t)$ is the complex envelope of the pulse, Ω is the carrier frequency, and t_0 is the time when some distinguishing point of the signal arrives. For narrowband signals the carrier frequency is so large that there are many cycles of the carrier within the duration of the pulse.

The time t_0 is proportional to the distance from the target to the receiving antenna. A small change in t_0 of the order of $(1/\Omega)$, corresponding to a change in the distance of the target of the order of a wavelength of the radiation, makes a very small change in the envelope $F(t-t_0)$, but a large change in the carrier phase $(-\Omega t_0)$. (A typical value of the pulse duration is 10^{-6} sec; $(1/\Omega)$ may be of the order of 10^{-9} sec.) The distance to the target will seldom be known accurately enough to determine this phase $(-\Omega t_0)$ within a fraction of 2π, although one may be able to time the arrival of the signal within a small fraction of the width of the pulse envelope $|F(t)|$. For this reason the phase $\psi = -\Omega t_0$ can be treated as a random variable, which can be expected to differ from trial to trial and whose value is unknown to the observer.

We wish, therefore, to study the problem of detecting one of an ensemble of signals $s(t;\ \psi)$ of the form

$$s(t;\psi) = \text{Rl}\ S(t;\psi)\ e^{i\Omega t}, \quad S(t;\psi) = F(t)e^{i\psi}, \tag{2.2}$$

in which the complex signal envelope $F(t)$ is assumed given. We are thus taking the time of arrival of the pulse envelope to be known. The signal phase ψ, however, is an unknown parameter whose value lies in the range $0 \leqslant \psi < 2\pi$. We seek an optimum strategy for deciding between the simple hypothesis (H_0) that noise alone is present in the input $v(t)$, and the composite hypothesis (H_1) that besides the noise there is also one of the possible signals $s(t;\ \psi)$. This detection problem might also arise in a communication system in which narrowband pulses are transmitted, but in which no attempt is made to maintain coherence of the radio-frequency phase from pulse to pulse.

For reasons of symmetry it is clear that the least favorable distribution $\tilde{z}(\psi)$ of the phase ψ is a uniform one,

$$\tilde{z}(\psi) = 1/2\pi, \quad 0 \leqslant \psi < 2\pi, \tag{2.3}$$

which implies maximum uncertainty in the value of ψ. If any particular values of the phase ψ were favored, filters matched to signals $s(t;\ \psi)$ with those phases could be used as described in the previous chapter; and by properly weighting their outputs the average probability of detection could be increased. The observer can be said to know least about the signal phase when all its values are equally likely. We shall derive a decision strategy using the Neyman–Pearson criterion in connection with the prior distribution of eq. (2.3). Then we shall compute the detection probability $Q_d(\psi)$ under this strategy for a signal with a given value of ψ, of which this probability will turn out to be independent. According to our discussion at the end of the previous section, this independence verifies our choice of eq. (2.3) as the least favorable distribution.

The noise is assumed to be Gaussian and narrowband. According to Section 6 of Chapter II, its autocovariance $\phi(\tau)$ can then be written $\phi(\tau) = \text{Rl}\,\tilde{\phi}(\tau)e^{i\Omega\tau}$ in terms of the complex autocovariance function $\tilde{\phi}(\tau)$. Later the detection strategy for white noise will be derived as a limiting case of that for narrowband noise.

The receiver must, as shown in Section 1, base its decision about the presence or absence of a signal on the value of an average likelihood ratio

$$\bar{\Lambda}[v(t)] = \int_0^{2\pi} \tilde{z}(\psi)\Lambda[v(t);\psi]\, d\psi, \tag{2.4}$$

where $\Lambda[v(t);\psi]$ is the likelihood ratio for the input $v(t)$ when the signal to be detected has the form given in eq. (2.2), but with a known phase ψ. This likelihood ratio can be determined by the methods of Section 3 or 4 of Chapter IV. One can, for instance, imagine the complex envelope $V(t)$ of the input sampled at uniformly spaced instants. The likelihood ratio for the samples is formed, and the number of samples is allowed to increase beyond all bounds. The result, as given in Problem 1 of Chapter IV, is

$$\begin{aligned}\Lambda[v(t);\psi] &= \exp\left[\text{Rl}\, e^{-i\psi}\int_0^T Q^*(t)V(t)\,dt - \tfrac{1}{2}\int_0^T Q^*(t)F(t)\,dt\right],\\ v(t) &= \text{Rl}\, V(t)e^{i\Omega t},\end{aligned} \tag{2.5}$$

where $Q(t)$ is the solution of the integral equation

$$F(t) = \int_0^T \tilde{\phi}(t-u)Q(u)\,du, \qquad 0 \leqslant t \leqslant T, \tag{2.6}$$

whose kernel is the complex autocovariance of the noise. This likelihood ratio must now be averaged over the phases ψ according to the least favorable distribution in eq. (2.3).

If we introduce the abbreviations

$$Re^{i\beta} = \int_0^T Q^*(t)V(t)\,dt, \qquad d^2 = \int_0^T Q^*(t)F(t)\,dt, \tag{2.7}$$

with R and β real, the average likelihood ratio in eq. (2.4) becomes

$$\bar{\Lambda}[v(t)] = \int_0^{2\pi} \exp\left[R\cos(\beta-\psi) - \tfrac{1}{2}d^2\right] d\psi/2\pi = e^{-d^2/2}I_0(R), \tag{2.8}$$

where $I_0(x)$ is the modified Bessel function of order 0,

$$I_0(x) = \int_0^{2\pi} e^{x\cos\theta}\, d\theta/2\pi. \tag{2.9}$$

The quantity $e^{-d^2/2}I_0(R)$ must be compared with a decision level Λ_0 to decide whether a signal is present. The only part of it depending on the input $v(t)$, however, is R; and as the Bessel function is monotone, the decision can as well be made by comparing the quantity

$$R = \left| \int_0^T Q^*(t)V(t)\,dt \right| \tag{2.10}$$

with a new decision level R_0. If R exceeds R_0, the receiver decides that a signal is present. The value of R_0 is selected so that the false-alarm probability Q_0 equals the preassigned value.

Now we shall show that the statistic R can be produced by passing the input $v(t)$ through a narrowband filter matched to the signal Rl $Q(t)e^{i\Omega t}$, rectifying the output, and comparing the value of this rectified output with the proper decision level. A filter matched to that signal has a complex impulse response (see Chapter I, Section 4)

$$\begin{aligned} k(\tau) &= Q^*(T-\tau), \qquad 0 < \tau < T, \\ &= 0, \qquad \tau < 0, \quad \tau > T. \end{aligned} \tag{2.11}$$

According to eq. (I, 4.5), the complex envelope $V_0(t)$ of the output of this filter at time t is, in the quasiharmonic approximation,

$$\begin{aligned} V_0(t) &= \int_0^\infty k(\tau)V(t-\tau)\,d\tau = \int_0^T Q^*(T-\tau)V(t-\tau)\,d\tau \\ &= \int_0^T Q^*(u)V(u+t-T)\,du. \end{aligned}$$

At time T the complex envelope is

$$V_0(T) = \int_0^T Q^*(u)V(u)\,du,$$

and the absolute value of this envelope is the statistic R we sought. In Section 3 of Chapter I we saw that the output of a rectifier is some monotone function of the absolute value of the complex envelope of its input. If we apply the filter output $v_0(t)$ to a linear rectifier, the value of the output of the rectifier at the end of the observation interval will be proportional to $|V_0(T)| = R$. This use of a matched filter and rectifier was proposed by Peterson, Birdsall, and Fox (1954).

The optimum detection system for a quasiharmonic signal of unknown phase in narrowband Gaussian noise consists of a filter followed by a rectifier. The filter is matched to a signal whose complex envelope $Q(t)$ is the solution of the integral equation (2.6), the kernel of which is the complex autocovariance function of the noise. The output of the rectifier at the end of the observation interval is proportional to the statistic R; it is compared with a decision level selected to yield a given false-alarm probability Q_0. If the output exceeds this decision level, an alarm can be made to indicate the decision that one of the signals $s(t; \psi)$ was present during the observation interval. In the next section the performance of this detection system will be analyzed, and the false-alarm and detection probabilities will be determined.

If the bandwidth of the input noise is much greater than that of the signal, and if the spectral density of the noise is nearly constant over the range of frequencies occupied by the spectrum of the signal, the autocovariance function $\tilde{\phi}(\tau)$ is narrow and sharply peaked in comparison with the signal envelope $F(t)$. When the noise bandwidth is much greater than both $(1/T)$ and the signal bandwidth, we can replace the complex autocovariance function of the noise by a delta-function,

$$\tilde{\phi}(\tau) = N\delta(\tau),$$

as in eq. (II, 6.22), where N is the unilateral spectral density of the noise in the neighborhood of the signal spectrum. The solution of the integral equation (2.6) in this limiting case is $Q(t) = F(t)/N$, and the test statistic R becomes

$$R = \frac{1}{N} \left| \int_0^T F^*(t)V(t)\,dt \right|. \tag{2.12}$$

It is proportional to the rectified output, at the end of the observation interval, of a filter matched to any of the expected signals $s(t; \psi)$. Since the bandwidth of the noise does not appear in eq. (2.12), the detection system must be optimum if the noise bandwidth is much greater than that of the signal, and hence even if the noise is white. As discussed in Chapter II, Section 6, removal of noise components of frequencies far from those of the signal by a filter of bandwidth much smaller than the carrier frequency Ω, but much greater than the bandwidth of the signal $s(t; \psi)$, can make little difference in the optimum detection of the signal. The representation of white noise in terms of quadrature components, eq. (II, 6.22), could have been used to derive the optimum detection system for quasi-harmonic signals in white noise and would have led finally to the statistic R of eq. (2.12).

3. THE DETECTABILITY OF SIGNALS OF UNKNOWN PHASE

The detection system derived in the last section can be evaluated on the basis of the probabilities Q_0 of a false alarm and Q_d of detection. In that system hypothesis H_0 is chosen when the statistic R of eq. (2.10) is less than the decision level R_0; hypothesis H_1 is chosen when it is greater. The probabilities in question are then

$$Q_0 = \int_{R_0}^{\infty} P_0(R)\, dR, \quad Q_d(\psi) = \int_{R_0}^{\infty} P_1(R; \psi)\, dR. \tag{3.1}$$

Here $P_0(R)$ is the probability density function of the statistic R when the input consists of noise alone; $P_1(R; \psi)$ is its p.d.f. when the input consists of noise plus the signal $s(t; \psi)$ of phase ψ. In eq. (3.1) we allow for the possibility that the probability of detection may be a function of the signal phase.

To determine the p.d.f.s of the statistic R we write it as

$$R = |x+iy| = \sqrt{x^2+y^2}, \tag{3.2}$$

where x and y are the real and imaginary parts of the complex number

$$x+iy = R\, e^{i\beta} = \int_0^T Q^*(t)\, V(t)\, dt. \tag{3.3}$$

These components x and y are Gaussian random variables, for they are the results of linear operations on the Gaussian random processes $X(t)$ and $Y(t)$, which are the quadrature components of the input $V(t) = X(t)+iY(t)$. Under hypothesis H_0 their mean values are zero, since $\overline{V(t)} = 0$. Their covariances can be calculated in the following way. First we take the average of the absolute square of $(x+iy)$,

$$\begin{aligned}\overline{|x+iy|^2} = \overline{x^2}+\overline{y^2} &= \int_0^T\int_0^T Q^*(t)\, Q(u)\, \overline{V(t)\, V^*(u)}\, dt\, du \\ &= 2\int_0^T\int_0^T Q^*(t)\, Q(u)\, \tilde{\phi}(t-u)\, dt\, du = 2\int_0^T Q^*(t)\, F(t)\, dt,\end{aligned} \tag{3.4}$$

where we have used eq. (6.11) of Chapter II and the integral equation (2.6). Similarly

$$\overline{(x+iy)^2} = \overline{x^2}+\overline{y^2}+2i\overline{xy} = \int_0^T\int_0^T Q^*(t)\, Q^*(u)\, \overline{V(t)\, V(u)}\, dt\, du = 0. \tag{3.5}$$

Therefore $\overline{x^2} = \overline{y^2}$ and $\overline{xy} = 0$, and from eq. (3.4),

$$\text{Var } x = \text{Var } y = \int_0^T Q^*(t)\, F(t)\, dt = d^2, \qquad \{x, y\} = 0. \tag{3.6}$$

The components x and y are statistically independent and have variances d^2. Under hypothesis H_0 their joint p.d.f. is thus

$$p_0(x, y) = (2\pi d^2)^{-1} \exp\,[-(x^2+y^2)/2d^2]. \tag{3.7}$$

The probability Q_0 of a false alarm is just the probability that the point with coordinates (x, y) lies outside a circle with radius R_0: $Q_0 = \Pr\{x^2+y^2 > R_0^2 \mid H_0\}$. This probability can be calculated by integrating the joint p.d.f. $p_0(x, y)$ over the region outside that circle,

$$\begin{aligned} Q_0 &= \iint_{R>R_0} p_0(x, y)\, dx\, dy = (2\pi\, d^2)^{-1} \iint_{R>R_0} \exp\,[-(x^2+y^2)/2d^2]\, dx\, dy \\ &= (1/d^2) \int_{R_0}^{\infty} R e^{-R^2/2d^2}\, dR = \exp\,(-R_0^2/2d^2), \end{aligned} \tag{3.8}$$

where we have evaluated the integral by changing to polar coordinates. Incidentally we have shown that the p.d.f. of the statistic R under hypothesis H_0 is

$$P_0(R) = \frac{R}{d^2}\, e^{-R^2/2d^2}; \tag{3.9}$$

this is known as the Rayleigh distribution.

When hypothesis H_1 is true and there is a signal $s(t; \psi)$ having a particular phase ψ present, the components x and y of eq. (3.3) are again Gaussian variables with covariances given by eq. (3.6). The mean value of the complex envelope $V(t)$ of the input is now, by eq. (2.2), $\overline{V(t)} = F(t)\, e^{i\psi}$, so that the mean values of the components x and y are given by

$$\begin{aligned} \bar{x} + i\bar{y} &= \int_0^T Q^*(t)\, \overline{V(t)}\, dt = \int_0^T Q^*(t)\, F(t)\, dt\, e^{i\psi} = d^2\, e^{i\psi}, \\ \bar{x} &= d^2 \cos \psi, \quad \bar{y} = d^2 \sin \psi. \end{aligned} \tag{3.10}$$

Therefore the joint p.d.f. of x and y under hypothesis H_1 is

$$\begin{aligned} p_1(x, y; \psi) &= (2\pi d^2)^{-1} \exp\,\{-[(x-d^2 \cos \psi)^2+(y-d^2 \sin \psi)^2]/2d^2\} \\ &= (2\pi d^2)^{-1} \exp\,\{-[x^2+y^2-2d^2(x \cos \psi+y \sin \psi)+d^4]/2d^2\}. \end{aligned} \tag{3.11}$$

The probability that the signal $s(t;\psi)$ is detected is now the probability that the point with coordinates (x, y) lies outside the circle of radius R_0,

$$Q_d(\psi) = \Pr\{x^2+y^2 > R_0^2 \mid H_1, \psi\} = \iint_{R>R_0} p_1(x, y; \psi)\, dx\, dy.$$

We introduce polar coordinates, $x = R\cos\beta$, $y = R\sin\beta$, to evaluate this integral. The element of area is $dx\,dy = R\,dR\,d\beta$. Using the definition, eq. (2.9), of the Bessel function $I_0(x)$, we find

$$Q_d(\psi) = (2\pi d^2)^{-1} \int_{R_0}^{\infty}\int_0^{2\pi} R\,dR\,d\beta \exp\{-[R^2-2d^2R\cos(\psi-\beta)+d^4]/2d^2\}$$

$$= (1/d^2)\int_{R_0}^{\infty} Re^{-(R^2+d^4)/2d^2} I_0(R)\,dR. \tag{3.12}$$

The probability density function of the statistic R under hypothesis H_1 that one of the signals $s(t;\psi)$ is present is

$$\begin{aligned} P_1(R;\psi) &= q(d, R/d)/d, \\ q(d, x) &= x\, e^{-(x^2+d^2)/2} I_0(dx). \end{aligned} \tag{3.13}$$

This density function $q(d, x)$ has been plotted in Fig. V.1 for a few values of d. The curve for $d = 0$ represents the Rayleigh distribution, eq. (3.9),

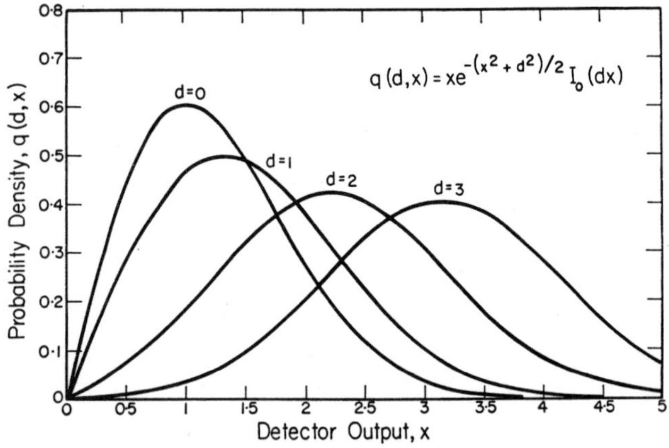

FIG. V.1. Probability density function of detector output.

for noise alone. We observe that for large values of d the density function looks very much like that for a Gaussian distribution. Indeed, with the asymptotic formula

$$I_0(x) \sim e^x/\sqrt{2\pi x}, \qquad x \gg 1,$$

for the Bessel function, the function $q(d, x)$ becomes

$$q(d, x) \sim \sqrt{\frac{x}{2\pi d}}\, e^{-(x-d)^2/2}, \qquad dx \gg 1.$$

The integral in eq. (3.12) cannot be evaluated in terms of ordinary functions. If we put

$$Q_d(\psi) = Q(d, R_0/d),$$

it is expressed in terms of the so-called "Q-function"

$$Q(\alpha, \beta) = \int_{\beta}^{\infty} x\, e^{-(x^2+\alpha^2)/2} I_0(\alpha x)\, dx. \tag{3.14}$$

This function has been extensively tabulated by Marcum (1950), and its properties have been studied by Rice (1944) and Marcum (1948). In particular we note the formulas

$$\begin{aligned} Q(\alpha, 0) &= 1, \quad Q(0, \beta) = e^{-\beta^2/2}, \\ Q(\alpha, \beta)+Q(\beta, \alpha) &= 1+e^{-(\alpha^2+\beta^2)/2} I_0(\alpha\beta) \end{aligned} \tag{3.15}$$

and the series expansions

$$\begin{aligned} Q(\alpha, \beta) &= e^{-(\alpha^2+\beta^2)/2} \sum_{n=0}^{\infty} (\alpha/\beta)^n I_n(\alpha\beta), \\ &= 1-e^{-(\alpha^2+\beta^2)/2} \sum_{n=1}^{\infty} (\beta/\alpha)^n I_n(\alpha\beta), \end{aligned}$$

in terms of the modified Bessel functions $I_n(x)$. Useful asymptotic formulas are

$$\begin{aligned} Q(\alpha, \beta) &\sim 1-\frac{1}{\alpha-\beta}\sqrt{\frac{\beta}{2\pi\alpha}}\, e^{-(\alpha-\beta)^2/2}, \qquad \alpha \gg \beta \gg 1, \\ Q(\alpha, \beta) &\sim \frac{1}{\beta-\alpha}\sqrt{\frac{\beta}{2\pi\alpha}}\, e^{-(\beta-\alpha)^2/2}, \qquad \beta \gg \alpha \gg 1. \end{aligned} \tag{3.16}$$

Further details concerning the Q-function are to be found in Appendix F.

When the Neyman–Pearson criterion is being used, the decision level R_0 on the statistic R is picked so that the false-alarm probability Q_0 of eq. (3.8) equals the preassigned value. The probability of detection $Q_d(\psi)$ of the signal $s(t; \psi)$ is then given by eq. (3.12). It is independent of the true phase ψ of the signal, a result to be expected because we used the least favorable prior distribution, eq. (2.3), for the signal phase.

The probability of detection Q_d is a function of the parameter d (eq. (3.6)), which we call the signal-to-noise ratio. In the case of white noise of spectral density N, as in Section 2, $Q(t) = F(t)/N$, and the signal-to-noise ratio d is given by

$$d^2 = \frac{1}{N} \int_0^T |F(t)|^2 \, dt.$$

For narrowband signals the quantity d is the same as that defined in Chapter IV, eqs. (1.13) and (3.11). To show this, put $s(t) = \text{Rl}\, F(t)\, e^{i\Omega t}$ and $q(t) = \text{Rl}\, Q(t)\, e^{i\Omega t}$ in eq. (3.11) of Chapter IV, and express these functions in terms of the real and imaginary parts of $F(t)$ and $Q(t)$. The integrand will then be found to have a group of terms with the factors $\cos 2\Omega t$ or $\sin 2\Omega t$; they oscillate much more rapidly than the other terms, which in the quasiharmonic approximation yield the formula in eq. (3.6) for d^2.

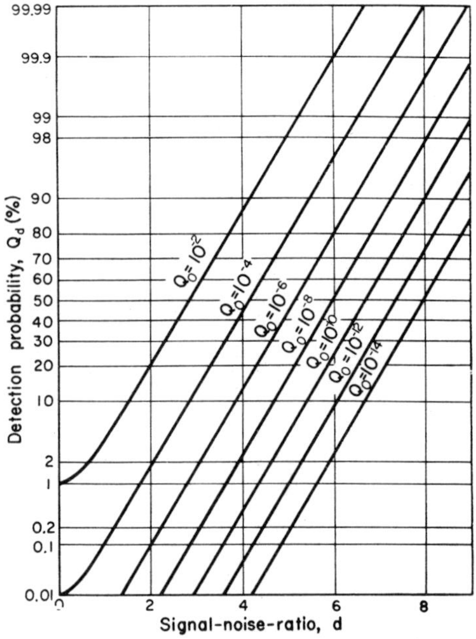

FIG. V.2. Probability of detection: signal of unknown phase.

We are justified, therefore, in calling the quantity d of eq. (3.6) the signal-to-noise ratio for the detection of narrowband signals. When the noise is white, d becomes the familiar $(2E/N)^{\frac{1}{2}}$, where E is the signal energy appearing within the observation interval.

In Fig. V.2 the probability Q_d of detection is plotted versus the signal-to-noise ratio d for various values of the probability Q_0 of a false alarm.

In Fig. V.3 the operating characteristics of this receiver are shown; they are curves of the detection probability Q_d versus the false-alarm probability Q_0 for fixed signal-to-noise ratio d. Comparison of these figures with Figs. IV.1 and IV.2 shows that the signal-to-noise ratio d required to attain a given probability of detection for the same false-alarm probability is slightly larger when the signal phase ψ is unknown than when all details of the signal are given. Thus for $Q_0 = 10^{-10}$, $Q_d = 0.90$, $d = 8.0$ for signals of unknown phase; when the phase is known, $d = 7.6$. This increase of about 0.4 in d appears throughout most of the graphs of Fig. V.2.

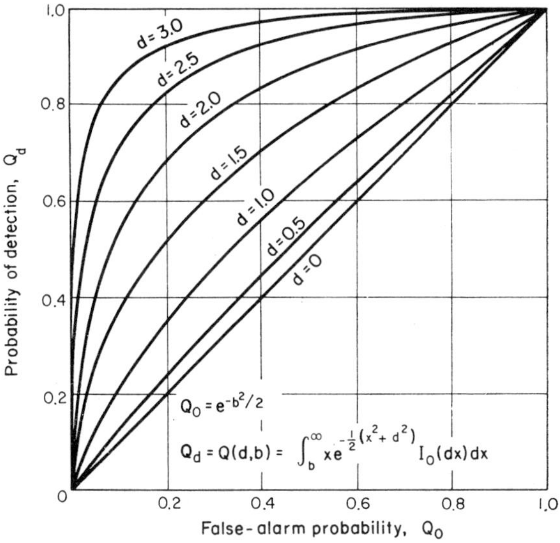

FIG. V.3. Receiver operating characteristics: signal of unknown phase.

As described in Chapter III, Section 2(d), the operating characteristics of Fig. V.3 can be used to determine the optimum strategy under the Bayes and minimax criteria; but for this the costs must be independent of the true signal phase—as is likely in any situation—and the uniform distribution, eq. (2.3), must be taken as the prior p.d.f. of the signal phase ψ.

4. DETECTION OF SIGNALS OF UNKNOWN AMPLITUDE AND PHASE

In this section we can discuss a problem that exhibits many practical features. A radar set is to determine whether a target is present at a certain distance from the transmitter. The receiver is gated so that signals and noise are observed only during an interval that might contain an echo signal from such a target. The interval during which the receiver is active corresponds to the observation interval $0 < t < T$ of previous sections. The receiver is to decide whether there is an echo signal of the form

$$s(t;\, A, \psi) = A \operatorname{Rl} F(t)\, e^{i(\Omega t+\psi)} \tag{4.1}$$

present in the input $v(t)$ during the interval. The signal shape $F(t)$ is known; it is determined by that of the transmitted pulse. The target is assumed stationary, so that the carrier frequency is also known. However, its location is not determined accurately enough for the signal phase to be known; and because the amount of scattering of the incident radiation by the target is unknown, the signal amplitude A is also an unknown parameter. We can assume that the amplitude A is positive, for a change in its sign corresponds to an undetectable change of π radians in the phase ψ. Here we have a problem in testing a simple hypothesis H_0 (noise alone present) versus a composite hypothesis H_1 (both noise and a signal of the form of eq. (4.1) are present). The unknown parameters of the signal are the amplitude A and the phase ψ. It is assumed that the noise is Gaussian and narrowband, with complex autocovariance function $\tilde{\phi}(\tau)$, as in Section 2.

If the signal amplitude were known, the optimum detection system would be that derived in Section 2, where we must replace $F(t)$ by $AF(t)$ in all formulas. This is equivalent to replacing $Q(t)$ by $AQ(t)$, where the new function $Q(t)$ is the solution of the integral equation

$$F(t) = \int_0^T \tilde{\phi}(t-u)\, Q(u)\, du, \qquad 0 < t < T. \tag{4.2}$$

There is now a factor of A in the optimum test statistic R of eq. (2.10), but this factor can be dropped if the decision level is changed proportionally. Hence the detection system for a signal of complex envelope $AF(t)e^{i\psi}$ and of unknown phase can as well be one that forms the new statistic

$$r = \left| \int_0^T Q^*(t)\, V(t)\, dt \right|, \tag{4.3}$$

where $V(t)$ is the complex envelope of the input and $Q(t)$ is the solution of the integral equation (4.2). The statistic r is compared with a decision level r_0; if $r > r_0$ the observer decides that one of the possible signals is present. The decision level r_0 is chosen so that the false-alarm probability

$$Q_0 = e^{-r_0^2/2f}, \quad f = \int_0^T Q^*(t)\, F(t)\, dt,$$

equals a preassigned value.

In this form the detection system does not depend on the signal amplitude A, and it is therefore optimum for any of the signals of the form of eq. (4.1) and of unknown amplitude. The "test" or detection system is uniformly most powerful with respect to the unknown signal parameter A, provided the unknown signal phase ψ is assigned its least favorable distribution, the uniform one. The detection probability $Q_d(A)$ is, of course, a function of the signal amplitude A; it is given by the formulas and graphs of Section 3, where the signal-to-noise ratio is $d = A\sqrt{f}$. The observer is assured that for signals of any phase ψ and any amplitude A the detection probability Q_d will not be less than $Q_d(A)$, for a given false-alarm probability Q_0; the detection system satisfies the Neyman–Pearson criterion in this sense.

Suppose that the detection system were built on the assumption that the signal phase is known, say $\psi = 0$. Then according to our work in Chapter IV, its use would involve reading the output of a filter matched to the signal $s(t;\, A,\, 0)$ precisely at the end of the observation interval. If the signal phase differed from that expected by an amount ψ, or if there were an error of an amount ψ/Ω in the time of measuring the filter output, the part of that output due to the signal would be reduced by a factor $\cos\psi$. This factor might even be negative, and there is a high probability that the observed filter output would be below the decision level and the signal would be missed.

The rectifier, on the other hand, averages over a number of cycles of the carrier, through the filtering action that removes components of frequency 2Ω and leaves only the modulus of the complex envelope of its input, as discussed in Chapter I, Section 3. When the matched filter of eq. (2.11) is used, the envelope of the signal component of its output reaches a maximum at the end of the observation interval; and for a fixed mean-square value of the noise component of the output, that terminal value of the amplitude of the signal component at the output is greater than for any other filter. In this way the use of a rectifier avoids the difficulties of uncertainty in the signal phase.

The detection system prescribed here is similar to what is used in an ordinary radar device that searches for a target at a given distance by gating its input so that it is observed only during a certain interval. The intermediate-frequency amplifier of such a radar corresponds roughly to the matched filter, since its bandwidth approximately equals that of the signal, although no attempt may be made to match details of the signal shape $F(t)$ exactly. The output of this amplifier is rectified and displayed on the screen of a cathode-ray oscilloscope. If the peak value of the output exceeds a certain level, the observer declares that a target is present at the distance in question.

5. SIGNALS OF UNKNOWN AMPLITUDE, PHASE, AND TIME OF ARRIVAL†

The most common use of a radar system is to search for targets whose range is not known in advance, so that the time at which the echo signal arrives at the receiver is unknown. The observer then cannot use the filter-rectifier system prescribed in the last section, for he does not know at what time to measure its output. And whatever detection strategy is used, the receiver input $v(t)$ must be observed over an interval $0 < t < T$ that is much longer than the duration of the echo signal. The length of the observation interval is usually determined by the pulse repetition period of the transmitter. Let us see how the decision theory developed at the beginning of this chapter can be applied to this problem.

The expected signal is now of the form

$$s(t;\, A, \psi, \tau) = A \,\mathrm{Rl}\, F(t-\tau)\, e^{i(\Omega t+\psi)}, \tag{5.1}$$

where τ is the time of arrival of a distinguishing point of the signal envelope; the other symbols have the same meanings as before. For targets not moving too rapidly we can assume that the carrier frequency Ω is known. We must test the simple hypothesis H_0 that no signal is present in the observation interval $0 < t < T$ against the composite hypothesis H_1 that a signal of the form of eq. (5.1) is present with some set of parameter values. For simplicity we assume that the observation interval is much longer than the duration of the signal and that the noise is Gaussian, with a bandwidth much larger than that of the signal. We shall use the Neyman–Pearson criterion.

Following the path traced in part (b) of Section 1, we seek a least favorable prior p.d.f. $\tilde{z}(A, \psi, \tau)$ of the unknown signal parameters, and with it we shall form an average likelihood ratio as in eq. (1.4),

$$\bar{\Lambda}[v(t)] = \iiint \tilde{z}(A, \psi, \tau)\, \Lambda[v(t);\, A, \psi, \tau]\, dA\, d\psi\, d\tau,$$

† This section may be omitted on first reading.

where $\Lambda[v(t); A, \psi, \tau]$ is the likelihood ratio for detecting a signal of the form given in eq. (5.1), but with specified values of amplitude, phase, and arrival time. If the noise is assigned a unilateral spectral density N, we can write down that likelihood ratio by replacing $F(t)$ in eq. (2.5) by $AF(t-\tau)$ and $Q(t)$ by $AF(t-\tau)/N$,

$$\bar{\Lambda}[v(t)] = \iiint \tilde{z}(A, \psi, \tau) \exp\left[\frac{A}{N} \operatorname{Rl} e^{-i\psi} \int_0^T F^*(t-\tau)\, V(t)\, dt - \frac{A^2}{2N} \int_0^T |F(t-\tau)|^2\, dt\right] dA\, d\psi\, d\tau. \tag{5.2}$$

This average likelihood ratio is to be compared with some critical value Λ_0, which depends on the preassigned false-alarm probability Q_0.

The least favorable situation is that in which the signal parameters are independent random variables, with no interrelationships of which the observer could take advantage to improve the probability of detection. Then we can write

$$\tilde{z}(A, \psi, \tau) = \tilde{z}_1(A)\, \tilde{z}_2(\psi)\, \tilde{z}_3(\tau).$$

Again the least favorable distribution of the signal phase ψ is the uniform one of eq. (2.3). Substituting it into eq. (5.2) and integrating over $0 \leqslant \psi < 2\pi$, we find for the average likelihood ratio

$$\bar{\Lambda}[v(t)] = \iint \tilde{z}_1(A)\, \tilde{z}_3(\tau)\, dA\, d\tau \exp\left[-\frac{A^2}{2N} \int_0^T |F(t-\tau)|^2\, dt\right] \cdot I_0\left(\frac{A}{N}\left|\int_0^T F^*(t-\tau)\, V(t)\, dt\right|\right). \tag{5.3}$$

Now the least favorable situation with regard to the signal amplitude A occurs when it is very small, as we have seen in Section 1, part (d). We are led to expand the Bessel and exponential functions in power series and to keep only the first two terms of each, obtaining

$$\bar{\Lambda}[v(t)] = 1 + \iint \tilde{z}_1(A)\, \tilde{z}_3(\tau)\, dA\, d\tau \left\{\frac{A^2}{4N^2}\left|\int_0^T F^*(t-\tau)\, V(t)\, dt\right|^2 - \frac{A^2}{2N} \int_0^T |F(t-\tau)|^2\, dt\right\}. \tag{5.4}$$

This is much like the threshold expansion in eq. (1.24). The integration over the range of amplitudes merely replaces A^2 by its mean value, and we see that instead of $\bar{\Lambda}[v(t)]$ we can use the test statistic

$$U = \int_0^T \tilde{z}_3(\tau) \left| \int_0^T F^*(t-\tau) V(t) \, dt \right|^2 d\tau = \int_0^T \int_0^T \gamma(t, u) V^*(t) V(u) \, dt \, du, \quad (5.5)$$

where

$$\gamma(t, u) = \int_0^T \tilde{z}_3(\tau) F^*(u-\tau) F(t-\tau) \, d\tau. \quad (5.6)$$

The statistic U is compared with some value U_0 depending on the false-alarm probability; if $U > U_0$ the observer decides that a signal is present.

To generate the statistic U would require a non-linear filter system of a rather complicated kind; see Chapter XI, Section 1, where the embodiment of a similar statistic is discussed. However, we are now concerned only with analyzing the behavior of such a detection system. To compute the false-alarm and detection probabilities we must find the p.d.f.s of the statistic U under hypotheses H_0 and H_1—in the latter case for the presence of a signal with a definite time of arrival τ_0.

When the observation time T is much longer than the duration of the signal, the quantity U is effectively the sum of a large number of independent random variables, and its p.d.f. is approximately Gaussian, in accordance with the central limit theorem mentioned in Chapter II, Section 4. This p.d.f. then depends only on the mean value $\bar{U}$ and on the variance Var U of the statistic. Under hypothesis H_0 we find, by eq. (II, 6.22),

$$\bar{U} = \int_0^T \int_0^T \gamma(t, u) \overline{V^*(t) V(u)} \, dt \, du = 2N \int_0^T \int_0^T \gamma(t, u) \, \delta(t-u) \, dt \, du$$
$$= 2N \int_0^T \gamma(t, t) \, dt. \quad (5.7)$$

To compute the variance we use eq. (II, 6.20), which gives the mean value of the product of four correlated Gaussian random variables:

$$\begin{aligned} \text{Var } U &= \iiiint \gamma(t, u) \gamma^*(t', u') \overline{V^*(t) V(u) V(t') V^*(u')} \, dt \, dt' \, du \, du' - \bar{U}^2 \\ &= 4N^2 \iiiint \gamma(t, u) \gamma^*(t', u') \, \delta(t-t') \, \delta(u-u') \, dt \, dt' \, du \, du' \\ &= 4N^2 \int_0^T \int_0^T |\gamma(t, u)|^2 \, dt \, du = \sigma_0^2. \end{aligned} \quad (5.8)$$

When the signal $s(A, \psi, \tau_0)$ is present, the mean value of the statistic U is

$$\bar{U} = 2N \int_0^T \gamma(t, t) \, dt + A^2 \int_0^T \int_0^T \gamma(t, u) F^*(t-\tau_0) F(u-\tau_0) \, dt \, du, \quad (5.9)$$

nd its variance becomes

$$\text{Var } U = \sigma_0^2+4NA^2 \int_0^T \int_0^T \int_0^T \gamma(t, u)\, \gamma^*(v, u)\, F^*(t-\tau_0)\, F(v-\tau_0)\, dt\, du\, dv = \sigma_1^2. \tag{5.10}$$

The probabilities of a false alarm and of detection are now given approximately by the equations

$$\begin{aligned} Q_0 &= \text{erfc } x, \quad Q_d(\tau_0) = \text{erfc } y(\tau_0), \\ y(\tau_0) &= \frac{\sigma_0}{\sigma_1}(x-d(\tau_0)), \\ [d(\tau_0)]^2 &= \frac{A^4}{\sigma_0^2}\left|\int_0^T \int_0^T \gamma(t, u)\, F^*(t-\tau_0)\, F(u-\tau_0)\, dt\, du\right|^2. \end{aligned} \tag{5.11}$$

The quantity $d(\tau_0)$ is the signal-to-noise ratio at the output of the system when that at the input is small. It and the probability of detection are functions of the time of arrival τ_0 of the signal.

When the observation interval is much longer than the signal, the least favorable distribution of the signal arrival time is approximately the uniform one

$$\tilde{z}_3(\tau) = 1/T, \qquad 0 < \tau < T, \tag{5.12}$$

for if any values of τ were more probable than others, a system that concentrated attention on them could attain a higher probability of detection. We shall see that when this prior p.d.f. is used, the probability of detection is approximately independent of the time of arrival of the signal. The only departure from this independence occurs at the ends of the interval $0 < \tau < T$, which become of negligible significance when the interval is very long.

Under this assumption of a long observation interval, the quantities in Eq. (5.11) can be shown to be approximately given by the following formulas:

$$\begin{aligned} d^2 &= \frac{E^2}{N^2T}\int_{-\infty}^{\infty} |\psi(s)|^2 ds / |\psi(0)|^2 \\ &= \frac{E^2}{N^2T}\int_{-\infty}^{\infty} |\Psi(\omega)|^2\, d\omega/2\pi \Bigg/ \left|\int_{-\infty}^{\infty} \Psi(\omega)\, d\omega/2\pi\right|^2, \\ \frac{\sigma_1^2}{\sigma_0^2} &= 1+\mu, \\ \mu &= \frac{2E}{NT}\,\frac{\int_{-\infty}^{\infty} |\Psi(\omega)|^3\, d\omega/2\pi}{\int_{-\infty}^{\infty} \Psi(\omega)\, d\omega/2\pi \int_{-\infty}^{\infty} |\Psi(\omega)|^2\, d\omega/2\pi}, \end{aligned} \tag{5.13}$$

where E is the signal energy,

$$E = \tfrac{1}{2}A^2 \int_{-\infty}^{\infty} |F(t)|^2 \, dt = \tfrac{1}{2}A^2 \psi(0), \tag{5.14}$$

and

$$\psi(\tau) = \int_{-\infty}^{\infty} F^*(v-\tau) \, F(v) \, dv,$$

$$\Psi(\omega) = \int_{-\infty}^{\infty} \psi(\tau) \, e^{-i\omega\tau} \, d\tau = |f(\omega)|^2, \tag{5.15}$$

where $f(\omega)$ is the Fourier transform of the signal envelope $F(t)$. We ca write

$$d = \frac{E}{N}\sqrt{\frac{\mathfrak{t}}{T}}, \quad \mu = 2bd\sqrt{\mathfrak{t}/T}, \quad y = (x-d)/\sqrt{1+\mu}, \tag{5.16}$$

with

$$\mathfrak{t} = \int_{-\infty}^{\infty} |\psi(\tau)|^2 \, d\tau / |\psi(0)|^2,$$

$$b = \int_{-\infty}^{\infty}\int_{-\infty}^{\infty} \psi(u_1)\, \psi(u_2)\, \psi^*(u_1+u_2)\, du_1\, du_2 / |\psi(0)|^3 \, \mathfrak{t}^2.$$

The time $\mathfrak{t}$ is of the order of the reciprocal bandwidth of the signal, an b is a dimensionless number depending only on the shape of the signal The following table gives some typical values:

	$\mathfrak{t}$	b
Rectangular pulse of duration T'	$2T'/3$	$99/80 = 1.2375$
Gaussian pulse of r.m.s. bandwidth $\Delta\omega$	$\pi^{\frac{1}{2}}/\Delta\omega$	$\sqrt{4/3} = 1.153$
Pulse with constant spectrum over $-W/2 < \omega/2\pi < W/2$; $f(\omega) = 0, \quad \lvert\omega\rvert/2\pi > W/2$	W^{-1}	1

Our results are derived on the assumption that the signal does no significantly overlap the ends of the observation interval, whereupon and μ and hence $Q_d(\tau_0)$ are independent of the time of arrival τ_0. Thus ou assumption of eq. (5.12) as the least favorable distribution in the limit c large T is borne out.

The validity of the Gaussian approximation, as shown in Chapter VI requires the ratio $\varkappa_3/\sigma_0^3$ to be much smaller than 1, where $\varkappa_3$ is the "thir cumulant" of the distribution of U under hypothesis H_0,

$$\varkappa_3 = \overline{U^3} - 3\bar{U}\sigma_0^2 - \bar{U}^3$$
$$= 3(2N)^3 \int_0^T \int_0^T \int_0^T \gamma(t, u)\, \gamma(u, v)\, \gamma(v, t)\, dt\, du\, dv.$$

When the observation interval is long,

$$\varkappa_3/\sigma_0^3 \cong 3b(\mathrm{t}/T)^{\frac{1}{2}},$$

and one can expect the Gaussian approximation to be the more accurate, the greater the ratio T/t.

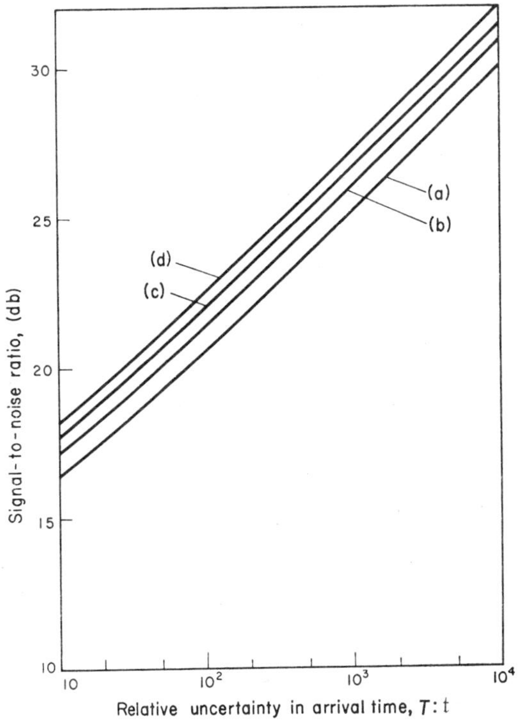

FIG. V.4. Detectability of a signal of unknown arrival time, threshold detector. $Q_d = 0.90$. Q_0: (a) 10^{-4}, (b) 10^{-6}, (c) 10^{-8}, (d) 10^{-10}.

When the input signal-to-noise ratio E/N is much smaller than the quantity T/t, μ is much less than 1, and the probability of detection depends only on the "effective signal-to-noise ratio" d; it is described by curves like those in Fig. IV.1. If $E/N < (T/\mathfrak{t})^{\frac{1}{2}}$, d is less than 1, and th probability of detection is very small for any feasible false-alarm proba bility Q_0. It is only for large input signal-to-noise ratios, $E/N \gg (T/\mathfrak{t})$ that the probability of detection approaches 1; and for a long observatio interval, $T \gg \mathfrak{t}$, E/N must be large indeed.

As an illustration, we have plotted in Fig. V.4. the signal-to-noise rati in decibels, $10 \log_{10} (2E/N)$, needed to attain a 90 percent probability o detecting a rectangular pulse of energy E in white noise of unilateral spec tral density N. The abscissa is the ratio $T/\mathfrak{t}$ of the duration of the obser vation interval to the characteristic time $\mathfrak{t}$. Curves are given for severa false-alarm probabilities Q_0. Since the constant b changes only slightl with the shape of the signal, these curves are approximately valid fo signals of any unimodal form. Our assumption that the statistic U i Gaussian is least reliable for small values of the ratio $T/\mathfrak{t}$ and for values o U in the tails of the distributions. The value of the decision level x use in the equation for $Q_d(\tau_0)$ may, therefore, be in error, but this affects onl the positions of the curves and not their general dependence on the ratio $T/\mathfrak{t}$

In Chapter IX we shall study another approach to the detection of sig nals of unknown arrival time, and a system will be developed emphasizin not the weakest signals, but rather those of large enough amplitudes tha there is a reasonable probability of detecting them. The method of "maxi mum-likelihood detection" applied there will be found superior at suc signal-to-noise ratios to the one derived here from the threshold expan sion, although at low signal-to-noise ratios it is certainly inferior.

PROBLEMS

1. A signal $Af(t)$, with $f(t)$ completely known, is to be detected in white Gaussia noise by observing an input $v(t)$ over an interval $(0, T)$. For the two cases discussed i Section 1, (a) A known to be positive, (b) A equally likely to be positive or negative plot the probability Q_d of detection versus the signal-to-noise ratio for a false-alarn probability $Q_0 = 10^{-6}$. For $Q_d = 0.90$, how much stronger a signal is needed in cas (b) than in case (a)? Give the ratio of the signal strengths in decibels.

2. A signal $Af(t)$ of known form and unknown amplitude is to be detected in whit Gaussian noise of unilateral spectral density N. Fix the cost matrix $\mathbf{C}$ and the prio probabilities ζ and $1-\zeta$ of hypotheses H_0 and H_1. Show that the false-alarm an detection probabilities are given as in eqs. (IV, 1.11, 1.12) with

$$x = \frac{1}{d} \ln \Lambda_0 + \frac{d}{2}, \quad d = (2E/N)^{\frac{1}{2}},$$

and with Λ_0 as given in eq. (III, 2.10). Find the minimum Bayes cost $\bar{C}_{\min}(d)$ as a func tion of the signal-to-noise ratio d, and show that as d goes to zero, $\bar{C}_{\min}(0) - \bar{C}_{\min}(d$ is proportional, for $d \ll 1$, to $d^3 \exp [-(\ln^2 \Lambda_0)/2d^2]$. This difference $\bar{C}_{\min}(0) - \bar{C}_{\min}(d$ of Bayes costs therefore approaches zero faster than any power of d.

3. Suppose that a narrowband signal

$$s(t;\, A,\, \psi) = A \text{ Rl } F(t) \exp{(i\Omega t + i\psi)}$$

s received with unknown phase ψ, and that all that is known about its amplitude A is hat it will be greater than a positive quantity A_0. In the space of the parameters $\boldsymbol{\theta} =$ $= (A, \psi)$ identify the regions Θ and Θ' associated with the least favorable p.d.f. (A, ψ), as described in Section 1, part (c).

4. Show that the likelihood ratio in eq. (2.8) is equal to dQ_d/dQ_0, where Q_0 and Q_d re the false-alarm and detection probabilities calculated in Section 3.

5. Let the amplitude A of the narrowband signal in problem 3 be distributed accord-ng to the Rayleigh distribution,

$$z(A) = (A/\sigma^2) \exp{(-A^2/2\sigma^2)}, \qquad A > 0,$$

nd let the phase ψ be uniformly distributed over $(0, 2\pi)$. Find the optimum detection tatistic and relate its decision level to the critical value Λ_0 associated with the Bayes riterion, eq. (III, 2.10). Calculate the minimum Bayes cost $\bar{C}_{\min}(\sigma)$ as a function of and investigate its behavior as σ approaches 0. Show that as σ vanishes, for $\Lambda_0 > 1$, $\bar{C}_{\min}(0) - \bar{C}_{\min}(\sigma)$ approaches 0 faster than any power of the average signal-to-noise atio. Take the noise as white and Gaussian.

6. Suppose that the complex autocovariance function $\tilde{\phi}(\tau)$ of narrowband Gaussian oise is real, so that the quadrature components X and Y are independent and identi-ally distributed. For two different times t_1 and t_2 let the complex envelope of the noise e $R_j \exp i\theta_j = X(t_j) + iY(t_j)$, $j = 1, 2$. Show that the joint probability density function f the amplitudes R_1 and R_2 is

$$p(R_1, R_2) = \frac{R_1 R_2}{\sigma^4(1-r^2)} \exp\left[-\frac{R_1^2 + R_2^2}{2\sigma^2(1-r^2)}\right] I_0\left(\frac{rR_1R_2}{\sigma^2(1-r^2)}\right),$$

$$\sigma^2 = \tilde{\phi}(0), \qquad r = \tilde{\phi}(t_2 - t_1)/\tilde{\phi}(0).$$

Hint. Convert eq. (II, 6.15) to the joint p.d.f. of R_1, R_2, θ_1, and θ_2, and integrate out he phases θ_1, θ_2 (Middleton, 1948).

7. For noise of the same kind as in Problem 6 find the p.d.f. of the phase difference $= \theta_2 - \theta_1$ by integrating the joint p.d.f. found in that problem over R_1 and R_2 nstead of over the phases. *Hint*. Change variables to (z, t), where $R_1 = \sigma z \cos t$, $R_2 = \sigma z \sin t$, and integrate first over $0 < z < \infty$, second over $0 < t < \pi/2$. *Answer:* ith $a = r \cos \psi$,

$$p(\psi) = (2\pi)^{-1}(1-r^2)(1-a^2)^{-\frac{3}{2}}\left[\sqrt{1-a^2} + a\left(\frac{\pi}{2} + \sin^{-1} a\right)\right]$$

Middleton, 1948).

8. A sinusoidal signal of amplitude A is added to Gaussian narrowband noise of ean-square amplitude $\sigma^2 = \tilde{\phi}(0)$. Show that the phase θ of the sum, measured with espect to that of the sinusoid, has the p.d.f.

$$p(\theta) = (2\pi)^{-1} \exp(-a^2/2) + (2\pi)^{-\frac{1}{2}} a \cos\theta \exp\left(-\tfrac{1}{2}a^2 \sin^2\theta\right)[1 - \operatorname{erfc}(a \cos\theta)],$$

ith $a = A/\sigma$. Work out a Gaussian approximation to this p.d.f. when $a \gg 1$ (Middle-on, 1948).

BIBLIOGRAPHY (V)

944 Rice, S. O., "The Mathematical Analysis of Random Noise", *Bell Sys. Tech. J.* **23,** 282–332 (July); **24,** 46–156 (Jan., 1945).

948 Marcum, J. I., "A Statistical Theory of Target Detection by Pulsed Radar", Rand Corp. Report RM–753 (July 1). Reprinted in *Trans. I.R.E.* **IT-6,** 59–267 (Apr. 1960).

MIDDLETON, D., "Some General Results in the Theory of Noise through Non-linear Devices", *Q. Appl. Math.* **5,** no. 4, 445–98.
1950 MARCUM, J. I., "Table of *Q*-Functions", Rand Corp. Report RM–339 (Jan. 1
WALD, A., *Statistical Decision Functions*, John Wiley & Sons, Inc., New York, N.Y.
1954 BLACKWELL, D. and GIRSHICK, M. A., *Theory of Games and Statistical Decision*, John Wiley & Sons, Inc., New York, N.Y.
PETERSON, W. W., BIRDSALL, T. G. and FOX, W. C., "The Theory of Signal Detectability", *Trans. I.R.E.* **PGIT-4,** 171–212 (Sept.).
1955 MIDDLETON, D. and VAN METER, D., "Detection and Extraction of Signals in Noise from the Point of View of Statistical Decision Theory", *J. Soc. Ind. Appl. Math.* (I) **3,** 192–253 (1955); (II) **4,** 86–119 (1956).
1960 MIDDLETON, D., *An Introduction to Statistical Communication Theory*, McGraw-Hill Book Co., New York, N.Y.
1961 RUDNICK, P., "Likelihood Detection of Small Signals in Stationary Noise", *J. Appl Phys.* **32,** 140–3 (Feb.).

VI

DIGITAL COMMUNICATIONS

1. THE TRANSMISSION OF DISCRETE INFORMATION

Information to be communicated from one point to another can be one of two distinct kinds, continuous or "analogue" information, and discrete or "digital" information. The sound of a voice as picked up by a microphone, the temperature of a place as measured by a thermocouple, and the intensity of light as sensed by a photocell typify continuous information that may have to be carried to a distant point. They are described by continuous functions of time that in a finite interval can appear in any of an infinite array of realizations. The messages keyed by a telegrapher and the output of a digital computer, on the other hand, constitute discrete information. They are expressed in sequences of symbols from a finite alphabet, and in a limited time they can assume only one of a finite set of possible forms.

The signals conveying information in a communication system are corrupted along the way by noise. Because of the noise, the receiver cannot be expected to reproduce continuous information exactly; it can only *estimate* what was sent. The receiver should be designed to minimize some average measure of the deviation between its output and that of the source of information. In a system carrying discrete information, however, the receiver has to *decide* what was sent by the transmitter. On the basis of its input during a given interval the receiver chooses one of a finite array of sequences as the one transmitted, and it should be able to pick the correct sequence with the highest possible probability. The two kinds of information are thus plainly distinguished by the operations needed at the receiver and by the measure of quality applied to them. Continuous information requires estimation with fidelity; discrete information requires decision with freedom from error.

Continuous information is sometimes converted into discrete by sampling it periodically and quantizing the amplitude of each sample into one of a finite number of values or "levels". The output of such an "analogue-to-digital converter" is a succession of numbers or of symbols representing numbers. When they are sent over a communication system, the receiver may simply print out the numbers, or it may change them back into as faithful a replica of the original continuous information as it can. Even voice signals are treated in this way by a pulse-code modulation system.

A conversion of this kind is a form of encoding. Digital information also may be encoded by translating it from one set of symbols into another, as when a telegrapher sends written messages by Morse code. The most drastic form of digital encoding is the translation of written words or numbers into a binary alphabet of only two symbols. Messages are sometimes encoded for secrecy, but more often the aim is efficiency of transmission over some communication system. To this end extra symbols or digits may be inserted into the messages for use later in detecting and correcting errors. The receiver must be able to translate, or "decode", the symbols it receives into an output message that should resemble the original message as closely as possible. A low probability of error and a high rate of dispatching messages are the primary demands imposed on a digital communication system. A quantitative measure of its ability to convey messages rapidly and correctly was established by Shannon (1948), who at the same time laid the theoretical foundations of the efficient encoding and decoding of both continuous and discrete information. Coding theory, particularly as applied to discrete messages, is now a flourishing subject of technical and scholarly endeavor.

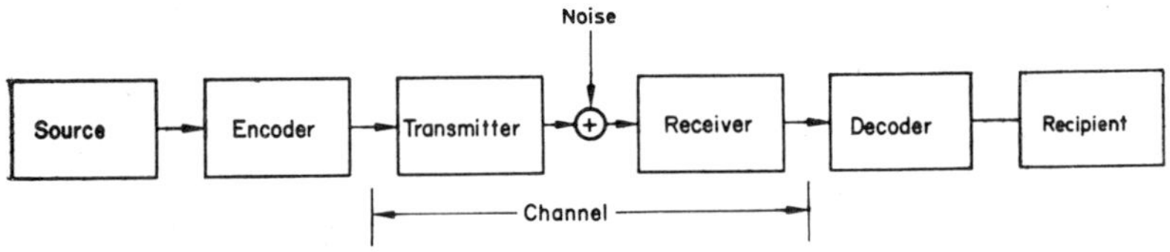

FIG. VI.1. A communication system.

The present chapter will treat the reception of discrete information in a communication system like that illustrated in Fig. VI.1. The encoder emits a succession of symbols drawn from an alphabet containing M symbols altogether; they appear at the rate of one every T seconds. We allow the possibility that the source may produce information already in this form and that no encoding is necessary. The "encoder" is then trivially a direct connection to the transmitter.

To each symbol of that alphabet is assigned a distinct signal pulse $f_i(t)$, $i = 1, 2, \ldots, M$, which is to be transmitted whenever the symbol appears. To avoid overlapping, the pulses $f_i(t)$ are of limited duration, at most T seconds. They appear at the receiver corrupted by random noise, which we shall assume to be Gaussian and simply additive. The receiver must decide, on the basis of its input $v(t)$, which of the M possible signals was actually transmitted during each of the intervals. After deciding that, say, the jth signal was sent during the interval in question, it emits the jth symbol of the alphabet. The output symbols flow into the decoder, and our concern with them stops at that point. The transmitter, the medium carrying the signals, and the receiver—as far as the decoder—make up the communication *channel.*

The input and the output of a discrete channel are sequences of symbols. The output symbols should be the same as the input symbols; when they differ, an error has occurred. The probabilities of the various possible errors characterize the channel. When the alphabet provides M different symbols, the channel is called "M-ary". With two symbols it is binary, with three ternary, with four quaternary. Special forms of these channels will be introduced later in the chapter. More general channels whose output symbols are drawn from a different alphabet from the one furnishing the input symbols can be envisioned, but we shall disregard them.

The output of the encoder, which is the input to the transmitter and to the channel, is treated as a stationary discrete random process. One does not know in advance which symbols will appear; one knows only the probabilities or relative frequencies with which the symbols or sequences are put forth. The relative frequency of the jth symbol will be denoted by ζ_j. For a sequence of n symbols, the joint probability of observing a particular set $i_1, i_2, \ldots, i_n$ is $\zeta(i_1, i_2, \ldots, i_n)$. If successive symbols are statistically independent,

$$\zeta(i_1, i_2, \ldots, i_n) = \prod_{k=1}^{n} \zeta_{i_k} .$$

These probabilities apply to the corresponding sequences of transmitted signals $f_i(t)$ as well.

With respect to a particular place in the sequence of input symbols, the task of the receiver can be viewed as that of choosing one of a set of M hypotheses $H_1, H_2, \ldots, H_M$. By H_j we denote the hypothesis, "The symbol in this place was the jth, and the jth signal $f_j(t)$ was transmitted". The prior probability of this hypothesis is ζ_j. If there exists an $M \times M$ matrix $\mathbf{C}$ whose (ij)-element is the cost of deciding that the ith signal was sent when the jth was actually transmitted, one might apply the Bayes criterion and design the receiver to minimize the average cost of each decision. It is seldom appropriate, however, to do more than regard all errors as equally expensive. The Bayes criterion is then equivalent to the requirement that the average probability of error be as small as possible, and this is the criterion we shall adopt.

When statistically independent signals are received in white noise, the receiver can decide about each transmitted pulse individually, using only its input $v(t)$ during the interval containing the signal in question. If the symbols being transmitted are not statistically independent, however, the input $v(t)$ during other intervals can be used to increase the probability of correctly deciding which signal arrived during a given interval.

The transmitter and the receiver are usually designed as though the symbols from the encoder were statistically independent, and it is left to the decoder to take account of what dependence may exist among them. To clarify this point by an example, let us consider the transmission of binary data that have been encoded by a "parity-check" or "group" code (Slepian, 1956). To each set of k successive binary digits (0's and 1's), a number $(n-k)$ of "check digits" are appended by the encoder. These check digits are selected in such a way that the resulting set of n digits satisfies $n-k$ parity equations; the binary sums of $n-k$ different combinations of the n digits vanish.

Even though the k original message digits might have been statistically independent, and are usually so considered, the n transmitted digits certainly are not. Nevertheless, the receiver may treat them as independent and decide individually about which digit was transmitted during each T-second interval. Its decisions are then passed on to the decoder as a stream of 0's and 1's, and the decoder applies a certain binary-arithmetic algorithm to each set of n digits to obtain k output digits for the recipient of the messages. The receiver is designed to make its decisions about individual transmitted signals with the minimum probability of error, but it disregards the relations between successive digits that were imposed by the encoder. The parity relations and the decoding algorithm are selected to minimize the average probability that each set of k output digits differs from the set originally submitted to the encoder.

Alternatively, the receiver might treat each set of n transmitted pulses as a single signal representing one of the 2^k possible sequences of k message digits and $(n-k)$ check digits. These sequences are now being regarded as symbols of a super-alphabet with $M = 2^k$ elements.The receiver uses what is known about the noise and about the relative frequencies of these sequences to decide, on the basis of its input during an interval of nT seconds, which of these 2^k sequences was transmitted, choosing in effect one of 2^k hypotheses. It makes these decisions with the least possible probability of error, and every nT seconds it emits the k message digits associated with the chosen hypothesis. No decoder is required. This procedure is more elaborate and expensive, but also more reliable, than the one involving individual detections and binary-arithmetic decoding.

In what follows we shall first deal with binary channels, to which the methods of the two previous chapters can be applied. Then we shall consider systems transmitting more than two symbols, treating only the more easily analyzed channels, and merely indicating how one might proceed with the complicated ones. The aim of this chapter is not to make a comprehensive survey of digital communication systems, but to show by some simple examples what detection theory can say about their design and to illustrate the evaluation of their performance.

2. BINARY CHANNELS

Digital communications often utilize binary signals transmitted at a constant rate. Both the theory of coding binary data and the theory of detecting binary signals are among the most extensively developed parts of communication theory. Referring to Fig. VI.1, we shall suppose the output of the encoder to be a stream of 0's and 1's appearing at a rate of one every T seconds. Each 0 causes the transmitter to send the signal $f_0(t)$; each 1 causes it to send $f_1(t)$. The relative frequencies of 0's and 1's are ζ_0 and ζ_1, respectively, with $\zeta_0+\zeta_1 = 1$.

In treating the detection of these signals we shall suppose the elements of the sequence of symbols they represent to be statistically independent, and each signal will be assumed to be restricted to an interval of T seconds' duration. Overlapping is excluded. With both the noise and the sequence of symbols taken as stationary random processes, all intervals are statistically alike, and we can confine our attention to the interval $(0, T)$. On the basis of its input $v(t)$ during that interval, the receiver is to choose between two hypotheses, (H_0) "signal $f_0(t)$ was sent" and (H_1) "signal $f_1(t)$ was sent". By a proper choice of units, $f_0(t)$ and $f_1(t)$ can be taken as the received signals, and their energies are

$$E_i = \int_0^T [f_i(t)]^2 \, dt, \quad i = 0, 1. \tag{2.1}$$

The noise will be assumed to be Gaussian.

(a) *Completely Known Signals*

If the forms $f_0(t)$ and $f_1(t)$ of the signals as received are completely known, and if the noise is stationary Gaussian with a known autocovariance function $\phi(\tau)$, the methods of Chapter IV can be simply adapted to the problem of detecting the signals with a minimum average probability of error. When the signals are narrowband modulations of a carrier, the phase of the carrier must be precisely known in each interval $(0, T)$; and when this is assured by preserving the same carrier phase through a great many intervals and synchronizing the transmitted carrier with a reference wave at the receiver, the signals are *coherent*.

The average probability of error will be least when the receiver forms from its input the likelihood ratio†

$$\Lambda[v(t)] = \frac{\exp\left[\int q_1(t)\, v(t)\, dt - \frac{1}{2}\int q_1(t) f_1(t)\, dt\right]}{\exp\left[\int q_0(t)\, v(t)\, dt - \frac{1}{2}\int q_0(t) f_0(t)\, dt\right]} \tag{2.2}$$
$$= \exp\left\{\int [q_1(t) - q_0(t)]\, v(t)\, dt - \tfrac{1}{2}(d_1^2 - d_0^2)\right\}$$

and compares it with the quantity

$$\Lambda_0 = \zeta_0/\zeta_1. \tag{2.3}$$

Here d_0 and d_1 are the signal-to-noise ratios defined by

$$d_i^2 = \int_0^T q_i(t) f_i(t)\, dt, \quad i = 0, 1, \tag{2.4}$$

and $q_0(t)$ and $q_1(t)$ are the solutions of the integral equation

$$f_i(t) = \int_0^T \phi(t-u)\, q_i(u)\, du, \quad 0 < t < T, \quad i = 0, 1. \tag{2.5}$$

If $\Lambda[v(t)] < \Lambda_0$, the receiver sends to the decoder a "0"; if $\Lambda[v(t)] > \Lambda_0$, it sends a "1".

The receiver can just as well make its decisions after passing the input $v(t)$ through a filter matched to the difference signal $q_1(t) - q_0(t)$. The output g of the filter at the end of each interval $(0, T)$ is

$$g = \int [q_1(t) - q_0(t)]\, v(t)\, dt, \tag{2.6}$$

and it is compared with the decision level

$$g_0 = \tfrac{1}{2}(d_1^2 - d_0^2) + \ln(\zeta_0/\zeta_1).$$

The statistic g is a Gaussian random variable. Its mean values when the signals $f_0(t)$ and $f_1(t)$ are present are, respectively,

$$\mathbf{E}[g \mid H_0] = h - d_0^2, \quad \mathbf{E}[g \mid H_1] = d_1^2 - h, \tag{2.7}$$

† In this section all unmarked integrals run from 0 to T.

where

$$h = \int q_0(t)\, f_1(t)\, dt = \iint q_0(t)\, \phi(t-u)\, q_1(u)\, dt\, du \\ = \int q_1(t)\, f_0(t)\, dt. \tag{2.8}$$

Under both hypotheses the variance of the statistic g is

$$\operatorname{Var} g = d_0^2 + d_1^2 - 2h = \sigma^2. \tag{2.9}$$

The average probability of error is thus

$$P_e = \zeta_0 \Pr\{g > g_0 | H_0\} + \zeta_1 \Pr\{g < g_0 | H_1\} \\ = \zeta_0 \operatorname{erfc} [(g_0 - h + d_0^2)/\sigma] + \zeta_1 \operatorname{erfc} [(d_1^2 - h - g_0)/\sigma] \\ = \zeta_0 \operatorname{erfc} \left(\frac{\sigma}{2} + \frac{L}{\sigma}\right) + \zeta_1 \operatorname{erfc} \left(\frac{\sigma}{2} - \frac{L}{\sigma}\right), \tag{2.10}$$

$$L = \ln (\zeta_0/\zeta_1), \quad \zeta_0 + \zeta_1 = 1,$$

where as before

$$\operatorname{erfc} x = (2\pi)^{-\frac{1}{2}} \int_x^\infty \exp(-t^2/2)\, dt.$$

If 0's and 1's occur equally often, $L = 0$ and the probability of error is simply

$$P_{e,\,\mathrm{sym}} = \operatorname{erfc} (\sigma/2). \tag{2.11}$$

Because the two signals enter the expression for σ^2 symmetrically, it is not hard to show that this is the maximum value of the probability of error as the relative frequencies ζ_0 and ζ_1 are varied.

When the noise is white and its unilateral spectral density is N,

$$d_i^2 = 2E_i/N, \quad i = 0, 1, \\ h = \frac{2}{N} \int_0^T f_0(t)\, f_1(t)\, dt = \lambda\, d_1\, d_2, \tag{2.12}$$

where

$$\lambda = \int f_0(t)\, f_1(t)\, dt \Big/ \left[\int [f_0(t)]^2\, dt \cdot \int [f_1(t)]^2\, dt \right]^{\frac{1}{2}} \tag{2.13}$$

is the "correlation coefficient" of the signals and has an absolute value less than or equal to 1. The maximum average probability of error is then $(\zeta_0 = \zeta_1 = \frac{1}{2})$

$$P_{e,\,\mathrm{sym}} = \operatorname{erfc} \left(\tfrac{1}{2}\sqrt{d_0^2 + d_1^2 - 2\lambda\, d_0\, d_1}\right), \tag{2.14}$$

and if the signals are received with equal energies, $E_0 = E_1 = Nd^2/2$,

$$P_{e,\,\mathrm{sym}} = \operatorname{erfc} \left(d \sqrt{(1-\lambda)/2}\right). \tag{2.15}$$

The combination of transmitter, medium, and receiver is then called a "binary symmetric channel". The probabilities of the two kinds of error are equal to $P_{e,\,\mathrm{sym}}$. This probability is in turn smallest when $\lambda = -1$ and the signals are "antipodal", $f_0(t) = -f_1(t)$, whereupon $P_{e,\,\mathrm{sym}} = \operatorname{erfc} d$.

For "on-off" signals in the "unilateral" or "one-sided" binary channel, $f_0(t) = 0$ and $f_1(t) \neq 0$. When both signals are transmitted equally often, the probability of error is

$$P_e = \operatorname{erfc}(d_1/2). \tag{2.16}$$

The unilateral channel is most aptly compared with the binary symmetric channel when both channels have the same average received power and white Gaussian noise of the same spectral density N. Then d_1 in eq. (2.16) must equal $\sqrt{2}$ times the d in eq. (2.15). Setting $\lambda = -1$ there, we find that the binary symmetric channel has the smaller probability of error.

(b) *Signals of Random Phase*

If the transmitted signals are narrowband pulse modulations of a carrier of frequency Ω,

$$f_j(t) = \mathrm{Rl}\, F_j(t) \exp(i\Omega t + i\psi_j), \quad j = 0, 1, \tag{2.17}$$

their phases ψ_0 and ψ_1 may be unknown at the receiver for several reasons. The transmitter may be pulsing a high-frequency oscillator with no attempt to make the phases of the output coherent from one signal to the next. Transmission over a multiplicity of paths of different and variable lengths, or rapidly varying delays in the propagation from transmitter to receiver, may change the phases of the received signals in ways the receiver cannot follow. Synchronization with the phase of the transmitted carrier may simply be too costly, and the designer may choose to disregard phase relations between successively received signals. We speak then of *incoherent* detection.

When the phases ψ_0 and ψ_1 of the received signal are unknown, their least favorable distribution is the uniform one,

$$\tilde{z}_j(\psi_j) = 1/2\pi, \quad 0 \leqslant \psi_j < 2\pi, \quad j = 0, 1. \tag{2.18}$$

The noise is taken as narrowband and Gaussian with the autocovariance

$$\phi(\tau) = \mathrm{Rl}\, \tilde{\phi}(\tau)\, e^{i\Omega\tau}. \tag{2.19}$$

From eqs. (1.8) and (2.5) of Chapter V we can obtain the average likelihood ratio — or better, ratio of average likelihoods — $\bar{\Lambda}[v(t)]$, which is to be compared with the decision level $\Lambda_0 = \zeta_0/\zeta_1$ for the purpose of deciding whether the received signal is a "0" or a "1". The ratio is

$$\bar{\Lambda}[v(t)] = \frac{\int_0^{2\pi} \exp\left[\mathrm{Rl}\, R_1 \exp i(\beta_1-\psi_1) - \tfrac{1}{2} d_1^2\right] d\psi_1/2\pi}{\int_0^{2\pi} \exp\left[\mathrm{Rl}\, R_0 \exp i(\beta_0-\psi_0) - \tfrac{1}{2} d_0^2\right] d\psi_0/2\pi}$$

$$= \exp\left[-\tfrac{1}{2}(d_1^2 - d_0^2)\right] I_0(R_1)/I_0(R_0), \tag{2.20}$$

where, with $j = 0, 1$,

$$d_j^2 = \int_0^T Q_j^*(t)\, F_j(t)\, dt, \quad R_j \exp i\beta_j = \int_0^T Q_j^*(t)\, V(t)\, dt, \tag{2.21}$$

with $Q_j(t)$ the solution of the integral equation

$$F_j(t) = \int_0^T \tilde{\phi}(t-u)\, Q_j(u)\, du, \qquad 0 < t < T. \tag{2.22}$$

Again $V(t)$ is the complex envelope of the input, $v(t) = \mathrm{Rl}\, V(t)\, e^{i\Omega t}$. The quantities R_0 and R_1 are the linearly rectified outputs, at the end of each interval $(0, T)$, of filters matched to the signals $\mathrm{Rl}\, Q_0(t) \exp i\Omega t$ and $\mathrm{Rl}\, Q_1(t) \exp i\Omega t$, respectively. The receiver compares the quantities

$$\gamma_0 = \zeta_0 \exp(-d_0^2/2)\, I_0(R_0) \quad \text{and} \quad \gamma_1 = \zeta_1 \exp(-d_1^2/2)\, I_0(R_1).$$

If $\gamma_0 > \gamma_1$, it chooses hypothesis H_0 and sends a "0" on to the decoder; if $\gamma_0 < \gamma_1$, it sends a "1". Because of the non-linearity of the operations by which γ_0 and γ_1 are generated, it is difficult to calculate their probability density functions under the two hypotheses and to determine the probabilities of the two kinds of errors.

(i) *The balanced binary incoherent channel.* If the "0"s and "1"s occur equally often, $\zeta_0 = \zeta_1$, and if $d_1 = d_0 = d$, the binary channel is appropriately termed "balanced". When the noise is white, both signals are being received with equal energies, $E_1 = E_2 = E$. There is complete symmetry between them. The receiver can then simply compare R_0 and R_1, deciding that the symbol "0" was sent if $R_0 > R_1$, and that "1" was sent if $R_1 > R_0$.

The probabilities of the two kinds of error are equal in the balanced channel. A rather long calculation, presented in Appendix G, shows that the probability of error is

$$P_e = \Pr\{R_1 > R_0 \mid H_0\} = Q(v_1 d, v_2 d) - \tfrac{1}{2} e^{-d^2/4} I_0(|\lambda|\, d^2/4)$$
$$= \tfrac{1}{2}[1 - Q(v_2 d, v_1 d) + Q(v_1 d, v_2 d)], \ \rule{2pt}{8pt} \tag{2.23}$$
$$v_1 = \tfrac{1}{2}(1 - \sqrt{1-|\lambda|^2})^{\frac{1}{2}}, \quad v_2 = \tfrac{1}{2}(1 + \sqrt{1-|\lambda|^2})^{\frac{1}{2}},$$

where λ is the correlation coefficient of the two signals,

$$\lambda = d^{-2} \int_0^T \int_0^T Q_0^*(t)\, \tilde{\phi}(t-u)\, Q_1(u)\, dt\, du, \tag{2.24}$$

and $Q(\alpha, \beta)$ is the Q-function of eq. (V, 3.14) and Appendix F. At high signal-to-noise ratios the probability of error is asymptotically

$$P_e \cong \sqrt{\frac{1+|\lambda|}{2|\lambda|}} \operatorname{erfc}\left(d\sqrt{(1-|\lambda|)/2}\right), \qquad |\lambda|\, d^2 \gg 1. \tag{2.25}$$

This formula was obtained by using eqs. (F.16), (F.17) of Appendix F in the second form for P_e in eq. (2.23). It should be compared with the probability of error for signals of known phase as given in eq. (2.15).

If $\lambda = 0$, the signals are orthogonal with respect to the interval $(0, T)$ and the kernel $\tilde{\phi}(t-u)$. The probability of error is then reduced to

$$P_e = Q(0, d) - \tfrac{1}{2} e^{-d^2/4} = \tfrac{1}{2} e^{-d^2/4}. \tag{2.26}$$

(ii) *The unilateral binary incoherent channel.* For a channel transmitting "on–off" pulses of random phase, $f_0(t) = 0$, and the received energy is

$$E = \int_0^T |f_1(t)|^2\, dt \cong \tfrac{1}{2} \int_0^T |F_1(t)|^2\, dt.$$

The signal-to-noise ratio d' is given by

$$d'^2 = \int_0^T F_1^*(t)\, Q_1(t)\, dt. \tag{2.27}$$

The receiver now uses the same decision scheme as was developed in Chapter V, Section 2. It compares the rectified output R of a filter matched to the signal $\mathrm{Rl}\, Q_1(t)\, e^{i\Omega t}$ with a decision level ϱ, and it sends a "1" to the decoder when $R > \varrho$. From eq. (VI, 2.20) or eq. (V, 2.8) we see that the decision level ϱ must satisfy the equation

$$\exp\left(-d'^2/2\right) I_0(\varrho) = \zeta_0/\zeta_1. \tag{2.28}$$

The average probability of error in this "unilateral" binary incoherent channel is

$$P_e = \zeta_0 \Pr\{R > \varrho \mid H_0\} + \zeta_1 \Pr\{R < \varrho \mid H_1\}, \tag{2.29}$$

and by using formulas from Chapter V, Section 3 we find

$$P_e = \zeta_0\, e^{-b^2/2} + \zeta_1 Q(d', b), \qquad b = \varrho/d', \tag{2.30}$$

where $Q(\alpha, \beta)$ is again the Q-function. By using eq. (F.12) and eq. (2.28) this expression can be simplified to

$$P_e = \zeta_1 Q(b, d'). \tag{2.31}$$

When $\zeta_0 = \zeta_1 = \frac{1}{2}$, pulses and blanks are being received equally often, and the "average signal-to-noise ratio" is $d_{av} = d'/\sqrt{2}$. If we compare the unilateral channel and the balanced channel, we should equate their average signal-to-noise ratios d_{av} and d, for the average power expended by the transmitter will then be the same for each. The unilateral channel has the smaller probability of error at all signal-to-noise ratios.

The probability of error at high signal-to-noise ratios can be estimated by using the asymptotic forms of the Bessel function and the Q-function. From eq. (2.28) with $\varrho = bd'$, $\zeta_0 = \zeta_1 = \frac{1}{2}$,

$$\exp(d'^2/2) \cong (2\pi bd')^{-\frac{1}{2}} e^{bd'},$$

so that approximately

$$\begin{aligned} b &\cong \tfrac{1}{2}d' + (2d')^{-1} \ln(2\pi bd') \cong \tfrac{1}{2}d' + (2d')^{-1} \ln(\pi d'^2), \\ d' - b &\cong \tfrac{1}{2}d' - (2d')^{-1} \ln(\pi d'^2). \end{aligned}$$

If we put this into the asymptotic form for the Q-function given in eq. (3.16), we obtain for the probability of error, with $d' = d\sqrt{2}$,

$$\begin{aligned} P_e &\cong \frac{1}{2(d'-b)} \sqrt{\frac{d'}{2\pi b}} \exp[-(d'-b)^2/2] \\ &\cong d'^{-1}\pi^{-\frac{1}{2}} \exp\{-\tfrac{1}{2}[\tfrac{1}{4}d'^2 - \tfrac{1}{2}\ln(\pi d'^2)]\} \\ &= (d\sqrt{2\pi})^{-\frac{1}{2}} \exp(-d^2/4). \end{aligned} \tag{2.32}$$

This should be compared with the value $\frac{1}{2}\exp(-d^2/4)$ for the balanced incoherent channel.

3. CHANNELS WITH MORE THAN TWO SIGNALS

In a communication channel using M signals to transmit messages encoded in an alphabet of M symbols, the receiver decides during each observation interval $(0, T)$ which of the signals $f_1(t), f_2(t), \ldots, f_M(t)$ is present in its input $v(t)$. Speaking in the language of hypothesis testing, we say that under hypothesis H_j, the input to the receiver is

$$v(t) = f_j(t) + n(t), \quad j = 1, 2, \ldots, M, \tag{3.1}$$

where $n(t)$ represents random noise of mean value 0. The receiver chooses one of the M hypotheses on the basis of measurements of its input $v(t)$. Having chosen, say, the kth, it sends the kth symbol on to the decoder. The receiver makes an error if it picks any other hypothesis than the correct one, and it is to be designed to make its choices with a minimum average probability of error.

We learned in Chapter III that with two hypotheses, the average probability of error is minimum if the receiver chooses the hypothesis with the greater posterior probability. The same principle can be applied to choices among multiple hypotheses (Woodward and Davies, 1952; Middleton and Van Meter, 1955).

Suppose that the receiver makes n measurements $x_1, x_2, \ldots, x_n$ of its input $v(t)$. We denote them collectively by the vector $\mathbf{x} = (x_1, x_2, \ldots x_n)$. Let $p_j(\mathbf{x})$ be the joint p.d.f. of these data under hypothesis H_j, and let ζ_j be the prior probability of that hypothesis. The ζ_j's are the relative frequencies with which the signals $f_j(t)$ are transmitted, and

$$\sum_{j=1}^{M} \zeta_j = 1. \tag{3.2}$$

The total probability of observing x_1 in (x_1, x_1+dx_1), x_2 in (x_2, x_2+dx_2), and so on, is

$$p(\mathbf{x})\, dx_1\, dx_2 \ldots dx_n = \sum_{j=1}^{M} \zeta_j p_j(\mathbf{x})\, dx_1\, dx_2 \ldots dx_n .$$

The posterior probability that hypothesis H_j is true and signal $f_j(t)$ was transmitted, given the observations $\mathbf{x}$, is then

$$p(H_j \mid \mathbf{x}) = \zeta_j p_j(\mathbf{x}) / p(\mathbf{x}).$$

The receiver chooses H_j if $p(H_j \mid \mathbf{x}) > p(H_i \mid \mathbf{x})$ for all $i \neq j$. Equivalently, it chooses the hypothesis corresponding to the largest value of the product $\zeta_i p_i(\mathbf{x})$, $i = 1, 2, \ldots, M$. We can put this prescription into more convenient form by introducing the p.d.f. $p_0(\mathbf{x})$ of the data $\mathbf{x}$ under a fictitious hypothesis H_0 that no signal at all is present in the input. It makes no difference if we divide all the other p.d.fs by $p_0(\mathbf{x})$, and we can say that hypothesis H_j is chosen if the quantity

$$\zeta_i p_i(\mathbf{x}) / p_0(\mathbf{x}) = \zeta_i \Lambda_i(\mathbf{x}), \qquad i = 1, 2, \ldots, M,$$

is greatest for the jth signal. The function $\Lambda_i(\mathbf{x})$ is the likelihood ratio for detecting the ith signal in the presence of random noise $n(t)$, that is, for choosing between the hypotheses H_0 and H_i, all the others being disregarded.

In terms of these Λ_i's we can make the transition to an infinite number of samples once for all, and we can state that the receiver must choose hypothesis H_j and send symbol j to the decoder if, for all $i \neq j$,

$$\zeta_j \Lambda_j[v(t)] > \zeta_i \Lambda_i[v(t)], \tag{3.3}$$

where $\Lambda_i[v(t)]$ is the likelihood ratio for detecting the ith signal $f_i(t)$ in the presence of the same kind of random noise. When the noise is Gaussian, as we shall assume in the remainder of this chapter, these likelihood ratios can be determined by the methods presented in Chapters IV and V.

(a) *Fully Known Signals*

If the signals as they appear at the input to the receiver are completely known, we can write down the likelihood ratios needed in eq. (3.3) from the results of Chapter IV. We suppose the noise to be stationary with autocovariance function $\phi(\tau)$, and in the usual notation we let $q_i(t)$ be the solution of the integral equation (2.5), in which the index i may run from 1 to M. Then by eq. (IV, 3.13) the ith likelihood ratio is

$$\begin{gathered} \Lambda_i[v(t)] = \exp\left(g_i - \tfrac{1}{2} d_i^2\right), \\ g_i = \int_0^T q_i(t) v(t)\, dt, \qquad d_i^2 = \int_0^T q_i(t) f_i(t)\, dt. \end{gathered} \tag{3.4}$$

The receiver decides that the jth signal is present if the inequality

$$g_j - \tfrac{1}{2} d_j^2 + \ln \zeta_j > g_i - \tfrac{1}{2} d_i^2 + \ln \zeta_i \tag{3.5}$$

holds for all $i \neq j$. As explained in Chapter IV, the quantity g_i is the output at the end of the interval $(0, T)$ of a filter matched to the signal $q_i(t)$.

The probability that a given transmitted signal, say the first, is correctly received is the probability that the $M-1$ quantities

$$t_i = g_1 - g_i + \tfrac{1}{2}(d_i^2 - d_1^2) + \ln(\zeta_1/\zeta_i), \qquad i = 2, 3, \ldots, M \tag{3.6}$$

are all positive. The t_i's are Gaussian random variables with expected values

$$\mathbf{E}(t_i \mid H_1) = \tfrac{1}{2}(d_i^2 - 2d_{i1} + d_1^2) + \ln(\zeta_1/\zeta_i) \tag{3.7}$$

and covariances

$$\{t_i, t_k\} = \varrho_{ik} = d_1^2 - d_{1k} - d_{1i} + d_{ik}, \tag{3.8}$$

where for all i, j the elements of the "signal correlation matrix" are

$$\begin{aligned} d_{ij} &= \int_0^T \int_0^T q_i(t)\, \phi(t-u)\, q_j(u)\, dt\, du, \\ d_{ii} &= d_i^2. \end{aligned} \tag{3.9}$$

The probability Q_1 of correctly choosing hypothesis H_1 is thus

$$Q_1 = \int_0^\infty dt_2 \int_0^\infty dt_3 \ldots \int_0^\infty dt_M p(t_2, t_3, \ldots, t_M), \tag{3.10}$$

where $p(t_2, t_3, \ldots, t_M)$ is an $(M-1)$-dimensional Gaussian density function—like the paradigm in eq. (II, 4.2)—with expected values as in eq. (3.8) and the covariance matrix $||\varrho_{ik}||$ as in eq. (3.9). For $M-1 = 2$, tables are available (National Bureau of Standards, 1959). For $M-1 > 2$ one must resort to numerical integration. The $M-1$ other probabilities $Q_2, Q_3, \ldots, Q_M$ for correctly receiving the remaining signals are similarly calculated. The average probability of error is

$$P_e = 1 - \sum_{j=1}^{M} \zeta_j Q_j.$$

(b) *The Balanced Coherent M-ary Channel*

If the M symbols appear equally often, and if the M signal-to-noise ratios are equal, $d_1 = d_2 = \ldots = d_M = d$, the receiver simply furnishes the decoder with the symbol corresponding to the greatest value of g_i, $i = 1, 2, \ldots, M$, or to the matched filter whose output at the end of the interval $(0, T)$ is largest. When the noise is white, the signals are received with equal energies E, and $d^2 = 2E/N$. An example is a "frequency-shift keying system", in which the signals are narrowband pulses Rl $F(t) \exp i\Omega_j t$ with the same envelope $F(t)$, but different carrier frequencies. For coherent reception the phases of the signals must be precisely known.

If the signals are orthogonal with respect to the kernel $\phi(t-u)$, $d_{ij} = 0$, $i \neq j$. For reception in white noise they are then orthogonal over the interval $(0, T)$ in the usual sense. The probability of mistaking any of these signals for any other is the same for all pairs of signals, and it equals $(M-1)^{-1}$ times the average probability of error. Such an M-ary channel might be called "balanced".

The average probability of correct reception, $1-P_e$, is equal to the probability under hypothesis H_1 that $g_1 > g_j$, for all $j \neq 1$,

$$1-P_e = \Pr\{g_1 > g_j,\ j \neq 1 \mid H_1\} = \int_{-\infty}^{\infty} p_1(g_1)\, dg_1 \left[\int_{-\infty}^{g_1} p_j(g_j)\, dg_j \right]^{M-1}. \tag{3.11}$$

Here $p_1(g_1)$ is the p.d.f. under hypothesis H_1 of the random variable g_1; $p_j(g_j)$ is the p.d.f., also under H_1, of any of the other variables $g_2, g_3, \ldots, g_M$, all of which have the same distribution under these conditions. All the g_i's are Gaussian variables, with expected values under hypothesis H_1 given by

$$\mathbf{E}(g_i \mid H_1) = d^2\delta_{i1} = \begin{cases} d^2, & i = 1, \\ 0, & i \neq 1, \end{cases} \tag{3.12}$$

and with equal variances

$$\operatorname{Var} g_i = d^2. \tag{3.13}$$

Since d_{ij} is assumed equal to 0, $i \neq j$, the g_i's are uncorrelated. Hence their p.d.f.s are

$$\begin{aligned} p_1(g_1) &= (2\pi d^2)^{-\frac{1}{2}} \exp\,[-(g_1 - d^2)^2/2d^2], \\ p_j(g_j) &= (2\pi d^2)^{-\frac{1}{2}} \exp\,(-g_j^2/2d^2), \end{aligned} \tag{3.14}$$

and from eq. (3.11) the probability of error is

$$P_e = 1-(2\pi)^{-\frac{1}{2}} \int_{-\infty}^{\infty} e^{-(x-d)^2/2}(1-\operatorname{erfc} x)^{M-1}\, dx. \tag{3.15}$$

Graphs of the probability P_e of error are given for several values of M by Viterbi (1961). For $M = 2$, as before,

$$P_e = \operatorname{erfc}(d/\sqrt{2}), \tag{3.16}$$

and for $M = 3$,

$$P_e = 2 \operatorname{erfc}(d/\sqrt{2}) - L(d/\sqrt{2}, d/\sqrt{2}, \tfrac{1}{2}), \tag{3.17}$$

where $L(h, k, r)$ is the cumulative bivariate normal distribution, which has been tabulated (National Bureau of Standards, 1959),

$$L(h, k, r) = \frac{1}{2\pi\sqrt{1-r^2}} \int_h^{\infty}\int_k^{\infty} \exp\left(-\frac{x^2+y^2-2rxy}{2(1-r^2)}\right) dx\, dy.$$

For $M > 3$, numerical integration is required.

For large signal-to-noise ratio, $d \gg 1$, an approximate value of the probability of error for the balanced M-ary coherent channel is obtained by expanding the factor $(1-\operatorname{erfc} x)^{M-1}$ in the integrand of eq. (3.15) and keeping only the first two terms,

$$P_e \cong (M-1) \operatorname{erfc}(d/\sqrt{2}) \cong \frac{M-1}{d\sqrt{\pi}} \exp(-d^2/4). \tag{3.18}$$

If the signals are not orthogonal, but happen to have equal correlation coefficients,

$$d_{ij} \equiv \lambda d^2, \quad i \neq j, \quad \text{all } i \text{ and } j,$$

and if $\zeta_j \equiv 1/M$ and $d_j^2 \equiv d^2$, the probability of error is given by a formula quite similar to eq. (3.15),

$$P_e = 1-(2\pi)^{-\frac{1}{2}} \int_{-\infty}^{\infty} e^{-(x-d')^2/2}(1-\text{erfc } x)^{M-1}\, dx, \qquad (3.19)$$
$$d' = d\sqrt{1-\lambda}$$

(Nuttall, 1962). For $M = 2$ the probability obtained from this formula is equal to that given by eq. (2.15).

When there are M signals of this kind available, the smallest possible value of λ is equal to $-(M-1)^{-1}$, as can be shown by an adaptation of the proof by Nuttall (1962). Because of the positive-definiteness of the covariance function $\phi(t-u)$,

$$0 \leqslant \int_0^T \int_0^T \left[\sum_{i=1}^{M} q_i(t)\right] \phi(t-u) \left[\sum_{j=1}^{M} q_j(t)\right] dt\, du$$
$$= \sum_{i=1}^{M} \sum_{j=1}^{M} d_{ij} = Md^2 + M(M-1)\lambda\, d^2,$$

which immediately yields the inequality $\lambda \geqslant -(M-1)^{-1}$.

A set of signals $f_i(t)$ for which the minimum value of λ is attained is said to be "maximally transorthogonal". The probability of error is then given by eq. (3.19) with $d' = d\sqrt{M/(M-1)}$. It is only slightly smaller when $M \gg 1$ than the probability of error for M orthogonal signals, but it represents the minimum possible probability of error among all sets of M signals with equal signal-to-noise ratios d_i and equal relative frequencies ζ_i (Landau and Slepian, 1966). The sum of the signals vanishes, their correlations d_{ij}, $i \neq j$, are equal, and they are said to form a "regular simplex".

Examples of transorthogonal signals composed of trains of positive and negative pulses are given by Baumert (1964). Their design requires choosing the signs of the component pulses of each of the M signals in such a way that the correlations equal $-d^2/(M-1)$. The formation of sets of orthogonal signals from such pulse trains is also described.

(c) *The Incoherent M-ary Channel*

When the signals are narrowband pulses modulating a radio-frequency carrier,

$$f_j(t) = \text{Rl}\, F_j(t) \exp(i\Omega t + i\psi_j), \qquad j = 1, 2, \ldots, M, \qquad (3.20)$$

the phases ψ_j must be known exactly by the receiver in order for the decision schemes of parts (a) and (b) to be optimum or even reliable. For reasons mentioned in Section 2, these phases ψ_j may be unknown, and it is appropriate to describe them as random variables with the least favorable uniform distribution over the interval $(0, 2\pi)$.

If the input to the receiver has a complex envelope $V(t)$, $v(t) = \text{Rl}\, V(t)e^{i\Omega t}$, the posterior probability, given $V(t)$, that the jth signal was transmitted is proportional to the average likelihood ratio

$$\bar{\Lambda}_j[v(t)] = \int_0^{2\pi} \Lambda_j[v(t); \psi]\, d\psi/2\pi \tag{3.21}$$

and to the prior probability ζ_j of hypothesis H_j. Here $\Lambda_j[v(t); \psi]$ is the likelihood ratio for detecting the signal

$$\text{Rl}\, F_j(t) \exp i(\Omega t + \psi)$$

in noise when the phase of the signal is known to be ψ. The receiver picks the signal with the greatest posterior probability, that is, with the greatest value of $\zeta_j \bar{\Lambda}_j[v(t)]$.

The same kind of analysis as in Section 2, part (b), informs us that when the signals arrive in narrowband Gaussian noise of autocovariance $\phi(\tau) = \text{Rl}\, \tilde{\phi}(\tau)\, e^{i\Omega\tau}$, the receiver should base its decisions on the M quantities

$$G_j = \zeta_j \exp(-d_j^2/2)\, I_0(R_j), \qquad j = 1, 2, \ldots, M, \tag{3.22}$$

with

$$d_j^2 = \int_0^T Q_j^*(t)\, F_j(t)\, dt, \qquad R_j = \left| \int_0^T Q_j^*(t)\, V(t)\, dt \right|$$

in the same notation as in eqs. (2.21), (2.22). The quantity R_j is the output, at the end of the interval $(0, T)$, of a linear rectifier following a filter matched to the signal $\text{Rl}\, Q_j(t)\, e^{i\Omega t}$. The receiver sends to the decoder the symbol corresponding to the largest of the M statistics G_j. As the reader can well imagine, it is in general hardly possible to express the probabilities of error of such a receiver in terms of ordinary functions.

If the signals occur equally often, $\zeta_j \equiv 1/M$, and arrive at the receiver with equal signal-to-noise ratios $d_j \equiv d$, the symbol issued by the receiver is determined simply by the largest of the rectified outputs R_j. If the signals are also orthogonal,

$$\int_0^T \int_0^T Q_i^*(t)\, \tilde{\phi}(t-u)\, Q_j(u)\, dt\, du = 0, \qquad i \neq j,$$

it is even possible to calculate the probability of error P_e. The outputs R_j are then statistically independent, and any signal has the same probability of being mistaken for any other. This channel might be labeled "balanced, incoherent, and M-ary". A formula much like eq. (3.11) holds, and we leave it to the reader to show that the probability of error is

$$\begin{aligned} P_e &= 1 - \int_0^\infty x(1-e^{-x^2/2})^{M-1}\, e^{-(x^2+d^2)/2} I_0(dx)\, dx \\ &= \frac{1}{M} \sum_{r=2}^{M} (-1)^r \binom{M}{r} e^{-(r-1)d^2/2r} \end{aligned} \tag{3.23}$$

(Reiger, 1958). For $M = 2$ this reduces to eq. (2.26).

For $M = 2$ correlated signals can be treated as shown in Section 2. Nuttall (1962) has dealt with the reception of signals for which all the correlations

$$\int_0^T \int_0^T Q_i^*(t)\, \tilde{\phi}(t-u)\, Q_j(u)\, dt\, du$$

are real and, for $i \neq j$, equal to a common value λd^2. He showed that the probability of correctly receiving each signal is given by the double integral

$$\begin{aligned} 1 - P_e = (1-\lambda)\, e^{-d^2/2} \int_0^\infty \int_0^\infty xy\, e^{-(x^2+y^2)/2} \cdot \\ I_0(d\sqrt{1-\lambda}x)\, I_0(\sqrt{\lambda}xy) \left[1 - Q(y\sqrt{\lambda}, x)\right]^{M-1} dx\, dy, \end{aligned} \tag{3.24}$$

where $Q(\alpha, \beta)$ is the Q-function. For $\lambda = 0$ this reduces to eq. (3.23).

4. THE RECEPTION OF OVERLAPPING PULSES

It is not always possible to keep the successive signals in a channel completely apart; the tail of each pulse may overlap one or more succeeding pulses, a condition known as "intersymbol interference". If the signal-to-noise ratio is high, the receiver can compensate by taking each of its decisions as correct, generating the remaining portion of each presumptive signal, and subtracting it from the input during the subsequent intervals. If the signal-to-noise ratio is so low that there is a significant probability of error, however, this procedure may be detrimental.

To see how detection theory can furnish a better scheme, let us consider a binary channel carrying "on–off" signals that are received in the presence of Gaussian noise. Every T seconds the transmitter sends the signal $f(t)$ when a "1" occurs in the output of the encoder; it sends nothing when a "0" occurs. The receiver decides about each transmitted signal T seconds after it begins arriving, but it bases its decision on its input received not only during the past T seconds, but also during M previous intervals; and it uses altogether $(M+1)T$ seconds of its input $v(t)$ for each decision. If the pulses die out rapidly, it may suffice to take $M = 1$; if the tail of each pulse survives through several intervals, M will have to be somewhat larger.

For definiteness we take the origin of time at the instant the pulse in question, if transmitted, will begin to arrive, and the input $v(t)$ from the interval $-MT < t < T$ is to be used. The receiver now has to take account of the 2^{M+1} sequences that may possibly have appeared during that interval. In deciding whether the most recent symbol was a "0" or a "1", it forms from the input $v(t)$ a likelihood ratio that includes in both numerator and denominator an average over the 2^M sequences that may have preceded the symbol in question. Only a single likelihood ratio is necessary because the receiver makes a binary decision, choosing between two hypotheses, (H_0) "the most recent symbol is a '0'", and (H_1) "the most recent symbol is a '1'".

We shall label the 2^M combinations of previous symbols by an index m, running from 1 to 2^M; these combinations can be arranged in any fixed order. Let $s_{1m}(t)$ be the received signal for the mth sequence of $(M+1)$ symbols, the last of which is a "1"; and let $s_{0m}(t)$ be the signal for the mth sequence ending in a "0". For instance, a list of sequences for $M = 2$ is

m	s_{0m}	s_{1m}	n_m
1	000	001	2
2	010	011	1
3	100	101	1
4	110	111	0

The prior probability of the mth sequence is

$$p_m = \zeta^{n_m}(1-\zeta)^{M-n_m},$$

where ζ and $(1-\zeta)$ are the relative frequencies of "0"s and "1"s, respectively, and n_m is the number of "0"s occurring in the mth sequence, not including the final symbol, about which the decision is to be made. The table lists values of n_m for the given arrangement of sequences.

The likelihood ratio upon which the receiver bases its decision about the most recent symbol can be written down by means of eq. (V, 1.8), if we regard the M preceding symbols as forming a discrete set of parameters $\boldsymbol{\theta}$ specifying the received signals and the associated probability distributions for the input $v(t)$. The prior p.d.f.s $z_0(\boldsymbol{\theta})$ and $z_1(\boldsymbol{\theta})$ in eq. (V, 1.8) are replaced by the prior probabilities p_m of the 2^M sets of signal parameters. Thus the likelihood ratio is

$$\Lambda[v(t)] = \frac{\sum_{m=1}^{2^M} p_m W_{1m} \exp g_{1m}}{\sum_{m=1}^{2^M} p_m W_{0m} \exp g_{0m}},$$

$$W_{im} = \exp\left(-\tfrac{1}{2} d_{im}^2\right), \qquad i = 0, 1, \tag{4.1}$$

$$g_{im} = \int_{-MT}^{T} q_{im}(t)\, v(t)\, dt, \qquad i = 0, 1,$$

where in notation that must by now be familiar, $q_{im}(t)$ is the solution of the integral equation

$$s_{im}(t) = \int_{-MT}^{T} \phi(t-u)\, q_{im}(u)\, du, \qquad -MT < t < T, \quad i = 0, 1, \tag{4.2}$$

whose kernel is the autocovariance of the noise. The signal-to-noise ratio d_{im} for the mth message under hypothesis H_i is given by

$$d_{im}^2 = \int_{-MT}^{T} q_{im}(t)\, s_{im}(t)\, dt, \qquad i = 0, 1. \tag{4.3}$$

The numerator and the denominator of $\Lambda[v(t)]$ in eq. (4.1) contain a term for each possible combination of the M previous symbols, and each term is multiplied by the prior probability p_m of the combination.

The quantity g_{im} is the output at time $t = T$ of a filter matched to the signal $q_{im}(t)$, which extends over an interval of $(M+1)T$ seconds. The receiver forms the likelihood ratio $\Lambda[v(t)]$ as a nonlinear function of the g_{0m}'s and g_{1m}'s, comparing it with a decision level $\Lambda_0 = (\zeta/1-\zeta)$. If the decision level is exceeded, the receiver sends a "1" to the decoder; otherwise it sends a "0".

The matched filters can be constructed as parallel banks of filters matched to signals $s(t)$ arriving in each of the $(M+1)$ intervals preceding the time of decision. The kth of these component filters is matched to the solution $q_k(t)$ of the integral equation

$$\int_{-MT}^{T} \phi(t-u)\, q_k(u)\, du = \begin{cases} s(t+kT), & -kT < t < T \\ 0, & -MT < t < -kT. \end{cases} \tag{4.4}$$

Its impulse response $K_k(\tau) = q_k(T-\tau)$ is the solution of the integral equation

$$\int_0^{(M+1)T} K_k(\tau)\,\phi(\tau-v)\,d\tau = \begin{cases} s[(k+1)\,T-v], & 0 < v < (k+1)T \\ 0, & (k+1)\,T < v < (M+1)\,T. \end{cases} \tag{4.5}$$

The filters matched to the various $q_{0m}(t)$ and $q_{1m}(t)$ are made up in the following way. If the mth sequence contains $(M-n_m)$ "1"s, the filter matched to $q_{0m}(t)$ consists of $(M-n_m)$ parallel filters $K_k(\tau)$, one for each "1" in the sequence. The filter $K_k(\tau)$ is used when a "1" appears in the place corresponding to the kth previous interval. The matched filter for $q_{1m}(t)$ is composed of the same $(M-n_m)$ filters, with an additional one of impulse response $K_0(\tau)$ in parallel. Referring to the table for the case $M = 2$, we see that the filter matched to $q_{14}(t)$ consists of K_0, K_1, and K_2 in parallel; the one matched to $q_{02}(t)$ has only K_1. There is no filter for the sequence "000"; in its place eq. (4.1) specifies that the constant amount ζ^2 be added to the denominator of the likelihood ratio.

A block diagram of such a system, using two previous pulse intervals, is shown in Fig. VI. 2. Although with proper interconnections the same filter

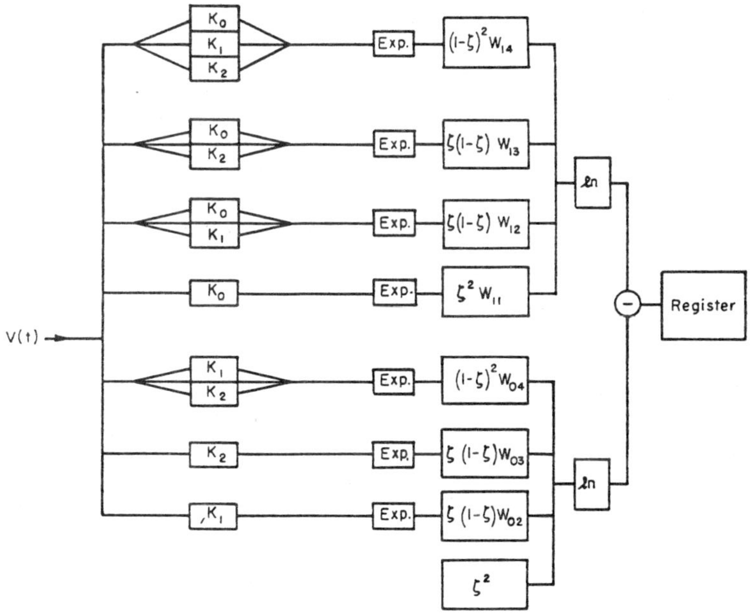

FIG. VI.2. A receiver taking account of interference by two previous signals.

$K_k(\tau)$ could be used in several branches of the receiver, this refinement has been avoided for the sake of clarity. The blocks marked "exp" form the exponential function of their input, and the blocks following them introduce the weighting factors p_m and $W_{im} = \exp\left(-\frac{1}{2} d_{im}^2\right)$. The block marked "ln" takes the logarithm of its input; the two logarithms are subtracted. The "register" samples the net output at the end of each interval and compares it with the decision level $\ln(\zeta/1-\zeta)$; if the sample is the larger, the register issues the symbol "1", otherwise the symbol "0". Among all systems taking into account $M = 2$ previous pulse intervals, this system will yield the minimum average probability of error. As M increases, the probability of error decreases.

A system with a probability of error even smaller could be designed by delaying the decision about a given symbol for some M' intervals and using additional information about the input. The length of the observation interval would then be $(M+M'+1)T$. The decision would be based on a likelihood ratio of the same nature as that in eq. (4.1); it would only be necessary also to take into account all possible combinations of symbols in the M' intervals following the one in question. For all such systems the probability of error is extremely difficult to calculate because of the nonlinearity of the operations performed on the input. Other ways of treating intersymbol interference have been discussed by Tufts (1965).

In a system utilizing quasiharmonic pulses, the transmitter may be able to maintain coherence between successive signals, but the delay between it and the receiver may not be known accurately enough to provide the receiver with a precise value of the phase of the carrier. The entire sequence of, say, $(M+1)$ pulses and blanks can then be considered as a narrowband signal

$$s_{jm}(t) = \mathrm{Rl}\, S_{jm}(t)\, e^{i\Omega t + i\psi}, \qquad j = 0, 1,$$

with a single unknown phase ψ. If this phase is assigned the least favorable prior p.d.f. $\tilde{z}(\psi) = 1/2\pi$, $0 \leqslant \psi < 2\pi$, the optimum decision statistic for the receiver can be found by replacing the numerator and denominator of eq. (4.1) by their proper forms for narrowband signals, as in eq. (V, 2.5), and averaging each over the phase ψ. The resulting average likelihood ratio is

$$\Lambda[v(t)] = \frac{\sum_{m=1}^{2M} p_m W_{1m} I_0(R_{1m})}{\sum_{m=1}^{2M} p_m W_{0m} I_0(R_{0m})}. \tag{4.6}$$

Here R_{jm}, $j = 0, 1$, is the rectified output at time $t = T$ of a filter matched to the signal

$$q_{jm}(t) = \text{Rl}\, Q_{jm}(t)\, e^{i\Omega t},$$

where $Q_{jm}(t)$ is the solution of the integral equation

$$S_{jm}(t) = \int_{-MT}^{T} \tilde{\phi}(t-u)\, Q_{jm}(u)\, du, \qquad -MT < t < T,$$

whose kernel is the complex autocovariance function $\tilde{\phi}(\tau)$ of the noise. The only change in the receiver of Fig. VI.2 is a replacement of each block marked "exp" with a rectifier whose output is $I_0(|W(t)|)$ for a quasiharmonic input $w(t) = \text{Rl}\, W(t)e^{i\Omega t}$. The net output of the system is sampled every T seconds by the register, which compares the samples with the decision level $\ln(\zeta/1-\zeta)$ and issues the appropriate symbols. This system also could use the input over a longer interval of duration $(M+M'+1)T$ to decide about a given symbol on the basis of the input both before and after the symbol arrived. In the limit $M \to \infty$, $M' \to \infty$ the receiver would be using all available information and would attain the minimum possible average probability of error.

A satellite transmitting on–off pulses might be able to maintain phase coherence for a period of time containing many signals, and if the velocity of the satellite relative to the receiver were known accurately enough to permit compensating for the Doppler shift of the carrier frequency Ω, the receiver could take the phase ψ of the carrier of a long string of pulses as a single unknown parameter. It could then use the method just described for deciding about each transmitted symbol. However, when M and M' are very large, the number of combinations of matched filters needed would be so huge that such a receiver would be prohibitively expensive. Detection theory prescribes the structure of the optimum receiver, but it does not guarantee that the receiver will be cheap.

Contemporary receivers of coherent signals from satellites track the phase of the incoming carrier by means of a "phase-locked loop". A nonlinear device yields an output voltage proportional to the deviation between the phases of the incoming carrier and a locally generated sinusoid. This voltage is applied to a voltage-controlled oscillator in such a way as to drive its phase toward that of the incoming carrier. In effect the system measures the phases of the received signals.

The measurement of the phase of each signal may be in error, however, because of the noise. The resulting uncertainty of the phase ψ can be expressed by a prior probability density function $z(\psi)$ of the value of ψ. Viterbi (1963) showed that for a simple type of phase-locked loop this prior p.d.f.

is given by

$$z(\psi) = [2\pi I_0(\alpha)]^{-1} \exp(\alpha \cos \psi), \qquad 0 \leqslant \psi < 2\pi,$$

the true phase being taken as $\psi = 0$. Here α is a parameter measuring the signal-to-noise ratio of the phase-locked loop; the greater α, the smaller the uncertainty of the phase ψ.

Viterbi (1965) has proposed that the receiver form an average likelihood ratio using this prior p.d.f. for the phase ψ. For detection in white noise of unilateral spectral density N, the average likelihood ratio is, by eq. (V, 2.5) with $Q(t) = F(t)/N$,

$$\bar{\Lambda}[v(t)] = \int_0^{2\pi} z(\psi) \exp\left[\mathrm{Rl}\, Re^{i(\beta-\psi)} - \tfrac{1}{2} d^2\right] d\psi,$$

where $V(t)$ is the complex envelope of the input, and

$$Re^{i\beta} = N^{-1} \int_0^T F^*(t)\, V(t)\, dt, \qquad d^2 = 2E/N = N^{-1} \int_0^T |F(t)|^2\, dt.$$

After carrying out the integration, one finds

$$\bar{\Lambda}[V(t)] = e^{-d^2/2} I_0(|Re^{i\beta} + \alpha|).$$

Thus the receiver can make its decision by comparing the quantity $Z = |Re^{i\beta} + \alpha|$ with a decision level Z_0 determined by the equation

$$e^{-d^2/2} I_0(Z_0) = \zeta/(1-\zeta).$$

It sends a "0" to the decoder when $Z < Z_0$, a "1" when $Z > Z_0$.

The receiver can form the statistic Z by adding a sinusoid of amplitude α and the proper phase, determined by the phase-locked loop, to the output of a filter matched to the signal $F(t)/N$. The sum is applied to a linear rectifier, whose output is sampled at the end of each interval $(0, T)$ and compared with a decision level Z_0. Details of this system with calculations and graphs of its average probability of error have been presented by Viterbi (1965). He has treated not only on–off signals, but also signals of equal energy with an arbitrary correlation coefficient, a special instance of which is a pair of orthogonal signals. A comprehensive study of phase-locked receivers is given by Viterbi (1966).

PROBLEMS

1. In a frequency-shift keying system the signals have the form Rl $F(t) \exp i\Omega_j t$, $j = 1, 2, \ldots, M$, with the same complex envelope, but different carrier frequencies. Express the elements of the signal correlation matrix in terms of the spectrum of $F(t)$, taking the noise to be white.

2. A ternary communication system transmits one of three signals $f(t)$, 0, or $-f(t)$ every T seconds. They are received with energy E or energy 0 in white Gaussian noise of spectral density N. At the end of each interval $(0, T)$ the output x of a filter matched to $f(t)$ is measured and compared with thresholds $+a$ and $-a$. If $x > a$, the decision is made that $+f(t)$ was sent; if $x < -a$, that $-f(t)$ was sent; and if $-a < x < a$, that 0 was sent. What is the average probability Q_r of correct reception as a function of a, E, and N when all three signals are sent equally often? What is the maximum possible value of Q_r and for what value of a is it attained?

3. A quaternary communication system transmits every T seconds one of four signals,

$$A = +f_1(t), \quad B = -f_1(t), \quad C = +f_2(t), \quad D = -f_2(t).$$

The signals are orthogonal,

$$\int_0^T f_1(t) f_2(t)\, dt = 0,$$

and are received with equal energies in white, Gaussian noise. The receiver has filters matched to $f_1(t)$ and $f_2(t)$ and observes their outputs y_1 and y_2 at the end of each interval $(0, T)$. It decides about the received signals by the following scheme:

$$y_1 > |y_2| \to A; \qquad y_1 < -|y_2| \to B; \qquad y_2 > |y_1| \to C; \qquad y_2 < -|y_1| \to D.$$

Calculate as a function of the signal-to-noise ratio the probability of correctly receiving each signal.

4. A quaternary communication system transmits every T seconds one of four signals,

$$A = a_1 f(t), \quad B = a_2 f(t), \quad C = -a_2 f(t), \quad D = -a_1 f(t), \quad 0 < a_2 < a_1.$$

The signals are sent with equal relative frequencies. They are received with a common attenuation μ in the presence of white Gaussian noise of spectral density N; i.e., if A is sent, $\mu a_1 f(t)$ is received, and so on. At the end of each interval $(0, T)$ the output y of a filter matched to $f(t)$ is compared with three thresholds b, 0, and $-b$, and the decisions about the transmitted signals are made on the basis of the scheme:

$$y > b \to A; \qquad 0 < y < b \to B; \qquad -b < y < 0 \to C; \qquad y < -b \to D.$$

Calculate the average probability of correct reception of the signals and choose the value of b that maximizes it. Show how you would determine the values of the amplitudes a_1 and a_2 to make this maximum probability of correct reception as large as possible under the constraint of fixed average transmitter power.

5. In an M-ary balanced channel one of M orthogonal signals is transmitted every T seconds with relative frequency $1/M$. The signals are received with energy E in white Gaussian noise of spectral density N, but with an unknown phase that can be taken as uniformly distributed over $(0, 2\pi)$. There is a possibility that fading might destroy the signals, and to indicate this a null-zone is provided in the decision mechanism (Bloom *et al.*, 1957). The rectified outputs of filters matched to each of the signals are compared at the end of each interval $(0, T)$, and the receiver sends to the decoder the symbol corresponding to the filter whose rectified output is the greatest, except that if all the outputs fall below a certain amplitude a, the receiver indicates an "erasure" E. Calculate the probabilities that the transmitted signal is correctly received, that an erasure is indicated, and that an incorrect symbol is sent on to the decoder.

BIBLIOGRAPHY (VI)

1948 SHANNON, C., "A Mathematical Theory of Communication", *Bell Sys. Tech. J.* **27**, 379–423 (July), 623–56 (Oct.).

1952 WOODWARD, P. M. and DAVIES, I. L., "Information Theory and Inverse Probability in Telecommunication", *Proc. I.E.E.* **99** (III), 37–44 (Mar.).

1955 MIDDLETON, D. and VAN METER, D., "On Optimum Multiple-alternative Detection of Signals in Noise", *Trans. I.R.E.* **IT-1**, no. 2, 1–9 (Sept.).

1956 SLEPIAN, D. "A Class of Binary Signaling Alphabets", *Bell Sys. Tech. J.* **35**, 203–34 (Jan.).

1957 BLOOM, F. J., CHANG, S. S. S. L., HARRIS, B., HAUPTSCHEIN, A. and MORGAN, K. C., "Improvement of Binary Transmission by Null-zone Reception", *Proc. I.R.E.* **45**, 963–75 (July).

1958 REIGER, S., "Error Rates in Data Transmission", *Proc. I.R.E.* **46**, 919–20 (May).

1959 NATIONAL BUREAU OF STANDARDS, *Tables of the Bivariate Normal Distribution*, NBS Appl. Math. Series no. 50, U.S. Government Printing Office, Washington, D.C.

1961 VITERBI, A. J., "On Coded Phase-coherent Communication", *Trans. I.R.E.* **SET-7**, 3–14 (Mar.).

1962 ARTHURS, E. and DYM, H., "On the Optimum Detection of Digital Signals in the Presence of White, Gaussian Noise—A Geometric Interpretation and a Study of Three Basic Data Transmission Systems", *Trans. I.R.E.* **CS-10**, 336–72 (Dec.).

NUTTALL, A. H., "Error Probabilities for Equicorrelated *M*-ary Signals under Phase-coherent and Phase-incoherent Reception", *Trans. I.R.E.* **IT–8**, 305–14 (July).

THOMAS, J. B. and WOLF, J. K., "On the Statistical Detection Problem for Multiple Signals", *Trans. I.R.E.* **IT-8**, 274–80 (July).

1963 VITERBI, A. J., "Phase-locked Loop Dynamics in the Presence of Noise by Fokker–Planck Techniques", *Proc. I.E.E.E.* **51**, 1735–53 (Dec.).

1964 BAUMERT, L. D., "Codes with Special Correlation", in *Digital Communications with Space Applications*, S. W. GOLOMB, ed., Prentice-Hall, Inc., Englewood Cliffs, N.J. pp. 47–64.

1965 TUFTS, D. W., "Nyquist's Problem—The Joint Optimization of Transmitter and Receiver in Pulse-Amplitude Modulations", *Proc. I.E.E.E.* **53**, 248–59 (Mar.)

VITERBI, A. J., "Optimum Detection and Signal Selection for Partially Coherent Binary Communication", *Trans. I.E.E.E.* **IT-11**, 239–46 (Apr.).

1966 LANDAU, H. J. and SLEPIAN, D., "On the Optimality of the Regular Simplex Code", *Bell Sys. Tech. J.* **45**, 1247–72 (Oct.).

VITERBI, A. J., *Principles of Coherent Communication*, McGraw-Hill Book Co., New York, N.Y.

VII
DETECTION BY MULTIPLE OBSERVATIONS

1. DETECTION OF A FIXED NUMBER OF SIGNALS

(a) *Multiple Signals in Radar and Communications*

Radar detection of a fixed target at a given range has been treated as a matter of deciding whether an echo signal of specified form is present in the input $v(t)$ to the receiver during a certain interval of time after an electromagnetic pulse has been transmitted toward the location in question. How the receiver should process its input $v(t)$ in order to make that decision most efficiently has been described in Chapters IV and V. Usually, however, a radar sends more than one pulse in the direction of a possible target, and the presence of a target is indicated by a train of echo signals appearing in the input to the receiver. If there is no target, the input contains only random noise.

Let M be the number of echoes expected, and represent them by the functions $s_k(t)$, $k = 1, 2, \ldots, M$. In the simplest situation of a fixed target at a given location, the input to the receiver is observed during a limited interval of duration T seconds following each transmitted pulse. The kth signal $s_k(t)$ will appear at a known time during the kth interval, and we can begin by assuming that it is known completely except, perhaps, for the phase of its high-frequency carrier. If we denote the input during the kth interval by $v_k(t)$, and the noise during that interval by $n_k(t)$, we can say that the receiver is confronted with two hypotheses between which to choose, $(H_0)\, v_k(t) = n_k(t)$, $k = 1, \ldots, M$, and $(H_1)\, v_k(t) = s_k(t)+n_k(t)$, $k = 1, \ldots, M$. The hypothesis H_1 is composite when the phases ψ_k of the M signals are unknown. In more complicated situations still other parameters of the signals may be known imprecisely or not at all.

In most radars the antenna rotates at a constant rate, and a given location is irradiated with pulses whose amplitudes follow the gain pattern of the transmitting antenna. If the same antenna is used for reception, the amplitudes of the echo signals will suffer an attenuation varying in accordance with the same pattern. Only a certain number of the echoes will provide a high enough signal-to-noise ratio to warrant attention by the system, and these are the M signals we shall deal with here.

It is possible, however, to move an antenna beam electronically rather than mechanically. The delays or phase shifts in the lines to a number of elements of the antenna can be changed rapidly and by just the right amounts to make the beam move as desired by the radar observer or his electronic counterpart. This flexibility makes it possible to control the number M of pulses transmitted toward a given location. In particular, the system can judge at any time whether it has enough information to make a reliable decision about the presence or the absence of a target, or whether it should send additional pulses in the same direction. A detection system that determines the number of its observations according to what it receives is said to operate *sequentially*. Sequential detection will be introduced in Section 3.

Although this discussion has been in terms of radar, these methods can also be applied to communications. A communication system sending messages coded in binary symbols might repeat each signal, $f_0(t)$ or $f_1(t)$, a fixed number of times as a simple way of increasing the probability that the "0" or the "1" will be correctly received. Alternatively, a feedback channel that is free or nearly free of noise might be used to control the number of times the transmitter sends each signal, with the receiver instructing the transmitter to go on to the next symbol in the message as soon as it considers its decision about the present symbol sufficiently reliable.

We shall speak of the M inputs $v_k(t)$ as if they appeared at the same receiver one after another, but they can alternatively be interpreted as simultaneous inputs to M different receivers. These receivers, which might be located in different places or be tuned to different frequencies, are directed to pick up a set of signals $s_k(t)$ that are either present or absent together. "Diversity" communication systems to combat fading or sporadic interference employ such multiple receivers, and the problem of how best to process their inputs to decide whether they contain the set $\{s_k(t)\}$ or not can be treated by methods related to those we shall now describe. Diversity techniques have been reviewed by Stein (1966).

(b) *The Likelihood-ratio Receiver*

By processing its inputs $v_k(t)$ during M observation intervals of duration T seconds, the receiver is to choose between the two hypotheses H_0 and H_1 just mentioned. The signals $s_k(t)$ are narrowband pulse modulations of a carrier of frequency Ω,

$$\begin{aligned} s(t;\,\psi_k) &= A_k \text{ Rl } F(t) \exp i(\Omega t+\psi_k), \\ 0 < t < T, &\qquad k = 1, 2, \ldots, M. \end{aligned} \tag{1.1}$$

For convenience we measure the time from the beginning of each interval (0, T). The complex envelope $F(t)$, the carrier frequency Ω, and the M amplitudes A_k are assumed known. The phases ψ_k, however, are unknown, and they are assumed to change in a random way from signal to signal, either because the erratic motions of the radar target change its distance by amounts of the order of a wavelength or more, or because the transmitted pulses are incoherent.

If the target is fixed, or moves with a known, constant velocity, and if an effort is made to control the phases of successive transmitted pulses, the target echoes $s_k(t;\,\psi_k)$ will be coherent, and the phases will not be independent. In that event the total signal $s_1(t)+s_2(t)+\ \ldots\ +s_M(t)$ can be treated as a single signal, and the methods of Chapter V can be applied. The observation interval is merely divided into a set of disconnected parts.

Here it will be assumed that the M phases ψ_k are statistically independent random variables, uniformly distributed over the range $0 \leqslant \psi_k < 2\pi$, as in eq. (V, 2.3). This is apparently the least favorable distribution, for any more detailed knowledge of the phases could be used to improve the detection of the signals.

Successive observation intervals are assumed to be far enough apart that the noise components $n_k(t)$ in each are statistically independent. For this it is only necessary that the time from the end of one interval to the beginning of the next be much longer than the correlation time of the noise. In terms of the complex envelopes $V_k(t)$ of the inputs $v_k(t) = \text{Rl } V_k(t)e^{i\Omega t}$ to the receiver during the M intervals, the likelihood ratio upon which the receiver is to base its decision can then be written down as the product of likelihood ratios of the form given in eq. (V, 2.5),

$$\begin{aligned} \Lambda_1[v(t)] = \prod_{k=1}^{M} \int_0^{2\pi} \exp \Big[A_k \text{ Rl} \exp(-i\psi_k) \int_0^T Q^*(t)\, V_k(t)\, dt \\ -\tfrac{1}{2} A_k^2 \int_0^T Q^*(t)\, F(t)\, dt \Big]\, d\psi_k, \end{aligned} \tag{1.2}$$

where $Q(t)$ is the solution of the integral equation

$$F(t) = \int_0^T \tilde{\phi}(t-u)\, Q(u)\, du, \qquad 0 < t < T, \tag{1.3}$$

whose kernel is the complex autocovariance $\tilde{\phi}(\tau)$ of the noise. This likeli-hood ratio has been averaged over the prior p.d.f.s of the random phases ψ_k. Upon carrying out the integrations we find as before that the average likelihood ratio is

$$\Lambda_1[v(t)] = \prod_{k=1}^{M} \exp(-D_k^2/2)\, I_0(D_k r_k), \tag{1.4}$$

where

$$r_k = \left| \int_0^T Q^*(t)\, V_k(t)\, dt \right| \cdot \left| \int_0^T Q^*(t)\, F(t)\, dt \right|^{-1/2} \tag{1.5}$$

is proportional to the linearly rectified output, at the end of the kth interval, of a filter matched to the signal Rl $Q(t)e^{i\Omega t}$. Here we introduced the signal-to-noise ratios D_k defined by

$$D_k^2 = A_k^2 \int_0^T Q^*(t)\, F(t)\, dt, \tag{1.6}$$

and for white noise of unilateral spectral density N,

$$D_k^2 = 2E_k/N,$$

where E_k is the energy of the kth signal.

The average likelihood ratio Λ_1 is to be compared with a fixed critical value Λ_0; if $\Lambda_1 < \Lambda_0$, the receiver decides that no signal is present. This procedure is equivalent to computing the logarithm of the likelihood ratio

$$\ln \Lambda_1 = \sum_{k=1}^{M} \ln I_0(D_k r_k) - \tfrac{1}{2} \sum_{k=1}^{M} D_k^2 \tag{1.7}$$

and comparing it with the decision level $\ln \Lambda_0$. Under the Neyman–Pearson criterion this decision level must be chosen to yield a preassigned false alarm probability.

The decision statistic $\ln \Lambda_1$ can be generated by amplifying the output of the matched filter during the kth interval by a factor proportional to the kth signal-to-noise ratio D_k and applying it to a rectifier whose characteristic is $\ln I_0(x)$, by which we mean that its output is $\ln I_0(|W(t)|)$ when its input is Rl $W(t)e^{i\Omega t}$. The outputs of the rectifier are sampled at the end of each interval, and the samples are summed and compared with the decision level

$$\ln \Lambda_0 + \tfrac{1}{2} \sum_{k=1}^{M} D_k^2 .$$

If the sum exceeds the decision level, an alarm indicates the decision that the train of signals arrived. Because of the non-linearity of the function n $I_0(x)$, it is very difficult to determine the false-alarm and detection probabilities for such a detector.

In Fig. VII.1 is shown the form of the rectifier characteristic $y = \ln I_0(x)$. For small values of x,

$$\ln I_0(x) = \tfrac{1}{4}x^2 - \tfrac{1}{64}x^4 + O(x^6), \tag{1.8}$$

and for large values

$$\ln I_0(x) = x - \tfrac{1}{2}\ln(2\pi x) + (8x)^{-1} + O(x^{-2}). \tag{1.9}$$

Hence for small values of $D_k r_k$ the optimum detector uses a rectifier that s nearly a quadratic device; for large values the rectifier is nearly a linear

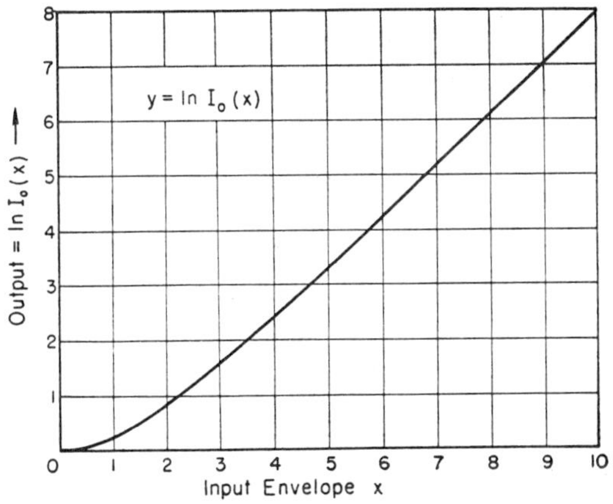

FIG. VII.1. Optimum rectifier characteristic.

one. This type of detector was derived by Marcum (1948), and its use has been discussed by Woodward and Davies (1950), Middleton (1953), Fleishman (1957), and others.

This detection system depends rigidly on the values of the signal amplitudes A_k. Even if they are all equal, it is necessary to know their common value. The system cannot provide a test for hypothesis H_0 versus hypothesis H_1 that is uniformly most powerful with respect to the amplitudes of the signal.

(c) *The Threshold Detector*

If the signal amplitudes are unknown, there are two courses the designer can follow. The first is to pick a typical set of amplitudes as specifying a standard set of signals for which the detector is to be optimum. The form of the detector is then given by eq. (1.4). The probability of detecting signals with some other set of amplitudes will be less than it might have been, had the amplitudes been known in advance, but the loss will in most cases not be serious.

A second course is to choose a joint probability density function $z(D_1, D_2, \ldots, D_M)$ for the signal-to-noise ratios and to have the receiver base its decisions on an average likelihood ratio

$$\Lambda_2 = \int_0^\infty dD_1 \ldots \int_0^\infty dD_M \, z(D_1, \ldots, D_M) \prod_{k=1}^{M} I_0(D_k r_k) \exp\left(-\tfrac{1}{2}D_k^2\right). \quad (1.10)$$

If the signals to be detected are communication signals that have passed through a fading channel, for instance, such a joint p.d.f. may be derivable from the nature of the channel. Alternatively, the least favorable distribution may be sought.

Detection is most difficult when the amplitudes A_k are all very small. Approaching the least favorable condition of vanishingly small amplitudes, we expand the product of exponential and Bessel functions in eq. (1.10), keeping only terms of second order in the amplitudes,

$$I_0(Dr) \exp\left(-\tfrac{1}{2}D^2\right) \doteq 1 + \tfrac{1}{4}(r^2-2)D^2.$$

Still neglecting terms of fourth order, we write

$$\prod_{k=1}^{M} I_0(D_k r_k) \exp\left(-\tfrac{1}{2}D_k^2\right) \doteq 1 + \tfrac{1}{4} \sum_{k=1}^{M} D_k^2(r_k^2-2).$$

Putting this into eq. (1.10) and denoting by $\langle D_k^2 \rangle$ the mean-square value of the kth signal-to-noise ratio, we find for the average likelihood ratio the approximate form

$$\Lambda_2 \doteq 1 + \tfrac{1}{4} \sum_{k=1}^{M} \langle D_k^2 \rangle (r_k^2-2), \quad \langle D_k^2 \rangle = \int_0^\infty D_k^2 \, z(D_k) \, dD_k. \quad (1.11)$$

If the signals to be detected are the M repetitions of a pulse conveying the symbol "1" of a binary message, and if these signals are perturbed by rapid, erratic fading during transmission, there is nothing to distinguish one signal from another, and their mean-square signal-to-noise ratios will be equal. The same will be true of the radar echoes from a rapidly fluctuating target when the antenna irradiating it is stationary. The average likelihood ratio in eq. (1.11) then depends on the input only through the threshold statistic

$$L = \sum_{k=1}^{M} r_k^2. \quad (1.12)$$

'he threshold detector contains a filter matched to the signal Rl $Q(t)e^{i\Omega t}$, 'hose output is applied to a quadratic rectifier. The output of the rectifier sampled at the end of each interval of duration T, and the sample values r_k^2 are summed to form the statistic L, which is compared with a decision :vel L_0 to decide whether the sequence of pulses is present or not. The alue of L_0 is chosen to produce a specified false-alarm probability.

If, on the other hand, the signals are echoes from a fixed target of onstant reflectivity, past which the antenna is rotating, the mean-square gnal-to-noise ratios $\langle D_k^2 \rangle$ will be proportional to a function representing ıe combined gains of the radar antenna on transmission and reception,

$$\langle D_k^2 \rangle = \langle D^2 \rangle f(\theta_k), \tag{1.13}$$

here θ_k is the azimuth of the antenna at the time the kth echo is received, ıeasured with respect to the azimuth of the target. The values of the beam factor" $f(\theta)$, if known, could be used to calculate an improved etection statistic of the form

$$L' = \sum_{k=1}^{M} f(\theta_k) r_k^2 .$$

requires more to be known about the signals $s_k(t)$ than the sum of quares in eq. (1.12). If the energies of the signals truly are proportional $f(\theta_k)$ as in eq. (1.13), the statistic L' will detect the train of signals more :liably than the statistic L of eq. (1.12).

2. DETECTION PROBABILITY OF THE QUADRATIC THRESHOLD DETECTOR

ı) *Exact Expressions*

The threshold detector proposed in the previous section involves passing ıe input $v(t)$ through a filter matched to the signal Rl $Q(t)e^{i\Omega t}$, where (t) is a solution of the integral equation (1.3). The output of this filter is pplied to a quadratic rectifier, whose outputs r_k^2 at the end of each bservation interval are stored and added. In this way the system forms ıe statistic

$$L = \sum_{k=1}^{M} (x_k^2 + y_k^2) = \sum_{k=1}^{M} r_k^2 ,$$

$$z_k = x_k + iy_k = \int_0^T Q^*(t)\, V_k(t)\, dt, \qquad r_k = |z_k|, \tag{2.1}$$

$$k = 1, 2, \ldots, M;$$

$V_k(t)$ is the complex envelope of the input during the kth interval o duration T, and for convenience we have normalized $F(t)$ so that

$$\int_0^T Q^*(t)\, F(t)\, dt = 1.$$

The sum L of rectifier outputs is compared with some decision level L to decide whether a signal is present. We must now calculate the false alarm and detection probabilities

$$Q_0 = \Pr\{L > L_0 \,|\, H_0\}, \quad Q_d = \Pr\{L > L_0 \,|\, H_1\}.$$

The $2M$ components x_k, y_k of the complex numbers z_k are independen Gaussian random variables. They are independent for different values o k because we took the intervals far enough apart that there is negligibl correlation between the noise voltages in separate ones. Under hypothesi H_0 that there is no signal present, the mean values of these variables ar zero, $\bar{x}_k = \bar{y}_k = 0$. Under hypothesis H_1 that one of the sets of signal of eq. (1.1) is present, the mean value of the input envelope for the kt interval is

$$\mathbf{E}[V_k(t)] = A_k F(t) \exp(i\psi_k), \qquad k = 1, 2, \ldots, M,$$

where A_k and ψ_k are the amplitude and phase of the kth signal. Hence w obtain

$$\mathbf{E}(z_k) = A_k \exp(i\psi_k) \int_0^T Q^*(t)\, F(t)\, dt = D_k \exp(i\psi_k),$$
$$\mathbf{E}(x_k) = D_k \cos\psi_k, \quad \mathbf{E}(y_k) = D_k \sin\psi_k. \quad (H_1) \qquad (2.2$$

The covariances of x_k and y_k under each hypothesis are derived in the sam manner as eq. (V, 3.6),

$$\text{Var}\, x_k = \text{Var}\, y_k = 1, \quad \{x_k, y_k\} = 0,$$
$$\{x_k, x_m\} = \{x_k, y_m\} = \{y_k, y_m\} = 0, \quad k \neq m. \qquad (2.3$$

The joint p.d.f. of the variables can be written down immediately from thes results. The statistic L whose distributions are sought is the sum of th squares of these $2M$ independent Gaussian variables.

A convenient method of finding the p.d.f. of the sum of a number o independent random variables utilizes their characteristic functions. Th characteristic function (ch.f.) of a random variable is the Fourier trans form of its p.d.f.,

$$h(z) = \int_{-\infty}^{\infty} p(x)\, e^{izx}\, dx \qquad (2.4$$

for all values of z at which the integral exists. Some of the properties of the characteristic function are described in Appendix B. In particular, the ch.f. of the sum of a number of independent random variables is the product of the ch.f.s of the individual variables, and from the ch.f. of the sum its p.d.f. can be found by an inverse Fourier transformation.

By virtue of eq. (B.6), the ch.f. of the sum L in eq. (2.1) is

$$h_L(z) = \int_{-\infty}^{\infty} p(L)\, e^{izL}\, dL = \prod_{j=1}^{M} h_{x_j^2}(z)\, h_{y_j^2}(z), \tag{2.5}$$

where

$$h_{x^2}(z) = \int_{-\infty}^{\infty} p(x) \exp(izx^2)\, dx, \quad h_{y^2}(z) = \int_{-\infty}^{\infty} p(y) \exp(izy^2)\, dy, \tag{2.6}$$

with $p(x)$ and $p(y)$ the p.d.f.s of x and y respectively. From eqs. (2.2) and (2.3) these p.d.f.s are, if we omit subscripts,

$$p(x) = (2\pi)^{-\frac{1}{2}} \exp[-(x-D\cos\psi)^2/2],$$

$$p(y) = (2\pi)^{-\frac{1}{2}} \exp[-(y-D\sin\psi)^2/2].$$

Therefore, the characteristic function of x^2 is

$$\begin{aligned} h_{x^2}(z) &= (2\pi)^{-\frac{1}{2}} \int_{-\infty}^{\infty} \exp\,[-\tfrac{1}{2}(x-D\cos\psi)^2 + izx^2]\, dx \\ &= (1-2iz)^{-\frac{1}{2}} \exp\left(\frac{izD^2\cos^2\psi}{1-2iz}\right), \end{aligned} \tag{2.7}$$

and a similar expression holds for the ch.f. of y^2, with $\cos^2\psi$ replaced by $\sin^2\psi$. The ch.f. of the sum L is then, by eq. (2.5),

$$h_L(z) = (1-2iz)^{-M} \exp[iSz/(1-2iz)], \tag{2.8}$$

where

$$S = \sum_{k=1}^{M} D_k^2 \tag{2.9}$$

is proportional to the total signal energy E_T received from the target. From eq. (2.8) we see that the p.d.f. of the sum L and hence also the probability Q_d of detection depend on the signal-to-noise ratios D_k only through the sum of their squares. The probability of detection is independent of the actual values of the signal phases ψ_k.

The inverse Fourier transform of $h_L(z)$ in eq. (2.8) is the p.d.f. of the statistic L under hypothesis H_1,

$$p_1(L) = \tfrac{1}{2}(L/S)^{(M-1)/2} \exp[-(L+S)/2]\, I_{M-1}(\sqrt{LS}), \quad L > 0, \tag{2.10}$$

where $I_{M-1}(x)$ is the modified Bessel function of order $(M-1)$. (This result is most easily obtained by looking up the transform in a table. For instance, after converting the integral to a Laplace transform by a change of variable, one can use eq. (18), p. 197 of vol. 1 of Erdélyi *et al.*, 1954.) Under hypothesis H_0, $S = 0$, and we find

$$p_0(L) = \frac{(L/2)^{M-1}\, e^{-L/2}}{2(M-1)!}, \tag{2.11}$$

by using the first term of the expansion of the modified Bessel function,

$$I_{M-1}(x) = \sum_{k=0}^{\infty} \frac{(x/2)^{M-1+2k}}{k!(M-1+k)!}, \tag{2.12}$$

and finally setting S equal to 0.

When there is no signal, the variable L is chi-squared distributed with $2M$ degrees of freedom, for it is the sum of $2M$ independent Gaussian variables of zero mean and unit variance. We derived the density function in eq. (2.11) by another method at the end of Section 3, Chapter III. The false-alarm probability for a detection system using a quadratic rectifier is given by

$$Q_0 = \int_{L_0}^{\infty} p_0(L)\, dL = 1 - I(L_0/2\sqrt{M},\ M-1), \tag{2.13}$$

in Pearson's (1934) notation for the incomplete gamma-function,

$$I(u, p) = \int_0^{u\sqrt{p+1}} v^p e^{-v}\, dv/p!. \tag{2.14}$$

By partial integration the false-alarm probability can be written down in closed form,

$$Q_0 = \exp(-L_0/2) \sum_{k=0}^{M-1} (L_0/2)^k/k!. \tag{2.15}$$

This formula involves too much computation if M is large. For small false-alarm probabilities, however, $L_0/2$ is large, and only a few terms of eq. (2.15) are needed,

$$Q_0 = [(M-1)!]^{-1}(L_0/2)^{M-1} \exp(-L_0/2)\,\cdot \left[1 + \frac{M-1}{(L_0/2)} + \frac{(M-1)(M-2)}{(L_0/2)^2} + \cdots\right].$$

Marcum (1948) suggested summing the bracket approximately as

$\left(1-\frac{M-1}{(L_0/2)}\right)^{-1}$, so that

$$Q_0 \cong \frac{(L_0/2)^M \exp(-L_0/2)}{(M-1)!\,(\frac{1}{2}L_0-M+1)}.$$

For large values of M one can use Stirling's formula for the factorial, finally obtaining the approximate equation

$$-\ln Q_0 \cong x+1-M\left[1+\ln\left(\frac{x}{M-1}\right)\right]+\ln(x-M+1)-\frac{1}{2}\ln\left(\frac{M-1}{2\pi}\right),$$
$$x = \tfrac{1}{2}L_0 \gg M-1 \gg 1. \tag{2.16}$$

This formula is sufficiently accurate in most problems. For the false-alarm probability $Q_0=10^{-p}$, where p is an integer from 1 to 12, and $1 \leqslant M \leqslant 150$, one can use Pachares's (1958) tables.

From eq. (2.10) the probability Q_d of detection is given by the integral

$$Q_d = \int_{L_0}^{\infty} p_1(L)\,dL = Q_M(S^{\frac{1}{2}}, L_0^{\frac{1}{2}}), \tag{2.17}$$

where

$$Q_M(\alpha, \beta) = \int_{\beta}^{\infty} x(x/\alpha)^{M-1}\, e^{-(x^2+\alpha^2)/2}\, I_{M-1}(\alpha x)\,dx \tag{2.18}$$

is a generalization of the Q-function defined in eq. (V, 3.14). These functions are related by the equation

$$Q_M(\alpha, \beta) = Q(\alpha, \beta)+e^{-(\alpha^2+\beta^2)/2}\sum_{r=1}^{M-1}(\beta/\alpha)^r\, I_r(\alpha\beta).$$

Using the tables of $Q(\alpha, \beta)$ compiled by Marcum (1950) and tables of modified Bessel functions, one can compute the detection probability, eq. (2.17). This is laborious, however, if M is large. In the next part we shall develop approximation formulas enabling one to evaluate the probability of detection for large values of M.

(b) *The Gram–Charlier Series*

For large values of M the probability density function of the statistic L is nearly Gaussian by virtue of the Central Limit Theorem, for it is then the sum of a large number of independent random variables (Cramér, 1946). We shall now derive an approximation to the p.d.f. $p_1(L)$ that exhibits this limiting Gaussian character and can be used to compute the probability Q_d of detection for a large number M of observations. The method is useful in many problems of this kind.

We expand the logarithm of the characteristic function $h(z)$ of a random variable x in a series of powers of (iz),

$$\ln h(z) = iz\bar{x} + \sigma^2(iz)^2/2 + \sum_{k=3}^{\infty} \varkappa_k (iz)^k/k!, \tag{2.19}$$

where $\bar{x}$ is the expected value of the random variable, $\sigma^2 = \mathbf{E}(x-\bar{x})^2$ is its variance, and $\varkappa_k$ is its so-called "kth cumulant" (or "semi-invariant"). For instance, using eq. (B. 3) and the power series for the logarithm, and collecting like powers of (iz), one can show that

$$\varkappa_3 = \overline{x^3} - 3\overline{x^2}\cdot\bar{x} + 2\bar{x}^3 = \overline{(x-\bar{x})^3},$$
$$\varkappa_4 = \overline{(x-\bar{x})^4} - 3\sigma^4,$$

and so on. It must be assumed, of course, that all moments of the distribution of x exist. The p.d.f. of x is the inverse Fourier transform of the ch.f., which can now be written

$$\begin{aligned} h(z) &= \exp[iz\bar{x} + \sigma^2(iz)^2/2 + r(z)] \\ &= \exp[iz\bar{x} + \sigma^2(iz)^2/2]\cdot\left[1 + \sum_{m=1}^{\infty} [r(z)]^m/m!\right], \end{aligned} \tag{2.20}$$
$$r(z) = \sum_{k=3}^{\infty} \varkappa_k (iz)^k/k!.$$

By collecting terms with like powers of (iz) we can write this as

$$h(z) = \exp[iz\bar{x} + \sigma^2(iz)^2/2]\cdot\left[1 + \sum_{k=3}^{\infty} c_k (iz)^k\right], \tag{2.21}$$

where the coefficients c_k are given by formulas like

$$c_3 = \varkappa_3/3!, \quad c_4 = \varkappa_4/4!, \quad c_5 = \varkappa_5/5!, \quad c_6 = (\varkappa_6 + 10\varkappa_3^2)/6!. \tag{2.22}$$

The inverse Fourier transform of eq. (2.21) is (Erdélyi *et al.*, 1954, vol. 1, p. 121, eq. (23))

$$\begin{aligned} p(x) &= (2\pi\sigma^2)^{-\frac{1}{2}} \exp[-(x-\bar{x})^2/2\sigma^2]\cdot\left[1 + \sum_{k=3}^{\infty} (c_k/\sigma^k)\, h_k(u)\right] \\ &= \sigma^{-1}\left[\phi^{(0)}(u) + \sum_{k=3}^{\infty} (-1)^k (c_k/\sigma^k)\, \phi^{(k)}(u)\right], \\ & \qquad u = (x-\bar{x})/\sigma. \end{aligned} \tag{2.23}$$

The Hermite polynomial $h_k(u)$ appearing here is defined by

$$\begin{aligned} (-1)^k e^{-u^2/2} h_k(u) &= \frac{d^k}{du^k}(e^{-u^2/2}) = (2\pi)^{\frac{1}{2}} \phi^{(k)}(u), \\ \phi^{(k)}(u) &= (-1)^k \phi^{(k)}(-u). \end{aligned} \tag{2.24}$$

The expansion in eq. (2.23) is known as a "Gram–Charlier series". The first term is the usual Gaussian error function; the others represent corrections to it. The functions $\phi^{(k)}(u)$ have been tabulated by the Harvard Computation Laboratory (1952) for $-1 \leqslant k \leqslant 20$, k integral. Here

$$\phi^{(-1)}(u) = (2\pi)^{-\frac{1}{2}} \int_0^u e^{-y^2/2}\, dy = \tfrac{1}{2} - \operatorname{erfc} u \tag{2.25}$$

is a form of the error-function integral. We note the formulas

$$\begin{aligned} \int_x^\infty \phi^{(k)}(t)\, dt &= -\phi^{(k-1)}(x), \qquad k \geqslant 1, \\ \int_x^\infty \phi^{(0)}(t)\, dt &= \tfrac{1}{2} - \phi^{(-1)}(x) = \operatorname{erfc} x. \end{aligned} \tag{2.26}$$

Fry (1965, p. 262) discusses calculations with the Gram–Charlier series. He points out that the natural order of the terms is not the best. In most problems the terms listed here in parentheses should be taken together: $k = (0), (3), (4, 6), (5, 7, 9), \ldots$, for the elements of these groups are usually of the same order of magnitude. Thus if one uses the terms through $k = 4$, one should also include the term $k = 6$.

To apply these formulas to calculating the detection probability Q_d, we must find the coefficients appearing in the expansion, eq. (2.23), of the p.d.f. $p_1(L)$. The simplest way is to take the logarithm of the characteristic function $h_L(z)$ of eq. (2.8),

$$\begin{aligned} \ln h_L(z) &= -M \ln (1-2iz) + \frac{iSz}{1-2iz} \\ &= \sum_{k=1}^{\infty} \left(\frac{M}{k} + \frac{S}{2} \right) (2iz)^k . \end{aligned} \tag{2.27}$$

Comparing terms with like powers of (iz) in eqs. (2.27) and (2.19), we obtain

$$\begin{aligned} \mathbf{E}(L) &= (2M+S), \quad \operatorname{Var} L = \sigma_L^2 = 4(M+S), \\ \varkappa_3 &= 8(2M+3S), \quad \varkappa_4 = 96(M+2S), \\ \varkappa_k &= 2^k(k-1)!\,(M+\tfrac{1}{2}kS) \end{aligned} \tag{2.28}$$

for the cumulants of the distribution of the statistic L under hypothesis H_1.

Substituting them into eq. (2.23), we find

$$p_1(L) = \sigma_L^{-1}\left[\phi^{(0)}(y) - \frac{2M+3S}{6(M+S)^{\frac{3}{2}}}\phi^{(3)}(y)\right.$$

$$\left. + \frac{M+2S}{4(M+S)^2}\phi^{(4)}(y) + \frac{12(M+3S)+(2M+3S)^2}{72\,(M+S)^3}\phi^{(6)}(y) + \ldots\right],$$

$$y = \frac{L-2M-S}{2(M+S)^{\frac{1}{2}}} \tag{2.29}$$

where we have grouped the terms in the manner suggested by Fry. The terms beyond the first become small for $M \gg 1$.

The probability Q_d of detection is given by the termwise integration of this density function, for which we can use the relations in eq. (2.26) to write

$$Q_d = \frac{1}{2} - \phi^{(-1)}(Y) + \frac{2M+3S}{6(M+S)^{\frac{3}{2}}}\phi^{(2)}(Y) - \frac{M+2S}{4(M+S)^2}\phi^{(3)}(Y)$$

$$- \frac{12(M+3S)+(2M+3S)^2}{72(M+S)^3}\phi^{(5)}(Y) - \ldots, \tag{2.30}$$

$$Y = \tfrac{1}{2}(M+S)^{-\frac{1}{2}}(L_0 - 2M - S).$$

This formula could also be used for the false-alarm probability Q_0 when the number M is large, by setting $S = 0$, but for very small values of the false-alarm probability, such as $Q_0 = 10^{-10}$, it is usually more efficient to use eq. (2.16).

(c) *Signal Detectability in Multiple Observations*

Using the formulas just derived, we can calculate the probability of detecting a signal $s_1(t)+\ldots+s_M(t)$ with a given set of amplitudes A_k by means of the threshold system worked out in Section 1, part (c). This system involved forming the sum L of the outputs, at the end of each observation interval, of a quadratic rectifier following a matched filter. The sum is compared with a decision level L_0; if $L > L_0$, the observer decides that one of the possible sets of signals was present. The decision level L_0 is a function of the desired false-alarm probability.

In Fig. VII.2 we have plotted the quantity $\frac{1}{2}L_0 - M + 1$ versus the false-alarm probability Q_0. It shows how the decision level increases, for fixed Q_0, as the number M of observations increases and causes the p.d.f. $p_0(L)$ to shift toward larger values of the sum L. In Fig. VII.3 the probability of detection is plotted, for $Q_0 = 10^{-10}$, versus the total signal-to-noise ratio $S^{\frac{1}{2}}$, as defined by eq. (2.9); curves are given for several values of M.

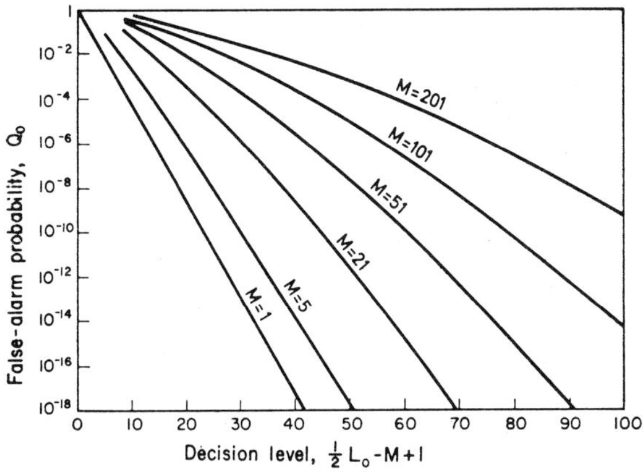

FIG. VII.2. Decision levels for multiple observations.

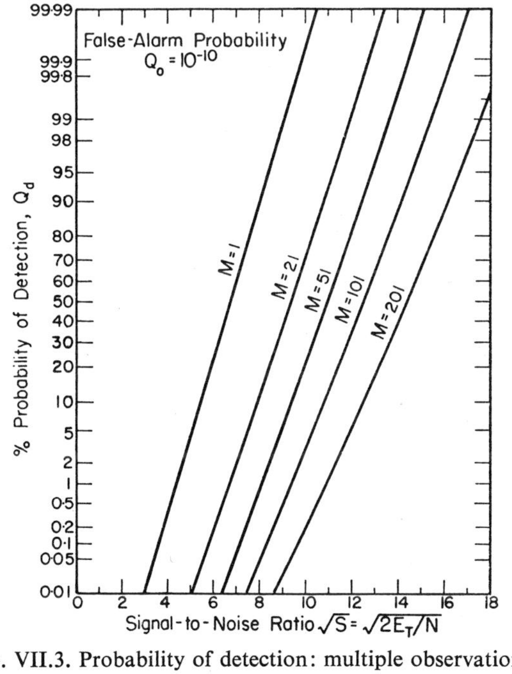

FIG. VII.3. Probability of detection: multiple observations.

When the noise is white, $S = 2E_T/N$, where E_T is the total energy received from the target during the entire observation, and N is the unilateral spectral density of the noise. From the graph it is seen that the total energy required to attain a given probability of detection increases with the number M of observations. That is, the signal is more difficult to detect when its total energy is divided among a number M of incoherent pulses than when the energy is concentrated into a single echo. On the other hand, for a given average energy per pulse, S/M, the probability of detection increases with the number M.

To put these remarks on a more quantitative basis, let us assume that the number M is so large that we need only the first two terms of eq. (2.30) to calculate both the false-alarm and detection probabilities. This approximation is reasonably good for $M > 100$, when both p.d.f.s $p_0(L)$ and $p_1(L)$ are nearly Gaussian. Then

$$Q_0 \cong \operatorname{erfc} x, \quad Q_d \cong \operatorname{erfc} y,$$
$$x = M^{-\frac{1}{2}}(\tfrac{1}{2}L_0 - M), \quad y = \left(x - \tfrac{1}{2}SM^{-\frac{1}{2}}\right)\sqrt{M/(M+S)}. \tag{2.31}$$

From these equations we can find the signal strength S required to attain a given probability of detection for a fixed false-alarm probability,

$$S = 2M^{\frac{1}{2}}\left(x - y\sqrt{(M+S)/M}\right) = 2\left(M^{\frac{1}{2}} - y\right)(x-y) + O\left(M^{-\frac{1}{2}}\right), \tag{2.32}$$

where x and y are the values obtained by solving the equations (2.31) with the given probabilities Q_0 and Q_d. For instance, for $Q_0 = 10^{-10}$ and $Q_d = 0.90$, $x = 6.36$ and $y = -1.282$.

From eq. (2.32) it is seen that for given values of Q_0 and Q_d the required total energy E_T is nearly proportional to $M^{\frac{1}{2}}$ for large values of the number M, and that the average energy per pulse E_T/M is proportional to $M^{-\frac{1}{2}}$. Thus the energy $E = E_T/M$ of the "minimum detectable signal", as defined in Chapter IV, is inversely proportional to the square-root of the number M of observations. To decrease this energy to one-tenth of its value for $M = 1$, it is necessary to take about 100 observations.

Our discussion of the least favorable distribution in Section 1 of Chapter V indicates that if the threshold detector is used with signals for which the signal-to-noise ratio exceeds some minimum value D_0, the probability of detection cannot be less than the value just calculated for $S = MD_0^2$, with a fixed false-alarm probability, no matter what the true prior p.d.f. of the signal-to-noise ratios D_k. However, if the observer knows that all signal-to-noise ratios are larger than some minimum value D_0, and if this minimum value is sufficiently large, he may be able to increase the average probability of detection by using a linear rectifier instead of a quadratic one, because of the behavior of the optimum rectifier characteristic (Fig. VII.1).

Let us briefly consider in more detail this question of the optimum rectifier characteristic. In Section 1 it was stated that for very small signal amplitudes the function $\ln I_0(D_k r_k)$ in the logarithm of the likelihood ratio, eq. (1.7), could be replaced by the first term, a quadratic one, in its power series, eq. (1.8). As we shall now demonstrate, however, for small numbers M and for reasonable values of the probabilities Q_0 and Q_d, the average value of $D_k r_k$ is so large that it is, for most of the observations, well beyond the quadratic part of the curve in Fig. VII.1, even when no signal is present.

From eq. (2.11) with $M = 1$ one obtains the p.d.f. of r_k^2 under hypothesis H_0, and from that expression it is easy to show that with no signal present $r = r_k$ has the Rayleigh distribution,

$$p_0(r) = re^{-r^2/2}, \qquad r > 0, \tag{2.33}$$

as in eq. (V, 3.9). The expected value of r is then

$$\bar{r} = \int_0^\infty rp_0(r)\,dr = (\pi/2)^{\frac{1}{2}}. \quad (H_0) \tag{2.34}$$

Hence if all pulses have equal amplitudes, the average value of the argument $D_k r_k$ of the function $\ln I_0(D_k r_k)$ in eq. (1.7) is $D_k \bar{r}_k = D_k(\pi/2)^{\frac{1}{2}} = (\pi S/2M)^{\frac{1}{2}}$ when no signal is present. If one is concerned with signals yielding, say, a detection probability $Q_d = 0.90$ for a false-alarm probability $Q_0 = 10^{-10}$, one can obtain values of S from the graph, Fig. VII.3, and can calculate the following average values of the arguments $D_k r_k$:

M	1	21	51	101	201
$D_k \bar{r}_k$	10.1	3.0	2.2	1.76	1.43

Referring to Fig. VII.1, one sees that all but the last of these are located on a part of the curve of $\ln I_0(x)$ that is nearly linear. When there is a signal present, the average value $D_k \bar{r}_k$ is even larger. Since the values of the random variables $D_k r_k$ tend to cluster about their averages $D_k \bar{r}_k$, most of them will lie on the linear part of the curve in Fig. VII.1, for values of the number M up to about 100 or 200.

It would seem, therefore, that for acceptable values of the false-alarm and detection probabilities and for small numbers M of observations, the functions $\ln I_0(D_k r_k)$ in the logarithm of the likelihood ratio, eq. (1.7), cannot be accurately approximated by the first term of the power series in eq. (1.8). Rather one should use the linear approximation, eq. (1.9), and build a detection system using linear rectifiers, for values of the number M up to 100 or so. Only when the number of observations is much larger are the minimum detectable signal amplitudes small enough to warrant the quadratic approximation.

Marcum (1948) presented formulas for calculating the false-alarm and detection probabilities for systems using linear rectifiers, as well as for those using quadratic ones. He calculated the signal strengths, as a function of the number M, required to attain a detection probability $Q_d = 0.50$ with a false-alarm probability of the order of 10^{-6}, for systems using both types of rectifier. His results showed that the linear rectifier is slightly better than the quadratic for values of M between 1 and 70; the latter is superior for $M > 70$. However, the ratio of signal strengths never exceeded about 0.19 db, and one can conclude that the quadratic rectifier is roughly as efficient as the linear one for all numbers M. His results do, however, bear out our deduction that the linear rectifier is more nearly optimum when only a few observations are made.

In the discussion thus far it has been assumed that the time of arrival of the signal is known and that the observer knows at what instants to measure the output of the rectifier. If the location of a possible radar target is unknown, receivers such as we have derived here cannot be used. We shall put off treating this situation until we have described methods of measuring the time of arrival of an echo from a target whose presence has been detected. They will be determined by means of the statistical theory of parameter estimation, the subject of the next chapter.

d) *Asymptotic Evaluation of Detectors*

When a number M of inputs $v_j(t)$ with independent noise components are available, a receiver, optimum or not, will in general base its decision about the presence or absence of a signal on a statistic that is the sum of statistics derived from each input. If we denote the M component statistics by $u_1, u_2, \ldots, u_M$ and their sum by U_M, the receiver will compare

$$U_M = u_1 + u_2 + \ldots + u_M \tag{2.35}$$

with a decision level Y; and if $U_M > Y$ it will choose hypothesis H_1. In this chapter we have studied receivers in which the u_j's are sampled outputs of a linear or a quadratic rectifier fed by a matched filter. The u_j's are independent random variables, and if the distributions of signals and noise are the same in all inputs $v_j(t)$, the u_j's will all have the same p.d.f. under each hypothesis.

The difficulty of calculating the p.d.f.s of the u_j's and of their sum U_M often prevents our evaluating such a receiver on the basis of its false-alarm and detection probabilities for arbitrary numbers M. When M is large, however, the Central Limit Theorem assures us in most cases that the distributions of the sum U_M are approximately Gaussian. We then need to know only its mean and its variance under each hypothesis, and these are the sums of the means and variances, respectively, of the individual statistics u_j. The mean and the variance of a statistic are usually much more easily calculated than its p.d.f.

When the number M is large, the probability of detecting a signal of strength a is approximately

$$\begin{aligned} Q_d(a) &\cong 1-\operatorname{erfc} y, \quad y = (\sigma_{M0}/\sigma_{M1})(D_M - x), \\ D_M &= D_M(a) = [\mathbf{E}(U_M \mid H_1, a) - \mathbf{E}(U_M \mid H_0)]/\sigma_{M0}, \\ \sigma_{M0}^2 &= \operatorname{Var}_0 U_M = \mathbf{E}(U_M^2 \mid H_0) - [\mathbf{E}(U_M \mid H_0)]^2, \\ \sigma_{M1}^2 &= \operatorname{Var}_1 U_M = \mathbf{E}(U_M^2 \mid H_1, a) - [\mathbf{E}(U_M \mid H_1, a)]^2, \end{aligned} \tag{2.36}$$

where x is determined by the false-alarm probability $Q_0 \cong \operatorname{erfc} x$. The quantities Q_d, y, σ_{M1}, and D_M all depend on the signal strength a, which might refer to the amplitude A of the signal, its square A^2, or some other monotone function of A. The quantity D_M we call the "equivalent signal-to-noise ratio".

Detectors are sometimes compared by specifying a pair of values (Q_0, Q_d) and asking how many inputs M are needed by each detector to attain this pair of probabilities for signals of the same strength a. As a vanishes and the numbers M_1 and M_2 of inputs to each detector grow toward infinity, their ratio $M_1 : M_2$ becomes independent of the fixed values of Q_0 and Q_d. The limiting value of this ratio is called the "asymptotic relative efficiency" (a.r.e.) of the detectors and is a measure of how much better one is than the other. Alternatively, the numbers M_1 and M_2 can be set equal and allowed to increase without bound, whereupon the ratio $a_1 : a_2$ of signal strengths needed to attain the "reliability" (Q_0, Q_d) ranks the detectors.

In the limit $a \to 0$ of vanishing signal strength, the equivalent signal-to-noise ratio can be expressed as

$$D_M = \frac{a}{\sigma_{M0}} \frac{\partial}{\partial a} \mathbf{E}(U_M \mid H_1, a) \bigg|_{a=0} . \tag{2.37}$$

If the u_j's are statistically independent and have the same p.d.f.s under each hypothesis, both the expected value and the variance of U_M will be proportional to M, and D_M will be proportional to $M^{\frac{1}{2}}$. It is therefore appropriate to define a quantity known as the "efficacy" of a detector by

$$\eta = \lim_{M\to\infty} D_M^2/Ma^2 = \lim_{M\to\infty} (M\sigma_{M0}^2)^{-1} \left[\frac{\partial}{\partial a} \mathbf{E}(U_M \mid H_1, a) \Big|_{a=0} \right]^2. \tag{2.38}$$

In the limit of vanishing signal strength the variance σ_{M1}^2 of the statistic U_M under hypothesis H_1 generally approaches σ_{M0}^2 rapidly enough that the ratio σ_{M1}/σ_{M0} can be set equal to 1, and eq. (2.36) shows that for $M \gg 1$ the probability of detection is approximately

$$Q_d \cong 1 - \operatorname{erfc}\left(a(M\eta)^{\frac{1}{2}} - x\right), \quad Q_0 \cong \operatorname{erfc} x. \tag{2.39}$$

The a.r.e. of two detectors with efficacies η_1 and η_2 is then

$$\lim_{a\to 0} M_1/M_2 = \eta_2/\eta_1. \tag{2.40}$$

For example, the a.r.e. of the detector using a linear rectifier with respect to one using a quadratic rectifier is $(1.093)^{-1}$ (Problem 8). For very weak signals, the detector requires 1.093 times as many independent inputs when it uses a linear rectifier as when it uses a quadratic one, in order to attain the same reliability (Q_0, Q_d) for signals of the same strength. This ratio measures the relative performances of two detectors only in the limit of infinitely many inputs, however, and it should be mistrusted when a receiver works with only a small number of inputs. In part (c) we reported Marcum's finding that the linear rectifier is slightly superior to the quadratic for M less than about 70, and we discussed the reasons. Caution is further warranted because in approximating the distributions of the statistic U_M by Gaussian p.d.f.s the tails of the distributions are least accurately handled. The smaller the specified values of Q_0 and $1-Q_d$, the greater the number of independent variates that must be summed before the Gaussian approximation is reliable.

(e) *The Threshold Detector*†

A comparison of detectors on the basis of their asymptotic relative efficiency favors the threshold detector, which is optimum in the limit of vanishingly small signal strengths by virtue of its derivation from the likelihood-ratio receiver. We shall now evaluate the efficacy of the threshold detector of signals depending not only on an unknown amplitude, but on other unknown parameters, such as arrival time, as well. The threshold detector has been analyzed by Middleton (1960, ch. 20; 1966) and Capon (1961).

† This section may be omitted on first reading.

The unknown parameters of the signal are divided into two classes, those that vary independently and randomly from one signal to another, and those that remain the same. Among the former are the strengths $a_1, a_2, \ldots, a_M$ of the signals; we single them out and assign them the prior p.d.f. $z(a_1, a_2, \ldots, a_M)$. To the rest of the independently varying parameters, such as the phases $\psi_1, \psi_2, \ldots, \psi_M$, we attribute their least favorable distributions, and we suppose that the density functions of the inputs under hypothesis H_1 have been averaged with respect to them. They are thus eliminated from the beginning. The parameters such as time of arrival and carrier frequency that although unknown are supposed to remain the same from one signal to the next are denoted collectively by the vector $\boldsymbol{\theta}'$. We suppose them governed by their least favorable prior p.d.f. $\tilde{z}'(\boldsymbol{\theta}')$ and independent of the strengths $\mathbf{a} = (a_1, \ldots, a_M)$. The data $\mathbf{x}_k = (x_{k1}, \ldots, x_{kn})$ obtained, say by sampling, from the kth input $v_k(t)$ have under hypothesis H_1 the joint p.d.f. $p_1(\mathbf{x}_k; a_k, \boldsymbol{\theta}')$; under H_0 they are distributed according to $p_0(\mathbf{x}_k)$. These p.d.f.s are assumed to have the same forms for all inputs $v_k(t)$.

The average likelihood ratio on which the receiver is to base its decision would, if the prior distributions were available, be given by

$$\Lambda[\{\mathbf{x}_k\}] = \int \ldots \int z(a_1, \ldots, a_M)\, \tilde{z}'(\boldsymbol{\theta}') \cdot \prod_{k=1}^{M} \Lambda(\mathbf{x}_k; a_k, \boldsymbol{\theta}')\, da_1 \ldots da_M\, d\boldsymbol{\theta}', \tag{2.41}$$

$$\Lambda(\mathbf{x}; a, \boldsymbol{\theta}') = p_1(\mathbf{x}; a, \boldsymbol{\theta}')/p_0(\mathbf{x}),$$

where $d\boldsymbol{\theta}'$ is a volume element in the space of the parameters $\boldsymbol{\theta}'$. To derive the threshold detector we proceed as in Section 1, part (c), and allow the signal strengths a_k to become very small, writing the likelihood ratio in this limit as

$$\Lambda(\mathbf{x}; a, \boldsymbol{\theta}') \doteq 1 + aL(\mathbf{x}; \boldsymbol{\theta}'),$$

$$L(\mathbf{x}; \boldsymbol{\theta}') = \frac{\partial}{\partial a} \ln \Lambda(\mathbf{x}; a, \boldsymbol{\theta}') \bigg|_{a=0}. \tag{2.42}$$

The convenient introduction of the logarithm here is correct because $\Lambda(\mathbf{x}; 0, \boldsymbol{\theta}') = 1$. The average likelihood ratio then becomes

$$\Lambda[\{\mathbf{x}_k\}] = \int \ldots \int z(a_1, \ldots, a_M)\, \tilde{z}'(\boldsymbol{\theta}') \cdot \left[1 + \sum_{k=1}^{M} a_k L(\mathbf{x}_k; \boldsymbol{\theta}')\right] da_1 \ldots da_M\, d\boldsymbol{\theta}' \tag{2.43}$$

$$= 1 + \langle a \rangle \sum_{k=1}^{M} L_1(\mathbf{x}_k),$$

where

$$L_1(\mathbf{x}) = \int \tilde{z}'(\boldsymbol{\theta}')\, L(\mathbf{x}; \boldsymbol{\theta}')\, d\boldsymbol{\theta}' \tag{2.44}$$

and $\langle a \rangle$ is the expected value of the signal strength a with respect to its prior p.d.f. In the limit $\langle a \rangle \to 0$ the receiver using the average likelihood ratio is equivalent to one that bases its decisions on the threshold statistic

$$W_M = \sum_{k=1}^{M} L_1(\mathbf{x}_k), \tag{2.45}$$

and this we call the threshold detector. We proceed to calculate its efficacy which will turn out to be simply the expected value of L_1^2 under hypothesis H_0.

When a set of signals of strengths $\mathbf{a} = (a_1, \ldots, a_M)$ and parameters $\boldsymbol{\theta}$ is present in the M inputs, the expected value of the threshold statistic W_M is

$$\begin{aligned} \mathbf{E}(W_M \mid H_1, \mathbf{a}, \boldsymbol{\theta}') &= \sum_{k=1}^{M} \int p_1(\mathbf{x}_k; a_k, \boldsymbol{\theta}')\, L_1(\mathbf{x}_k)\, d^n\mathbf{x}_k \\ &\doteq \sum_{k=1}^{M} a_k \int \frac{\partial}{\partial a} p_1(\mathbf{x}; a, \boldsymbol{\theta}') \bigg|_{a=0} L_1(\mathbf{x})\, d^n\mathbf{x} \end{aligned} \tag{2.46}$$

when the strengths a_k are very small. If we denote the average signal strength in the set by

$$\bar{a} = M^{-1} \sum_{k=1}^{M} a_k,$$

we can put for the expected value of W_M under H_1

$$\begin{aligned} \mathbf{E}(W_M \mid H_1, \mathbf{a}, \boldsymbol{\theta}') &= M\bar{a} \int \frac{\partial}{\partial a} \Lambda(\mathbf{x}; a, \boldsymbol{\theta}') \bigg|_{a=0} p_0(\mathbf{x})\, L_1(\mathbf{x})\, d^n\mathbf{x} \\ &= M\bar{a} \int L(\mathbf{x}; \boldsymbol{\theta}')\, p_0(\mathbf{x})\, L_1(\mathbf{x})\, d^n\mathbf{x}. \end{aligned} \tag{2.47}$$

It can furthermore be shown that $\mathbf{E}(W_M|H_0) = 0$ (Problem 9). The variance of the statistic W_M under hypothesis H_0 is

$$\sigma_{M0}^2 = \mathrm{Var}_0\, W_M = M \int p_0(\mathbf{x})\, [L_1(\mathbf{x})]^2\, d^n\mathbf{x} = M\, \mathbf{E}(L_1^2 \mid H_0), \tag{2.48}$$

and from eq. (2.37) the equivalent signal-to-noise ratio is, in the threshold limit,

$$D_M(\bar{a}, \boldsymbol{\theta}') = \bar{a} M^{\frac{1}{2}} [\mathbf{E}(L_1^2 \mid H_0)]^{-\frac{1}{2}} \int L(\mathbf{x}; \boldsymbol{\theta}')\, p_0(\mathbf{x})\, L_1(\mathbf{x})\, d^n\mathbf{x}. \tag{2.49}$$

The least favorable distribution, as we learned in Section 1 of Chapter V, assigns positive probability—$\tilde{z}'(\boldsymbol{\theta}') > 0$—to a certain region Θ of the space of the parameters $\boldsymbol{\theta}'$, and zero probability to the rest. Furthermore the probability $Q_d(a, \boldsymbol{\theta}')$ of detection is independent of $\boldsymbol{\theta}'$ for parameters $\boldsymbol{\theta}'$ lying in Θ, and the average probability of detection under the leas avorable distribution $\tilde{z}'(\theta')$ is equal to $Q_d(a, \theta')$ for any θ' in Θ. In the hreshold limit of vanishing signal strength, on the other hand, eq. (2.36) hows that $Q_d(a, \theta')$ depends on θ' only through the equivalent signal-to-oise ratio $D_M(\bar{a}, \theta')$, which is given by eq. (2.49). This signal-to-noise atio must, therefore, like the probability of detection itself, be indepen-lent of θ' for θ' in Θ; and we can replace $D_M(\bar{a}, \theta')$ by its average over θ' vith respect to the least favorable prior p.d.f. $\tilde{z}'(\theta')$. We first carry out that verage over the expected value $\mathbf{E}(W_M \mid H_1, \mathbf{a}, \theta')$ in eq. (2.47), which be-omes in the limit of weak signals

$$\begin{aligned} &\mathbf{E}(W_M \mid H_1, \mathbf{a}, \theta') \\ &\quad = M\bar{a} \int \tilde{z}'(\theta')\, d\theta' \int L(\mathbf{x}; \theta')\, p_0(\mathbf{x})\, L_1(\mathbf{x})\, d^n\mathbf{x} \\ &\quad = M\bar{a} \int p_0(\mathbf{x})\, [L_1(\mathbf{x})]^2\, d^n\mathbf{x} = M\bar{a}\mathbf{E}(L_1^2 \mid H_0). \end{aligned} \tag{2.50}$$

ere we have used the definition of $L_1(\mathbf{x})$ in eq. (2.44). Putting this result nto eq. (2.49) we obtain for the equivalent signal-to-noise ratio of the ıreshold detector

$$D_M = \bar{a} M^{\frac{1}{2}} [\mathbf{E}(L_1^2 \mid H_0)]^{\frac{1}{2}}, \tag{2.51}$$

nd in the limit $\bar{a} \to 0$ the probability of detecting the signal is

$$Q_d \cong 1 - \operatorname{erfc}\,(D_M - x), \qquad Q_0 \cong \operatorname{erfc} x.$$

ccording to eq. (2.38) the efficacy of the threshold detector is

$$\eta = \mathbf{E}(L_1^2 \mid H_0) = \int [L_1(\mathbf{x})]^2\, p_0(\mathbf{x})\, d^n\mathbf{x}. \tag{2.52}$$

In Chapter V, Section 5 we studied the threshold detector for signals rriving at an unknown time τ within an interval $(0, T)$ much longer than e signals themselves. When M inputs $v_k(t) = \mathrm{Rl}\, V_k(t)\, e^{i\Omega t}$ are available stead of only one, the threshold statistic is, from eq. (V, 5.4),

$$\begin{aligned} W_M &= \sum_{k=1}^{M} \left[(2N)^{-2}\, U_k - (2N)^{-1} \int_{-\infty}^{\infty} |F(t)|^2\, dt \right], \\ U_k &= \int_0^T \int_0^T \gamma(t, u)\, V_k^*(t)\, V_k(u)\, dt\, du, \end{aligned} \tag{2.53}$$

here $F(t)$ is the complex envelope of the signal, N is the unilateral spec-al density of the noise, assumed white, and $\gamma(t, u)$ is defined as in eq. (V, 6). In the limit of very long intervals the least favorable p.d.f. of the ar-val times is uniform over each interval, $\tilde{z}(\tau) \equiv 1/T$. If we identify the signal rength a with the square A^2 of the amplitude, the equivalent signal-to-noise ratio for this threshold detector is, from eq. (V, 5.16),

$$D_M = (M\mathfrak{t}/T)^{\frac{1}{2}} \frac{E}{N} \tag{2.54}$$

with the time width $\mathfrak{t}$ as defined in Chapter V, and with E the average energy of the signal, $E = \frac{1}{2}\bar{a} \int |F(t)|^2 \, dt$. The reader may verify that these results agree with the general formulas in eqs. (2.45) and (2.51).

3. SEQUENTIAL DETECTION

(a) *The Sequential Probability Ratio Test*

A receiver is presented in succession with the inputs $v_1(t)$, $v_2(t)$, $v_3(t)$, . . . each occupying an interval of T seconds' duration. All the inputs either consist only of random noise of mean zero, $v_k(t) = n_k(t)$ (hypothesis H_0), or contain besides the noise a sequence of signals $s_k(t; \boldsymbol{\theta}_k)$,

$$v_k(t) = s_k(t; \boldsymbol{\theta}_k) + n_k(t), \qquad k = 1, 2, 3, \ldots, \tag{3.1}$$

(hypothesis H_1). We assume as before that the noise inputs $n_k(t)$ are statistically independent from one interval to another. The receiver is to decide which of the hypotheses best describes the set of inputs. The vectors $\boldsymbol{\theta}$ represent sets of parameters specifying the signals. Much or little may be known in advance about these parameters, and they may differ from signal to signal.

It is convenient to divide the parameters into two classes, the random parameters and the nonrandom parameters. The random parameters will be assumed to be statistically independent from one signal to another and to be described by given prior probability density functions, perhaps the least favorable ones. An example of such a random parameter is the r.f. phase ψ_k of each of a train of quasiharmonic pulses. The nonrandom parameters may be unknown, but no prior p.d.f.s describing them are postulated, and in determining likelihood ratios they must be assigned certain fixed, "standard" values. The amplitudes A_k of a set of pulses are an example.

A radar system that must decide whether a target is present at a certain location is confronted with a problem of this kind. Each input $v_k(t)$ is observed after the location has been irradiated by a radar pulse, and the question is whether it contains an echo or not. In Section 1, part (b), it was assumed that only M inputs $v_1(t)$, $v_2(t)$, . . ., $v_M(t)$ are available, and that the only unknown parameters are the phases of the signals. The receiver bases its decision on an average likelihood ratio formed from all M inputs. Because the noise inputs $n_k(t)$ and the random phases were assumed statistically independent, the receiver was designed to form, at the end of each interval, the logarithm of an average likelihood ratio for detecting the signal $s_k(t; \theta_k)$ in the presence of noise with given statistical properties,

$$z_k = \ln \bar{\Lambda}[v_k(t)], \qquad k = 1, 2, \ldots, M. \tag{3.2}$$

The receiver makes its decision by comparing the sum

$$Z_M = z_1 + z_2 + \ldots + z_M \tag{3.3}$$

with a decision level that is set to yield a preassigned false-alarm probability. The terms z_k of this sum we call "logarithmic likelihood ratios" (l.l.r.). When as in Section 1, part (b) the amplitudes A_k, but not the phases, of the signals are fixed and the noise is Gaussian, the l.l.r. takes the form

$$z = \ln I_0(Dr) - \tfrac{1}{2}D^2, \tag{3.4}$$

where r is the rectified output of a filter matched to the signal, and D is, with proper normalization, the signal-to-noise ratio. A test that is thus based on a fixed number of independent data such as $z_1, z_2, \ldots, z_M$ is called by statisticians a "fixed-sample-size" (f.s.s.) test.

The number M of observations is in radar inversely proportional to the scanning rate of the antenna, and this rate—and hence the number M—may be selected so that for a given false-alarm probability, signals of a certain strength will be detected with a specified probability. In binary communications the number M of times that a signal will be repeated may also be set by requiring the receiver to attain a certain probability of detecting the entire sequence of signals. Such a pair (Q_0, Q_d) of probabilities of a false alarm and of a detection is conveniently termed the "reliability" of the detection process, and a signal that governs the structure and the parameters of a receiver through the requirement that it be detected with a specified reliability might be called the "standard signal". The parameters of the standard signal will be denoted by θ_0.

Certain parameters, such as the phase, of the standard signal may be random variables with accepted prior probability density functions; if so, the probability of detection meant is a corresponding average with respect to them. The probability density functions describing the inputs under hypothesis H_1 are also supposed to have been averaged with respect to the independently random parameters, and they are omitted from the set θ_0. We shall assume, although it is not strictly necessary, that the same set θ_0 specifies the standard signal in each observation interval. The standard signal is sometimes assigned the minimum amplitude that one believes is necessary or feasible to detect, whereupon it assumes the role of a "minimum detectable signal".

Sequential detection is possible when the number of inputs $v_k(t)$ to be used need not be fixed in advance and once for all, but can be controlled by the receiver. At any stage, the receiver judges on the basis of its previous inputs whether it has adequate information to make a reliable decision. If so, it chooses one hypothesis or the other; if not, it asks for more information. In radar, the transmitter is ordered to send out another pulse, and the input during the subsequent T-second interval is appended to the data at hand. The total number of inputs $v_1(t), v_2(t), \ldots$, observed before coming to a decision is now a random variable and may differ from one trial of the procedure to the next. A specified reliability can be attained with an average number of inputs or "stages" of the test that is smaller than the number required by a fixed-sample-size test.

What we have learned so far about decision theory persuades us that the decisions made by the receiver at each stage should be based on a likelihood ratio formed from the available data. At the first stage of the test the receiver possesses only the input $v_1(t)$, from which it forms an average likelihood ratio $\Lambda_1[v_1(t)]$ for detecting a signal $s(t; \theta_0)$ in the presence of the noise $n_1(t)$. This likelihood ratio is compared with two decision levels A_1 and B_1, $A_1 > B_1$. If $\Lambda_1[v_1(t)] > A_1$, the receiver decides that a signal is present, and it selects hypothesis H_1. If $\Lambda_1 < B_1$, it selects H_0, the hypothesis that no signal is present. If $B_1 < \Lambda_1 < A_1$, the receiver postpones the selection of a hypothesis and waits until the next input $v_2(t)$ is available. A similar procedure is followed at subsequent stages of the test; the receiver chooses one of three alternatives, H_0, H_1, or postponement, on the basis of what information it has so far received.

Specifically, at the kth stage of the sequential test, the receiver has the k inputs $v_1(t), v_2(t), \ldots, v_k(t)$, from which it forms the likelihood ratio $\Lambda_k[v_1(t), v_2(t), \ldots, v_k(t)]$, comparing it with two levels A_k and B_k, $A_k > B_k$. If $\Lambda_k < B_k$, it chooses hypothesis H_0; if $\Lambda_k > A_k$, H_1; but if $B_k < \Lambda_k < A_k$ it decides to wait until the next input $v_{k+1}(t)$ is available. In radar search the receiver orders the transmitter to send another pulse in the direction of the location being examined.

When, as we have assumed, the noise inputs $n_k(t)$ and the random parameters are statistically independent, the likelihood ratio Λ_k is the product of likelihood ratios for each interval, and it is convenient to use instead its logarithm,

$$\ln \Lambda_k[v_1(t), \ldots, v_k(t)] = Z_k = z_1 + z_2 + \ldots + z_k, \quad (3.5)$$

where $z_j = \ln \Lambda[v_j(t)]$ is the logarithmic likelihood ratio defined as before for detecting the signal $s(t; \theta_0)$ in the noise $n_j(t)$. The sum Z_k is compared with the levels $b_k = \ln B_k$, $a_k = \ln A_k$ to decide whether to accept one of the hypotheses or to observe a $(k+1)$th input. A statistical test of this kind is called a "sequential probability ratio test".

The question now arises how best to choose the levels $B_1, A_1, B_2, A_2, \ldots$. If the designer knows the prior probabilities ζ and $1-\zeta$ of each hypothesis, the costs associated with a choice of one or the other hypothesis, and the cost of obtaining each input $v_j(t)$, he can adopt a Bayesian viewpoint and determine the levels by minimizing the average cost of the sequential procedure. Calculating the optimum decision levels is a formidable problem.

Abraham Wald (1945) cut this Gordian knot by proposing that all the upper limits on the sums Z_k be set at a common level A, and all the lower ones at a common level B, with A and B to be chosen to provide a test of a specified size and power. At the same time he furnished an approximate but simple way of determining the levels A and B. In the context of detection theory, they are set to such values as guarantee detecting a certain standard set of signals with a given reliability.

The Bayes criterion prescribes such constant decision levels for a sequential test utilizing statistically independent data $z_1, z_2, \ldots, z_k$ when the cost of collecting each datum z, and the p.d.f.s of z under the two hypotheses, are the same at all stages. In this situation, the decisions at each stage can be based on the ratio of the posterior probabilities of the two hypotheses,

$$\frac{p(H_1 \mid z_1, \ldots, z_k)}{p(H_0 \mid z_1, \ldots, z_k)} = \frac{1-\zeta}{\zeta} \Lambda_k[v_1(t), \ldots, v_k(t)],$$

which embodies all the past data. Because the costs and the distributions of the data are invariant, the optimum decision at any stage depends only on this ratio; it is irrelevant how many stages the test has already passed through. The limits on this ratio, and hence also on the likelihood ratio Λ_k, must be the same at each stage.

As such an invariance of costs and distributions from stage to stage is commonly met both in statistical applications and in signal detection, Wald's artifice of equalizing the decision levels is quite acceptable. It has been shown (Wald, 1947) that in a sequential probability ratio test with constant decision levels, one hypothesis or the other will eventually be chosen, and the test will terminate. There is no chance of its continuing for ever.

(b) *Properties of the Sequential Test*

That the decision levels A and B should be determined by the false-alarm probability and by the probability of detecting a standard set of signals is consistent with our preference for the Neyman–Pearson criterion. The levels might be calculated by first working out the probabilities, under both H_0 and H_1, that the sum Z_k—eq. (3.5)—will exceed the upper decision level $a = \ln A$ before passing below the lower one $b = \ln B$, a problem that was formulated by Samuelson (1948) and Kemperman (1950) in terms of integral equations. The probabilities $Q_0(a, b)$ and $Q_d(a, b)$ so determined are functions of the levels a and b. When they are respectively set equal to the preassigned false-alarm probability Q_0 and to the desired probability Q_d of detecting the standard signal $s(t; \theta_0)$, a pair of simultaneous equations for the levels a and b is obtained. This calculation is difficult, however, and it usually suffices to adopt the approximations given by Wald (1947),

$$A = e^a \cong Q_d/Q_0, \quad B = e^b \cong (1-Q_d)/(1-Q_0). \tag{3.6}$$

The approximations leading to eq. (3.6) require that the average size of the increments z_j of the logarithmic likelihood ratio Z_k be much smaller than $a-b = \ln (A/B)$. As a result, the average number of stages in the sequential test is very large. The signal-to-noise ratio of the standard signal is small, and the sequential detector is operating in the threshold régime. To obtain precise formulas when the average number of stages is small is, as we have indicated, very difficult; and in what follows we shall quote formulas based on the threshold approximation. For their derivation we refer to Wald (1947). The formulas were applied to sequential detection by Bussgang and Middleton (1955), Blasbalg (1957), and others.

Signals of the same form as the standard signal, but weaker, will be detected with a smaller average probability, those of greater amplitude with a larger average probability, than the standard signal. The graph of probability of detection versus signal strength or signal-to-noise ratio is called the "operating characteristic" of the sequential test. If other parameters than the amplitude are considered nonrandom, it may be of interest to calculate the dependence of the detection probability on their values as well. In order to use the method now to be presented, it is necessary to take the nonrandom parameters as the same for each of the signals $s_k(t; \theta_k)$, and to assume that the other parameters are independently random with invariable prior distributions.

Let us denote by $x_1, x_2, \ldots, x_k$ the data available at the kth stage for deciding whether to choose one of the hypotheses or to take further observations. Ideally the datum x_j will be a monotone function of the likelihood ratio $\Lambda[v_j(t)]$ for detecting the signal $s(t;\ \theta_0)$ in the jth input, but we can allow for the possibility that it is not. The input $v_j(t)$ might, for instance, have been processed by a filter imprecisely matched to the signal $s(t;\ \theta_0)$. We denote by $p_0(x_j)$ the p.d.f. of x_j under hypothesis H_0, and by $p(x_j;\ \theta_0)$ its p.d.f. when the standard signal is present in the input $v_j(t)$. The sequential test is to operate by summing the l.l.r.s $z_1, z_2, \ldots, z_k$, where

$$z_j = \ln p(x_j;\ \theta_0)/p_0(x_j), \tag{3.7}$$

and at each stage it compares the sum

$$Z_k = z_1 + z_2 + \ldots + z_k$$

with the decision levels $a = \ln A$ and $b = \ln B$ as described earlier. The p.d.f. $p(x;\ \theta_0)$ has, we assume, been averaged over the random parameters and, like $p_0(x)$, is the same from stage to stage.†

When a signal with the nonrandom parameters θ is present, the "moment generating function" (m.g.f.) of the l.l.r. z is defined by the formula

$$\phi(h;\ \theta) = \mathbf{E}[e^{zh} \mid H_1, \theta] = \int_{-\infty}^{\infty} e^{zh} p(z;\ \theta)\, dz = \int_{-\infty}^{\infty} \left[\frac{p(x;\ \theta_0)}{p_0(x)}\right]^h p(x;\ \theta)\, dx. \tag{3.8}$$

The moment-generating function differs from the characteristic function described in Appendix B only by a factor of i in the independent variable, a factor that would be inconvenient here and is omitted.

As a function of the real variable h, the m.g.f. $\phi(h;\ \theta)$ is convex downward, and the equation

$$\phi(h;\ \theta) = 1 \tag{3.9}$$

has in general two roots, one of which is $h = 0$. The second root, which is the one we shall deal with, is a function of the nonrandom parameters θ, $h = h(\theta)$. It takes on the special values

$$h(0) = 1, \quad h(\theta_0) = -1,$$

if we indicate the absence of a signal by $\theta = 0$.

When, for instance, the data x are Gaussian variables, as in detecting a signal of known form, but unknown amplitude in Gaussian noise,

$$h(d) = 1 - 2d/d_0, \tag{3.10}$$

† It is recommended that the student work Problem 5, p. 246 as he reads the remainder of this section.

where d is the signal-to-noise ratio for a signal of arbitrary amplitude, as defined in Chapter IV, and d_0 is that for the standard amplitude. In general, if the third and higher cumulants of the l.l.r. z are negligible,

$$h(\theta) \cong -2\mathbf{E}(z \mid \theta)/\text{Var}\, z, \tag{3.11}$$

where the expectations are with respect to the p.d.f. $p(z; \theta)$.

After these preliminaries, the probability $Q_d(\theta)$ of detection, averaged over the random parameters, can be calculated approximately by the formula

$$Q_d(\theta) = (1-B^h)/(A^h-B^h), \quad h = h(\theta). \tag{3.12}$$

For the two pairs of values $\theta = 0$, $h = 1$ and $\theta = \theta_0$, $h = -1$, this yields the equations

$$Q_0 = \frac{1-B}{A-B}, \quad Q_d(\theta_0) = \frac{A(1-B)}{A-B}, \tag{3.13}$$

which are equivalent to eq. (3.6).

The number of stages in the sequential test, or the number of inputs $v_j(t)$ used to make the final decision, is a random variable, which will differ from one application of the test to another, even if the parameters θ are the same. To judge the performance of a sequential detection system it is important to know the average number of stages $\bar{n}(\theta) = \mathbf{E}(n \mid H_1, \theta)$ as a function of the non-random parameters θ. (Again there is an average over the random parameters according to their prior p.d.f.s.) Wald (1947) showed that this "average sample number" is approximately

$$\bar{n}(\theta) = \{Q_d(\theta) \ln A + [1-Q_d(\theta)] \ln B\}/\mathbf{E}(z \mid H_1, \theta), \tag{3.14}$$

where the denominator is the expected value of the l.l.r. z when a signal with nonrandom parameters θ is present. The function $Q_d(\theta)$ is to be obtained from eq. (3.12).

There is a signal strength roughly midway between 0 and that of the standard signal for which $h = 0$ and the fraction in eq. (3.14) takes the indeterminate form 0/0. An application of l'Hôpital's rule then yields the special value

$$\bar{n}(\theta) = -(\ln A)(\ln B)/\text{Var}\, z, \quad \mathbf{E}(z \mid H_1, \theta) = 0. \tag{3.15}$$

As a function of the signal amplitude, the average number $\bar{n}$ of stages exhibits a peak between zero and the amplitude of the standard signal. As the amplitude increases beyond the standard value, the average number $\bar{n}$ decreases toward 0. It is appropriate to compare the value of $\bar{n}(\theta)$ with the number M of stages needed by a fixed-sample-size test that attains the same reliability (Q_0, Q_d) as the sequential test when detecting the same standard signal. In general $\bar{n}(0)$ and $\bar{n}(\theta_0)$ are less than this number M. In the absence of any signal, or in the presence of the standard signal, the sequential test attains the specified reliability with a smaller average number of stages than required by the f.s.s. test. For signal amplitudes midway between 0 and the standard, however, the average number $\bar{n}(\theta)$ of stages may exceed M.

A further aspect of the randomness of the number n of stages of a sequential test is that n may occasionally be very large. The p.d.f. of the number n is difficult to calculate, but some indication of the variability of n is provided by its variance, for which the following rather complicated, but approximate formula can be derived,

$$\operatorname{Var} n = [\mathbf{E}(z)]^{-2}\left\{\left[1+\frac{2h(a-b)}{e^{ah}-e^{bh}}\right]\mathbf{E}(n)\operatorname{Var} z-3(a-b)^2 Q_d(1-Q_d)\right\}, \tag{3.16}$$

$$a = \ln A, \quad b = \ln B, \quad h = h(\theta),$$

with all elements evaluated for the nonrandom parameters θ. This equation holds approximately under the same conditions as for the previous ones. For such parameter values that $\mathbf{E}(z \mid H_1, \theta) = 0$, we must again apply l'Hôpital's rule, and we obtain

$$\begin{aligned} \operatorname{Var} n &= -ab(a^2+b^2)/3(\operatorname{Var} z)^2, \\ a = \ln A, \quad b &= \ln B, \quad \mathbf{E}(z) = 0. \end{aligned} \tag{3.17}$$

At signal strengths intermediate between 0 and the standard strength, both $\bar{n}$ and Var n are relatively large. Signals of these amplitudes may draw out the sequential test to inordinate lengths before a decision is reached. If such signals are likely to be present, it may be advisable to force the test to yield a decision after a certain fixed number of stages. Such a truncation of the procedure affects the reliability in a way that is difficult to calculate.

(c) *Sequential Detection of Signals of Random Phase*

When the signals $s_k(t; \theta)$ are quasiharmonic pulses with phases independently random from one signal to the next, but with a common though unknown amplitude A—not to be confused with the upper threshold in the sequential test—we can use the methods just described to set up and evaluate a sequential test for deciding whether or not a train of such signals is present in the inputs $v_1(t)$, $v_2(t)$, ..., successively observed by the receiver. We shall briefly summarize the necessary formulas, leaving their derivation to the interested reader.

The signal-to-noise ratio of an arbitrary signal is defined as in eq. (1.6); in the notation of Section 1, part (b),

$$D^2 = A^2 \int_0^T F^*(t)\, Q(t)\, dt. \tag{3.18}$$

The random variable defined by

$$r = \left| \int_0^T Q^*(t)\, V(t)\, dt \right| \cdot \left| \int_0^T Q^*(t)\, F(t)\, dt \right|^{-1/2}, \tag{3.19}$$

where $V(t)$ is the complex envelope of the input to the receiver, is distributed according to the familiar p.d.f.

$$p(r;\, D) = r \exp\left[-(r^2 + D^2)/2\right] I_0(Dr) \tag{3.20}$$

when a signal is present with amplitude A. When no signal is present, the p.d.f. of r is

$$p_0(r) = p(r;\, 0) = re^{-r^2/2}. \tag{3.21}$$

The l.l.r. is, as before,

$$z = \ln\left[p(r;\, D_0)/p_0(r)\right] = \ln I_0(D_0 r) - \tfrac{1}{2} D_0^2, \tag{3.22}$$

where D_0 is the signal-to-noise ratio of the standard signal. The statistic r is a monotone function of the l.l.r. z. At the end of each interval of duration T, the l.l.r. z is calculated or otherwise determined from the input $v(t) = \mathrm{Rl}\, V(t)\, e^{i\Omega t}$, and it is added to the sum Z carried over from the previous interval. The new value of Z is compared with the thresholds $a = \ln A$ and $b = \ln B$. If $Z < b$, the receiver decides that its inputs have contained only noise; if $Z > a$, it decides that signals of some positive but unknown amplitude have also been present. In either event the test ends. If $b < Z < a$ the receiver chooses to await further information.

To determine the probability $Q_d(D)$ of detection as a function of the signal-to-noise ratio D, one must first calculate the m.g.f. of the l.l.r. z, which is given by eq. (3.8),

$$\phi(h;\, D) = \int_0^\infty \left[\frac{p(r;\, D_0)}{p_0(r)}\right]^h p(r;\, D)\, dr = \exp(-hD_0^2/2) \int_0^\infty [I_0(D_0 r)]^h\, p(r;\, D)\, dr. \tag{3.23}$$

This function cannot be obtained in closed form. A power series can be worked out by expanding the function $[I_0(x)]^h$ in powers of x, substituting into eq. (3.23), and integrating term by term by means of eq. (F.6) of

Appendix F. The result is, in terms of $S_0 = D_0^2/2$ and $S = D^2/2$,

$$\phi(h;\, D) = 1+\tfrac{1}{2}h(h-1)\, S_0^2[1+\tfrac{2}{3}(h-2)\, S_0+\tfrac{1}{4}(3h^2-11h+11)\, S_0^2] + hSS_0[1+(h-1)\, S_0+\tfrac{1}{2}(h-1)(3h-4)\, S_0^2]+\tfrac{1}{4}h(2h-1)\, S^2S_0^2+\dots \quad (3.24)$$

When a signal whose signal-to-noise ratio is $D = (2S)^{\frac{1}{2}}$ is present, the expected value and the variance of the l.l.r. z are

$$\mathbf{E}(z \mid H_1,\, D) = -\tfrac{1}{2}S_0^2(1-\tfrac{4}{3}S_0+\tfrac{11}{4}S_0^2)+SS_0(1-S_0+2S_0^2)-\tfrac{1}{4}S^2S_0^2+\dots \quad (3.25)$$

$$\operatorname{Var} z = S_0^2(1+2S-2S_0)+O(S_0^4),$$

and the root of the equation $\phi(h;\, D) = 1$ is approximately

$$h(D) \cong 1-2S/S_0. \quad (3.26)$$

These results can be put into the equations given previously for calculating the probability of detection, the average sample number, and the variance of the number of stages. The approximation is most reliable when both S and S_0 are small and the average sample number $\bar{n}(D)$ is very large.

It is a temptation to approximate the l.l.r. in eq. (3.22) by expanding the logarithm as in eq. (1.8) and keeping only the term proportional to r^2. The system would then accumulate the statistics

$$z' = -\tfrac{1}{2}D_0^2+\tfrac{1}{4}D_0^2r^2$$

from each observation interval. However, as Bussgang and Mudgett (1960) and Blasbalg (1961) have pointed out, the expected value of z' when no signal is present vanishes, $\mathbf{E}(z' \mid H_0) = 0$, and the test may run through many stages before a decision is reached. They suggested replacing the term of fourth order in the expansion

$$z = -\tfrac{1}{2}D_0^2+\tfrac{1}{4}D_0^2r^2-\tfrac{1}{64}D_0^4r^4+O(r^6)$$

by its expected value under hypothesis H_0 to obtain the approximate test statistic

$$z'' = -\tfrac{1}{2}D_0^2+\tfrac{1}{4}D_0^2r^2-\tfrac{1}{8}D_0^4.$$

By solving the integral equations arising in the exact analysis of the sequential test, Kendall (1965) calculated the false-alarm probability Q_0 and the average number $\bar{n}(0)$ of stages under H_0 for a sequential test using the statistic

$$z = -\tfrac{1}{2}D_0^2+\tfrac{1}{4}D_0^2r^2+\beta,$$

where β is an arbitrary constant. He found that both Q_0 and $\bar{n}(0)$ are much larger when $\beta = 0$ and $z = z'$ than when $\beta = -D_0^4/8$ and $z = z''$. The principal reason for preferring z' or z'' over z of eq. (3.22) is that a quadratic rectifier is more easily constructed than one having the characteristic $\ln I_0(x)$. The approximation actually used, however, must be carefully selected if the advantages of the sequential test are to be preserved.

(d) *Sequential Detection of Targets of Unknown Distance*

In searching for targets by means of radar, it is usually necessary to detect those lying anywhere in a range many times longer than the spatial length of a signal. The echoes may arrive at any time during the so-called "interpulse interval" T_p between transmitted pulses. We have already briefly treated the problem of detecting a signal of unknown arrival time in the input $v(t)$ during a single interpulse interval, and we shall return to it in Chapter IX. At the risk of prematurity we wish to describe here some efforts to apply sequential detection to this task.

It is customary to divide the interpulse interval T_p into subintervals of a duration T of the order of the reciprocal bandwidth of the signals to be detected. The total number of subintervals will be denoted by $K = T_p/T$. Attention is focused on signals whose leading edges reach the receiver at the beginning of a subinterval; they are substantially past by the end of the same subinterval. In our discussion we suppose the target to be stationary, so that its echoes appear at the same relative position in each interpulse interval.

The receiver contains a filter matched to such a signal over an interval of duration T, and the output of this filter is rectified and sampled at the end of each subinterval to provide a statistic r of the form of eq. (3.19). (In practice the matching may be imprecise.) During the jth interpulse interval T_p the receiver thus generates K samples $r_1^{(j)}, r_2^{(j)}, \ldots, r_K^{(j)}$, which are statistically nearly independent. It is on these that its decisions are based.

In the sequential detection system proposed by Marcus and Swerling (1962) it is postulated that at most one signal is present, and that it may appear with equal probability $1/K$ in each of the subintervals. At the end of each interpulse interval the receiver forms an average likelihood ratio for the data received since the beginning of the test. Under the approximation that the data $r_k^{(j)}$ are statistically independent, the average likelihood ratio at the end of the mth interpulse interval is

$$\Lambda_m = K^{-1} \sum_{s=1}^{K} \prod_{j=1}^{m} [p_1(r_s^{(j)})/p_0(r_s^{(j)})], \tag{3.27}$$

where $p_0(r)$ is the p.d.f. of the datum r when no signal is present, and $p_1(r) = p(r; \theta_0)$ is the p.d.f. of r when a standard signal is present, an average having been taken over any random parameters such as the phase. Since a standard signal can appear in no more than one subinterval, the terms in the summation in eq. (3.27) contained factors $p_0(r_i^{(j)})$, $i \neq s$, which cancelled from numerator and denominator.

This average likelihood ratio $\bar{\Lambda}_m$ is compared with decision levels A and B determined by Wald's approximations as in eq. (3.6), and the decisions are made as previously described. If $B < \bar{\Lambda}_m < A$, the transmitter is ordered to send out another pulse, and data are collected from the following interval to permit forming a new likelihood ratio $\bar{\Lambda}_{m+1}$. Marcus and Swerling simulated such a sequential test on a digital computer and obtained average sample numbers as functions of the signal-to-noise ratio and the reliability of detection. The test was found to require a somewhat smaller signal-to-noise ratio than a fixed-sample-size test with the same reliability and a total number M of stages equal to the average sample number of the sequential test. The saving in signal-to-noise ratio was the smaller, the greater the number K of subintervals. They also observed that for signal strengths intermediate between 0 and the standard strength the average number of stages did not become much larger than the average sample numbers for the zero and the standard strengths. Truncation of such a sequential test to avoid excessive lengths may be unnecessary.

An alternative suggested by Kendall and Reed (1963) allows a signal to appear in any subinterval with a probability q; the probability distribution of the total number of targets is then binomial. They presented the form of the likelihood ratio for this test and pointed out that as with the Marcus and Swerling test, simulation would be necessary to evaluate its performance.

In another form of sequential detection a sequential test is applied to the data from each subinterval. Pulses are transmitted in a certain direction until the tests of all K subintervals have terminated. If at the kth stage, for instance, the sequential test for the jth subinterval has not yet reached a final decision, the receiver will use the data $r_j^{(1)}, r_j^{(2)}, \ldots, r_j^{(k)}$ to form a likelihood ratio

$$\Lambda_j^{(k)} = \Lambda(r_j^{(1)}, \ldots, r_j^{(k)}) = \prod_{s=1}^{k} p_1(r_j^{(s)})/p_0(r_j^{(s)}),$$

which is compared with two levels A and B. If $\Lambda_j^{(k)} < B$, the receiver decides that no target is present in the jth subinterval, and if $\Lambda_j^{(k)} > A$, it decides that there is a target there. In either event the test for the jth subinterval terminates, and the data $r_j^{(i)}$ from future interpulse intervals $(i > k)$ are disregarded. If on the other hand $B < \Lambda_j^{(k)} < A$, the jth subinterval will be examined again after the $(k+1)$th pulse is transmitted.

The average number of pulses needed to attain a specified reliability with such a system has been calculated in some representative cases by Reed and Selin (1963) and Bussgang and Ehrman (1965). The writer has worked out the median number of pulses transmitted when no signal is present, as a function of the number K of subintervals. This number roughly determines the average time needed to scan a fixed portion of the sky that is empty of targets (Helstrom, 1962). The ratio of the median number to the number M of pulses needed by an f.s.s. system of the same reliability is, for low standard signal-to-noise ratios, independent of the strength of the standard signal. This ratio ranges from about 0.3 to about 0.6 as K increases from 10 to 1000, for detection probabilities between 0.9 and 0.999 and an average false-alarm probability for all K subintervals of 10^{-6}. Thus the sequential system enables a given part of the sky to be scanned in about half the time needed by a conventional radar, when few targets are present.

(e) *Sequential Detection of a Single Coherent Signal*

Suppose that a signal $s(t)$ known in all details, including time of arrival and phase, is to be detected in additive Gaussian noise $n(t)$. The receiver begins observing its input $v(t)$ at time $t = 0$. Instead of waiting until the end of an interval of fixed duration T, it makes a decision as soon as it can do so with some specified reliability. The length τ of the observation interval is now a continuous random variable. Such a sequential detection procedure has been analyzed by Selin (1964).

The system is simplest when the signal is constant, $s(t) \equiv s$, and the noise is white. At each time τ the receiver must generate the l.l.r.

$$z(\tau) = (2s/N) \int_0^\tau v(t)\, dt - s^2\tau/N,$$

whose form follows directly from eq. (IV, 1.14) as adapted to an observation interval of duration τ. The l.l.r. $z(\tau)$ is compared at each instant τ with two decision levels $a = \ln A$ and $b = \ln B$ chosen by Wald's formulas, eq. (3.6), which for this continuous sequential procedure are exact. As soon as $z(\tau)$ crosses one level or the other, the test stops and the corresponding hypothesis is adopted. To implement the procedure it is only necessary to integrate the input and to compare $\int_0^\tau v(t)\, dt$ with linearly increasing limits $Nb/2s+\frac{1}{2}s\tau$ and $Na/2s+\frac{1}{2}s\tau$.

A binary communication system utilizing such continuous sequential detection has been studied by Viterbi (1965). The symbol "1" is sent as a continuous sinusoid; for the symbol "0" the transmitter is cut off. The receiver observes its input until the logarithmic likelihood ratio crosses one of two limits selected for a preassigned probability of error, $Q_0 = 1 - Q_d = \varepsilon$. At that instant the receiver signals the transmitter over a noiseless feed-back channel to drop the current message symbol and to begin sending the next one.

Viterbi showed that if the signals could be sent instantaneously, this sequential system could operate with about one-fourth the average power needed by a system transmitting signals of fixed duration with the same probability of error. He also analyzed a system sending M symbols by continuous sinusoids of widely separated frequencies; similar savings were discovered. A finite delay in the transmission of the message and the feed-back signals reduces the saving in average power.

Turin (1965) has treated a system in which the l.l.r. itself is returned to the transmitter over a noiseless channel. There it determines the form of the transmitted signal as well as the time when the transmitter goes on to the next symbol. The optimum forms of the signals under average- and peak-power constraints were worked out. This problem has been discussed further by Horstein (1966). Coding and decoding for a communication system equipped with a noiseless feedback channel has been analyzed by Schalkwijk and Kailath (1966).

PROBLEMS

1. Show that an equation of the form of eq. (III, 2.17) holds for the average probability of detecting a signal $s(t; \boldsymbol{\theta})$ in noise when the parameters $\boldsymbol{\theta}$ of the signal are distributed according to a given prior p.d.f. $z(\boldsymbol{\theta})$.

2. In certain rapidly fading communication channels the amplitude A of the signal can be described by the Rayleigh distribution,

$$z(A) = (A/s^2) \exp(-A^2/2s^2),$$

and the amplitudes of successive signals can be assumed statistically independent. In a binary communication system operating over such a channel, a signal proportional to $\text{Rl}\, F(t)e^{i\Omega t}$ is repeated M times and received as $s_k(t)$ of eq. (1.1), $k = 1, 2, \ldots, M$, with its phases ψ_k independently random and its amplitudes A_k distributed as just stated. Assuming that the noise is white and Gaussian, show that the optimum detector at all signal-to-noise ratios uses the statistic L of eq. (1.12). Show that L is chi-squared distributed under both hypotheses, and find the probabilities of mistaking a "1" for a "0" and vice versa.

Hint. In the last part use the result of Problem 1.

3. Derive the chi-squared distribution under hypothesis H_1 for the statistic L of the previous problem by averaging the characteristic function of eq. (2.8) over the distribution of the amplitudes A_k, taken as statistically independent.

4. For any statistic g we can define an equivalent signal-to-noise ratio D by the equation

$$D^2 = [\mathbf{E}(g \mid H_1) - \mathbf{E}(g \mid H_0)]^2/\mathrm{Var}_0\, g,$$

where the variance $\mathrm{Var}_0\, g$ is evaluated under hypothesis H_0. When the statistic g is nearly Gaussian, as it will be, by the Central Limit Theorem, if it is the sum of a large number of random variables, the detectability of a signal depends largely on the value of D. Calculate the equivalent signal-to-noise ratios D for the two threshold detectors of Section 1, part (c), when the squared signal amplitudes are proportional to the beam factor $f(\theta_k)$, and show by Schwarz's inequality that the second detector has the greater value of D.

5. The signals $s_k(t)$ are known completely except for a common amplitude A. They arrive at a known time in the midst of white Gaussian noise of unilateral spectral density N, and in the kth observation interval of duration T the input to the receiver is either $(H_0)\ v_k(t) = n_k(t)$ or $(H_1)\ v_k(t) = s_k(t) + n_k(t)$. Take a standard signal of energy E_0 and signal-to-noise ratio $d_0 = (2E_0/N)^{\frac{1}{2}}$, which is to be detected with probability $Q_d(d_0)$, and set up a sequential probability ratio test of the kind described in Section 3. (a) Express the logarithmic likelihood ratio z_j for the jth interval in terms of the input $v_j(t)$ during that interval. (b) Show that z_j is Gaussian and derive its mean and variance when a signal of energy E is present. (c) Let $d = (2E/N)^{\frac{1}{2}}$. Find the moment-generating function $\phi(h;\, d)$ of the statistic z, and prove eq. (3.10). (d) Write down formulas for the probability $Q_d(d)$ of detection and the average number $\bar{n}(d)$ of stages of the sequential test. (e) Plot $\bar{n}(d)$ and $Q_d(d)$ as functions of the signal-to-noise ratio d for $0 < d < d_0 = 1$, with $Q_d(d_0) = 0.90$, $Q_0 = 10^{-6}$. Use the approximations given in the text.

6. Work out a sequential system for deciding whether the variance of a Gaussian noise input is N_0 or N_1, $N_1 > N_0$. The second variance N_1 may represent the sum of the variance N_0 of ordinary noise and the variance $N_s = N_1 - N_0$ of an independent noise-like signal added to it. Such a signal could be the output of a radar jamming transmitter. Available are independent samples $x_1, x_2, \ldots$ of the input; their mean values are 0. (a) Find the 1.1.r. $z_j = \ln\, [p_1(x_j)/p_0(x_j)]$, where $p_0(x_j)$ and $p_1(x_j)$ are Gaussian p.d.f.s of mean 0 and variances N_0, N_1 respectively. (b) Show that if the true variance of the data is N, $N > N_0$, the m.g.f. of the statistic z is

$$\phi(h;\, N) = (N_0/N_1)^{h/2}\left[1 - \frac{(N_1 - N_0)N}{N_0 N_1}\,h\right]^{-\frac{1}{2}}.$$

(c) Calculate the mean and variance of z when the true noise variance is N. (d) Show how to determine the probability of detection and the average number $\bar{n}$ of stages of the test as functions of N. Use the approximate formulas given in the text.

7. Outline a sequential system to detect the 0's and 1's transmitted over the fading channel of Problem 2. Suppose that there is a noiseless channel whereby the receiver can tell the transmitter when to stop repeating one symbol of the message and go on to the next. Assume that the signal amplitudes and phases are independently random, and set the system up for signals arriving with amplitudes drawn from a standard Rayleigh distribution with the parameter s equal to s_0. Determine the 1.1.r. z, and calculate its m.g.f. $\phi(h;\, s)$, its mean, and its variance when the true parameter of the Rayleigh distribution is s (Basharian and Fleishman, 1959).

8. For detectors using linear and quadratic rectifiers, as described in Section 1, show that the asymptotic relative efficiency of the latter with respect to the former is equal to $4(4-\pi)/\pi = 1.0926$. Use eqs. (F.7–F.9) of Appendix F for the required moments.

9. Show that in the notation of part (e), Section 2, $\mathbf{E}[L_1(\mathbf{x}) \mid H_0] = 0$. *Hint.* Start with the formula $\int p_1(\mathbf{x};\, a,\, \boldsymbol{\theta}')\, d^n\mathbf{x} = 1$, differentiate with respect to a, and pass to the limit $a \to 0$.

BIBLIOGRAPHY (VII)

1934 PEARSON, K., *Tables of the Incomplete Gamma-Function*, Cambridge University Press, Cambridge, England.

1945 WALD, A., "Sequential Tests of Statistical Hypotheses", *Ann. Math. Stat.* **16,** 117–86 (June).

1946 CRAMÉR, H., *Mathematical Methods of Statistics*, Princeton University Press, Princeton, N.J.

1947 WALD, A., *Sequential Analysis*, John Wiley & Sons, Inc., New York, N.Y.

1948 MARCUM, J. I., *A Statistical Theory of Target Detection by Pulsed Radar*, Rand Corp. Rept. RM-753, July 1, 1948. Reprinted in *Trans. I.R.E.* **IT-6,** 59–267 (Apr. 1960).

SAMUELSON, P. A., "Exact Distribution of Continuous Variables in Sequential Analysis", *Econometrica* **16,** 191–8.

1950 KEMPERMAN, H. H. B., "The General One-dimensional Random Walk with Absorbing Barriers with Applications to Sequential Analysis", M.A. Thesis, University of Amsterdam.

MARCUM, J. I., *Tables of Q-Functions*, Rand Corp. Rept. RM-339, Jan. 1, 1950.

WOODWARD, P. M. and DAVIES, I. L., "A Theory of Radar Information", *Phil. Mag.* **41,** 1001–17 (Oct.).

1952 HARVARD COMPUTATION LABORATORY, *Tables of the Error Function and of its First Twenty Derivatives*, Harvard University Press, Cambridge, Mass.

1953 MIDDLETON, D., "Statistical Criteria for the Detection of Pulsed Carriers in Noise", *J. Appl. Phys.* **24,** 371–8, 379–91 (Apr.).

1954 ERDÉLYI, A. *et al.*, *Tables of Integral Transforms*, vol. 1, McGraw-Hill Book Co., New York, N.Y.

1955 BUSSGANG, J. J. and MIDDLETON, D., "Optimum Sequential Detection of Signals in Noise", *Trans. I.R.E.* **IT-1,** 5–18 (Dec.).

1957 BLASBALG, H., "The Relationship of Sequential Filter Theory to Information Theory and its Application to the Detection of Signals in Noise by Bernoulli Trials", *Trans. I.R.E.* **IT-3,** 122–31 (June).

BLASBALG, H., "The Sequential Detection of a Sine-wave Carrier of Arbitrary Duty Ratio in Gaussian Noise", *Trans. I.R.E.* **IT-3,** 248–56 (Dec.).

FLEISHMAN, B. S., "On the Optimal Detector with a log I_0 Characteristic for the Detection of a Weak Signal in the Presence of Noise", *Radio Engrg. and Elect. Phys.* **2,** no. 6, 75–85.

1958 PACHARES, J., "A Table of Bias Levels useful in Radar Detection Problems", *Trans. I.R.E.* **IT-4,** 38–45 (Mar.).

1959 BASHARIAN, A. E. and FLEISHMAN, B. S., "The Application of Sequential Analysis to Binary Communication Systems with a Rayleigh Distribution of Signal Intensity Fluctuations", *Radio Engrg. and Elect. Phys.* **4,** no. 2, 1–9.

1960 BUSSGANG, J. J. and MUDGETT, W. L., "A Note of Caution on the Square-law Approximation to an Optimum Detector", *Trans. I.R.E.* **IT-6,** 504–5 (Sept.).

MIDDLETON, D., *An Introduction to Statistical Communication Theory*, McGraw-Hill Book Co., New York, N.Y.

1961 BLASBALG, H., "On the Approximation to Likelihood Ratio Detectors [*sic*] Laws (The Threshold Case)", *Trans. I.R.E.* **IT-7,** 194–5 (July).

CAPON, J., "On the Asymptotic Efficiency of Locally Optimum Detectors", *Trans. I.R.E.* **IT-7,** 67–71 (Apr.).

1962 HELSTROM, C. W., "A Range-sampled Sequential Detection System", *Trans. I.R.E.* **IT-8,** 43–47 (Jan.).

MARCUS, M. B. and SWERLING, P., "Sequential Detection in Radar with Multiple Resolution Elements", *Trans. I.R.E.* **IT-8**, 237–45 (Apr.).

1963 KENDALL, W. B. and REED, I. S., "A Sequential Test for Radar Detection of Multiple Targets", *Trans. I.E.E.E.* **IT-9**, 51–53 (Jan.).

REED, I. S. and SELIN, I., "A Sequential Test for the Presence of a Signal in One of *k* Possible Positions", *Trans. I.E.E.E.* **IT-9**, 286–8 (Oct.).

1964 SELIN, I., "The Sequential Estimation and Detection of Signals in Normal Noise", *Info. and Control*, (I) **7**, 512–34 (Dec.), (II) **8**, 1–35 (Feb. 1965).

1965 BUSSGANG, J. J. and EHRMAN, L., "A Sequential Test for a Target in One of *k* Range Positions", *Proc. I.E.E.E.* **53**, 495–6 (May).

DILLARD, G. M., "The Binomial Marcus and Swerling Test", *Trans. I.E.E.E.* **IT-11**, 145–7 (Jan.).

FRY, T. C., *Probability and its Engineering Uses*, 2nd ed., D. Van Nostrand Co., Princeton, N.J.

GAGLIARDI, R. M. and REED, I. S., "On Sequential Detection of Emerging Targets", *Trans. I.E.E.E.* **IT-11**, 260–3 (Apr.).

KENDALL, W.B., "Performance of the Biased Square-law Sequential Detector in the Absence of Signal", *Trans. I.E.E.E.* **IT-11**, 83–90 (Jan.).

TURIN, G., "Signal Design for Sequential Detection Systems with Feedback", *Trans. I.E.E.E.* **IT-11**, 401–8 (July).

VITERBI, A., "The Effect of Sequential Decision Feedback on Communication over the Gaussian Channel", *Info. and Control* **8**, 80–92 (Feb.).

1966 HORSTEIN, M., "On the Design of Signals for Sequential and Nonsequential Detection Systems with Feedback", *Trans. I.E.E.E.* **IT-12**, 448–55 (Oct.).

MIDDLETON, D., "Canonically Optimum Threshold Detection", *Trans. I.E.E.E.* **IT-12**, 230–43 (Apr.).

SCHALKWIJK, J. P. M. and KAILATH T., "A Coding System for Additive Noise Channels with Feedback—Part I: No Bandwidth Constraint", *Trans I.E.E.E.* **IT-12**, 172–82 (Apr.).

SCHALKWIJK, J. P. M., "A Coding System for Additive Noise Channels with Feedback—Part II: Band-Limited Signals", *Trans. I.E.E.E.* **IT-12**, 183–9 (Apr.).

STEIN, S., "Decision-oriented Diversity for Digital Transmission", chap. XI, pp. 490–584, in *Communication Systems and Techniques*, M. SCHWARTZ, W. R. BENNETT and S. STEIN, McGraw-Hill Book Co., New York, N.Y.

TURIN, G. L., "Comparison of Sequential and Nonsequential Detection Systems with Uncertainty Feedback", *Trans. I.E.E.E.* **IT–12**, 5–8 (Jan.).

VIII

THE ESTIMATION OF SIGNAL PARAMETERS

1. THE THEORY OF ESTIMATION

A radar has more to do than simply detect targets; it must find where they are and how they are moving. For this purpose it must estimate the values of certain parameters of the received echo signals, and because of the noise the estimates will be in error. The theory of estimation shows us how to design the receiver to minimize errors due to noise, and it tells us how large the irreducible residual errors will on the average be.

The location of a target involves its distance and its direction. The distance is proportional to the interval between transmission of a radar pulse and reception of its echo, and to measure it the radar must determine the instant when the echo arrives. It might do so by timing the peak of the received signal, but exactly when this peak occurs is made uncertain by the noise. The azimuth of the target can be estimated by comparing the amplitudes of successive echoes as the radar antenna rotates. By changing those amplitudes in a random, unpredictable way the noise introduces error. A measurement of the Doppler-shifted carrier frequency of the echo yields the component of the target velocity in the direction of the radar; this too will be falsified by the noise.

A radar echo can be represented in the form

$$s(t; A, \psi, \tau, \Omega) = A \operatorname{Rl} F(t-\tau) \exp (i\Omega t + i\psi), \tag{1.1}$$

where $F(t)$ is the complex envelope of the pulse, A its amplitude, τ its time of arrival or *epoch*, Ω its carrier frequency, and ψ its r.f. phase. The input to the receiver is

$$v(t) = s(t; A, \psi, \tau, \Omega) + n(t), \tag{1.2}$$

with $n(t)$ the random noise; and from the input $v(t)$ observed during a certain interval the receiver is to determine the values of the unknown parameters A, τ, and Ω. The joint p.d.f. of a set $\mathbf{x} = \{v(t_i)\}$ of samples of the input at times t_i depends on those parameters through the signal,

$$p(\mathbf{x}; A, \psi, \tau, \Omega) = p_0(\{x_i - s(t_i; A, \psi, \tau, \Omega)\}), \tag{1.3}$$

where $p_0(\{n(t_i)\})$ is the joint p.d.f. of samples of the random noise at times t_i. In this way the unknowns become parameters of the distribution of the observations $\mathbf{x}$.

The phase ψ carries no useful information about the target when, as often, the phase of the transmitted pulse is uncontrolled. Over such an uninformative parameter the joint p.d.f. will generally be averaged with respect to an accepted prior distribution,

$$p(\mathbf{x};\, A, \tau, \Omega) = \int_0^{2\pi} z(\psi)\, p(\mathbf{x};\, A, \psi, \tau, \Omega)\, d\psi, \tag{1.4}$$

to provide a joint density function of the observations that depends only on the quantities of interest. We seek values of A, τ, and Ω for which the joint p.d.f. $p(\mathbf{x};\, A, \tau, \Omega)$ in some sense best describes the observations $\mathbf{x}$.

Signal parameters may also have to be estimated in communications. Suppose that we wish to transmit numerical data that can take on arbitrary values within a limited range, as in telemetry when the temperature or pressure at a point is to be conveyed periodically to a distant observer. The amplitudes of a succession of pulses might be set by the data, or their carrier frequencies might be caused to deviate proportionally from a reference frequency stored at transmitter and receiver. The receiver would then have to estimate the amplitudes or the frequencies as the pulses arrive mixed with random noise, and it should be able to do so as accurately as possible.

The theory of estimation presupposes that one knows the probability density $p(\mathbf{x};\, \boldsymbol{\theta})$ of the outcomes of a set of measurements as a function of m unknown parameters $\boldsymbol{\theta} = (\theta_1, \theta_2, \ldots, \theta_m)$. One seeks a strategy that on the basis of measured values of the n random variables $\mathbf{x} = (x_1, x_2, \ldots, x_n)$ assigns some value $\hat{\theta}_k$ as an estimate of the kth parameter; such an estimation strategy is expressed as a function $\hat{\theta}_k = \hat{\theta}_k(x_1, x_2, \ldots, x_n) = \hat{\theta}_k(\mathbf{x})$ of the data. The collection of m such estimates we can designate by the vector $\hat{\boldsymbol{\theta}} = (\hat{\theta}_1, \hat{\theta}_2, \ldots, \hat{\theta}_m) = \hat{\boldsymbol{\theta}}(\mathbf{x})$. It is not always necessary to estimate all the unknown parameters; some may be uninformative. We shall assume that the dependence on uninformative parameters has been removed by averaging with respect to some prior p.d.f. and that the m unknown parameters $\boldsymbol{\theta}$ remaining are all to be estimated.

Since the data $\mathbf{x}$ are random variables, no two experiments will yield the same values of the estimate $\hat{\boldsymbol{\theta}}(\mathbf{x})$, even though the true set of parameters $\boldsymbol{\theta}$ is the same in both. The most one can hope for is that the estimates $\hat{\theta}_k$ will be close to the true values θ_k "on the average". Given a set of strategies, or "estimators" $\hat{\boldsymbol{\theta}}(\mathbf{x})$, and the joint p.d.f.s $p(\mathbf{x};\, \boldsymbol{\theta})$, one can calculate a conditional p.d.f. $p(\hat{\boldsymbol{\theta}}; \boldsymbol{\theta})$ of the estimates $\hat{\boldsymbol{\theta}}$. One would like this conditional p.d.f. to be sharply peaked in the neighborhood of the true values $\boldsymbol{\theta}$.

If the expected value $\mathbf{E}(\hat{\theta}_k(\mathbf{x}) \mid \boldsymbol{\theta})$ equals θ_k, the estimate of this parameter is said to be *unbiased*; if not, the difference $\mathbf{E}(\hat{\theta}_k \mid \boldsymbol{\theta}) - \theta_k$ is called the *bias* of the estimate. Both the bias of an estimate and its variance should be small, and it is often necessary to compromise between these requirements. Just as it was necessary in the testing of hypotheses (Chapter III) to adopt a criterion specifying the quality of a decision strategy, we must before seeking an estimation strategy establish a criterion by which to measure its effectiveness and value.

(a) *Bayes Estimates*

(i) *The Bayes risk*. Sometimes it is possible to specify both the cost of an error in estimation and the prior p.d.f.s of the unknown parameters, much as in hypothesis testing the costs of incorrect decisions and the prior probabilities of the hypotheses may be available. The cost to the experimenter of assigning a set of estimates $\hat{\boldsymbol{\theta}}$ to the parameters when their true values are given by $\boldsymbol{\theta} = (\theta_1, \theta_2, \ldots, \theta_m)$ will be a function $C(\hat{\boldsymbol{\theta}}, \boldsymbol{\theta})$ of the true values and the estimates. As a function of the estimates, it is smallest for $\hat{\boldsymbol{\theta}} = \boldsymbol{\theta}$, often depending only on the differences $(\hat{\theta}_k - \theta_k)$ between the estimates and the true values of the parameters. Given such a prior p.d.f. $z(\boldsymbol{\theta})$ and a cost function $C(\hat{\boldsymbol{\theta}}, \boldsymbol{\theta})$, the observer is in a position to adopt the Bayes criterion that the estimation strategy should yield the minimum average risk per experiment.

If one makes a fixed number n of measurements $\mathbf{x} = (x_1, x_2, \ldots, x_n)$, whose joint p.d.f. is $p(\mathbf{x}; \boldsymbol{\theta})$, the risk $R\big(\hat{\boldsymbol{\theta}}(\mathbf{x}); \boldsymbol{\theta}\big)$ incurred by using the estimator $\hat{\boldsymbol{\theta}}(\mathbf{x})$ is

$$R\big(\hat{\boldsymbol{\theta}}(\mathbf{x}); \boldsymbol{\theta}\big) = \int C\big(\hat{\boldsymbol{\theta}}(\mathbf{x}), \boldsymbol{\theta}\big)\, p(\mathbf{x}; \boldsymbol{\theta})\, d^n\mathbf{x} \tag{1.5}$$

when the true parameters are $\boldsymbol{\theta}$. (Compare this expression with the risk defined in Chapter III, Section 2.) The average risk per experiment is obtained by averaging with respect to the prior p.d.f. of the parameters $\boldsymbol{\theta}$,

$$\begin{aligned} \bar{C} = \bar{C}\big[\hat{\boldsymbol{\theta}}(\mathbf{x})\big] &= \int z(\boldsymbol{\theta})\, R\big(\hat{\boldsymbol{\theta}}(\mathbf{x}); \boldsymbol{\theta}\big)\, d^m\boldsymbol{\theta} \\ &= \int d^n\mathbf{x} \int d^m\boldsymbol{\theta}\, z(\boldsymbol{\theta})\, C\big(\widehat{\boldsymbol{\theta}}(\mathbf{x}), \boldsymbol{\theta}\big)\, p(\mathbf{x}; \boldsymbol{\theta}). \end{aligned} \tag{1.6}$$

A set $\hat{\boldsymbol{\theta}}(\mathbf{x})$ of estimators that minimizes this average risk provides the *Bayes estimates*, and the minimum value $\bar{C}_{\min}$ of the average risk they entail is called the *Bayes risk*.

(ii) *The conditional risk*. As in hypothesis testing, the Bayes strategy can be described as the one that minimizes the conditional risk $C(\hat{\boldsymbol{\theta}} \mid \mathbf{x})$, which we shall now define. It involves the posterior probability density function $p(\boldsymbol{\theta} \,|\, \mathbf{x})$ of the parameters $\boldsymbol{\theta}$, given the measured values of the random variables $\mathbf{x}$,

$$\begin{aligned} p(\boldsymbol{\theta} \,|\, \mathbf{x}) &= z(\boldsymbol{\theta})\, p(\mathbf{x}; \boldsymbol{\theta})/p(\mathbf{x}), \\ p(\mathbf{x}) &= \int d^m\boldsymbol{\theta}\, z(\boldsymbol{\theta})\, p(\mathbf{x}; \boldsymbol{\theta}), \end{aligned} \tag{1.7}$$

where $p(\mathbf{x})$ is the over-all p.d.f. of the outcomes $\mathbf{x}$. Of all experiments in which data close to the vector $\mathbf{x}$ are obtained, the fraction in which the true values of the parameters lie in a small volume element $d^m\boldsymbol{\theta}$ about the point $\boldsymbol{\theta} = (\theta_1, \theta_2, \ldots, \theta_m)$ is $p(\boldsymbol{\theta} \,|\, \mathbf{x})\, d^m\boldsymbol{\theta}$.

The conditional risk $C(\hat{\boldsymbol{\theta}} \,|\, \mathbf{x})$ is the average risk to the experimenter in all such trials in which sets of outcomes near $\mathbf{x}$ are obtained; that is,

$$\begin{aligned} C(\hat{\boldsymbol{\theta}} \,|\, \mathbf{x}) &= \int C(\hat{\boldsymbol{\theta}}, \boldsymbol{\theta})\, p(\boldsymbol{\theta} \,|\, \mathbf{x})\, d^m\boldsymbol{\theta} \\ &= \int d^m\boldsymbol{\theta}\, z(\boldsymbol{\theta})\, C(\hat{\boldsymbol{\theta}}, \boldsymbol{\theta})\, p(\mathbf{x}; \boldsymbol{\theta})/p(\mathbf{x}). \end{aligned} \tag{1.8}$$

This conditional risk is a function of the outcomes $\mathbf{x}$ and the resultant values $\hat{\boldsymbol{\theta}}$ of the estimates. In terms of it the average risk $\bar{C}$ given in eq. (1.6) is

$$\bar{C} = \int C(\hat{\boldsymbol{\theta}} \,|\, \mathbf{x})\, p(\mathbf{x})\, d^n\mathbf{x}.$$

Since the p.d.f. $p(\mathbf{x})$ is positive over the range of possible values of the outcomes $\mathbf{x}$, the average risk $\bar{C}$ is minimized by making the conditional risk $C(\hat{\boldsymbol{\theta}} \,|\, \mathbf{x})$ as small as possible for each value of $\mathbf{x}$.

The requirement that $C(\hat{\boldsymbol{\theta}} \,|\, \mathbf{x})$ be minimum for each value of $\mathbf{x}$ defines the set of functions $\hat{\boldsymbol{\theta}}(\mathbf{x})$ making up the Bayes estimate. If the conditional risk is a continuous function of the estimates $\hat{\boldsymbol{\theta}}$, the estimators $\hat{\boldsymbol{\theta}}(\mathbf{x})$ can be found by solving the equations

$$\partial C(\hat{\boldsymbol{\theta}} \,|\, \mathbf{x})/\partial\hat{\theta}_k = 0, \quad k = 1, 2, \ldots, m,$$

and using the set of roots for which the conditional risk in eq. (1.8) takes on its smallest value.

(iii) *The quadratic cost function.* In estimating a single parameter θ it is often convenient to adopt a cost function proportional to the square of the difference between the true value and the estimate,

$$C(\hat{\theta}, \theta) = \gamma(\theta)\, (\hat{\theta} - \theta)^2, \tag{1.9}$$

where $\gamma(\theta)$ is independent of the estimate $\hat{\theta}$. Any convex cost function that is continuous and differentiable can be expanded in a Taylor series in $\hat{\theta}$ about the point $\hat{\theta} = \theta$; eq. (1.9) is the leading term of such an expansion. When $\gamma(\theta) \equiv 1$, using the quadratic cost function and the Bayes criterion is equivalent to demanding an estimate whose mean-square error, averaged with respect to $z(\theta)$, is minimum.

By minimizing the conditional risk, eq. (1.8), we find that with the quadratic cost function the Bayes estimate of the parameter θ is

$$\hat{\theta}(\mathbf{x}) = \int \theta\gamma(\theta)\, p(\theta \,|\, \mathbf{x})\, d\theta \Big/ \int \gamma(\theta)\, p(\theta \,|\, \mathbf{x})\, d\theta. \tag{1.10}$$

For $\gamma(\theta) \equiv 1$, the Bayes estimate is simply the conditional expected value of the parameter θ,

$$\hat{\theta}(\mathbf{x}) = \mathbf{E}(\theta \,|\, \mathbf{x}) = \int \theta p(\theta \,|\, \mathbf{x})\, d\theta. \tag{1.11}$$

This estimate remains a functional of the prior p.d.f. $z(\theta)$ of the unknown parameter.

The conditional expected value is the Bayes estimate under somewhat more general circumstances. What is required is that as a function of θ, the posterior p.d.f. $p(\theta \,|\, \mathbf{x})$ have a single peak, about which it is symmetrical, and that the cost function have the properties

$$\begin{aligned} C(\hat{\theta}, \theta) &= c(\hat{\theta}-\theta), \\ c(x) &= c(-x) \geqslant 0, \\ c(x_1) &\geqslant c(x_2) \quad \text{for} \quad |x_1| \geqslant |x_2|. \end{aligned} \tag{1.12}$$

Such cost functions are quite common. They include not only the ubiquitous quadratic function $(\hat{\theta}-\theta)^2$, but also the absolute value $|\hat{\theta}-\theta|$, the function

$$C(\hat{\theta}, \theta) = 0, \quad |\hat{\theta}-\theta| < A; \quad C(\hat{\theta}, \theta) = 1, \quad |\hat{\theta}-\theta| \geqq A,$$

and the function

$$C(\hat{\theta}, \theta) = \begin{cases} 0, & |\hat{\theta}-\theta| < A, \\ \dfrac{|\hat{\theta}-\theta|-A}{B-A} & A < |\hat{\theta}-\theta| < B, \\ 1, & |\hat{\theta}-\theta| > B, \end{cases}$$

with A and B positive constants (Sherman, 1958).

When several parameters $\boldsymbol{\theta}$ are to be estimated, what corresponds to the quadratic cost function is the positive-definite quadratic form

$$C(\hat{\boldsymbol{\theta}}, \boldsymbol{\theta}) = \sum_{i=1}^{m} \sum_{j=1}^{m} \gamma_{ij}(\hat{\theta}_i-\theta_i)(\hat{\theta}_j-\theta_j), \tag{1.13}$$

in which the γ_{ij} may be, but seldom are, functions of the true values θ. If the γ_{ij} are independent of θ, the Bayes estimates are again the conditional expected values,

$$\hat{\theta}_k = \int \theta_k p(\boldsymbol{\theta} \,|\, \mathbf{x})\, d^m\boldsymbol{\theta}, \qquad k = 1, 2, \ldots, m. \tag{1.14}$$

In particular, if the p.d.f.s $z(\boldsymbol{\theta})$ and $p(\mathbf{x}; \boldsymbol{\theta})$ are multivariate Gaussian functions of both the n data x_k and the m parameters θ_k, the posterior p.d.f. $p(\boldsymbol{\theta} \mid \mathbf{x})$ is also Gaussian, and the Bayes estimate $\hat{\boldsymbol{\theta}}(\mathbf{x})$ is a linear function of $x_1, x_2, \ldots, x_n$.

(iv) *Minimax estimates.* If the prior p.d.f. $z(\boldsymbol{\theta})$ of the parameters is unknown, one can, as in the testing of composite hypotheses, seek its least favorable form. The Bayes risk $\bar{C}_{\min}$ depends on the prior p.d.f. $z(\boldsymbol{\theta})$, and the least favorable distribution is the one that maximizes this Bayes risk. The Bayes estimate for the least favorable p.d.f. $\tilde{z}(\boldsymbol{\theta})$ is a *minimax* estimate.

For all those values of the parameters assigned a positive probability density by the least favorable prior p.d.f., the risks $R(\hat{\boldsymbol{\theta}}(\mathbf{x}); \boldsymbol{\theta})$ are equal when the minimax estimate is employed,

$$\begin{aligned} R(\hat{\boldsymbol{\theta}}(\mathbf{x}); \boldsymbol{\theta}) &\equiv \int \tilde{z}(\boldsymbol{\theta})\, R(\hat{\boldsymbol{\theta}}(\mathbf{x}); \boldsymbol{\theta})\, d^m\boldsymbol{\theta} = \bar{C}_{\text{minimax}}, &\quad \tilde{z}(\boldsymbol{\theta}) > 0; \\ R(\hat{\boldsymbol{\theta}}(\mathbf{x}); \boldsymbol{\theta}) &< \bar{C}_{\text{minimax}}, &\quad \tilde{z}(\boldsymbol{\theta}) = 0, \end{aligned} \tag{1.15}$$

where $\bar{C}_{\text{minimax}}$ is the minimax risk. In using the minimax estimate the observer is assured that the average risk is never larger than $\bar{C}_{\text{minimax}}$, no matter what the true prior p.d.f. of the parameters $\boldsymbol{\theta}$. If in estimating a single parameter θ the quadratic cost function $(\hat{\theta}-\theta)^2$ is adopted, the minimax estimate when unbiased is said to have "uniformly minimum variance". The variance of the estimate $\hat{\theta}$ is then independent of the true value of the parameter.

A least favorable p.d.f. $\tilde{z}(\boldsymbol{\theta})$ may not strictly exist, as when the range of possible values of a parameter is unbounded. The least favorable situation is then one of complete ignorance about the values of the parameter. As the prior p.d.f. $z(\theta)$ for such a parameter becomes wider and wider, the Bayes risk $\bar{C}_{\min}$ continues to increase, and its least upper bound may not be attained for any ordinary probability density function $z(\theta)$. In estimating the parameters of a signal of unknown amplitude, on the other hand, the least favorable condition is the limiting one of vanishing amplitude, to which the so-called "threshold estimators" pertain.

(v) *Estimating the mean of a Gaussian distribution.* As a simple example to illustrate these ideas, let us estimate the mean m of a Gaussian distribution with known variance δ^2 by n independent observations $x_1, x_2, \ldots, x_n$ of a random variable x. Their probability density function is

$$p(\mathbf{x}; m) = (2\pi\delta^2)^{-n/2} \exp\left[-\sum_{k=1}^{n} (x_k - m)^2/2\delta^2 \right]. \tag{1.16}$$

Let us assume that previous experiments have shown the true mean m to be normally distributed with expected value μ and variance β^2,

$$z(m) = (2\pi\beta^2)^{-\frac{1}{2}} \exp[-(m-\mu)^2/2\beta^2]. \tag{1.17}$$

From the definition, eq. (1.7), we can compute the posterior p.d.f. of the true mean m, given the set of outcomes $\mathbf{x}$,

$$\begin{gathered} p(m \mid \mathbf{x}) = (2\pi\gamma^2)^{-\frac{1}{2}} \exp\left\{-\left[m-\gamma^2\left(\frac{nX}{\delta^2}+\frac{\mu}{\beta^2}\right)\right]^2 \Big/ 2\gamma^2\right\}, \\ \gamma^{-2} = n\delta^{-2}+\beta^{-2}, \end{gathered} \tag{1.18}$$

where X is the sample mean, $X = \sum_{k=1}^{n} x_k/n$.

We shall use the quadratic cost function $C(\hat{m}, m) = (\hat{m}-m)^2$. According to eq. (1.11) the Bayes estimate is then the conditional expected value

$$\hat{m}(\mathbf{x}) = \int mp(m \mid \mathbf{x})\, dm = \gamma^2\left(\frac{nX}{\delta^2}+\frac{\mu}{\beta^2}\right) = \frac{\beta^2 X+\mu\delta^2/n}{\beta^2+\delta^2/n}. \tag{1.19}$$

As always when the distributions of the observations and of the parameters are Gaussian functions of both the observations and the parameters, this estimate is a linear function of the data $\mathbf{x}$.

Upon examining the estimate given in eq. (1.19), we see that if the initial uncertainty β in the value of the mean is very large, $\beta^2 \gg \delta^2/n$, the Bayes estimate is nearly equal to the sample mean, $\hat{m} \sim X$. If, on the other hand, the error variance of the measurements is very large, $\delta^2/n \gg \beta^2$, the estimate $\hat{m}$ is close to the prior expected value μ, and the observations contribute little new information about the value of the mean m.

The estimate $\hat{m}$ in eq. (1.19) is biased, for its expected value is

$$\mathbf{E}(\hat{m} \mid m) = \langle\hat{m}\rangle = \frac{\beta^2 m+\mu\delta^2/n}{\beta^2+\delta^2/n} \tag{1.20}$$

when the true value of the mean is m. As the number n of measurements increases, this expected value $\langle\hat{m}\rangle$ approaches the true mean m, and one can say the estimate is "asymptotically unbiased".

The risk associated with a true mean m is, according to the definition in eq. (1.5),

$$\begin{aligned} R(\hat{m}(\mathbf{x}); m) &= R(m) = \int [\hat{m}(\mathbf{x})-m]^2\, p(\mathbf{x}; m)\, d^n\mathbf{x} \\ &= \int [\hat{m}(X)-m]^2\, p(X; m)\, dX = \frac{\delta^2}{n} \cdot \frac{\beta^4+(\mu-m)^2\,\delta^2/n}{(\beta^2+\delta^2/n)^2}, \end{aligned} \tag{1.21}$$

where $p(X; m)$ is the p.d.f. of the sample mean X when the true mean is m. This p.d.f. $p(X; m)$ is Gaussian, with expected value m and variance (δ^2/n). By writing the estimate as $\hat{m}(X)$ we emphasize that it depends on the data $\mathbf{x}$ only through the sample mean X, as in eq. (1.19).

The Bayes risk is the average of the risk in eq. (1.21) with respect to the prior p.d.f. $z(m)$ in eq. (1.17),

$$\bar{C}_{\min} = \int z(m)\, R(m)\, dm = \frac{\delta^2}{n} \cdot \frac{\beta^2}{\beta^2 + \delta^2/n} \,. \tag{1.22}$$

As the variance β^2 of the prior p.d.f. $z(m)$ increases, the Bayes risk $\bar{C}_{\min}$ increases toward its least upper bound δ^2/n.

In the least favorable situation there is complete prior ignorance of the true mean, corresponding to the limit $\beta \to \infty$. In this limit the estimate in eq. (1.19) becomes $\hat{m} = X$. If the observer uses this estimate, the risk $R(m)$ associated with any value of the true mean is, according to eq. (1.21),

$$R(m) = \delta^2/n = \text{l.u.b. } \bar{C}_{\min} \,, \tag{1.23}$$

and it is independent of the true mean. The use of the sample mean X as the estimator corresponds to the minimax strategy and the value (δ^2/n) to the minimax risk. The average risk is then (δ^2/n) no matter what the true prior p.d.f. $z(m)$ of the means m turns out to be, and the observer is assured that his average cost will never exceed that value. The estimate $\hat{m} = X$ possesses uniformly minimum variance. If, however, the observer has prior information about the parameter m, expressed in a p.d.f. $z(m)$ such as that in eq. (1.17), the average risk, or the mean-square error, can be reduced by using a Bayes estimate based upon it.

(b) *Maximum-likelihood Estimates*

(i) *Bayes' rule and maximum likelihood.* When no cost function is available to assess the seriousness of errors in parameter estimates, a natural way of choosing an estimation strategy is to maximize the posterior p.d.f. $p(\boldsymbol{\theta}|\mathbf{x})$ given in eq. (1.7), or what is equivalent, to find the values of the parameters that maximize the product $z(\boldsymbol{\theta})\, p(\mathbf{x}; \boldsymbol{\theta})$. The estimate $\hat{\boldsymbol{\theta}}(\mathbf{x})$ is then the set of parameter values that appear most likely in view of the outcome of one's measurements. For instance, the estimate of the mean of a Gaussian distribution as given in eq. (1.19) is the one for which the posterior p.d.f. in eq. (1.18) is maximum. This estimation strategy is simply an application of Bayes' rule of inverse probability (Woodward, 1953).

Bayes' rule, however, like the estimators developed in part (a), requires one to know a prior probability density function $z(\boldsymbol{\theta})$ for the unknown parameters, and this is more likely than a cost function to be missing. If one had a prior p.d.f., one would usually be content to minimize the error variance, and one would adopt the quadratic cost function. To see what to do in the absence of a prior p.d.f., consider what would happen if Bayes' rule were applied to estimating a parameter θ so vaguely known in advance that its prior p.d.f. $z(\theta)$ is very wide. If the data $\mathbf{x}$ are to be of any use in making one's knowledge of θ more precise, the posterior p.d.f. $p(\theta|\mathbf{x})$ must be much narrower than the prior p.d.f. $z(\theta)$; and this requires the joint p.d.f. $p(\mathbf{x}; \theta)$, regarded as a function of θ, to be sharply peaked at some value of θ when the observations $\mathbf{x}$ are substituted. If the p.d.f. $z(\theta)$ is much broader than this peak in $p(\mathbf{x}; \theta)$, $z(\theta)$ will only slightly influence the location of the maximum of the posterior p.d.f. $p(\theta|\mathbf{x})$. The less is known in advance about θ, the smaller is the effect of $z(\theta)$. In the least favorable situation of complete ignorance of the parameter θ, the estimate obtained by this reasoning is simply the value of θ for which the joint p.d.f. $p(\mathbf{x}; \theta)$ of the measurements is maximum. This is the *maximum-likelihood estimate.*

The maximum-likelihood estimator of a set of m parameters $\boldsymbol{\theta}$ selects that set $\hat{\boldsymbol{\theta}}$ for which $p(\mathbf{x}; \hat{\boldsymbol{\theta}}) > p(\mathbf{x}; \boldsymbol{\theta}')$ for all $\boldsymbol{\theta}'$ different from $\hat{\boldsymbol{\theta}}$. It can be found by solving the set of simultaneous equations

$$\frac{\partial}{\partial \theta_k} p(\mathbf{x}; \boldsymbol{\theta}) = 0, \qquad k = 1, 2, \ldots, m. \tag{1.24}$$

In general these equations have many roots, and one must pick the set of solutions $\hat{\boldsymbol{\theta}}(\mathbf{x})$ that yields the highest peak of the function $p(\mathbf{x}; \boldsymbol{\theta})$. In our example of estimating the mean of a Gaussian distribution the maximum-likelihood estimate is the sample mean

$$\hat{m} = X = \sum_{k=1}^{n} x_k/n.$$

In most estimation problems it is desirable that the same value of a parameter θ be obtained whether one estimates θ itself or some monotone function $f(\theta)$ of that parameter. For instance, if one estimates θ^2 and takes the square root of the result, one would like to get the same value that a direct estimate of θ would yield. Maximum-likelihood estimates possess this property. Bayes estimates, however, based on some prior p.d.f. $z(\theta)$, in general do not, because of the different weightings assigned to corresponding ranges of the parameter. For a discussion of such matters as applied to physical measurements, the article by Annis, Cheston, and Primakoff

(1953) and the books by Jeffreys (1961) and Jánossy (1965) may be consulted.

(ii) *The variance of a maximum-likelihood estimate.* An approximate formula for the variance of the maximum-likelihood estimate of a single parameter θ will now be obtained. The formula is the more accurate, the better the estimate; and it can be applied in two situations, when a great many independent measurements contribute to estimating θ or when, in estimating a parameter of a signal, the signal-to-noise ratio is very large. The formula may be said to have asymptotic validity.

Maximizing the joint p.d.f. $p(\mathbf{x};\,\theta)$ is the same as maximizing its logarithm $g(\mathbf{x};\,\theta) = \ln p(\mathbf{x};\,\theta)$, and it involves solving the equation

$$g_\theta(\mathbf{x};\,\theta) = 0, \tag{1.25}$$

in which we have indicated by a subscript θ partial differentiation with respect to θ. In the favorable situation we are concerned with, the derivative $g_\theta(\mathbf{x};\,\theta)$ can be expanded in a Taylor series about the true value of the parameter, which we denote here by θ_0,

$$g_\theta(\mathbf{x};\,\theta_0)+(\theta-\theta_0)\,g_{\theta\theta}(\mathbf{x};\,\theta_0) \cong 0.$$

Terms of order $(\theta-\theta_0)^2$ have been dropped. The maximum-likelihood estimate is now given by

$$\hat{\theta}-\theta_0 \cong -g_\theta(\mathbf{x};\,\theta_0)/g_{\theta\theta}(\mathbf{x};\,\theta_0). \tag{1.26}$$

Provided that $\mathbf{E}[g_{\theta\theta}(\mathbf{x};\theta_0)]$ exists and is different from 0, the denominator of the right-hand side of eq. (1.26) can in the limiting situation of interest be approximated by its expected value. The numerator, on the other hand, has an expected value of 0—the estimate is asymptotically unbiased—and its random variation about 0 accounts for most of the deviation of the estimate $\hat{\theta}$ from the true value θ_0.

That $\mathbf{E}[g_\theta(\mathbf{x};\,\theta_0)] = 0$ is proved by differentiating the equation

$$\int p(\mathbf{x};\,\theta)\,d^n\mathbf{x} = 1$$

with respect to θ,

$$\int \frac{\partial}{\partial\theta}\,p(\mathbf{x};\,\theta)\,d^n\mathbf{x} = \int g_\theta(\mathbf{x};\,\theta)\,p(\mathbf{x};\,\theta)\,d^n\mathbf{x} = \mathbf{E}[g_\theta(\mathbf{x};\,\theta)] = 0. \tag{1.27}$$

The variance of the error $\hat{\theta}-\theta_0$ is now approximately

$$\operatorname{Var}\hat{\theta} \cong \mathbf{E}\{[g_\theta(\mathbf{x};\,\theta_0)]^2\}/\{\mathbf{E}[g_{\theta\theta}(\mathbf{x};\,\theta_0)]\}^2, \tag{1.28}$$

the numerator of which can be evaluated by differentiating eq. (1.27) once more with respect to θ and setting θ equal to θ_0,

$$\int g_{\theta\theta}(\mathbf{x};\theta)\, p(\mathbf{x};\theta)\, d^n\mathbf{x} + \int [g_\theta(\mathbf{x};\theta)]^2\, p(\mathbf{x};\theta)\, d^n\mathbf{x} = 0.$$

Therefore,

$$\mathbf{E}[g_{\theta\theta}(\mathbf{x};\theta_0)] = -\mathbf{E}[g_\theta(\mathbf{x};\theta_0)]^2.$$

Thus we obtain for the asymptotic variance of the maximum-likelihood estimate of θ

$$\begin{aligned}\operatorname{Var}\hat{\theta} &\cong [\mathbf{E}\{[g_\theta(\mathbf{x};\theta_0)]^2\}]^{-1} = -\{\mathbf{E}[g_{\theta\theta}(\mathbf{x};\theta_0)]\}^{-1}\\ &= \left\{\int \left[\frac{\partial}{\partial\theta_0}\ln p(\mathbf{x};\theta_0)\right]^2 p(\mathbf{x};\theta_0)\, d^n\mathbf{x}\right\}^{-1}.\end{aligned} \tag{1.29}$$

If, for instance, the data $x_1, x_2, \ldots, x_n$ are statistically independent and identically distributed,

$$p(\mathbf{x};\theta) = \prod_{k=1}^{n} p(x_k;\theta),$$

the variance of the maximum-likelihood estimate is, in the limit $n \gg 1$,

$$\operatorname{Var}\hat{\theta} \cong \frac{1}{n}\left[\int \left[\frac{\partial}{\partial\theta_0}\ln p(x;\theta_0)\right]^2 p(x;\theta_0)\, dx\right]^{-1}. \tag{1.30}$$

This formula was discovered by R. A. Fisher (1922).

When several parameters $\boldsymbol{\theta}$ are being estimated, their estimates will not in general be statistically independent. By a method similar to what led to eq. (1.29) one can show that the covariance of the estimates of two parameters θ_j and θ_k is approximately

$$\gamma_{jk} \cong \{\hat{\theta}_j, \hat{\theta}_k\}, \qquad j, k = 1, 2, \ldots, m, \tag{1.31}$$

where the matrix $||\gamma_{jk}||$ is the inverse of the matrix

$$\begin{aligned}||\Gamma_{jk}|| &= ||\gamma_{jk}||^{-1},\\ \Gamma_{jk} &= \mathbf{E}\left[\frac{\partial}{\partial\theta_j} g(\mathbf{x};\boldsymbol{\theta})\cdot\frac{\partial}{\partial\theta_k} g(\mathbf{x};\boldsymbol{\theta})\right] = -\mathbf{E}\left[\frac{\partial^2}{\partial\theta_j\,\partial\theta_k} g(\mathbf{x};\boldsymbol{\theta})\right]\\ &= \int \frac{\partial}{\partial\theta_j}[\ln p(\mathbf{x};\boldsymbol{\theta})]\cdot\frac{\partial}{\partial\theta_k}[\ln p(\mathbf{x};\boldsymbol{\theta})]\, p(\mathbf{x};\boldsymbol{\theta})\, d^n\mathbf{x},\end{aligned} \tag{1.32}$$

in which the derivatives are evaluated at the true values of the parameters $\boldsymbol{\theta}$. The variances of the estimates $\hat{\theta}_j$ are the diagonal elements γ_{jj} of the inverse $||\Gamma_{jk}||^{-1}$. These results are again asymptotically valid for a large number of independent measurements or for a large signal-to-noise ratio.

(iii) *The Cramér–Rao inequality.* A more precise form of eq. (1.29) is embodied in the Cramér–Rao inequality (Cramér, 1946, section 32.3; Rao, 1945). For any estimate satisfying certain easy conditions of good behavior, the mean-square error is subject to a lower bound,

$$\mathbf{E}(\hat{\theta}-\theta)^2 \geqslant \frac{(\partial\langle\hat{\theta}\rangle/\partial\theta)^2}{\mathbf{E}\left[\dfrac{\partial}{\partial\theta}\ln p(\mathbf{x};\theta)\right]^2} \tag{1.33}$$

where

$$\langle\hat{\theta}\rangle = \mathbf{E}[\hat{\theta}(\mathbf{x})\,|\,\theta] = \int \hat{\theta}(\mathbf{x})\,p(\mathbf{x};\theta)\,d^n\mathbf{x}, \tag{1.34}$$

and where θ is the true value of the parameter. For an unbiased estimate the numerator of the right-hand side equals 1, and the left-hand side is the variance of the estimate of θ. A generalization applicable to the estimation of several parameters $\boldsymbol{\theta}$ is given by Cramér (1946, sections 32.6, 32.7); it involves the matrix $||\Gamma_{jk}||$ of eq. (1.32).

An estimate that is unbiased and whose variance attains the lower bound given by the right-hand side of eq. (1.33) is called an *efficient* estimate. There are two conditions, beyond lack of bias, for an efficient estimate. The estimate $\hat{\theta}(\mathbf{x})$ must be a sufficient statistic for estimating θ, and the equation

$$\frac{\partial}{\partial\theta}\ln p(\mathbf{x};\theta) = k(\theta)\,[\hat{\theta}(\mathbf{x})-\theta], \tag{1.35}$$

where $k(\theta)$ is independent of $\mathbf{x}$, must hold.

When we say that $\hat{\theta}(\mathbf{x})$ is a sufficient statistic, we mean that the joint p.d.f. $p(\mathbf{x};\theta)$ can be written in the form

$$p(\mathbf{x};\theta) = q[\hat{\theta}(\mathbf{x});\theta]\,r(\mathbf{x}) \tag{1.36}$$

with the factor $r(\mathbf{x})$ independent of the parameter θ. The factor $r(\mathbf{x})$ will then cancel out when the joint p.d.f. $p(\mathbf{x};\theta)$ is substituted into eq. (1.7) for the conditional p.d.f. $p(\theta\,|\,\mathbf{x})$, and $p(\theta\,|\,\mathbf{x})$ will depend on the observations $\mathbf{x}$ only through the statistic $\hat{\theta}(\mathbf{x})$. Any Bayes estimate of the parameter θ, as well as the maximum-likelihood estimate, will then involve the observations only through $\hat{\theta}(\mathbf{x})$.

Efficient estimates are rare. When they exist, they are maximum-likelihood estimates, for combining eqs. (1.24) and (1.35) leads immediately to the equation $\theta = \hat{\theta}(\mathbf{x})$. It is customary to measure the *efficiency* of an unbiased estimate by the ratio of the minimum possible variance, given by the right-hand side of eq. (1.33), to the actual variance of the estimate. This efficiency is a number between 0 and 1.

In applying these concepts to the estimate of the mean m of a Gaussian distribution, which we studied in part (a), we show first from eq. (1.16) that

$$\mathbf{E}\left\{\left[\frac{\partial}{\partial m} \ln p(\mathbf{x}; m)\right]^2\right\} = n/\delta^2$$

and second from eq. (1.20) that for the estimate in eq. (1.19)

$$\partial\langle\hat{m}\rangle/\partial m = \beta^2/(\beta^2+\delta^2/n).$$

Hence the right-hand side of the Cramér–Rao inequality (1.33) is

$$\left(\frac{\beta^2}{\beta^2+\delta^2/n}\right)^2 \frac{\delta^2}{n}.$$

The left-hand side is just the risk $R(m)$ evaluated in eq. (1.21). It is greater than the right-hand side except when the true mean m happens to take on the value μ. However, the two sides of the inequality (1.33) become identically equal in the limit $\beta \to \infty$ to δ^2/n, which is the variance of the estimate $\hat{m} = X = \sum_k x_k/n$. This estimate is unbiased and efficient. The reader can easily check that eq. (1.35) is satisfied and that the p.d.f. $p(\mathbf{x}; m)$ can be written in the form of eq. (1.36). The sample mean is a sufficient statistic for estimating the true mean of a set of independent Gaussian random variables.

A maximum-likelihood estimate is asymptotically normal, unbiased, and efficient; when the number n of independent measurements is large, the p.d.f. $p(\hat{\boldsymbol{\theta}} \mid \boldsymbol{\theta})$ of the estimate is nearly a multivariate Gaussian distribution with expected values $\mathbf{E}(\hat{\boldsymbol{\theta}})$ nearly equal to the true values of the parameters $\boldsymbol{\theta}$, and with a covariance matrix $||\gamma_{jk}||$ given by eqs. (1.31), (1.32) (Cramér, 1946, section 33.3). The larger the number of independent measurements, the better these approximations. Because the distribution of the estimates $\boldsymbol{\theta} = (\theta_1, \theta_2, \ldots, \theta_m)$ narrows down about the true values $\boldsymbol{\theta}$ as the number of independent data increases, the estimates are *consistent*; the probability $P(\varepsilon)$ that the largest error, $\max_k |\hat{\theta}_k - \theta_k|$, is greater than a fixed amount ε decreases to zero as the number of independent data increases. These properties of asymptotic efficiency and consistency further dispose us to adopt the maximum-likelihood estimate.

2. ESTIMATING SIGNAL PARAMETERS

(a) *The Maximum-likelihood Estimate*

When a signal $s(t; \theta)$ depending on certain parameters θ is received in additive noise $n(t)$, the input $v(t)$ to the receiver during an observation interval $(0, T)$ is

$$v(t) = s(t; \theta) + n(t), \quad 0 < t < T. \tag{2.1}$$

On the basis of this input $v(t)$ the observer is to estimate the values of the parameters θ. As we said earlier, these parameters might typically be the amplitude, the epoch, and the carrier frequency of a narrowband pulse.

Let the input $v(t)$ be sampled at n times t_i to provide the data $\mathbf{x} = (x_1, x_2, \ldots, x_n)$, $x_k = v(t_k)$. If by $p_0(\mathbf{y})$ we denote the joint p.d.f. of the noise $n(t)$ sampled at the same times,

$$p_0(\mathbf{y}) = p_0(\{n(t_i)\}), \quad y_k = n(t_k),$$

the joint p.d.f. of the data $\mathbf{x} = \{v(t_i)\}$ is

$$p(\mathbf{x}; \theta) = p_0(\{x_i - s(t_i; \theta)\}). \tag{2.2}$$

If the signal were absent, the joint p.d.f. of the observations would be $p_0(\mathbf{x})$, which is independent of the signal parameters. It is convenient to introduce here again the likelihood ratio $\Lambda(\mathbf{x}; \theta) = p(\mathbf{x}; \theta)/p_0(\mathbf{x})$, for it is then often possible to pass to the limit of an infinite number of densely spaced samples $v(t_i)$ and to replace $\Lambda(\mathbf{x}; \theta)$ with its limiting form $\Lambda[v(t); \theta]$. For signals in Gaussian noise we have already calculated this likelihood ratio $\Lambda[v(t); \theta]$. In most of the estimation formulas $p(\mathbf{x}; \theta)$ can be replaced by $\Lambda[v(t); \theta]$.

The conditional p.d.f. of the parameters θ, for instance, which was defined in eq. (1.7), can as well be expressed in terms of the likeloihod ratio,

$$\begin{aligned} p(\theta \,|\, \mathbf{x}) &= z(\theta)\, \Lambda(\mathbf{x}; \theta)/\Lambda(\mathbf{x}), \\ \Lambda(\mathbf{x}) &= \int d^m\theta\, z(\theta)\, \Lambda(\mathbf{x}; \theta), \end{aligned} \tag{2.3}$$

by simply dividing the numerator and the denominator in eq. (1.7) by $p_0(\mathbf{x})$, which is independent of θ. Passing to the limit of infinitely many samples, we can write the conditional p.d.f. of the parameters θ, given the input $v(t)$, as

$$\begin{aligned} p(\theta \,|\, v(t)) &= z(\theta)\, \Lambda[v(t); \theta]/\Lambda[v(t)], \\ \Lambda[v(t)] &= \int d^m\theta\, z(\theta)\, \Lambda[v(t); \theta]. \end{aligned} \tag{2.4}$$

The conditional risk of an estimator can also be treated as a functional of the input,

$$C(\hat{\theta} \,|\, v(t)) = \int C(\hat{\theta}, \theta)\, p(\theta \,|\, v(t))\, d^m\theta. \tag{2.5}$$

The Bayes estimate of the parameters $\boldsymbol{\theta}$ is the set $\hat{\boldsymbol{\theta}}$ that minimizes this conditional risk.

A Bayes estimate of the parameters $\boldsymbol{\theta}$ will therefore involve the input $v(t)$ only through the likelihood ratio $\Lambda[v(t); \boldsymbol{\theta}]$. The same is true of a maximum-likelihood estimate. Maximizing $p(\mathbf{x}; \boldsymbol{\theta})$ with respect to $\boldsymbol{\theta}$ is the same as maximizing $\Lambda(\mathbf{x}; \boldsymbol{\theta}) = p(\mathbf{x}; \boldsymbol{\theta})/p_0(\mathbf{x})$, for $p_0(\mathbf{x})$ is independent of $\boldsymbol{\theta}$; and we can again pass to the limit and determine the maximum-likelihood estimate $\hat{\boldsymbol{\theta}}$ as the value of $\boldsymbol{\theta}$ for which the likelihood ratio $\Lambda[v(t); \boldsymbol{\theta}]$ is largest. In this way the likelihood ratio embodies all the information in the input $v(t)$ contributing to an estimate of the signal parameters; and when it can be obtained explicitly, we can dispense with sampling.

If certain unknown parameters, such as the phase ψ of a narrowband pulse, are uninformative and are not to be estimated, the joint p.d.f. $p(\mathbf{x}; \boldsymbol{\theta})$ will, we assume, have been averaged over them with respect to an accepted prior p.d.f., possibly a least favorable one. The likelihood ratio $\Lambda[v(t); \boldsymbol{\theta}]$ can similarly be averaged, and we henceforth take it to depend only on the parameters $\boldsymbol{\theta}$ whose values we want to estimate. The remaining unknown parameters, we suppose, have been eliminated by averaging.

Prior distributions of the parameters to be estimated are seldom available, and when they are given or can be assumed, they are usually much broader than the posterior p.d.f.s we expect to result from our measurements. It is then appropriate to use the maximum-likelihood estimate, and we shall treat it exclusively. We shall take as the estimate $\hat{\theta}$ $[v(t)]$ of a set of signal parameters the value of $\boldsymbol{\theta}$ for which the likelihood ratio $\Lambda[v(t); \boldsymbol{\theta}]$ is largest.

An approximate formula for the variance of the maximum-likelihood estimate $\hat{\theta}$ of a single parameter θ of a signal can be derived by a simple modification of the argument of Section 1, part (b). It is only necessary to replace $g(\mathbf{x}; \theta) = \ln p(\mathbf{x}; \theta)$ there by $g(\mathbf{x}; \theta) = \ln p(\mathbf{x}; \theta) - \ln p_0(\mathbf{x}) = \ln \Lambda(\mathbf{x}; \theta)$. Nothing is changed, for we are subtracting a quantity independent of θ. We can again pass to the limit of an infinite number of samples to show that the error variance is, from eq. (1.29), given by

$$\operatorname{Var} \hat{\theta} \cong \left[\mathbf{E}\left\{ \frac{\partial}{\partial \theta} \ln \Lambda[v(t); \theta] \right\}^2 \right]^{-1} = -\left[\mathbf{E}\left\{ \frac{\partial^2}{\partial \theta^2} \ln \Lambda[v(t); \theta] \right\} \right]^{-1}, \tag{2.6}$$

when the signal-to-noise ratio is large. The Cramér–Rao inequality, eq. (1.33), can similarly be expressed in terms of the likelihood ratio $\Lambda[v(t); \theta]$. Furthermore, the covariance matrix $||\gamma_{jk}|| = ||\{\hat{\theta}_j, \hat{\theta}_k\}||$ of a set of estimates of the m parameters $\boldsymbol{\theta}$ is, in the limit of large signal-to-noise ratio, the inverse of a matrix $\|\Gamma_{jk}\|$ whose elements are

$$\Gamma_{jk} = \mathbf{E}\left\{\frac{\partial}{\partial\theta_j}\ln \Lambda[v(t);\,\boldsymbol{\theta}]\cdot\frac{\partial}{\partial\theta_k}\ln \Lambda[v(t);\,\boldsymbol{\theta}]\right\}$$
$$= -\mathbf{E}\left\{\frac{\partial^2}{\partial\theta_j\,\partial\theta_k}\ln \Lambda[v(t);\,\boldsymbol{\theta}]\right\}, \tag{2.7}$$

as in eq. (1.32). The expectations in eqs. (2.6) and (2.7) are taken with respect to the distributions of the input $v(t)$ in the presence of the signal $s(t;\,\boldsymbol{\theta})$.

If several independent inputs $v_j(t)$ are available, and if the unknown parameters not to be estimated are statistically independent from one input to another, the over-all likelihood ratio is the product of the individual likelihood ratios. If the distributions of the noise are the same from one input to the next, the variances and covariances as found above for a single input are divided by the total number of independent inputs used in the estimate.

(b) *Parameter Estimation for a Signal in Gaussian Noise*

Suppose that the signal $s(t;\,\boldsymbol{\theta})$ is received in Gaussian noise of autocovariance $\phi(t, u)$ and that all the signal parameters $\boldsymbol{\theta}$ are to be estimated. The logarithm of the likelihood ratio for the input $v(t)$ is, as in eq. (IV, 3.13),

$$\ln \Lambda[v(t);\,\boldsymbol{\theta}] = \int_0^T q(t;\,\boldsymbol{\theta})\, v(t)\, dt - \tfrac{1}{2}\int_0^T q(t;\,\boldsymbol{\theta})\, s(t;\,\boldsymbol{\theta})\, dt, \tag{2.8}$$

where $q(t;\,\boldsymbol{\theta})$ is the solution of the integral equation

$$s(t;\,\boldsymbol{\theta}) = \int_0^T \phi(t, u)\, q(u;\,\boldsymbol{\theta})\, du, \quad 0 < t < T, \tag{2.9}$$

and $(0, T)$ is the observation interval. The maximum-likelihood estimate $\hat{\boldsymbol{\theta}}$ of the parameters is that set for which the right-hand side of eq. (2.8) is largest. When the noise is white, with a unilateral spectral density N, the logarithmic likelihood ratio (l.l.r.) is

$$\ln \Lambda[v(t);\,\boldsymbol{\theta}] = \frac{2}{N}\int_0^T s(t;\,\boldsymbol{\theta})\, v(t)\, dt - \frac{1}{N}\int_0^T [s(t;\,\boldsymbol{\theta})]^2\, dt. \tag{2.10}$$

The matrix elements Γ_{jk} of the inverse of the covariance matrix of the estimates are now, from eqs. (2.7), (2.8),

$$\Gamma_{jk} = \int_0^T \frac{\partial q(t;\,\boldsymbol{\theta})}{\partial\theta_j}\cdot\frac{\partial s(t;\,\boldsymbol{\theta})}{\partial\theta_k}\, dt \tag{2.11}$$

for reception in noise of autocovariance $\phi(t, u)$, or

$$\Gamma_{jk} = \frac{2}{N} \int_0^T \frac{\partial s(t; \boldsymbol{\theta})}{\partial \theta_j} \cdot \frac{\partial s(t; \boldsymbol{\theta})}{\partial \theta_k} \, dt \tag{2.12}$$

for reception in white noise. In particular, the mean-square error of the estimate of a single parameter θ is, by the Cramér–Rao inequality, bounded below by

$$\mathbf{E}(\hat{\theta} - \theta)^2 \geqslant \frac{(\partial \langle \hat{\theta} \rangle / \partial \theta)^2}{\int_0^T [\partial q(t; \theta)/\partial \theta] \cdot [\partial s(t; \theta)/\partial \theta] \, dt}. \tag{2.13}$$

When the signal-to-noise ratio is large, the maximum-likelihood estimate will be unbiased, $\partial \langle \hat{\theta} \rangle / \partial \theta \cong 1$, and the right-hand side of this equation will be approximately the variance of the estimate (Slepian, 1954).

The function

$$H(\boldsymbol{\theta}_1, \boldsymbol{\theta}_2) = \int_0^T q(t; \boldsymbol{\theta}_1) \, s(t; \boldsymbol{\theta}_2) \, dt \tag{2.14}$$

is known as the "generalized ambiguity function" for the signals $s(t; \boldsymbol{\theta})$ in noise of covariance function $\phi(t, u)$. Special forms of it will be treated in detail later when we discuss the resolution of signals. For the present we remark that the elements of the inverse $\boldsymbol{\Gamma}$ of the asymptotic covariance matrix $\boldsymbol{\gamma}$ are

$$\Gamma_{jk} = \left. \frac{\partial^2 H}{\partial \theta_{1j} \, \partial \theta_{2k}} \right|_{\boldsymbol{\theta}_1 = \boldsymbol{\theta}_2 = \boldsymbol{\theta}}. \tag{2.15}$$

The form of the generalized ambiguity function for white noise is obtained by putting $q(t; \boldsymbol{\theta}_1) = (2/N) \, s(t; \boldsymbol{\theta}_1)$ into eq. (2.14).

As a simple example, consider estimating the amplitude A of a signal $s(t; A) = Af(t)$ that is otherwise completely known. Then $q(t; A) = Ag(t)$, where $g(t)$ is the solution of the integral equation

$$f(t) = \int_0^T \phi(t, u) \, g(u) \, du, \quad 0 < t < T. \tag{2.16}$$

From eq. (2.8) the logarithmic likelihood ratio is now

$$\ln \Lambda[v(t); A] = A \int_0^T g(t) \, v(t) \, dt - \tfrac{1}{2} A^2 \int_0^T g(t) f(t) \, dt. \tag{2.17}$$

It is maximized by the linear estimate

$$\hat{A} = \int_0^T g(t) \, v(t) \, dt \Big/ \int_0^T g(t) f(t) \, dt, \tag{2.18}$$

which is proportional to the output, at the end of the observation interval, of a filter matched to the signal $g(t)$. This is the same filter as would be used to detect the signal $f(t)$ in Gaussian noise of autocovariance $\phi(t, u)$.

When the signal $s(t; A) = Af(t)$ is present, the expected value of the estimate of its amplitude is

$$\mathbf{E}(\hat{A} \mid A) = A; \tag{2.19}$$

the estimate is unbiased. Its variance is a constant,

$$\operatorname{Var} \hat{A} = \left[\int_0^T g(t) f(t)\, dt \right]^{-1}, \tag{2.20}$$

and it is easy to verify that the Cramér–Rao inequality in eq. (2.13) here becomes an equality. This maximum-likelihood estimate is sufficient, efficient, and unbiased. In general, maximum-likelihood estimates that are linear functions of the measurements are efficient.

When besides the amplitude $A = \theta_1$ other parameters $(\theta_2, \theta_3 \dots, \theta_m) = \boldsymbol{\theta}'$ are unknown, we write the signal as $s(t; \boldsymbol{\theta}) = Af(t; \boldsymbol{\theta}')$ and maximize

$$\ln \Lambda[v(t); A, \boldsymbol{\theta}'] = A \int_0^T g(t; \boldsymbol{\theta}')\, v(t)\, dt - \tfrac{1}{2} A^2 \int_0^T g(t; \boldsymbol{\theta}') f(t; \boldsymbol{\theta}')\, dt \tag{2.21}$$

where $g(t; \boldsymbol{\theta}')$ is the solution of the integral equation

$$f(t; \boldsymbol{\theta}') = \int_0^T \phi(t, u)\, g(u; \boldsymbol{\theta}')\, du, \quad 0 < t < T. \tag{2.22}$$

The maximum-likelihood estimate of the amplitude is now

$$\hat{A} = \int_0^T g(t; \hat{\boldsymbol{\theta}}')\, v(t)\, dt \Big/ \int_0^T g(t; \hat{\boldsymbol{\theta}}')\, f(t; \hat{\boldsymbol{\theta}}')\, dt, \tag{2.23}$$

into which the maximum-likelihood estimates $\hat{\boldsymbol{\theta}}'$ of the $(m-1)$ other parameters must be substituted. These are found by maximizing the function

$$\ln \Lambda[v(t); \hat{A}, \boldsymbol{\theta}'] = \left[\int_0^T g(t; \boldsymbol{\theta}')\, v(t)\, dt \right]^2 \Big/ 2 \int_0^T g(t; \boldsymbol{\theta}') f(t; \boldsymbol{\theta}')\, dt. \tag{2.24}$$

One way of determining these estimates $\boldsymbol{\theta}'$ is to construct a bank of parallel filters matched to the signals $g(t; \boldsymbol{\theta}')$ for a dense array of discrete values of the parameters $(\theta_2, \theta_3, \dots, \theta_m)$, and to weight their outputs with the reciprocal of the square-root of the denominator in eq. (2.24). The filter whose weighted output at the end of the interval $(0, T)$ has the greatest absolute magnitude provides an estimate of the parameters $\boldsymbol{\theta}'$. This estimate can be made as close as desired to the maximum-likelihood estimate $\hat{\boldsymbol{\theta}}'$ by building a sufficient number of matched filters. There is little to be gained, however, by spacing the parameters of the filters by much less than the r.m.s. values of the errors introduced by the noise.

The function in the denominator of eq. (2.24) is often independent of the parameters θ' over the greater part of their ranges. This is so, for instance, when the arrival time of a signal is being estimated and the observation interval is so long that signals overlapping its ends can be disregarded. In such circumstances the estimate of the amplitude A is asymptotically uncorrelated with the estimates of the remaining parameters θ'.

It is useful to define a reduced ambiguity function by

$$H'(\theta_1', \theta_2') = \int_0^T g(t; \theta_1') f(t; \theta_2') \, dt, \tag{2.25}$$

from which the signal amplitudes have been eliminated. Then it follows from the positive-definiteness of the autocovariance function $\phi(t, s)$ that

$$|H'(\theta_1', \theta_2')|^2 \leq H'(\theta_1', \theta_1') H'(\theta_2', \theta_2'); \tag{2.26}$$

this is version of the Schwarz inequality. The denominator in eq. (2.24) is $H'(\theta', \theta')$, and if this is independent of θ', the reduced ambiguity function $H'(\theta_1', \theta_2')$ is maximum when $\theta_1' = \theta_2'$. In that case

$$\frac{\partial}{\partial \theta_{1j}} H'(\theta_1', \theta_2') \bigg|_{\theta_1' = \theta_2' = \theta'} = 0, \quad j = 2, 3, \ldots, m.$$

Under these conditions the elements of the inverse asymptotic covariance matrix $\mathbf{\Gamma}$ are given by

$$\begin{aligned} \Gamma_{11} &= H'(\theta', \theta'), \\ \Gamma_{1j} &= 0, \quad j = 2, 3, \ldots, m, \\ \Gamma_{jk} &= A^2 \frac{\partial^2}{\partial \theta_{1j} \, \partial \theta_{2k}} H'(\theta_1', \theta_2') \bigg|_{\theta_1' = \theta_2' = \theta'}, \\ & \qquad j, k = 2, 3, \ldots, m, \end{aligned} \tag{2.27}$$

into which the true values of the parameters A, θ' must be substituted.

Hence at large signal-to-noise ratios $d \gg 1$,

$$\begin{aligned} \operatorname{Var} \hat{A} &= [H'(\theta', \theta')]^{-1} = A^2/d^2, \\ \{\hat{A}, \hat{\theta}_j\} &= 0, \quad j = 2, 3, \ldots, m, \\ \{\hat{\theta}_j, \hat{\theta}_k\} &= A^{-2} \gamma_{jk}', \quad j, k = 2, 3, \ldots, m, \end{aligned} \tag{2.28}$$

where $||\gamma_{jk}'||$ is the inverse of the $(m-1) \times (m-1)$ matrix $\mathbf{\Gamma}'$ whose elements are the Γ_{jk} given in the third line of eq. (2.27), but divided by A^2. The variance of the estimate of a single additional parameter θ' will be, at large signal-to-noise ratio,

$$\operatorname{Var} \hat{\theta}' = A^{-2} \left[\int_0^T \frac{\partial g(t; \theta')}{\partial \theta'} \cdot \frac{\partial f(t; \theta')}{\partial \theta'} \, dt \right]^{-1}, \tag{2.29}$$

provided that the function $H'(\theta', \theta')$ is independent of θ'. This estimate is then the value of θ' that maximizes $\left| \int_0^T g(t; \theta') \, v(t) \, dt \right|$.

(c) *Estimating the Parameters of Narrowband Signals*

In dealing with quasiharmonic signals it is usually desirable to distinguish both the amplitude $A = \theta_1$ and the phase $\psi = \theta_2$ from the rest of the unknown parameters, which can be collected as a vector $\boldsymbol{\theta}'' = (\theta_3, \theta_4, \ldots, \theta_m)$ of $(m-2)$ components. One of these parameters might be the carrier frequency Ω of the signal, which we shall assume to be found in the neighborhood of a fixed reference frequency Ω_r, with respect to which the complex envelope of the signal is defined. Another parameter might be the time τ of arrival of the signal. These parameters $\boldsymbol{\theta}''$ we call "essential parameters", for they provide a basis for distinguishing signals.

The signal is now written as

$$s(t; \boldsymbol{\theta}) = A \operatorname{Rl} F(t; \boldsymbol{\theta}'') \exp (i\Omega_r t + i\psi), \tag{2.30}$$

and as in eq. (V, 2.5) the likelihood ratio is

$$\Lambda[v(t); A, \psi, \boldsymbol{\theta}''] = \exp \left[A \operatorname{Rl} e^{-i\psi} \int_0^T G^*(t; \boldsymbol{\theta}'') \, V(t) \, dt - \tfrac{1}{2} A^2 \int_0^T G^*(t; \boldsymbol{\theta}'') \, F(t; \boldsymbol{\theta}'') \, dt \right], \tag{2.31}$$

where $V(t)$ is the complex envelope of the input $v(t) = \operatorname{Rl} V(t) \exp i\Omega_r t$, and where $G(t; \boldsymbol{\theta}'')$ is the solution of the integral equation

$$F(t; \boldsymbol{\theta}'') = \int_0^T \tilde{\phi}(t-u) \, G(u; \boldsymbol{\theta}'') \, du, \quad 0 < t < T, \tag{2.32}$$

whose kernel $\tilde{\phi}(\tau)$ is the complex autocovariance function of the noise, taken as stationary and quasiharmonic. If the noise is white and has a unilateral spectral density N, the substitutions $\tilde{\phi}(\tau) = N\delta(\tau)$, $G(t; \boldsymbol{\theta}'') = N^{-1} F(t; \boldsymbol{\theta}'')$ yield the necessary forms. With these narrowband signals the reduced ambiguity function

$$H'(\boldsymbol{\theta}_1'', \boldsymbol{\theta}_2'') = \int_0^T G^*(t; \boldsymbol{\theta}_1'') \, F(t; \boldsymbol{\theta}_2'') \, dt \tag{2.33}$$

is associated.

There are three approaches to estimation of the parameters θ''. When as usual the phase ψ is uninformative, the likelihood ratio in eq. (2.31) can be averaged with respect to its least favorable distribution, the uniform one, and the amplitude A and the parameters θ'' estimated by the method of maximum likelihood. If the amplitude A is also uninformative and nothing whatever can be assumed about its magnitude, the least favorable situation of a vanishingly small amplitude might be supposed to exist and the threshold estimators of the remaining parameters θ'' be adopted. A third plan is to estimate the amplitude A and the phase ψ, though they may be uninformative, and to discard the estimates. At large signal-to-noise ratios the first and the third methods yield nearly the same estimates. The second is most appropriate when the signal-to-noise ratio is expected to be small and a number of independent inputs are available.

Taking the first approach, we average the likelihood ratio in eq. (2.31) with respect to the uniform prior p.d.f. $z(\psi) = (2\pi)^{-1}$, $0 \leq \psi < 2\pi$, to obtain

$$\Lambda[v(t); A, \theta''] = \exp\left[-\tfrac{1}{2}A^2 H'(\theta'', \theta'')\right] I_0\left(AR(\theta'')\right), \tag{2.34}$$

where

$$R(\theta'') = \left| \int_0^T G^*(t; \theta'')\, V(t)\, dt \right|. \tag{2.35}$$

This is the linearly rectified output of a filter matched to the signal Rl $G(t; \theta'') \exp i\Omega_r t$. The maximum-likelihood estimate of the amplitude A is determined by solving the equation

$$AH'(\hat{\theta}'', \hat{\theta}'') = R(\hat{\theta}'')\, I_1\left(AR(\hat{\theta}'')\right) / I_0\left(AR(\hat{\theta}'')\right), \tag{2.36}$$

into which the maximum-likelihood estimates $\hat{\theta}''$ of the remaining parameters are to be substituted. When the signal-to-noise ratio is large, the estimated amplitude is approximately, by eq. (VII, 1.9),

$$\hat{A} = R(\hat{\theta}'')/H'(\hat{\theta}'', \hat{\theta}''). \tag{2.37}$$

The maximum-likelihood estimates of the other parameters are then approximately those values for which the function

$$W(\theta'') = [R(\theta'')]^2/H'(\theta'', \theta'') \tag{2.38}$$

is maximum. When the signal-to-noise ratio cannot be assumed to be large, it will be more difficult to calculate the maximum-likelihood estimates of the parameters θ''.

If, however, the function $H'(\theta'', \theta'')$ is independent of the parameters θ'', as is often the case, it is only necessary to find the values of θ'' for which the function $R(\theta'')$ is maximum. A bank of parallel filters, matched to the signals Rl $G(t; \theta'') \exp i\Omega_r t$ for a dense array of values of the parameters θ'' and followed by linear rectifiers, can be attached to the receiver; and the filter with the largest rectified output at the end of the interval $(0, T)$ identifies the set of parameters θ'' closest to the maximum-likelihood estimate $\hat{\theta}''$. This method is appropriate for estimating the arrival time or, in the presence of effectively white noise, the carrier frequency of a narrowband signal.

In the least favorable situation of a vanishingly small amplitude A, the logarithmic likelihood ratio in eq. (2.34) can be expanded in powers of A, and by keeping only the terms proportional to A^2 one finds that the remaining parameters θ'' are estimated by maximizing the function

$$J(\theta'') = [R(\theta'')]^2 - 2H'(\theta'', \theta''). \tag{2.39}$$

If $H'(\theta'', \theta'')$ is independent of θ'', the same estimates of the parameters θ'' as before are obtained. The amplitude itself can be estimated only by keeping terms of higher order in A from the expansion.

If one cannot be sure that the amplitude of the signal is great enough to warrant the approximation leading to eq. (2.37), one might choose to estimate both the amplitude A and the phase ψ, even though the results might be useless apart from their contributions to the estimation of θ''. Equivalently one can estimate the real and imaginary parts u and v of

$$A\, e^{i\psi} = u + iv. \tag{2.40}$$

If we put

$$x + iy = \int_0^T G^*(t; \theta'')\, V(t)\, dt, \tag{2.41}$$

we find that we must choose values of u, v, and θ'' that maximize the l.l.r.

$$\ln \Lambda[v(t); u, v, \theta''] = xu + yv - \tfrac{1}{2}(u^2 + v^2)\, H'(\theta'', \theta''). \tag{2.42}$$

The maximum-likelihood estimates of u and v are then

$$\hat{u} = x_1/H'(\hat{\theta}'', \hat{\theta}''), \quad \hat{v} = y_1/H'(\hat{\theta}'', \hat{\theta}''), \tag{2.43}$$

in which x_1 and y_1 are obtained from eq. (2.41) by substituting $\hat{\theta}''$ for θ''. The maximum-likelihood estimates of the rest of the parameters are those that maximize

$$\max_{u, v} \ln \Lambda[v(t); u, v, \theta''] = [R(\theta'')]^2/2H'(\theta'', \theta''), \tag{2.44}$$

the same prescription as derived before in the limit of large signal-to-noise ratio. The reason is not hard to find. The estimate of the phase ψ will be meaningful only when its r.m.s. error is much less than 2π, and this requires such a large signal-to-noise ratio that eq. (2.37) gives a valid estimate of the amplitude A. Indeed, eq. (2.43) leads also to the estimate $\hat{A}$ in eq. (2.37).

The variances and the covariances of estimates such as these are simple to calculate only when the signal-to-noise ratio is very large. As we have seen, the maximum-likelihood estimates of the parameters $\boldsymbol{\theta}''$ are then obtained by maximizing the right-hand side of eq. (2.44) and are the same whether the phase ψ is estimated or not. We can therefore assume that all m parameters $\boldsymbol{\theta}$ of the signal $s(t;\,\boldsymbol{\theta}) = \text{Rl}\ S(t;\,\boldsymbol{\theta}) \exp i\Omega_r t$ are being estimated, and we can apply eq. (2.7) to determining the covariances of the estimates in the limit of large signal-to-noise ratio,

$$\{\hat{\theta}_j, \hat{\theta}_k\} = \gamma_{jk}, \tag{2.45}$$

where $\boldsymbol{\gamma}$ is the inverse of the matrix $\boldsymbol{\Gamma} = \boldsymbol{\gamma}^{-1}$ whose elements are

$$\Gamma_{jk} = \text{Rl} \int_0^T \frac{\partial Q^*(t;\,\boldsymbol{\theta})}{\partial \theta_j} \cdot \frac{\partial S(t;\,\boldsymbol{\theta})}{\partial \theta_k}\, dt, \tag{2.46}$$

where in our previous notation

$$S(t;\,\boldsymbol{\theta}) = A\, e^{i\psi} F(t;\,\boldsymbol{\theta}''), \quad Q(t;\,\boldsymbol{\theta}) = A\, e^{i\psi} G(t;\,\boldsymbol{\theta}'').$$

The derivation of eq. (2.46) follows the same lines as that of eq. (2.11) except that one starts with the likelihood ratio in eq. (2.31) instead of with eq. (2.8). When, as often, $H'(\boldsymbol{\theta}'', \boldsymbol{\theta}'')$ is independent of $\boldsymbol{\theta}''$, the variance of the estimate of amplitude is given by

$$\text{Var}\ \hat{A} = A^2/d^2, \tag{2.47}$$

where d, defined by

$$d^2 = A^2 H'(\boldsymbol{\theta}'', \boldsymbol{\theta}''), \tag{2.48}$$

is the same signal-to-noise ratio as before. For a signal of energy E in white, Gaussian noise of unilateral spectral density N, $d = (2E/N)^{\frac{1}{2}}$. The estimate of the amplitude will in this case be independent of the estimates of the other parameters and of the phase.

(d) *Estimates from Multiple Inputs*

In radar, target parameters such as range and radial velocity may be measured on the basis not of one, but of a number of successive echo signals, which are received following the periodically transmitted pulses. It is possible simply to average the estimates provided by each echo, but better estimators can sometimes be constructed by the methods of the previous sections.

Let us suppose that there are M received signals altogether, of which a typical one has the quasiharmonic form

$$s_k(t; \theta) = \text{Rl } S_k(t; \theta) \exp i\Omega_k t, \qquad k = 1, 2, \ldots, M, \tag{2.49}$$

where Ω_k is a known reference frequency, which may, but need not, differ from one signal to the next. The kth signal appears with random noise to make up the kth input

$$v_k(t) = \text{Rl } V_k(t) \exp i\Omega_k t, \tag{2.50}$$

which is observed during an interval $0 < t < T$, the time being measured from the beginning of each interval. The additive noise components of the inputs $v_k(t)$ are taken as Gaussian and independent from one interval to the next. The intervals need not follow each other in time, although in radar they normally do. The inputs $v_k(t)$ might, for instance, be received simultaneously in frequency bands well enough separated that the noise associated with one is independent of the noise in each of the others.

The amplitudes A_k and the phases ψ_k may differ from signal to signal, but we suppose that the rest of the parameters θ'', the ones whose values most concern us, remain the same for all signals. The signals then have complex envelopes of the form

$$S_k(t; \theta) = A_k \exp (i\, \psi_k)\, F_k(t; \theta''),$$

in which the functions $F_k(t; \theta'')$ are presumed known, though not necessarily identical. The parameters θ'' might, for example, be the radial velocity of a target and its range at the beginning of the observation. These govern the frequency deviations and the arrival times of successive echo signals.

Since the noise is independent from one interval to another, the likelihood ratio for the set of inputs $\{v_k(t)\}$ is the product of likelihood ratios for each interval, as given by eq. (2.31),

$$\Lambda[\{v_k(t)\}; \mathbf{A}, \boldsymbol{\psi}, \theta''] = \prod_{k=1}^{M} \exp \left[A_k \text{ Rl} \exp(-i\psi_k) \int_0^T G_k^*(t; \theta'')\, V_k(t)\, dt \right.$$
$$\left. - \tfrac{1}{2} A_k^2 \int_0^T G_k^*(t; \theta'')\, F_k(t; \theta'')\, dt \right], \tag{2.51}$$

where $G_k(t; \theta'')$ is related to $F_k(t; \theta'')$ by an integral equation like eq. (2.32), and where we have denoted by $\mathbf{A}$ and $\boldsymbol{\psi}$ the sets of amplitudes and phases.

In part (c) we showed how the essential parameters θ'' could be estimated in three different ways, which differed in their treatment of the unknown amplitude and phase of the signal. The same alternatives appear when there are M pairs of amplitudes and phases, with the additional question whether the amplitudes or the phases are independently random from signal to signal. If both amplitude and phase are the same for all signals, the entire set $\{s_k(t; \theta)\}$ can be treated as a single signal, to which the methods of part (c) can be applied, and nothing more need be said.

If the unknown phases ψ_k are assumed independently random and uniformly distributed over $(0, 2\pi)$, the likelihood ratio in eq. (2.51) can be averaged over them. As before, non-linear equations for the unknown amplitudes are then obtained, and the same approximations can, when appropriate, be applied. The assumptions of large signal-to-noise ratio and a common signal amplitude, for instance, lead to an estimator of θ'' involving the sum of the linearly rectified outputs of filters matched to the signals Rl $G_k(t; \theta'') \exp i\Omega_k t$.

Owing to fading the signal amplitudes may differ, and in the least favorable situation they will be independently random. Both the set $\mathbf{A} = (A_1, A_2, \ldots, A_M)$ of amplitudes and the set $\boldsymbol{\psi} = (\psi_1, \psi_2, \ldots, \psi_M)$ of phases can then be estimated along with the parameters θ''. An analysis similar to what led to eq. (2.44) shows that when this is done, the parameters θ'' are estimated as the values for which

$$\ln \Lambda[\{v_k(t)\}; \hat{\mathbf{A}}, \hat{\boldsymbol{\psi}}, \theta''] = \tfrac{1}{2} \sum_{k=1}^{M} \{[R_k(\theta'')]^2 / H_k'(\theta'', \theta'')\} \tag{2.52}$$

is largest, where

$$\begin{aligned} R_k(\theta'') &= \left| \int_0^T G_k^*(t; \theta'') \, V_k(t) \, dt \right|, \\ H_k'(\theta_1'', \theta_2'') &= \int_0^T G_k^*(t; \theta_1'') \, F_k(t; \theta_2'') \, dt. \end{aligned} \tag{2.53}$$

A bank of parallel filters matched to the signals Rl $G_k(t; \theta'') \exp i\Omega_k t$ for a dense array of values of the parameters θ'' are connected to quadratic rectifiers, whose weighted outputs are sampled and summed to generate a set of values of the l.l.r. in eq. (2.52). The greatest of the summed outputs specifies the estimate $\hat{\theta}''$.

When all the parameters are estimated in this way, the covariances of the estimates will be given at large signal-to-noise ratio by a $(2M+m-2) \times$ $\times (2M+m-2)$ matrix $\boldsymbol{\gamma}$ that is the inverse of a matrix $\boldsymbol{\Gamma} = \boldsymbol{\gamma}^{-1}$ whose elements are

$$\Gamma_{jn} = \sum_{k=1}^{M} \mathrm{Rl} \int_0^T \frac{\partial Q_k^*(t; \theta)}{\partial \theta_j} \cdot \frac{\partial S_k(t; \theta)}{\partial \theta_n} \, dt, \tag{2.54}$$

where $S_k(t;\,\theta) = A_k \exp(i\psi_k)\, F_k(t;\,\theta'')$, $Q_k(t;\,\theta) = A_k \exp(i\psi_k)\; G_k(t;\,\theta'')$, and where it is assumed that $H_k'(\theta'', \theta'')$ is independent of θ'' for all k.

If the complex envelopes $F_k(t;\,\theta'')$ are the same for all M signals, the covariances γ_{jn} of the parameters other than amplitude and phase are inversely proportional to $\sum_k A_k^2$ or, for estimation in the presence of white noise, to $d_T^2 = 2E_T/N$, where E_T is the total received energy. How this energy happened to be divided among the signals is irrelevant. If, however, the signals have equal energies, the covariances are simply those obtained before for a single signal, divided by the total number M of signals; and they are equal to the covariances of estimates that are sample means of the M estimates provided by each signal independently. Only when the energies of the signals might differ can the accuracy of the estimates be enhanced by the methods just prescribed.

If the expected signal energies are both equal and very small, it is best to adopt the threshold estimator, which requires the summation of functions $J(\theta'')$—eq. (2.39)—for each input $v_k(t)$ and the maximization of the sum with respect to θ''. If one were to estimate θ'' from each of these weak signals independently and then average the estimates, the result would be in error by much more than eqs. (2.46) and (2.54) would indicate; for the function $J(\theta'')$ might well have peaks caused by the noise that are taller than the one due to the signal. With weak signals the summation must be performed before the maximization.

3. ESTIMATION OF SIGNAL ARRIVAL TIME

To measure the distance of a radar target it is necessary to estimate the time τ at which the echo from it arrives at the receiver. If time is counted from the transmission of the radar pulse, the distance is $c\tau/2$, where c is the velocity of electromagnetic radiation. The received signal will have the form

$$s(t;\,A,\tau) = Af(t-\tau) \tag{3.1}$$

with the function $f(t)$ completely known if the phase of the transmitted pulse has been retained at the receiver,

$$f(t) = \text{Rl}\; F(t)\; e^{i\Omega t}, \tag{3.2}$$

where Ω is the radar carrier frequency. We shall assume that the target is stationary and that Ω is known. The amplitude A contains information about the radar cross-section of the target, and we shall presume that it too is to be estimated. The noise, we shall suppose, is white and Gaussian with unilateral spectral density N.

From what has been said in previous sections we know that the maximum likelihood estimates $\hat{A}$ and $\hat{\tau}$ of the amplitude and the epoch are the values that maximize the l.l.r.

$$\ln \Lambda[v(t); A, \tau] = \frac{2A}{N} \int_0^T f(t-\tau)\, v(t)\, dt - \frac{A^2}{N} \int_0^T [f(t-\tau)]^2\, dt, \qquad (3.3)$$

and as in eq. (2.23) the estimate of the signal amplitude A is

$$\hat{A} = \int_0^T f(t-\hat{\tau})\, v(t)\, dt \Big/ \int_0^T [f(t-\hat{\tau})]^2\, dt, \qquad (3.4)$$

into which the estimate $\hat{\tau}$ of the arrival time, as yet undetermined, must be substituted. Putting eq. (3.4) back into eq. (3.3), we see, as in eq. (2.24), that $\hat{\tau}$ is the value of the epoch that maximizes the function

$$\ln \Lambda[v(t); \hat{A}, \tau] = \left[\int_0^T f(t-\tau)\, v(t)\, dt\right]^2 \Big/ N \int_0^T [f(t-\tau)]^2\, dt. \qquad (3.5)$$

The observation interval $(0, T)$ is usually so much longer than the signal pulse $f(t)$ that the possibility that the signal overlaps the ends of the interval can be disregarded. The denominator of eq. (3.5) is then independent of τ, the limits of integration in the numerator can be taken as $-\infty$ and $+\infty$, and estimating the time τ requires us to maximize the quantity

$$w(\tau) = \left[\int_{-\infty}^{\infty} f(t-\tau)\, v(t)\, dt\right]^2. \qquad (3.6)$$

If the signal $f(t)$ is confined to an interval $0 < t < T'$, outside of which its values are insignificant, the quantity $w(\tau)$ can be generated by passing the input $v(t)$ through a filter whose impulse response is

$$\begin{aligned} K(s) &= f(T'-s), \quad 0 < s < T', \\ &= 0, \qquad\qquad s < 0,\ s > T'. \end{aligned} \qquad (3.7)$$

The output of this matched filter at time t is

$$v_0(t) = \int_0^{T'} f(T'-u)\, v(t-u)\, du = \int_{-\infty}^{\infty} f(s)\, v(t-T'+s)\, ds, \qquad (3.8)$$

and the quantity $w(\tau)$ is given by

$$w(\tau) = |v_0(T'+\tau)|^2. \qquad (3.9)$$

It is the square of the output of the filter at the time $T'+\tau$. To estimate the time of arrival, therefore, a squaring device is connected to the output of the matched filter, and the time at which its output is greatest is equal to $T'+\hat{\tau}$.

At very large signal-to-noise ratios the time at which this squared output is greatest will be displaced by the noise only slightly from the time $T'+\tau_0$, τ_0 being the true arrival time of the signal. Since this displacement is as likely to be in one direction as in the other, the estimate $\hat{\tau}$ is unbiased. The mean-square error $\mathbf{E}(\hat{\tau}-\tau_0)^2$, or the variance of the estimate $\hat{\tau}$, is given by eq. (2.29), into which we put $f(t;\,\theta') = f(t-\tau)$, $g(t;\,\theta') = (2/N)f(t-\tau)$. With the duration of the observation interval effectively infinite we obtain for the variance of the estimate

$$\operatorname{Var}\hat{\tau} \cong 1/d^2\beta^2, \tag{3.10}$$

where as before $d = (2E/N)^{\frac{1}{2}}$, with E the energy of the signal, and where

$$\beta^2 = \int_{-\infty}^{\infty} [f'(t)]^2\,dt \Big/ \int_{-\infty}^{\infty} [f(t)]^2\,dt, \tag{3.11}$$

the prime denoting differentiation with respect to t. In terms of the spectrum of the signal,

$$F(\omega) = \int_{-\infty}^{\infty} f(t)\,e^{-i\omega t}\,dt, \tag{3.12}$$

the quantity β, which has the dimensions of angular frequency, is given by

$$\beta^2 = \int_{-\infty}^{\infty} \omega^2\,|F(\omega)|^2\,d\omega \Big/ \int_{-\infty}^{\infty} |F(\omega)|^2\,d\omega. \tag{3.13}$$

When as in radar the signal is a narrowband pulse modulating a high-frequency carrier, eq. (3.2), β is approximately equal to the carrier frequency Ω, which is much greater than the bandwidth $\Delta\omega$ of the envelope $F(t)$ as defined in Chapter I, Section 5. Then

$$\operatorname{Var}\hat{\tau} \cong 1/d^2\Omega^2, \tag{3.14}$$

which asserts that when the signal-to-noise ratio is large, the arrival time of the radar echo can be measured within a fraction of a period of its carrier, and the range of the target can be specified within less than a wavelength of the radiation.

To attain such accuracy the oscillations of frequency 2Ω in the squared output $[v_0(t)]^2$ of the matched filter must be observed to determine which is highest. Only when the signal is very strong will this be possible without ambiguity. With weaker signals, even though the output stands well above the noise level, the noise may give a neighboring cycle of the oscillations a greater excursion from the zero line, and the error in the estimate will be some multiple of the period π/Ω of the oscillations. If the measurement is repeated several times, the observed maximum will jump erratically from one cycle to another in the vicinity of the time $T'+\tau_0$.

When this is happening, knowledge of the phase of the transmitted pulse is no longer of any use; and even if that phase were uncontrolled, the estimate of the arrival time of the echo would not be much altered. This estimate and its accuracy will then be nearly the same as for the time of arrival of a quasiharmonic signal

$$s(t;\, A, \psi, \tau) = A \text{ Rl } F(t-\tau)\, e^{i\Omega t+i\psi} \tag{3.15}$$

of unknown phase ψ.

The arrival time of such a signal of unknown phase is estimated, as shown in part (c) of Section 2, by the value of τ that maximizes the quantity

$$[R(\tau)]^2 = \left| N^{-1} \int_{-\infty}^{\infty} F^*(t-\tau)\, V(t)\, dt \right|^2 \tag{3.16}$$

where $V(t)$ is the complex envelope of the input $v(t) = \text{Rl } V(t)\, e^{i\Omega t}$. By the same reasoning as before, we can say that this quantity is proportional to the quadratically rectified output, at time $T'+\tau$, of a filter matched to the signal $\text{Rl } F(t)\, e^{i\Omega t}$,

$$[R(\tau)]^2 = V_d(T'+\tau)/N^2,$$

$$V_d(t) = \left| \int_{-\infty}^{\infty} F^*(s)\, V(t-T'+s)\, ds \right|^2.$$

This system, illustrated in Fig. VIII.1, estimates the signal epoch by timing the peak of the envelope of the output of the matched filter. It is this peak

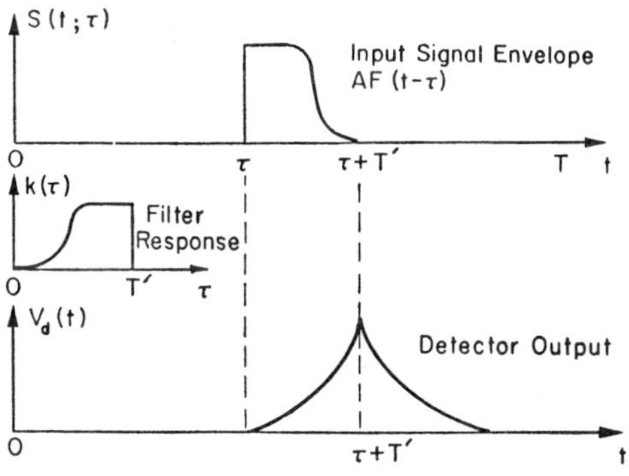

FIG. VIII.1. Estimation of target range.

that determines which of the cycles in the previous output $[v_0(t)]^2 = w(t-T')$ has the greatest excursion from the zero line.

When the phase ψ is taken as unknown and random, the variance of the estimate $\hat{\tau}$ of the arrival time of the signal in eq. (3.15) is given, at large signal-to-noise ratio, by eq. (2.45) as

$$\operatorname{Var}\hat{\tau} \cong (N/A^2)\left[\int_{-\infty}^{\infty} |\partial F(t-\tau)/\partial\tau|^2\, dt\right]^{-1} = 1/d^2\,\Delta\omega^2, \qquad (3.17)$$

where again $d = (2E/N)^{\frac{1}{2}}$, and where $\Delta\omega^2$ is given as in Chapter I, Section 5, by

$$\Delta\omega^2 = \int_{-\infty}^{\infty} |F'(t)|^2\, dt \bigg/ \int_{-\infty}^{\infty} |F(t)|^2\, dt, \qquad (3.18)$$

the carrier frequency Ω having been chosen so that the mean frequency deviation $\bar{\omega}$, eq. (I, 5.1), vanishes.

Swerling (1959) showed that the arrival time can be determined with a variance given by eq. (3.14) when the signal-to-noise ratio is so large that $d \gg \Omega/\Delta\omega$. When $1 \ll d \ll \Omega/\Delta\omega$, however, the variance is limited by $1/d^2\Delta\omega^2$ as in eq. (3.17). It is not hard to see why the dividing line between the ranges of validity of the two formulas should occur at a signal-to-noise ratio of the order of $\Omega/\Delta\omega$. In order to measure the time τ within a fraction of a period of the carrier, it must be possible to locate the peak of the envelope of the output of the matched filter with an error somewhat smaller than π/Ω. Hence the signal-to-noise ratio must, by eq. (3.17), be large enough that

$$(\operatorname{Var}\hat{\tau})^{\frac{1}{2}} \cong 1/d\,\Delta\omega \ll \pi/\Omega,$$

from which we obtain the condition $d \gg \Omega/\pi\,\Delta\omega$.

The system just derived closely resembles a conventional radar range-measuring device. The intermediate amplifier of a radar corresponds to the matched filter, although it is not usually matched precisely to the signal, but merely has an approximately equal bandwidth. The target range is measured by timing the peak of the rectifier output as displayed on an "*A*-scope". This output has many peaks due to the noise, but whenever the signal-to-noise ratio suffices for practically certain detection, there is one peak representing the signal and standing out above the rest. The noise displaces the highest point of this peak by an amount whose mean-square magnitude is given approximately by the variance $\operatorname{Var}\hat{\tau}$ in eq. (3.17).

The greater the bandwidth $\Delta\omega$ of the signal, the more accurately the time of arrival τ can be estimated. One way of achieving this is to transmit a single narrow pulse, to whose width $\Delta\omega$ will be inversely proportional. Another way is to transmit a number M of pulses with different carrier frequencies, but with accurately controlled phases. The individual pulses can then be longer, and a given total energy can be transmitted with a smaller peak power. The bandwidth $\Delta\omega$ determining the accuracy of an estimate of τ will now be of the order of the difference between the largest and the smallest carrier frequencies.

The disadvantage of this second method is that the signal output of the matched filter will have several peaks. In particular, if the transmitted frequencies are uniformly spaced by w rad/sec, the output will crest at times separated by $2\pi/w$. The width of each peak will be of the order of $2\pi/\Delta\omega$, and their number will be about $wt_p/2\pi$, where t_p is the duration of each pulse. The noise may cause the wrong peak to appear tallest, and a large error in the estimate $\hat{\tau}$ will ensue. If several targets are present at nearly the same range, their echoes may appear inextricably confused.

If, on the other hand, the phases of the transmitted pulses are uncontrolled and the echoes are taken to have individually random phases ψ_k, the best that can be done is to rectify the pulses individually and sum, as indicated by eq. (2.52). Ambiguity of the kind just described will be avoided, but the mean-square error of the arrival time will be given by $1/d_T^2(\Delta'\omega)^2$ instead of by $1/d_T^2(\Delta\omega)^2$, where $\Delta'\omega$ is the bandwidth of an individual pulse and $d_T = (2E_T/N)^{\frac{1}{2}}$ is the net signal-to-noise ratio. The same accuracy could be attained by periodically transmitting M pulses of a single frequency and uncontrolled phase.

4. ESTIMATION OF SIGNAL ARRIVAL TIME AND CARRIER FREQUENCY

a) *The Estimating System*

If the radar target is not stationary, as assumed in Section 3, but is moving toward or away from the antenna, the carrier frequency Ω of the echo differs from that of the transmitted pulse because of the Doppler effect. If we pick the transmitted frequency as our reference frequency, the echo will have the form

$$s(t; \tau, w) = A \operatorname{Rl} F(t-\tau) \exp [i(w+\Omega_r)(t-\tau)+i\psi], \tag{4.1}$$

where A is its amplitude, ψ its phase, τ its epoch, and $w = \Omega - \Omega_r$ the change in carrier frequency. This "Doppler shift" w is given by

$$w = \Omega - \Omega_r = (2v/c)\,\Omega_r \tag{4.2}$$

where v is the component of target velocity in the direction of the radar antenna and c is the velocity of electromagnetic radiation. The pulse envelope $F(t)$ is also compressed by a factor $(1+2v/c)^{-1}$, but for targets of ordinary velocities this factor differs negligibly from 1. For a target moving at a rate of 500 m.p.h., and for a carrier frequency $\Omega_r = 2\pi \cdot 3 \cdot 10^9$ rad/sec (3000 MHz), the frequency shift is $w = 2\pi \cdot 4{\cdot}5 \cdot 10^3$ rad/sec (4500 Hz), an appreciable fraction of the l-megahertz bandwidth typical of a radar pulse. For the much larger velocities encountered in tracking missiles and satellites the Doppler shift will be even greater.

When the echo signal suffers a Doppler shift comparable with its bandwidth, the response to it of a filter matched to the transmitted pulse is much reduced; and the signal may be missed in the noise. Only if the target velocity is known can the receiver filter be properly matched to the echo pulse. On the other hand, if the Doppler shift can be measured, the observer can calculate the component of the target velocity in the direction of his radar antenna, obtaining valuable information for tracking the target efficiently. The possibility thus arises of measuring both the distance of the target and its velocity, by estimating the time τ of arrival of the echo signal and the frequency shift w of its carrier. In this section we shall indicate how this can be done by the methods of the statistical theory of estimation.

As the time τ of arrival is unknown, we can combine the term $-\Omega_r \tau$ in eq. (4.1) with the unknown phase ψ and write the signal instead as

$$s(t; A, \psi, \tau, w) = A \text{ Rl } F(t; \tau, w) \exp (i\Omega_r t + i\psi), \tag{4.3}$$

with

$$F(t; \tau, w) = F(t-\tau)\, e^{iw(t-\tau)}. \tag{4.4}$$

This signal is received in the presence of white, Gaussian noise of unilateral spectral density N, during an observation interval $(0, T)$ that is so long that signals overlapping its ends can be disregarded.

In our previous notation the unknown parameters are denoted by $\theta_1 = A$, $\theta_2 = \psi$, $\theta_3 = \tau$, $\theta_4 = w$, and from eq. (2.33) the reduced ambiguity function is

$$H'(\theta_1'', \theta_2'') = N^{-1} \int_{-\infty}^{\infty} F^*(t-\tau_1)\, F(t-\tau_2) \exp i(w_2 - w_1)t \, dt. \tag{4.5}$$

Since $H'(\theta'', \theta'')$ is independent of the parameters $\theta'' = (\tau, w)$, the maximum-likelihood estimates of the arrival time τ and the frequency shift w are, as shown in Section 2, part (c), those values for which the quantity

$$R(\tau, w) = N^{-1} \left| \int_{-\infty}^{\infty} F^*(t-\tau)\, e^{-iw(t-\tau)} V(t)\, dt \right| \tag{4.6}$$

is largest, where $V(t)$ is the complex envelope of the input $v(t) = \text{Rl } V(t) \exp i\Omega_r t$.

This quantity $R(\tau, w)$ can be generated for a dense set of values of the frequency shift w by means of a bank of parallel filters followed by linear rectifiers. The filter for a particular shift w is matched to a signal Rl $F(t) \exp i(w+\Omega_r)t$; its complex impulse response, referred to the frequency Ω_r, is

$$\begin{aligned} k_w(s) &= F^*(T'-s)\, e^{-iw(T'-s)}, \qquad 0 < s < 2T', \\ &= 0, \qquad s < 0, \quad s > 2T', \end{aligned} \tag{4.7}$$

where T' is large enough for the signal envelope $|F(t)|$ to be entirely contained within the interval $(-T', T')$. (The interval is taken thus because we shall later want the envelope to be so defined that its mean epoch $\bar{t}$—eq. (I, 5.4)—is 0.) The complex envelope of the output of this filter is

$$\begin{aligned} V_w(t) &= \int_0^{2T'} F^*(T'-s)\, e^{-iw(T'-s)}\, V(t-s)\, ds \\ &= \int_{-\infty}^{\infty} F^*(u)\, e^{-iwu}\, V(t-T'+u)\, du, \end{aligned} \tag{4.8}$$

and the output of a linear rectifier following this filter is, at time t, proportional to $R(t-T', w)$.

The rectified outputs of all these matched filters must be watched, and the largest values they attain during the interval $(T', T'+T)$ must be recorded. The filter whose rectified output reaches the highest value specifies the estimate $\hat{w}$ of the frequency shift, and the time t at which that peak value appears determines the estimate of the arrival time of the signal through $\hat{\tau} = t-T'$.

Alternatively, all the filters can be matched to a signal Rl $F(t) \exp i\Omega_i t$, where Ω_i is a fixed intermediate frequency. Each filter is preceded by a mixer in which the input is beaten against a wave of frequency $(\Omega_r+w-\Omega_i)$ for one of a uniformly spaced set of values of w. The output of each filter is applied to a linear rectifier, and the branch of the array whose peak output is largest identifies the estimate $\hat{w}$. If the input can be recorded, the best value of the shift w can be sought by passing the input again and again through a mixer with a variable local oscillator frequency and observing the peak output. Searching for the signal frequency in this way is, in radar, seldom practical.

The closer are the frequency shifts for which matched filters are constructed, the nearer will the estimate obtained in this way lie to the maximum-likelihood estimate $\hat{w}$. There is little to be gained, however, by spacing the values of w by much less than the r.m.s. error $(\mathrm{Var}\,\hat{w})^{\frac{1}{2}}$ introduced by the noise. The noise will tend to make the maximum output appear in some other filter-rectifier branch than the correct one, and the time at which it occurs will deviate from the time $T'+\tau_0$ when it would occur in the absence of noise. In this way errors are introduced into the estimates.

(b) *The Error Variances*

The magnitudes of the errors and their relationships can be assessed by working out the variances $\mathrm{Var}\,\hat{\tau}$ and $\mathrm{Var}\,\hat{w}$ and the covariance $\{\hat{\tau}, \hat{w}\}$ of the maximum-likelihood estimates by the method of Section 2, which is applicable when the signal-to-noise ratio is large. From eq. (2.46) we find for the inverse asymptotic covariance matrix

$$\mathbf{\Gamma} = \begin{bmatrix} d^2/A^2 & 0 & 0 & 0 \\ 0 & d^2 & -d^2(\bar{\omega}+w) & d^2\bar{t} \\ 0 & -d^2(\bar{\omega}+w) & d^2(\overline{\omega^2}+2w\bar{\omega}+w^2) & -d^2(\overline{\omega t}+w\bar{t}) \\ 0 & d^2\bar{t} & -d^2(\overline{\omega t}+w\bar{t}) & d^2\overline{t^2} \end{bmatrix} \tag{4.9}$$

where the moments of time and frequency are defined as in Section 5 of Chapter I. If we assume for simplicity that the complex envelope of the signal has been so defined that $\bar{t} = 0$ and $\bar{\omega} = 0$, we obtain for the covariance matrix $\boldsymbol{\gamma} = \mathbf{\Gamma}^{-1}$

$$\boldsymbol{\gamma} = d^{-2}C^{-1} \begin{bmatrix} A^2C & 0 & 0 & 0 \\ 0 & C+w^2\,\Delta t^2 & w\,\Delta t^2 & w\,\Delta(\omega t) \\ 0 & w\,\Delta t^2 & \Delta t^2 & \Delta(\omega t) \\ 0 & w\,\Delta(\omega t) & \Delta(\omega t) & \Delta\omega^2 \end{bmatrix} \tag{4.10}$$

in which we have put $\Delta(\omega t) = \overline{\omega t} - \bar{\omega}\bar{t}$, $C = \Delta\omega^2\,\Delta t^2 - [\Delta(\omega t)]^2$.

From eq. (4.10) we learn that the estimate $\hat{A}$ of the amplitude is asymptotically uncorrelated with the rest of the estimates, and its relative variance $(\mathrm{Var}\,\hat{A})/A^2$ is equal to d^{-2}, where $d = (2E/N)^{\frac{1}{2}}$ is the usual signal-to-noise ratio for a signal of energy E. The errors in the estimates of arrival time and frequency shift have second moments given at large signal-to-noise ratios by

$$\mathrm{Var}\,\hat{\tau} = \Delta t^2/d^2C, \quad \{\hat{\tau}, \hat{w}\} = \Delta(\omega t)/d^2C, \quad \mathrm{Var}\,\hat{w} = \Delta\omega^2/d^2C,$$
$$C = \Delta\omega^2\,\Delta t^2 - [\Delta(\omega t)]^2. \tag{4.11}$$

If the signal contains no frequency modulation, $\Delta(\omega t)$ vanishes, and the moments of the errors become simply

$$\mathrm{Var}\,\hat{\tau} = 1/d^2\,\Delta\omega^2, \quad \mathrm{Var}\,\hat{w} = 1/d^2\,\Delta t^2, \quad \{\hat{\tau}, w\} = 0. \tag{4.12}$$

The first of these is the same as eq. (3.17) for the variance of the estimate of the time when an echo arrives from a fixed target; it is inversely proportional to the mean-square bandwidth of the signal. The variance of the estimate of the frequency shift w is inversely proportional to the mean-square duration Δt^2 of the signal, and the estimates of epoch and frequency are uncorrelated.

For a given signal shape an increase in the bandwidth $\Delta\omega$ entails a decrease in the r.m.s. duration Δt, and the variance of the estimate of the epoch τ cannot be reduced without at the same time accepting less precise measurements of the frequency shift w unless a marked change is made in the shape of the transmitted pulse itself. Still considering signals without frequency modulation, we observe that the product $\Delta\omega^2 \cdot \Delta t^2$ can be made large by using signals whose spectra are, for a given bandwidth $\Delta\omega$, distributed as much toward high frequencies as possible. This can be achieved by giving the pulses very sharp corners. Such signals will yield the most accurate simultaneous estimates of arrival time and frequency. The increased accuracy will not be gained, however, unless filters properly matched to the signals are built into the receiver.

At large signal-to-noise ratios the estimates of the parameters τ and w have a joint Gaussian distribution, and the variances in eq. (4.11) determine the distribution as

$$p(\hat{\tau}, \hat{w}) = \left(C^{\frac{1}{2}}E/\pi N\right) \exp\left\{-\frac{E}{N}\left[\Delta\omega^2(\hat{\tau}-\tau_0)^2 - 2\Delta(\omega t)(\hat{\tau}-\tau_0)(\hat{w}-w_0) + \Delta t^2(\hat{w}-w_0)^2\right]\right\}, \quad (4.13)$$

which can be derived from eq. (II, 4.2). Referring to eq. (5.15) of Chapter I we see that the contours of constant probability density $p(\hat{\tau}, \hat{w})$ are ellipses similar to the "uncertainty ellipse" defined there. Figure I.7 shows that when the signal pulse is frequency modulated, $\Delta(\omega t) \neq 0$, the errors in the estimates of the epoch τ and the shift w are correlated, large values of one error tending to accompany large values of the other. As the signal-to-noise ratio $(2E/N)^{\frac{1}{2}}$ increases, the surface $p(\hat{\tau}, \hat{w})$ becomes more and more peaked in the neighborhood of the true values τ_0 and w_0, but its contours remain similar to the uncertainty ellipse.

The Gaussian pulse with complex envelope

$$F(t) = A \exp(-Bt^2/2), \quad \mathrm{Rl}\, B > 0,$$

has an uncertainty ellipse of the greatest possible area, and it entails the largest errors in estimates of signal arrival time and frequency shift among all pulses having the same total energy E. There is, on the other hand, no limit to how small the combined error variances can be made, for the area $\pi C^{-\frac{1}{2}}$ of the uncertainty ellipse can be diminished as much as desired by properly selecting the shape of the signal.

(c) *Estimation by Multiple Signals*

In the previous section we learned that by transmitting pulses of a number of carrier frequencies occupying a spectral band much wider than the spectrum of a single pulse, the accuracy of a radar range measurement could be enhanced. In a similar way the radial velocity v of a target can be measured more accurately if the transmitter sends out a train of coherent pulses of the same carrier frequency. Such a composite signal might take the form

$$f(t) = \text{Rl} \sum_{k=1}^{M} F(t-(k-1)\,T) \exp\,[i\Omega_r(t-(k-1)\,T)], \tag{4.14}$$

where T denotes the time between two pulses. From a target whose range is initially $r_0 = \frac{1}{2}(c+v)\tau$ an echo will be received that is described approximately by

$$s(t;\tau,w) = A\;\text{Rl} \sum_{k=1}^{M} F(t-(k-1)\,T-\tau+(2v/c)(k-1)\,T)\cdot$$
$$\exp\left[i(\Omega_r+w)\,(t-\tau-(k-1)T)\left(1-\frac{2v}{c}\right)\right], \tag{4.15}$$

with $w = (2v/c)\Omega_r$. In writing the echo signal in this way it is assumed that the coherence of the signals is preserved upon reflection from the target and during propagation. The radial velocity v has been taken constant during entire MT seconds occupied by the train of pulses.

The frequency shift w and the epoch τ can be estimated by the same method as before. It is only necessary to build an array of filters matched to the signals

$$\text{Rl} \sum_{k} F\left(t-(k-1)T+\frac{w}{\Omega_r}(k-1)T\right)\cdot$$
$$\exp\left[i(\Omega_r+w)\left(t-(k-1)T+\frac{w}{\Omega_r}(k-1)T\right)\right]$$

for a densely spaced set of values of the frequency shift w. Each of these matched filters can perhaps more simply be constructed as a combination of a tapped delay line and a filter matched to the signal $\text{Rl}\,F(t)\exp i(\Omega_r+w)\,t$. The delay line retards the input $v(t)$ by integral multiples of $(1-w/\Omega_r)T$

and feeds the retarded inputs to the matched filter. The output of this combination is applied to a linear rectifier. The branch of this array whose output attains the largest value during the interval $(\overline{M-1}T, MT)$ following the Mth transmitted pulse determines the estimate $\hat{w}$ of the frequency shift, and the time at which that largest rectified output occurs provides an estimate of the epoch τ.

The accuracy with which the frequency shift w can be measured by such a system is given at large signal-to-noise ratios by the approximate formula

$$\operatorname{Var} \hat{w} \cong d^{-2}(MT)^{-2},$$

$d = (2E/N)^{\frac{1}{2}}$, for the r.m.s. duration Δt of the signal is now roughly equal to the length MT of the train of pulses. The energy E is the total energy in the set of pulses.

Here again ambiguity can arise. The spectrum of the signal and the transfer functions of the matched filters consist of a number of peaks separated in angular frequency by $2\pi/T$. The entire spectrum occupies a band of frequencies whose width is of the order of the bandwidth of a component pulse Rl $F(t)$ exp $(i\Omega_r t)$; this width is inversely proportional to the duration of each pulse. Hence, when an echo appears, a number of the matched filters will produce large outputs, namely those filters designed for frequency shifts w differing from the true Doppler shift by approximately integral multiples of $2\pi/T$. The noise may cause one of these extraneous peaks to be taller than the peak output of the correct matched filter, and an error in w amounting to some multiple of $2\pi/T$ will be incurred.

The rectified outputs of each of these filters will exhibit a series of peaks separated by T seconds as the component pulses of the echo arrive. The tallest of these determines the estimate $\hat{\tau}$ of the signal epoch, which will be in error by an integral multiple of T if the noise makes the wrong peak appear tallest. We are confronted with ambiguities in measurements of both time of arrival and frequency. It might be thought that by spacing the pulses in an erratic or quasirandom way, such ambiguities could be avoided, but it appears quite difficult to do so. Some of the limitations on the elimination of ambiguities will be discussed in Chapter X when we treat the ambiguity function in detail.

Target scintillations or erratic delays in propagation may render the components of the echo incoherent. If so, the individual received signals must be assigned random phases, and a bank of matched filters and delay lines of the kind just described will be ineffectual. According to what we have said in part (d) of Section 2, the best that can be done will in most cases be to form the test function

$$R(\tau, w) = N^{-1} \sum_{k=1}^{M} \left| \int_{-\infty}^{\infty} F^*(t'-\tau+(k-1)wT/\Omega_r) \exp\,[-iw(t'-\tau)]\, V_k(t')\, dt' \right|^2, \tag{4.16}$$

where $V_k(t')$ is the complex envelope of the input during the interval following the kth transmitted pulse. (The time t' in the integral is measured from the beginning of each interval.) The maximum-likelihood estimates of the epoch and the frequency shift are the values of τ and w that maximize $R(\tau, w)$. This function can be generated for a set of values of w by passing the input through filters matched to signals of the form Rl $F(t) \exp i(\Omega_r+w)t$ and followed by quadratic rectifiers and tapped delay lines. The rectified and delayed outputs are summed to produce, during the final interval, a set of functions $R(t'+T', w)$, where T' is the delay in each matched filter. Again the branch with the largest output specifies the estimate of the shift w.

The variances and the covariance of the estimates $\hat{\tau}$ and $\hat{w}$ obtained by maximizing $R(\tau, w)$ can be calculated from eq. (2.54). The signal $S_k(t; \theta)$ is taken as

$$S_k(t; \theta) = A \exp\,(i\psi_k)\, F(t-\tau+\mu_k w)e^{iw(t-\tau)},$$
$$\mu_k = (k-1)T/\Omega_r,$$

and $Q_k(t; \theta) = N^{-1}S_k(t; \theta)$. After some algebra one finds, in particular, for the variance of the estimate of frequency the formula

$$\text{Var}\,\hat{w} = \left\{ d_T^2 \Delta t^2 + \Delta\omega^2 \left[\sum_{k=1}^{M} \mu_k^2 d_k^2 - d_T^{-2} \left(\sum_{k=1}^{M} \mu_k d_k^2 \right)^2 \right] \right\}^{-1},$$
$$d_k^2 = 2E_k/N, \quad d_T^2 = 2E_T/N, \tag{4.17}$$

in which it has been assumed that there is no frequency modulation in the pulses, $\Delta(\omega t) = 0$. Here E_k is the energy of the kth echo and E_T is the total energy in all M echoes.

To elucidate this result let us suppose that all the signals have equal energies, and $d_k^2 \equiv d_T^2/M = d^2$. Then we find

$$\sum_{k=1}^{M} \mu_k^2 d_k^2 - d_T^{-2} \left(\sum_{k=1}^{M} \mu_k d_k^2 \right)^2 = \tfrac{1}{12}(M^2-1)T^2\, d_T^2/\Omega_r^2\,.$$

The term with $\Delta\omega^2$ in eq. (4.17) is usually larger than Δt^2, and the variance of the corresponding estimate $\hat{v}$ of the radial velocity is

$$\text{Var}\,\hat{v} \cong (c^2/4\Omega_r^2)\ \text{Var}\,\hat{w} \cong (\text{Var}\,\hat{r})\,[\tfrac{1}{12}M(M^2-1)T^2]^{-1}, \tag{4.18}$$

where Var $\hat{r} = c^2/(4d^2 \Delta\omega^2)$ is the variance of an estimate of the range of the target based on a single echo. The error variance in eq. (4.18) is the same as the mean-square error in a target velocity v estimated by simply fitting a straight line $r(t) = r_0 - vt$ by the method of least squares to a set of M measurements of the range of the target at times spaced T seconds apart.

If the velocity of the target is not constant, one can at least for a short span of time attribute to it a constant acceleration. There are then three unknown parameters, the acceleration, the initial range, and the initial radial velocity, to be estimated. The methods presented in this chapter can be applied to calculating the asymptotically minimum variances that such estimates can attain, but the analysis is too lengthy to be given here. The problem has been treated by Bello (1960) and Kelly (1961).

PROBLEMS

1. Show that the Bayes estimate of the parameters $\boldsymbol{\theta}$ with a cost function $C(\hat{\boldsymbol{\theta}}, \boldsymbol{\theta}) = A - B\delta(\hat{\boldsymbol{\theta}} - \boldsymbol{\theta})$, where A and B are positive constants, is equivalent to the estimate that maximizes the posterior probability density function of the parameters $\boldsymbol{\theta}$.

2. Given are n independent measurements $(v_1, v_2, \ldots, v_n)$ of the noise voltage v at a certain point in a receiver. If v is Gaussian with mean value 0, what is the maximum-likelihood estimate of the variance of the noise? Calculate the expected value and the variance of this estimate as functions of the true variance. Give a sufficient statistic for estimating Var v.

3. Suppose that in Problem 2 both the mean value and the variance of the voltage v are unknown. Work out their maximum-likelihood estimates based on the same n measurements.

4. A narrowband signal appears at a known time in the midst of stationary narrowband Gaussian noise. Unknown are its amplitude, its phase, and the deviation w of its carrier frequency from a fixed reference frequency Ω_r. Determine the maximum-likelihood estimates of these three unknown parameters and evaluate the variance of the estimate of frequency at high signal-to-noise ratio. Under the assumption that the observation interval is much longer than the signal, express Var $\hat{w}$ in terms of the spectrum of the signal and the spectral density of the noise. Specialize to estimation in white noise.

5. Prove eq. (2.26) by using the positive-definiteness of the autocovariance function $\phi(t, u)$. *Hint.* Write a double integral involving the function $f(t; \boldsymbol{\theta}_1) - \lambda f(t; \boldsymbol{\theta}_2)$ and minimize with respect to λ.

6. Show that at large signal-to-noise ratio the maximum-likelihood estimate of the azimuth θ of a target, based on echoes received by a radar antenna scanning at a uniform rate, is inversely proportional to both the net squared signal-to-noise ratio $d_T^2 = 2E_T/N$ and the mean-square beamwidth Θ^2, defined by

$$\Theta^2 = \int_0^{2\pi} [\varrho'(\theta)]^2 \, d\theta \Bigg/ \int_0^{2\pi} [\varrho(\theta)]^2 \, d\theta,$$

where $\varrho(\theta)$ is the amplitude-gain pattern of the antenna. Take the received signals as

$$f_k(t) = \text{Rl}\, A\varrho(\theta_0 + k\delta)\, F(t) \exp(i\psi_k + i\Omega t),$$

where the amplitude A, the azimuth θ_0 of the target, and the phases ψ_k are independent and unknown, and all are to be estimated. The noise is white and Gaussian of unilateral spectral density N, and E_T is the total received energy. Show how the maximum-likelihood estimate of θ_0 can be obtained at large signal-to-noise ratios. In evaluating its variance, use eq. (2.54) and assume that the angle δ through which the antenna turns between reception of one echo and the next is small enough that summations over k can be replaced by integrations over azimuth. It was assumed in writing the equation for $f_k(t)$ that the transmitting antenna is fixed and that all pulses incident on the target have the same energy. References to studies of the angular accuracy of radar are given in the bibliography of this chapter.

7. Let $v(t)$ be a realization of Gaussian random noise of autocovariance $\phi(t, s) = B\varrho(t, s)$, where B is positive but unknown. If $v(t)$ is given only over a finite interval $(0, T)$, the multiplicative constant B can be estimated as accurately as desired. To show this, consider the estimator

$$b_n = n^{-1} \sum_{k=1}^{n} v_k^2/\lambda_k,$$

where $v_k = \int_0^T v(t) f_k(t)\, dt$, with $\{f_k(t)\}$ the orthonormal eigenfunctions and $\{\lambda_k\}$ the eigenvalues of the integral equation

$$\lambda f(t) = \int_0^T \varrho(t, s) f(s)\, ds,$$

$\lambda_1 \geqslant \lambda_2 \geqslant \ldots \geqslant \lambda_n > 0$. Show that b_n is an unbiased estimate of B and that Var $b_n \to 0$ as $n \to \infty$. Hence the accuracy of the estimate is the greater, the larger the number n of terms in b_n.

8. Average the likelihood ratio in eq. (2.51) over the independently random and uniformly distributed phases ψ_k. Assume that the amplitudes A_k are equal to an unknown positive constant A. Derive an equation from which the maximum-likelihood estimate of A can be found, and solve it in the limit of large signal-to-noise ratio. Show how the maximum-likelihood estimates of the essential parameters $\boldsymbol{\theta}''$ can be obtained in this case. Compare with the result for $M = 1$ in eq. (2.38.).

BIBLIOGRAPHY (VIII)

1922 Fisher, R. A., "On the Mathematical Foundations of Theoretical Statistics", *Phil. Trans. Roy. Soc.* A **222**, 309–68.

1945 Rao, C. R., "Information and the Accuracy Attainable in the Estimation of Statistical Parameters", *Bull. Calcutta Math. Soc.* **37**, 81–91.

1946 Cramér, H. *Mathematical Methods of Statistics*, Princeton University Press, Princeton, N.J.

1950 Woodward, P. M. and Davies, I. L., "A Theory of Radar Information", *Phil. Mag.* **41**, 1001–17 (Oct.).

1953 Annis, M., Cheston, W. and Primakoff, H., "On Statistical Estimation in Physics", *Rev. Mod. Phys.* **25**, 818–30 (Oct.).

Woodward, P. M., *Probability and Information Theory, with Applications to Radar*, McGraw-Hill Book Co., New York, N.Y.; Pergamon Press, Ltd., Oxford, England.

1954 Slepian, D., "Estimation of Signal Parameters in the Presence of Noise", *Trans. I.R.E.* **PGIT-3**, 68–89 (Mar.).

1956 Swerling, P., "Maximum Angular Accuracy of a Pulsed Search Radar", *Proc. I.R.E.* **44,** 1146–55 (Sept.).

1958 Sherman, S., "Non-Mean-Square Error Criteria", *Trans. I.R.E.* **IT-4**, 125–6 (Sept.).

1959 Swerling, P., "Parameter Estimation for Waveforms in Additive Gaussian Noise", *J. Soc. Ind. Appl. Math.* **7,** 152–66 (June).

1960 Bello, P., "Joint Estimation of Delay, Doppler, and Doppler Rate", *Trans. I.R.E.* **IT-6,** 330–41 (June).

Skolnik, M. I., "Theoretical Accuracy of Radar Measurements", *Trans. I.R.E.* **ANE-7,** 123–9 (Dec.).

1961 Brennan, L. E., "Angular Accuracy of a Phased Array Radar", *Trans. I.R.E.* **AP-9,** 268–75 (May).

Jeffreys, H., *Theory of Probability*, Oxford University Press, London, England.

Kelly, E. J., "The Radar Measurement of Range, Velocity, and Acceleration", *Trans. I. R. E.* **MIL-5**, 51 – 57 (Apr.).

1964 Swerling, P., "Parameter Estimation Accuracy Formulas", *Trans. I.E.E.E.* **IT-10,** 302–14 (Oct.).

Urkowitz, H., "The Accuracy of Maximum Likelihood Angle Estimates in Radar and Sonar", *Trans. I.E.E.E.* **MIL–8,** 39–45 (Jan.).

1965 Jánossy, L., *Theory and Practice of the Evaluation of Measurements*, Oxford University Press, London, England.

Sakrison, D. J., "Estimation of Signals containing Unknown Parameters: Comparison of Linear and Arbitrary Unbiased Estimates", *J. Soc. Ind. Appl. Math.* **13,** 706–19 (Sept.).

1966 Swerling, P., "Topics in Generalized Least Squares Signal Estimation", *SIAM J. Appl. Math.* **14,** 998–1031 (Sept.).

IX

DETECTION OF SIGNALS WITH UNKNOWN PARAMETERS

1. MAXIMUM-LIKELIHOOD DETECTION

(a) *The Application of Estimation Theory*

When the signal to be detected is not unique, but depends on one or more parameters whose values are unknown or uncertain, the methods of statistical decision theory cannot be applied unless a prior probability distribution of the parameters is available. There may be situations in which past experience suffices to determine a prior distribution, but more often than not it is necessary to go ahead without one. In Chapter V it was suggested that one might seek the least favorable prior p.d.f. of the unknown parameters, for which the average probability of detection, with a given false-alarm probability, is smallest. The receiver is then to base its decisions on a likelihood ratio averaged with respect to this least favorable distribution.

When the amplitude of the signal is unknown, the least favorable distribution entails our taking the signals as vanishingly small and adopting the threshold detector, which is obtained by expanding the likelihood ratio in a power series in the amplitude and using as detection statistic the term of lowest positive order. When additional parameters such as the arrival time of the signal are known only within wide limits, this statistic must further be averaged over them. The resulting threshold detector, as we found in Chapter V, Section 5, attains a useful combination of false-alarm and detection probabilities only for excessive signal strengths. The emphasis on signals too weak to be reliably detected is an unsatisfactory aspect of adopting least favorable distributions for unknown parameters.

In practice the ranges of unknown parameters such as arrival time and carrier frequency are broad but finite, and any search for the signal would be confined to a finite region of the parameter space. We may call this region the "expected domain" of the parameter values $\boldsymbol{\theta} = (\theta_1, \theta_2, \ldots, \theta_m)$. Were a signal known to be present, its unknown parameters could be estimated by one of the methods set forth in the previous chapter. One might, for instance, find for what values of $\boldsymbol{\theta}$ in the expected domain the likelihood ratio is largest. This could be done by passing the input through a bank of parallel filters matched to densely spaced values of the parameters and looking for the filter with the greatest rectified output, a procedure that suggests a receiver in which the outputs of such a filter bank are compared with a decision level. Whenever the level is surpassed, a signal is taken to be present. Since the outputs are monotonely related to the values of the likelihood ratio, the observer is in effect deciding about the presence of a signal on the basis of the maximum value of the likelihood ratio,

$$\Lambda(\mathbf{x}; \hat{\boldsymbol{\theta}}) = \max_{\boldsymbol{\theta}} \Lambda(\mathbf{x}; \boldsymbol{\theta}) = \max_{\boldsymbol{\theta}} p_1(\mathbf{x}; \boldsymbol{\theta})/p_0(\mathbf{x}), \tag{1.1}$$

where $p_0(\mathbf{x})$ and $p_1(\mathbf{x}; \boldsymbol{\theta})$ are the joint p.d.f.s of the data under the two hypotheses, H_0 that the signal is absent and H_1 that it is present. Here $\hat{\boldsymbol{\theta}}$ is the maximum-likelihood estimate of the parameters $\boldsymbol{\theta}$ under the assumption that a signal really is at hand. The maximum likelihood ratio $\Lambda(\mathbf{x}; \hat{\boldsymbol{\theta}})$ is compared with a decision level Λ_l set by the preassigned false-alarm probability, a strategy known as *maximum-likelihood detection* (Kelly, Reed, and Root, 1960).

Now we shall relate this idea to our previous approach, whereby an average likelihood ratio, defined in terms of a prior p.d.f. $z(\boldsymbol{\theta})$ of the unknown parameters by

$$\Lambda(\mathbf{x}) = \int z(\boldsymbol{\theta})\, \Lambda(\mathbf{x}; \boldsymbol{\theta})\, d^m\boldsymbol{\theta}, \tag{1.2}$$

was to be compared with the decision level Λ_0. When the expected domain of the parameters $\boldsymbol{\theta}$ is very broad, the prior p.d.f. $z(\boldsymbol{\theta})$ will be only a slowly varying function of $\boldsymbol{\theta}$. If now the likelihood ratio itself has a relatively sharp peak near the point $\boldsymbol{\theta} = \hat{\boldsymbol{\theta}}$, the main contribution to the integral in eq. (1.2) will come from the neighborhood of $\hat{\boldsymbol{\theta}}$, and the average likelihood ratio will be proportional to the peak value $\Lambda(\mathbf{x}; \hat{\boldsymbol{\theta}})$. Comparing the average likelihood ratio with a decision level is then nearly equivalent to comparing the maximum likelihood ratio $\Lambda(\mathbf{x}; \hat{\boldsymbol{\theta}})$ with a related decision level. The difference between the two procedures will be the smaller, the greater the signal-to-noise ratio. Since we are looking for a system that is at least nearly optimum at signal strengths offering a useful probability of detection, the concept of maximum likelihood invites our attention.

In maximum-likelihood detection the receiver seeks the largest value $\Lambda(\mathbf{x}; \hat{\boldsymbol{\theta}})$ of the likelihood ratio in the expected domain of the parameters and compares it with a decision level Λ_l. If $\Lambda(\mathbf{x}; \hat{\theta})$ exceeds Λ_l, the receiver accepts hypothesis H_1. When, as often, the data $\mathbf{x} = (x_1, x_2, \ldots, x_n)$ are samples of the input $v(t)$ of the receiver at uniformly spaced times and it is possible to pass to the limit of a large number of dense samples, the receiver can instead work with the likelihood ratio $\Lambda[v(t); \theta]$. If $\Lambda[v(t); \theta]$ is less than a decision level Λ_l for all values of the parameters θ within the expected domain, the receiver decides that no signal is present. If $\Lambda[v(t); \theta] > \Lambda_l$ for some value or values of θ, a signal is declared present, and its parameters are estimated by the vector θ for which $\Lambda[v(t); \theta]$ is largest.

When a signal must be detected in Gaussian noise whose spectral density depends on a finite number of unknown parameters, such as a multiplicative constant or a bandwidth, both hypotheses H_0 and H_1 are composite. In such a situation the principle of maximum likelihood requires the receiver to compare the ratio

$$\Lambda_{ml}(\mathbf{x}) = \max_{\theta} p_1(\mathbf{x}; \theta)/\max_{\theta} p_0(\mathbf{x}; \theta) \tag{1.3}$$

with an appropriate decision level and to choose hypothesis H_1 if the level is exceeded and H_0 if it is not. Now one is estimating the parameters θ in both the p.d.f.s $p_0(\mathbf{x}; \theta)$ and $p_1(\mathbf{x}; \theta)$ as if each hypothesis were true, and one is using these estimates in the likelihood ratio. The principle of maximum likelihood in this form is discussed by Lehmann (1959, pp. 14–16).

It may happen that the likelihood ratio $\Lambda[v(t); \theta]$ exceeds the decision level Λ_l in a number of disconnected regions of the parameter space. If as in radar there may be more than one signal present, each of the peak values of $\Lambda[v(t); \theta]$ surpassing the decision level can be attributed to a signal, and the location of each peak estimates the parameters of the associated signal. When the false-alarm probability is very small and the level Λ_l correspondingly high, the probability is just as small that any such peaks higher than Λ_l would not have been caused by a signal. If, on the other hand, as in communications at most one signal can be expected during the observation interval $(0, T)$, only the tallest peak of the likelihood ratio should be considered as due to a signal.

It is conceivable that the function $\Lambda[v(t); \theta]$ could have more than one local maximum near the true value θ_0 of the parameters of a single signal, these additional maxima having been caused by noise fluctuations. The question how far apart in θ should maxima of $\Lambda[v(t); \theta]$ be before the receiver should attribute them to more than one signal is related to the problem of resolving signals, which will be treated in the next chapter.

(b) *Maximum-likelihood Detection of Signals in Gaussian Noise*

The principle of maximum-likelihood detection is most simply applied to the detection in Gaussian noise of a signal $s(t) = Af(t)$ completely known except for its amplitude A. As we showed in Chapter IV, the likelihood ratio is given by

$$\Lambda[v(t); A] = \exp\left[A \int_0^T g(t)\, v(t)\, dt - \tfrac{1}{2}A^2 \int_0^T g(t)\, f(t)\, dt\right], \qquad (1.4)$$

where $v(t)$ is the input to the receiver and $g(t)$ is the solution of the usual integral equation (VIII, 2.16), whose kernel is the autocovariance of the noise. This likelihood ratio is maximized when the amplitude is taken as

$$\hat{A} = \int_0^T g(t)\, v(t)\, dt \Big/ \int_0^T g(t) f(t)\, dt, \qquad (1.5)$$

and the maximum value of the likelihood ratio is

$$\Lambda[v(t); \hat{A}] = \exp\left\{\left[\int_0^T g(t)\, v(t)\, dt\right]^2 \Big/ 2 \int_0^T g(t) f(t)\, dt\right\}. \qquad (1.6)$$

Comparing this with a decision level Λ_l is the same as comparing with some other decision level the absolute value of the output of a filter matched to the signal $g(t)$. The detection system is the same as the one obtained in Chapter V, Section 1 for a signal whose unknown amplitude might be positive or negative. In effect one is pretending that a signal $Af(t)$ is present in the input $v(t)$, estimating its amplitude A by the method of maximum likelihood, and comparing the absolute value $|\hat{A}|$ of the estimate with an appropriate decision level. If $|\hat{A}|$ is the smaller of the two, one is led to conclude that the peak in $\Lambda[v(t); A]$ resulted from a noise fluctuation and that there is no signal present after all, and one selects hypothesis H_0.

In this simple example it is easy to determine the value of the decision level Λ_l required to yield a preassigned false-alarm probability. We have already done so in Chapter V. When additional parameters $\boldsymbol{\theta}$ of the signal are unknown, however, it is harder to find the proper value of Λ_l. Under hypothesis H_0 the function $\Lambda(\mathbf{x}; \boldsymbol{\theta})$ or $\Lambda[v(t); \boldsymbol{\theta}]$ may have a number of local maxima in the expected domain of the parameters, and the probability that at least one of these exceeds a value Λ_l is in general very difficult to calculate. An example in which an approximate solution can be obtained will appear in the next sections when we treat the detection of a signal whose time of arrival is unknown.

The results of Section 2 of Chapter VIII can be used directly to obtain the maximum-likelihood receivers of signals to be detected in Gaussian noise. Suppose, for instance, that the signal $s(t; \boldsymbol{\theta}) = Af(t; \boldsymbol{\theta}')$ depends on

$(m-1)$ unknown parameters $\boldsymbol{\theta}' = (\theta_2, \ldots, \theta_m)$ besides an unknown amplitude $A = \theta_1$. The maximum value of the likelihood ratio is then given by eq. (VIII, 2.24) as

$$\Lambda[v(t); \hat{A}, \hat{\boldsymbol{\theta}}'] = \max_{\boldsymbol{\theta}'} \exp \left\{ \left[\int_0^T g(t; \boldsymbol{\theta}')\, v(t)\, dt \right]^2 \Big/ 2 \int_0^T g(t; \boldsymbol{\theta}')\, f(t; \boldsymbol{\theta}')\, dt \right\}, \tag{1.7}$$

where $v(t)$ is the input to the receiver and $g(t; \boldsymbol{\theta}')$ is the solution of the integral equation (VIII, 2.22), whose kernel is the autocovariance $\phi(t, s)$ of the noise.

The quantity in eq. (1.7) is to be compared with a decision level Λ_l, but according to eq. (VIII, 2.23) this is equivalent to comparing with some other level the quantity $|\hat{A}|\,|H'(\hat{\boldsymbol{\theta}}', \hat{\boldsymbol{\theta}}')|^{\frac{1}{2}}$, where $H'(\boldsymbol{\theta}', \boldsymbol{\theta}')$ is given in eq. (VIII, 2.25), and where

$$\hat{A} = \int_0^T g(t; \hat{\boldsymbol{\theta}}')\, v(t)\, dt / H'(\hat{\boldsymbol{\theta}}', \hat{\boldsymbol{\theta}}') \tag{1.8}$$

is the maximum-likelihood estimate of the amplitude A. When, as often, the function in the denominator is independent of $\hat{\boldsymbol{\theta}}'$, maximum-likelihood detection is the same as deciding that a signal is present when the maximum-likelihood estimate of its amplitude, under the supposition that a signal is really there, has an absolute value $|\hat{A}|$ greater than a certain magnitude.

We can similarly use the results of part (c) of Section 2, Chapter VIII, to work out the maximum-likelihood receiver of a quasiharmonic signal in narrowband noise. Referred to a reference carrier frequency Ω_r, the signal is written as

$$s(t; \boldsymbol{\theta}) = A \text{ Rl } F(t; \boldsymbol{\theta}'') \exp(i\Omega_r t + i\psi), \tag{1.9}$$

and it has $(m-2)$ parameters $\boldsymbol{\theta}'' = (\theta_3, \ldots, \theta_m)$ unknown besides the amplitude $A = \theta_1$ and the phase $\psi = \theta_2$. According to eq. (VIII, 2.44) the maximum-likelihood receiver forms the quantity

$$\max_{\boldsymbol{\theta}''} \ln \Lambda[v(t); A, \psi, \boldsymbol{\theta}''] = \max_{\boldsymbol{\theta}''} [R(\boldsymbol{\theta}'')]^2 / 2H'(\boldsymbol{\theta}'', \boldsymbol{\theta}''), \tag{1.10}$$

and compares it with a decision level. Here

$$R(\boldsymbol{\theta}'') = \left| \int_0^T G^*(t; \boldsymbol{\theta}'')\, V(t)\, dt \right| \tag{1.11}$$

is the output of a linear rectifier following a filter matched to the signal Rl $G(t; \boldsymbol{\theta}'') \exp i\Omega_r t$, where $G(t; \boldsymbol{\theta}'')$ is the solution of the integral equation (VIII, 2.32), $V(t)$ is the complex envelope of the input Rl $V(t) \exp i\Omega_r t$, and by eq. (VIII, 2.33),

$$H'(\theta'', \theta'') = \int_0^T G^*(t; \theta'') F(t; \theta'') \, dt. \tag{1.12}$$

When the quantity $H'(\theta'', \theta'')$ is independent of θ'', it is the output $R(\theta'')$ of the linear rectifier itself that can be compared with the decision level, and this is proportional to the maximum-likelihood estimate $\hat{A}$ of the amplitude of the signal.

The maximum-likelihood receiver can be approximately realized by passing the input through a bank of parallel filters matched to the signals Rl $G(t; \theta'') \exp i\Omega_r t$ for a number of closely spaced values of the parameters θ'' throughout their expected domain. The outputs of the filters are passed through linear rectifiers to a decision device, which samples the rectified outputs at the end of the observation interval and issues an alarm if any of them exceed a fixed decision level. If when there is an alarm the receiver can also determine which of the matched filters had the largest rectified output, it can produce, at least approximately, the maximum-likelihood estimate $\hat{\theta}$ of the signal parameters as well. This simultaneous detection of a signal and estimation of its parameters is an advantage of the method of maximum likelihood.

When multiple inputs $v_i(t)$ are available and their noise components are statistically independent, the maximum-likelihood receiver will utilize an appropriate one of the estimation procedures described in Chapter VIII, Section 2, part (d). It is merely necessary to append a decision device.

2. DETECTION OF A SIGNAL OF UNKNOWN ARRIVAL TIME

(a) *The Maximum-likelihood Detector*

The most immediate application of maximum-likelihood detection is to a radar that must search for targets in a narrow cone many miles long. The echo signal must be expected to arrive at any time within an interval $(0, T)$ that is much longer than the duration of the echo itself. Any prior distribution of the arrival time will be so broad that the value of an average likelihood ratio will be governed by the peak value of the likelihood ratio as a function of the parameters.

In this section we shall consider only echoes from stationary targets, and we shall assume that the input $v(t)$ to the receiver consists of narrowband Gaussian noise of given complex autocovariance $\tilde{\phi}(\tau)$, to which there may be added a quasiharmonic signal of the form

$$s(t; A, \psi, \tau) = A \text{ Rl } F(t-\tau) \exp i(\Omega t+\psi). \tag{2.1}$$

The amplitude A and the phase ψ, as well as the arrival time τ of the signal, are unknown. With the target stationary, the carrier frequency Ω equals that of the transmitter and is known.

After the maximum-likelihood estimates $\hat{A}$ and $\hat{\psi}$ of the amplitude and phase of the signal have been substituted into the likelihood ratio, it becomes, according to eq. (VIII, 2.44),

$$\Lambda[v(t); \hat{A}, \hat{\psi}, \tau] = \exp \{[R(\tau)]^2/2H'(\tau, \tau)\}, \tag{2.2}$$

where, by eqs. (VIII, 2.35) and (VIII, 2.33),

$$\begin{aligned} R(\tau) &= \left| \int_0^T G^*(t; \tau)\ V(t)\ dt \right|, \\ H'(\tau, \tau) &= \int_0^T G^*(t; \tau)\ F(t-\tau)\ dt, \end{aligned} \tag{2.3}$$

with $G(t; \tau)$ the solution of the integral equation—cf. eq. (VIII, 2.32)—

$$F(t-\tau) = \int_0^T \tilde{\phi}(t-u)\ G(u; \tau)\ du, \quad 0 < t < T. \tag{2.4}$$

Again $V(t)$ is the complex envelope of the input $v(t) = \text{Rl } V(t)e^{i\Omega t}$. The receiver must determine whether for any values of the time τ the likelihood ratio in eq. (2.2) exceeds the decision level. If so, the presence of a signal is indicated.

If we once more assume that the signal is much briefer than the observation interval $(0, T)$, we can disregard those echoes that overlap the ends of the interval, and in implementing the maximum-likelihood prescription we can take the integrals in eqs. (2.3) and (2.4) over the infinite range. Then the function $G(t; \tau)$ has the form $G(t-\tau)$, where $G(t)$ is the solution of the integral equation

$$F(t) = \int_{-\infty}^{\infty} \tilde{\phi}(t-u)\ G(u)\ du, \tag{2.5}$$

and according to the convolution theorem for Fourier transforms—see Appendix A—it is given by

$$G(t) = \int_{-\infty}^{\infty} \frac{f(\omega)}{2\tilde{\Phi}(\omega)}\ e^{i\omega t}\ d\omega/2\pi, \tag{2.6}$$

where

$$f(\omega) = \int_{-\infty}^{\infty} F(t)e^{-i\omega t}\, dt, \quad \tilde{\Phi}(\omega) = \tfrac{1}{2} \int_{-\infty}^{\infty} \tilde{\phi}(\tau)\, e^{-i\omega\tau}\, d\tau. \tag{2.7}$$

The function $f(\omega)$ is the narrowband spectrum of the signal, and $\tilde{\Phi}(\omega)$ is what we called in Chapter II the narrowband spectral density of the noise. When the noise is white, as we said there, we can take $\tilde{\Phi}(\omega) = N/2$ and $G(t; \tau) = N^{-1}F(t-\tau)$, where N is the unilateral spectral density of the noise. In any case, we assume that the spectrum $f(\omega)$ drops to 0 so much more rapidly than the density $\tilde{\Phi}(\omega)$ as $|\omega|$ goes to infinity that the Fourier transform of their quotient exists.

If we can find an interval $(-T', T')$ much shorter than the observation interval $(0, T)$, yet long enough to contain substantially all of the function $G(t)$, we can again generate the quantity $R(\tau)$ as the rectified output of a matched filter. The complex impulse response of this narrowband filter is taken as

$$\begin{aligned} k(s) &= G^*(T'-s), \qquad 0 < s < 2T', \\ &= 0, \qquad\qquad s < 0, \quad s > 2T', \end{aligned} \tag{2.8}$$

when referred to the carrier frequency Ω. At time t the output of this filter has a complex envelope

$$V_0(t) = \int_0^{2T'} G^*(T'-s)\, V(t-s)\, ds = \int_{-\infty}^{\infty} G^*(u)\, V(t-T'+u)\, du. \tag{2.9}$$

Therefore,

$$R(\tau) \cong \left| \int_{-\infty}^{\infty} G^*(t-\tau)\, V(t)\, dt \right| = |V_0(\tau+T')|. \tag{2.10}$$

With our neglect of signals that overlap the ends of the interval,

$$H'(\tau, \tau) \cong \int_{-\infty}^{\infty} G^*(t-\tau)\, F(t-\tau)\, dt = \int_{-\infty}^{\infty} G^*(s)\, F(s)\, ds \tag{2.11}$$

is independent of the arrival time τ.

The decision about the presence of a signal can therefore, by eq. (2.2), be made by comparing the rectified output $|V_0(t)|$ of the matched filter with a decision level. If it exceeds the level at any time during the interval $(T', T'+T)$, the presence of a signal is indicated. The receiver can estimate the arrival time of this signal as $\hat{\tau} = t^* - T'$, where t^* is the time at which the output $|V_0(t)|$ attains its greatest value. If several echoes may be present, every excursion of $|V_0(t)|$ above the decision level is attributed to a signal. It is apparent that this receiver is much like a conventional radar receiver for detecting stationary or slowly moving targets and at the same time measuring their ranges. To the description in Chapter VIII, Section 2, of the system for estimating range it is only necessary to add a decision level and an alarm device at the output of the receiver.

The height of the level with which the output $|V_0(t)|$ must be compared is determined by the false-alarm probability, which is the probability that $|V_0(t)|$ will exceed the decision level sometime during the interval $(T', T'+T)$ when only noise is present at the input to the receiver. Later in this section we shall describe a way of at least approximately calculating this probability, and there the performance of the maximum-likelihood receiver will be assessed.

(b) *Detection of a Train of Signals*

The probability of detecting a target is increased if a number $M > 1$ of pulses are transmitted and the input is observed during the intervals in which the echoes of these pulses are expected to appear. If we measure time in each interval from its beginning, we can write the signal that arrives in the kth interval as

$$s_k(t; A_k, \psi_k, \tau) = A_k \text{ Rl } F(t-\tau) \exp i(\Omega t+\psi_k) \tag{2.12}$$

when the target is stationary. The amplitudes A_k, the phases ψ_k, and the time τ are usually unknown. As discussed earlier, if there is no coherence of the transmitted pulses, the phases ψ_k are independent random variables.

When there is no serious fading, the amplitudes of the signals can be assumed to have a common value $A_k \equiv A$, and the quantity to be compared with the decision level is, according to Problem 8, Chapter VIII,

$$\left[\sum_{k=1}^{M} R_k(\tau)\right]^2 \Big/ \sum_{k=1}^{M} H_k'(\tau, \tau),$$

where $R_k(\tau)$ and $H_k'(\tau, \tau)$ are given for each interval by eq. (2.3) when $V(t)$ is replaced for the kth interval by $V_k(t)$, the complex envelope of the input during that interval. When again the intervals are much longer than the signals, $H_k'(\tau, \tau)$ is independent of τ and can be dropped, and the quantity $R_k(\tau)$ can be generated by passing the input Rl $V_k(t) \exp i\Omega t$ through the matched filter of eq. (2.8) and applying the output to a linear rectifier. The outputs $|V_{k0}(t+T')|$ of this rectifier are stored and added at corresponding times t to form the test function

$$\sum_{k=1}^{M} |V_{k0}(t+T')|, \quad T' < t < T' + T.$$

This sum is finally displayed, and if it exceeds the decision level at any time during the interval $T' < t < T'+T$ following the last transmitted pulse, a signal is reported to be present.

When the signals fade rapidly or the radar target scintillates, owing perhaps to the motion of a propeller, the amplitudes A_k are taken as statistically independent and are estimated separately. After the estimates of the amplitudes A_k and the phases ψ_k are substituted into the likelihood ratio, we find, as in part (d) of Section 2, Chapter VIII, that the maximum-likelihood receiver can operate by comparing the quantity

$$\sum_{k=1}^{M} \{[R_k(\tau)]^2/H_k'(\tau, \tau)\}$$

with a decision level. This means in the present case that it needs only to apply the outputs of the matched filter to a quadratic rectifier and sum to form the test function

$$\sum_{k=1}^{M} |V_{k0}(t+T')|^2, \quad T' < t < T'+T,$$

whose crossings of a decision level during the interval $T' < t < T'+T$ indicate the presence of echoes. As always, the height of this decision level is determined by the preassigned false-alarm probability.

The rectified outputs of the matched filter might be summed as shown in Fig. IX.1. The delay line must retard its input by a time accurately equal to the interval T between transmitted pulses. Its output is fed back to its input, where it is added to the output of the linear or quadratic rectifier. During the final observation interval the alarm circuit is activated, and if the output of the adder crosses the decision level, it signals the presence of an echo. At the same time it can turn on another circuit, not shown, to measure the time t^* at which the total output reaches its peak value, thus estimating the range of the target.

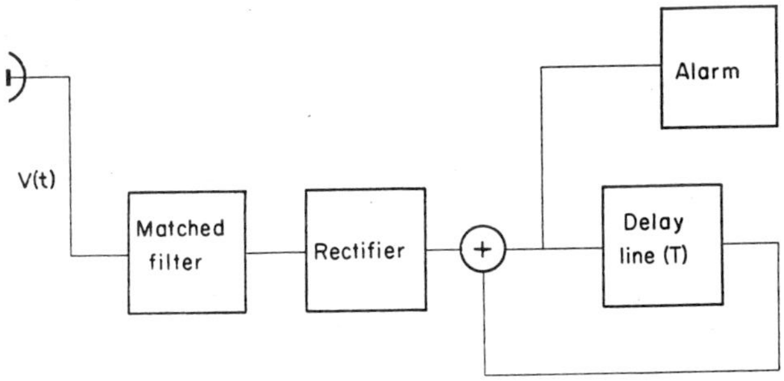

FIG. IX.1. Receiver for signals of unknown arrival time.

In ordinary radar the rectified outputs of the matched filter are displayed on the face of a cathode-ray tube during each interpulse interval. Any summing—or "integration", as it is often called—takes place in the eye and the brain of the radar operator. Such a system is less sensitive, but simpler and cheaper, than the maximum-likelihood receiver. If the target is moving, however, and the maximum-likelihood receiver has been designed only for stationary targets, the probability that it will detect the target decreases, and the simpler system may gain superiority.

(c) *The False-alarm Probability*

(i) *The first-passage time problem.* The maximum-likelihood receiver for detecting a signal of unknown arrival time in Gaussian noise must determine whether a certain stochastic process crosses a fixed level during the observation interval. For a receiver working with a single input $v(t)$ this process is the rectified output of a filter matched to the expected signal. When several inputs with independent noise components are available, the process is the sum of a number of such rectified outputs. The false-alarm probability is the probability that the stochastic process crosses the decision level during the interval of observation when the receiver input contains only noise. Now we shall attack the problem of calculating this probability.

The stochastic process of interest will be denoted by $r(t)$; it is stationary. The probability Q_0 that $r(t)$ will exceed a level $r = a$ sometime during an observation interval $0 < t < T$ is given by

$$Q_0 = 1-P(T), \quad P(t) = \Pr\{r(t') < a, 0 \leqslant t' \leqslant t\}. \tag{2.13}$$

The function $P(t)$ is the probability that a process $r(t')$ drawn at random from its ensemble lies below the level $r = a$ throughout the interval $(0, t)$. From the value $P(0) = \Pr\{r(0) < a\}$ at $t = 0$ this function $P(t)$ decreases to 0 as the time t goes to infinity.

The negative derivative $q(t) = -\partial P/\partial t$, $0 < t < \infty$, is the so-called "first-passage-time probability density function"; $q(t)\,dt$ is the probability that the process $r(t)$ crosses the level $r = a$ from below for the first time in the interval $(t, t+dt)$. Calculating the density function $q(t)$ is essentially the same problem as finding the probability $P(t)$, and it has been solved for only a few types of stochastic process $r(t)$.

Initiatory work on first-passage-time probabilities was summarized by Siegert (1951) in a paper in which he presented a general solution for stochastic processes of the type known as "Markov processes". We recall from Chapter II, Section 3 that for a Markov process $r(t)$ the conditional p.d.f. of r at time t, given the values $r_k = r(t_k)$ of the process at an arbitrary set of M previous times $t_M < t_{M-1} < \ldots < t_1 < t$, is a function only of r and $r_1 = r(t_1)$,

$$p(r, t \mid r_1, t_1; r_2, t_2; \ldots; r_M, t_M) = p(r, t \mid r_1, t_1).$$

The function $p(r, t \mid r_1, t_1)$ is called the "transition p.d.f." of the process. The p.d.f. of the value $r(t)$ of a Markov process at any time t in the future depends only on its p.d.f. at the present, and not on the past history of the process. Siegert showed how the Laplace transform of the p.d.f. $q(t)$ could be written in terms of the Laplace transform of the transition p.d.f. of the process.

The stationary Gaussian Markov process, for example, has an autocovariance $\phi(\tau) = \phi(0) \exp(-\mu|\tau|)$, and the Laplace transform of its first-passage-time p.d.f. is a quotient of Weber-Hermite functions. When the interval is so long that $\mu T \gg 1$, the p.d.f. $q(t)$ is governed mainly by the pole of this Laplace transform lying nearest the origin, and if the level $r = a$ is much higher than the r.m.s. value $[\phi(0)]^{\frac{1}{2}}$ of the process, the probability Q_0 that it will be crossed at least once during an interval $(0, T)$ is approximately

$$\begin{gathered} Q_0 \cong 1-e^{-\nu T}, \quad \nu = \mu a[2\pi\phi(0)]^{-\frac{1}{2}} \exp[-a^2/2\phi(0)], \\ \mu T \gg 1, \quad a \gg [\phi(0)]^{\frac{1}{2}}, \end{gathered} \tag{2.14}$$

where ν is the reciprocal of the mean first-passage time and has been calculated by Siegert's formulas.

A second Markov process lending itself to this kind of analysis is the envelope

$$r(t) = \{[x(t)]^2 + [y(t)]^2\}^{\frac{1}{2}} \tag{2.15}$$

of a narrowband Gaussian process whose complex autocovariance is the exponential function $\tilde{\phi}(\tau) = \tilde{\phi}(0) \exp(-\mu|\tau|)$. This process, whose quadrature components $x(t)$ and $y(t)$ are independent Gaussian Markov processes, has been treated by Rice (1958), Tikhonov (1961), and the writer (1959). The Laplace transform of its first-passage-time p.d.f. can be expressed as a quotient of confluent hypergeometric functions. When $\mu T \gg 1$ and $a^2 \gg \tilde{\phi}(0)$, the probability Q_0 that the level $r = a$ will be crossed at least once in $(0, T)$ is asymptotically

$$\begin{gathered} Q_0 \cong 1-e^{-\nu T}, \quad \nu = [\mu a^2/\tilde{\phi}(0)] \exp[-a^2/2\tilde{\phi}(0)], \\ \mu T \gg 1, \quad a \gg [\tilde{\phi}(0)]^{\frac{1}{2}}. \end{gathered} \tag{2.16}$$

A Gaussian process whose spectral density is a rational function of the frequency can be considered as one component of a vector Markov process. The number of components of the stochastic vector equals the degree of the denominator of the spectral density as a polynomial in ω^2. The methods proposed by Siegert can in principle be applied to calculating the first-passage-time p.d.f. for such a process, but the required computations appear prohibitively difficult (Helstrom, 1957). One must either solve a certain multidimensional integral equation whose kernel is the transition p.d.f. of the vector process, or find the solution of a Fokker–Planck partial differential equation with certain boundary conditions in the space of the components and the time.

When the expected value of the process $r(t)$ is 0 and $a = 0$, the problem of calculating the p.d.f. $q(t)$ or the distribution $P(t)$ is known as the "zero-crossing problem". It has been extensively studied in recent years by Longuet-Higgins, McFadden, Rainal, Slepian, and others, whose papers are listed in the bibliography at the end of this chapter. Besides the first-passage-time p.d.f. they have investigated the distribution of the number of times $r(t)$ crosses the level $r=0$ in a given interval and the distributions of the lengths of the intervals between such crossings. Although some of the methods, particularly those of Longuet-Higgins, might be applied to the crossings of a non-zero level $r = a$, the calculations required would be formidable, involving multivariate Gaussian integrals, and nothing of this kind seems to have been published.

(ii) *The crossing-rate approximation.* In a radar receiver that is to detect signals of unknown epoch the false-alarm probability must be kept much smaller than 1, simply because the user cannot afford to let it be large. For instance, in a defensive system based on radar it is so costly to send missiles to attack apparent targets that only a very few sorties in a day or a week can be permitted. It can therefore be assumed that the level a is so much larger than the r.m.s. value of the process $r(t)$ that there is only a small probability that the output $r(t)$ of the receiver will exceed it at any time during the observation interval $(0, T)$. In addition, the interval $(0, T)$ is much longer than the correlation time of the stochastic process $r(t)$, which is of the order of the reciprocal of the bandwidth of the signal. Over most of the interval $(0, T)$ the process $r(t)$ has negligible correlation with its initial value $r(0)$ and its initial time derivatives, and the probability $Q_0 = 1 - P(T)$ will be almost independent of them as well. Under these conditions it is useful to define an average rate $\lambda(a)$ with which the stochastic process $r(t)$ crosses the level $r = a$ from below. In an interval of length τ the average number of crossings is $\lambda\tau$, and for a stationary process this rate λ is constant.

When the decision level $r = a$ is very high, crossings from below are rare events and occur so far apart on the average that they can be considered statistically independent. The number n of times the process $r(t)$ crosses $r = a$ from below in an interval of duration T can therefore be roughly described by the Poisson distribution, which characterizes independent rare events,†

$$p_n(T) = (\lambda T)^n e^{-\lambda T}/n! \tag{2.17}$$

(Cramér, 1966). Then the probability Q_0 that $r(t)$ will cross $r = a$ at least once during the interval is given by

$$Q_0 = 1 - e^{-\lambda T}, \tag{2.18}$$

which has the same form as eqs. (2.14) and (2.16). We shall mainly be concerned with intervals that are much longer than the reciprocal bandwidth of the process $r(t)$, yet short enough that $\lambda T \ll 1$. The probability of more than one crossing during the interval is then negligible, and the probability $Q_0 \doteq \lambda T$ is proportional to the length of the interval. We must now see how to calculate the rate λ, which in radar theory is called the "false-alarm rate".

(iii) *The crossing rate of a stochastic process.* To determine the false-alarm rate for a detection system we can use a formula given by Rice (1944, eq. 3.3–5),

$$\lambda(a) = \int_0^\infty \dot{r}\, p(a, \dot{r})\, d\dot{r}, \tag{2.19}$$

where $\dot{r} = dr/dt$ is the rate of change of the stochastic process $r(t)$, which must be at least once differentiable. The joint probability density function of the output r and its rate $\dot{r}$ of change is $p(r, \dot{r})$. We now present a brief derivation of this formula.

We take a small interval of length τ and ask for the fraction of members of an ensemble of time series $r(t)$ that cross the level $r = a$ from below during that interval. Let $r_1 = r(t)$ and $r_2 = r(t+\tau)$. If the duration of the interval is much shorter than the correlation time of the stochastic process, the probability sought is equal to the joint probability that $r(t) = r_1$ is less than a and $r(t+\tau) = r_2$ is greater than a, which is

$$\lambda(a)\tau = \int_{-\infty}^{a} dr_1 \int_a^\infty dr_2\, P(r_1, r_2),$$

† For the zero-crossings of a mean-zero stochastic process, the assumption of a Poisson distribution is unwarranted (Longuet-Higgins, 1962, p. 578).

where $P(r_1, r_2)$ is the joint p.d.f. of r_1 and r_2 (see Fig. IX.2a). When the time interval is very short, we can write approximately

$$r_2 = r(t+\tau) \doteq r_1+\dot{r}_1\tau,$$

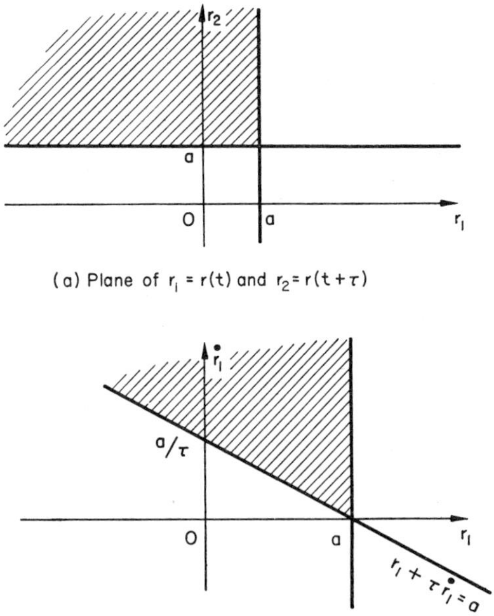

(a) Plane of $r_1 = r(t)$ and $r_2 = r(t+\tau)$

(b) Plane of $r_1 = r(t)$ and $\dot{r}_1 = dr/dt$

FIG. IX.2. Regions of integration for the mean crossing rate.

where $\dot{r}_1$ is the rate of change of $r(t)$ at the beginning of the interval; we are approximating the noise wave $r(t)$ by a straight line in the interval. The double integral can then be simplified by changing the variables from (r_1, r_2) to $(r_1, \dot{r}_1)$, with

$$P(r_1, r_2)\, dr_1\, dr_2 = p(r_1, \dot{r}_1)\, dr_1\, d\dot{r}_1.$$

The region of integration in the new coordinates is the area shaded in Fig. IX.2b, and we find for the fraction of members of the ensemble crossing $r = a$ during the interval

$$\lambda(a)\tau = \int_0^\infty d\dot{r}_1 \int_{a-\dot{r}_1\tau}^{a} dr_1\, p(r_1, \dot{r}_1).$$

When the duration τ of the interval is very short, the second integral equals approximately the length $\dot{r}_1\tau$ of the range of integration multiplied by the value of the integrand at any point of that range,

$$\lambda(a)\tau = \int_0^\infty d\dot{r}_1 \dot{r}_1 \tau \, p(a, \dot{r}_1) + O(\tau^2),$$

from which Rice's formula, eq. (2.19), follows immediately.

(iv) *The chi-process and its crossing rate.* The false-alarm rate of the maximum-likelihood receiver for detecting a signal of unknown epoch is equal to the number of times per second that the process $r(t) = |V_0(t)|^2$ crosses a decision level $r = a$. Here

$$V_0(t) = x(t) + iy(t)$$

is the complex envelope of the output of a filter matched to the expected signal, as described in part (a). When the input to the receiver contains only Gaussian noise, the quadrature components $x(t)$ and $y(t)$ are Gaussian random processes with expected value 0, and

$$r(t) = [x(t)]^2 + [y(t)]^2. \tag{2.20}$$

We shall denote the complex autocovariance of the process Rl $V_0(t)e^{i\Omega t}$ by $\psi(\tau)$,

$$\mathbf{E}[V_0(t_1)\, V_0^*(t_2)] = 2\psi(t_1 - t_2), \quad \mathbf{E}[V_0(t_1)\, V_0(t_2)] = 0. \tag{2.21}$$

For simplicity we shall assume that $\psi(\tau)$ is real; $x(t)$ and $y(t)$ are accordingly independent Gaussian processes with autocovariances $\psi(\tau)$.

When M inputs are available, $M > 1$, and it is assumed that the amplitudes of the suspected signals, as well as the noise components, are independent from one input to another, the maximum-likelihood receiver forms the sum of the quadratically rectified outputs of the matched filter,

$$r(t) = \sum_{k=1}^{M} |V_{k0}(t)|^2 = \sum_{k=1}^{M} \{[x_k(t)]^2 + [y_k(t)]^2\}. \tag{2.22}$$

Under hypothesis H_0 the process $r(t)$ is thus the sum of the squares of $2M$ independent Gaussian processes, and it is chi-squared distributed. We want the average number of times $r(t)$ crosses the decision level $r = a$ from below during the observation interval.

A process that is the sum of the squares of n independent stationary Gaussian processes of expected value 0,

$$r(t) = \sum_{k=1}^{n} [x_k(t)]^2, \tag{2.23}$$

has been called a "chi-process" (Silverman, 1958). We assign to the processes $x_k(t)$ the real autocovariance function $\psi(\tau)$. Our interest lies mainly in the cases $n = 2$ and $n = 2M$.

To find the rate with which the chi-process $r(t)$ crosses a level $r = a$ we must first determine the joint p.d.f. of $r(t)$ and its first derivative $\dot{r}(t)$,

$$\dot{r}(t) = 2 \sum_{k=1}^{n} x_k \dot{x}_k . \tag{2.24}$$

At any time t the random variables x_k and $\dot{x}_k$ are independently Gaussian. Their expected values are 0, and their variances are $\psi(0)$ and $|\psi''(0)|$, respectively, where $\psi''(\tau) = d^2\psi/d\tau^2$.

To derive the joint p.d.f. $p(r, \dot{r})$ we shall use the rules for conditional probabilities. We can express it as

$$\begin{aligned} p(r, \dot{r})\, dr &= \int_{(dr)} \ldots \int p(x_1, \ldots, x_n, \dot{r})\, dx_1 \ldots dx_n \\ &= \int_{(dr)} \ldots \int p(\dot{r}\,|\,x_1, \ldots, x_n)\, p(x_1, \ldots, x_n)\, dx_1 \ldots dx_n, \end{aligned} \tag{2.25}$$

in which the multiple integral marked "dr" is taken over the spherical shell

$$r < x_1^2 + x_2^2 + \ldots + x_n^2 < r + dr$$

in n-dimensional Euclidean space. Now from eq. (2.24) we observe that when the variables $x_1, \ldots, x_n$ are fixed, $\dot{r}$ is a linear combination of Gaussian random variables with mean 0 and variance $\text{Var}\, \dot{x}_k = |\psi''(0)|$. Hence $\dot{r}$ is conditionally Gaussian with mean 0 and variance

$$\text{Var}\, \dot{r} = \mathbf{E}(\dot{r}^2\,|\,x_1, \ldots, x_n) = 4 \sum_{k=1}^{n} x_k^2 \,\text{Var}\, \dot{x}_k = 4\,|\psi''(0)|\,r, \tag{2.26}$$

and the conditional p.d.f. of $\dot{r}$ depends on the x_k's only through the sum of their squares,

$$p(\dot{r}\,|\,x_1, \ldots, x_n) = [8\pi\,|\psi''(0)|\,r]^{-\frac{1}{2}} \exp\,[-\dot{r}^2/8\,|\psi''(0)|\,r] = p(\dot{r}\,|\,r).$$

We can therefore take it outside of the integral in eq. (2.25), and we find that $p(r, \dot{r})\, dr = p(\dot{r}\,|\,r)\, p(r)\, dr$, where $p(r)$ is the p.d.f. of the variable alone.

We can now use Rice's formula, eq. (2.19), to obtain the crossing rate

$$\lambda(a) = \int_0^\infty \dot{r}\, p(\dot{r}\,|\,a)\, p(a)\, d\dot{r} = p(a)\, [2|\psi''(0)|\,a/\pi]^{\frac{1}{2}} . \tag{2.27}$$

An alternative derivation of this result was given by Silverman (1958). The p.d.f. $p(r)$ appearing in it is related to the chi-square distribution and is, by eq. (III, 3.17),

$$\begin{aligned} p(r) &= \frac{r^{(n-2)/2} e^{-r/2\psi(0)}}{[2\psi(0)]^{n/2}\, \Gamma(n/2)}, \quad & r > 0, \\ &= 0, & r < 0. \end{aligned} \tag{2.28}$$

(v) *The false-alarm probability.* For the maximum-likelihood receiver operating with a single input, $n = 2$ and the false-alarm probability is, by eqs. (2.18), (2.27),

$$Q_0 \cong \lambda(a)T = \beta T[a/2\pi\psi(0)]^{\frac{1}{2}} \exp[-a/2\psi(0)], \qquad \beta^2 = |\psi''(0)/\psi(0)|, \tag{2.29}$$

when $Q_0 \ll 1$ (Middleton, 1948). In terms of the narrowband spectral density $\Psi(\omega)$ of the process Rl $V_0(t)e^{i\Omega t}$,

$$\beta^2 = \int_{-\infty}^{\infty} \omega^2 \, \Psi(\omega) \, d\omega \Big/ \int_{-\infty}^{\infty} \Psi(\omega) \, d\omega.$$

Our assumption that $\psi(\tau)$ is real is equivalent to taking $\Psi(\omega)$ as an even function of ω. If this is not so, it can be shown as in Problem 1 at the end of this chapter that the formula in eq. (2.29) remains the same, but β must be defined by

$$\beta^2 = \overline{\omega^2} - \bar{\omega}^2, \tag{2.30}$$

where

$$\overline{\omega^n} = \int_{-\infty}^{\infty} \omega^n \, \Psi(\omega) \, d\omega \Big/ \int_{-\infty}^{\infty} \Psi(\omega) \, d\omega \tag{2.31}$$

is the nth moment of the narrowband spectral density of the process. Thus β is simply the r.m.s. bandwidth of the noise process Rl $V_0(t)e^{i\Omega t}$.

If the spectral density $\Psi(\omega)$ has the form

$$\Psi(\omega) = \mu\psi(0)/(\mu^2 + \omega^2),$$

the bandwidth β is infinite, $|\psi''(0)|$ does not exist, and the crossing-rate is meaningless. The probability Q_0 that $r(t)$ will cross the level $r = a$ at least once in the interval $(0, T)$, which is what we really need, can in this case be obtained when $a \gg \psi(0)$ by means of eq. (2.16), but with a^2 there replaced by a.

When the receiver utilizes M inputs, and the process $r(t)$ is defined by eq. (2.22), the false-alarm probability is given by eqs. (2.27), (2.28) with $n = 2M$,

$$Q_0 \cong \lambda(a)T = \frac{\beta T \pi^{-\frac{1}{2}}}{(M-1)!} [a/2\psi(0)]^{(2M-1)/2} \exp[-a/2\psi(0)]. \tag{2.32}$$

It remains for us to evaluate the narrowband spectral density $\Psi(\omega)$ of the output of the matched filter and to determine its r.m.s. bandwidth β. The narrowband transfer function $y(\omega)$ of the matched filter is obtained by taking the Fourier transform of $k(\tau)$ in eq. (2.8),

$$y(\omega) = g^*(\omega)e^{-i\omega T} = \frac{f^*(\omega)e^{-i\omega T}}{2\tilde{\Phi}(\omega)}, \qquad (2.33)$$

where $f(\omega)$ is the Fourier transform of the signal envelope $F(t)$ and $\tilde{\Phi}(\omega)$ is the narrowband spectral density of the noise at the input. From eq. (II, 6.6) we find for the narrowband spectral density of the output of the matched filter

$$\Psi(\omega) = \tilde{\Phi}(\omega)\,|y(\omega)|^2 = |f(\omega)|^2/4\tilde{\Phi}(\omega), \qquad (2.34)$$

and the variance $\psi(0)$ of each quadrature component is

$$\psi(0) = 2\int_{-\infty}^{\infty} \Psi(\omega)\, d\omega/2\pi = \frac{1}{2}\int_{-\infty}^{\infty} \frac{|f(\omega)|^2}{\tilde{\Phi}(\omega)}\frac{d\omega}{2\pi}.$$

The bandwidth β in the formulas for the false-alarm rate is now obtained by using eq. (2.34) in eqs. (2.30), (2.31).

When the input noise is white and has a unilateral spectral density N, $\tilde{\Phi}(\omega) = N/2$, and we find

$$\psi(0) = \int_{-\infty}^{\infty} |f(\omega)|^2\, d\omega/2\pi N = \int_{-\infty}^{\infty} |F(t)|^2\, dt/N.$$

The quantity β is now equal to the r.m.s. bandwidth $\Delta\omega$ of the signal as defined in Chapter I, Section 5.

To estimate the order of magnitude of the false-alarm rate $\lambda(a)$ for a single input, as given in eq. (2.29), it is useful to write it in the form

$$\lambda(a) = \beta\sqrt{a/2\pi\psi(0)}\ \Pr\{|V_0(t)|^2 > a\}. \qquad (2.35)$$

Here the probability

$$\Pr\{|V_0(t)|^2 > a\} = \exp\left[-a/2\psi(0)\right] = Q$$

is the false-alarm probability for a system detecting a target of known location, as derived in Chapter V. There will thus on the average be Q such false alarms in a time $\beta^{-1}\sqrt{2\pi\psi(0)/a}$. The factor $\sqrt{a/2\pi\psi(0)}$ is usually of the order of 1; for $Q = 10^{-10}$ it equals 2.71. One false-alarm can be expected in a time of the order of $1/\beta Q$.

This observation suggests an approximate way of calculating the false-alarm probability when we are unable to evaluate Rice's formula, eq. (2.19), for the crossing rate. If we suppose that in the interval $(0, T)$ the receiver produces βT equally spaced samples of the process $r(t)$ and that an alarm occurs if any of them surpasses the decision level $r = a$, eq. (2.35) shows that the false-alarm probability can be obtained approximately by assuming that the samples are statistically independent. It will then be roughly given by βT times the probability that a single sample of $r(t)$ exceeds the decision level,

$$Q_0 \cong \beta T \Pr\{r > a \mid H_0\}. \tag{2.36}$$

Since the decision level a is insensitive to the value of Q_0—eq. (2.29) shows it to be only logarithmically dependent on Q_0—the value of a will not be much in error when calculated by this approximation. The effect of this error in turn on the probability of detection will be slight.

For a receiver that sums the outputs of linear rectifiers following the matched filter, as in detecting a set of signals of equal amplitudes and random phases, it does not seem to be possible to determine the joint p.d.f. of

$$r(t) = \sum_{k=1}^{M} |V_{k0}(t)|$$

and its derivative $\dot{r}$. The approximation in eq. (2.36) is then useful, although the distributions under hypotheses H_0 and H_1 of the sum r are themselves difficult to calculate. Approximations based on the Gram–Charlier series have been given by Marcum (1960, pp. 183–9).

(d) *The Probability of Detection*

The probability of detection in receivers like those treated in part (a) is even more difficult than the false-alarm probability to calculate precisely, for the random process $r(t)$ is no longer stationary; the signal makes its statistical properties, even its mean and its variance, into functions of time. However, it is a good approximation at large signal-to-noise ratios to set the probability Q_d of detection equal to what it would be if the arrival time of the signal were known. We have already calculated this probability as a function of the decision level and the signal strength—in Chapter V, Section 3 for a signal of unknown phase in a single input, in Chapter VII, Section 2 for a train of M signals with independent amplitudes and phases. In effect we are equating the probability that the peak value of the process $r(t)$ exceeds the decision level $r = a$ with the probability that a sample of $r(t)$, taken at the proper instant for detecting a signal of known arrival time, will exceed the same level.

The reason for this is that when a strong signal is present, the peak value of the output

$$r(t) = |V_0(t)|^2 \quad \text{or} \quad r(t) = \sum_{k=1}^{M} |V_{k0}(t)|^2$$

occurs at a time $t^* = \hat{\tau}+T'$ that is very close to the time $t_0 = \tau_0+T'$ at which the output $r(t)$ would be sampled if the true epoch τ_0 of the signal were known. (T' is the delay in the matched filter, as in eq. (2.8).) The noise in this output $r(t)$ varies significantly only in a time of the order of the reciprocal bandwidth $(\Delta\omega)^{-1}$ of the signal because of the correlation imposed on it by the matched filter. Hence, if the signal is strong enough for the peak value of the output $r(t)$ to be well above the level $r = a$, it is unlikely that the noise will change enough in the time $|\tau_0-\hat{\tau}|$ to carry the output below the level at the time τ_0+T'. Therefore

$$Q_d = \Pr\left\{\max_{\tau} r(\tau+T') > a\right\} \cong \Pr\{r(\tau_0+T') > a\}. \tag{2.37}$$

The right-hand side of this equation is the probability of detection calculated before. For a receiver working with a single input $v(t)$, the probability of detection is approximately

$$Q_d = Q(d, b), \quad d^2 = A^2 \int_{-\infty}^{\infty} G^*(t)\, F(t)\, dt,$$

$$b = [a/\psi(0)]^{\frac{1}{2}} = a \left| \int_{-\infty}^{\infty} G^*(t)\, F(t)\, dt \right|^{-\frac{1}{2}}, \tag{2.38}$$

where $Q(\alpha, \beta)$ is the Q-function defined in eq. (V, 3.14). The quantity d is the signal-to-noise ratio defined previously, and for a signal of energy E received in white noise of unilateral spectral density N it is the familiar $d = (2E/N)^{\frac{1}{2}}$.

The observation time T in effect measures the uncertainty of the observer's knowledge of the location of a possible target; it is proportional to the range interval over which he must search. A range uncertainty Δr corresponding to a value $\beta T = 1$ is equal to $c/2\beta$, where c is the velocity of light. For a signal bandwidth $\beta = 2\pi \cdot 10^6$ rad/sec (one megahertz), this range uncertainty is $\Delta r = 78$ feet.

We can define a minimum detectable signal in terms of the signal-to-noise ratio d required to yield a detection probability of, say, $Q_d = 0.90$ for a fixed false-alarm probability such as $Q_0 = 10^{-10}$. Then we can plot the signal-to-noise ratio d versus the uncertainty parameter βT by first using eq. (2.29) to calculate the decision level $r = a$ and then applying eq. (2.38) to determine the value of the signal-to-noise ratio attaining the specified value of Q_d. Such a graph is given in Fig. IX.3. Because of the approximations we had to make in calculating the false-alarm and detection probabilities, the curves are reliable only for $\beta T \gg 1$. It is apparent that the strength of the minimum detectable signal depends only weakly on the uncertainty in the time of arrival; a change in the parameter βT by a factor of 10^4 corresponds to an increase of about 2 db in the required signal-to-noise ratio.

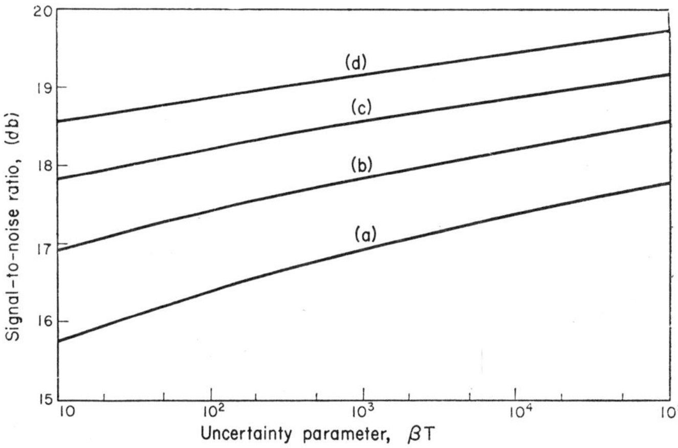

FIG. IX.3. Detectability of a signal of unknown arrival time, maximum-likelihood detector. $Q_d = 0.90$. Q_0: (a) 10^{-4}, (b) 10^{-6}, (c) 10^{-8}, (d) 10^{-10}.

The threshold detector of signals of unknown arrival time, on the other hand, displays a much greater sensitivity to the uncertainty in the arrival time. A comparison of the curves in Fig. V.4 with those in Fig. IX.3 shows that as βT increases, the strength of the minimum detectable signal rises much more rapidly for the threshold detector than for the maximum-likelihood receiver. For most signals, the signal duration t used in Chapter V, Section 5 is of the order of the reciprocal bandwidth $\beta^{-1} = (\Delta\omega)^{-1}$ entering our definition of the uncertainty parameter βT, and we see that for $\beta T \sim 10$ the threshold and the maximum-likelihood detectors are about equally sensitive. For larger values of βT, however, the maximum-likelihood detector is superior in that it attains a detection probability Q_d of 0.90 for a somewhat smaller signal strength than the threshold detector, the difference being of the order of 8 db at $\beta T = 1000$. For signals of much smaller amplitudes the threshold detector must be superior by virtue of its theoretical provenance, but when the uncertainty βT is large, this superiority is maintained only for signals whose probability of detection is too small to be of interest.

In Chapter VIII we learned that the r.m.s. error of an estimate of the arrival time is inversely proportional to the bandwidth $\beta = \Delta\omega$. By using signals of greater bandwidth, the accuracy of the estimate is increased. However, the parameter βT then increases, and so does the strength of the minimum detectable signal. An improvement in accuracy is paid for by a loss of detectability, but the cost is seldom large.

It would perhaps be useful to find a detection system that yielded a maximum probability of detection for a given false-alarm rate. The system described in this section does not necessarily possess this property; and this problem has not, to the writer's knowledge, been solved. From eq. (2.29) it would seem that if a somewhat smaller filter bandwidth were used, the false-alarm probability for a given decision level a might be reduced without changing the peak value of the rectified signal output very much. Then the decision level could be lowered to restore the original value of the false-alarm probability Q_0, leading to a smaller minimum detectable signal. However, the insensitivity of the decision level, for fixed false-alarm probability Q_0, to changes in the parameter βT, displayed by the slow variation of the curves in Fig. IX.3, leads one to doubt that much improvement in detectability would be provided by such an optimum system.

3. DETECTION OF A SIGNAL OF UNKNOWN ARRIVAL TIME AND CARRIER FREQUENCY

In radar search neither the locations nor the velocities of targets are usually known with any precision, and great uncertainty attaches to both the time τ at which an echo might arrive and the carrier frequency Ω that it might have. The maximum-likelihood detection strategy in this situation involves the tentative assumption that the input $v(t) = \text{Rl } V(t) \exp i\Omega_r t$ contains a signal of the form

$$\begin{aligned} s(t; A, \psi, \tau, w) &= A \text{ Rl } F(t; \tau, w) \exp (i\Omega_r t + i\psi), \\ F(t; \tau, w) &= F(t-\tau)e^{iw(t-\tau)}, \end{aligned} \tag{3.1}$$

whose unknown amplitude A, phase ψ, arrival time τ, and frequency shift w must be estimated. Here $F(t)$ is a known signal envelope and Ω_r a reference carrier frequency.

From Section 1 we know that the maximum-likelihood receiver can decide about the presence or absence of a signal by comparing with some decision level the test function

$$h(\tau, w) = [R(\tau, w)]^2/H'(\tau, w; \tau, w), \tag{3.2}$$

where

$$\begin{aligned} R(\tau, w) &= \left| \int_0^T G^*(t; \tau, w)\, V(t)\, dt \right|, \\ H'(\tau, w; \tau, w) &= \int_0^T G^*(t; \tau, w)\, F(t-\tau) e^{iw(t-\tau)}\, dt, \end{aligned} \tag{3.3}$$

with $G(t; \tau, w)$ the solution of the integral equation

$$F(t-\tau)e^{iw(t-\tau)} = \int_0^T \tilde{\phi}(t-s)\, G(s;\tau,w)\, \cancel{\tilde{\phi}(s)\, G(t-s; \tau, w)}\, ds, \qquad 0 < t < T, \tag{3.4}$$

whose kernel $\tilde{\phi}(s)$ is the complex autocovariance of the noise.

If we again postulate an observation interval $(0, T)$ long enough that we can disregard signals overlapping one or the other end, we can solve eq. (3.4) by Fourier transforms, obtaining

$$\begin{aligned} G(t; \tau, w) &= G_1(t-\tau; w), \\ G_1(t; w) &= \frac{1}{2} \int_{-\infty}^{\infty} \frac{f(\omega - w)}{\tilde{\Phi}(\omega)}\, e^{i\omega t}\, d\omega/2\pi, \end{aligned} \tag{3.5}$$

where as before $f(\omega)$ is the Fourier transform of the signal envelope $F(t)$ and $\tilde{\Phi}(\omega)$ is the narrowband spectral density of the noise. If we can find an interval $(-T', T')$ long enough to contain substantially all of the signal $G_1(t; w)$, yet short enough that $2T' \ll T$, a filter of the type given in eq. (2.8) can be built to match it for any value of the frequency shift w. The quantity $H'(\tau, w; \tau, w)$ is now

$$H'(\tau, w; \tau, w) = \int_{-\infty}^{\infty} \frac{|f(\omega - w)|^2}{2\tilde{\Phi}(\omega)} \frac{d\omega}{2\pi}, \tag{3.6}$$

and it is independent of the arrival time τ but not, in general, of the shift w. For white noise of unilateral spectral density N, $\tilde{\Phi}(\omega) = N/2$, and the dependence on w disappears. The signals $G_1(t; w)$ are then all alike except for a frequency shift.

The maximum-likelihood receiver can be approximated by applying the input to a bank of parallel filters, each matched to a signal Rl $G_1(t; w)$

exp $i\Omega_r t$ with one of a dense set of values of the shift w in the expected domain. The outputs of these filters are passed to a quadratic rectifier whose output is weighted by the factor $[H'(\tau, w; \tau, w)]^{-1}$ as given by eq. (3.6). These weighted outputs are compared with a common decision level, and if during the interval $(T', T'+T)$ any of them cross it, a signal is considered present. The frequency shift w of the signal can be estimated by the value of w associated with the filter whose subsequent peak value is highest, and the time t^* at which that highest peak occurs provides an estimate of the arrival time through the relation $\hat{\tau} = t^* - T'$. Again, if a number of inputs, in which the signals are expected to have independently random amplitudes, are utilized, the weighted and rectified outputs can be delayed and summed before being compared with the decision level, as shown in Fig. IX.1 and described in Chapter VIII, Section 2(d).

The height of the decision level is again to be determined by the acceptable false-alarm probability Q_0, that is, by the probability that at least one of the rectified outputs of the bank of matched filters will cross it during the interval $(T', T'+T)$. This probability is difficult to compute exactly, but it can be estimated in terms of the false-alarm rate of the rectified output of each of the filters, which was calculated in Section 2, part (b). We assume for simplicity that the noise at the input is white.

The rectified outputs of filters with adjacent values of the shift w are correlated, and they tend to reach their peak values at nearly the same time. Only for filters with values of w separated by more than about the reciprocal $(\Delta t)^{-1}$ of the signal duration—as defined in Chapter I, Section 5—are the noise outputs so weakly correlated that they can be considered independent random variables. One can say, therefore, that if the total range of values of w under observation is W, the number of such independent outputs is roughly equal to $W\,\Delta t$, and the total false-alarm rate is approximately $W\,\Delta t$ times the rate for an individual filter. Hence, from eq. (2.29) the false-alarm probability is

$$\begin{aligned} Q_0 &\cong (W\,\Delta t)(\Delta\omega T)\left(b\pi^{-\frac{1}{2}}\right) \exp(-b^2/2), \\ b &= [a/\psi(0)]^{\frac{1}{2}}, \quad \psi(0) = \int_{-\infty}^{\infty} |F(t)|^2\,dt/N, \end{aligned} \tag{3.7}$$

provided that $Q_0 \ll 1$, $W\,\Delta t \gg 1$, and $\Delta\omega T \gg 1$. If on the other hand the range W is less than about $(\Delta t)^{-1}$, all the filters tend to reach their peak values together, and the false-alarm probability is given approximately by eq. (3.7) with the factor $W\Delta t$ replaced by 1. Here a is the decision level for the test function

$$[R(t-T', w)]^2 = \left| \int_{-\infty}^{\infty} G_1^*(s; w)\, V(s+t-T')\, ds \right|^2$$
$$= \left| \int_{-\infty}^{\infty} F^*(s)\, V(s+t-T') e^{-iws}\, ds/N \right|^2 .$$

When at a time τ_0 a signal with a frequency shift w_0 arrives with a signal-to-noise ratio d somewhat larger than the quantity b appearing in eq. (3.7), a number of the matched filters with values of the shift w near w_0 will produce rectified outputs surpassing the decision level. The range of values of w over which this happens will be of the order of $(\Delta t)^{-1}$ in width, and since it is over such a range that the noise components of the outputs are correlated, we can take for granted that the probability that the combined output due to both signal and noise exceeds the decision level is approximately equal to the probability of detection of a signal with a known time of arrival and a known carrier frequency. The probability of detection will then be approximately equal to $Q_d \cong Q(d, b)$, as in eq. (2.38).

4. NON-PARAMETRIC DETECTION

(a) *Parametric and Non-parametric Hypotheses*

In everything we have done so far we have postulated that the statistical structure of the noise, embodied in its set of probability density functions, is given. Indeed, in all examples we have taken the noise to be of the ubiquitous Gaussian type, with expected value 0 and a given autocovariance function—the only realistic kind of noise for which p.d.f.s of arbitrary order can even be written down. We have also assumed that the signals, when present, combine additively with the noise, and that we know everything about them except perhaps a limited number of parameters. When certain statistical properties of the noise are unknown, however, the detection problem becomes one of choosing between composite hypotheses, and a detection theory is more difficult to establish.

There are various levels of ignorance to contend with. If everything is known about the p.d.f.s of the noise and of the sum of signal and noise except for the values of a finite set of parameters governing them, the two hypotheses H_0 and H_1 are said to be *parametric*. In detecting signals in white Gaussian noise, for instance, the only unknown quantity may be the spectral density of the noise. With colored Gaussian noise, the only undetermined parameters may be the variances and the bandwidths of certain components.

If on the other hand the very forms of the distributions of the noise are unknown, a finite number of parameters will not suffice to specify them, and the hypotheses are called *non-parametric*. Even Gaussian noise whose autocovariance function or spectral density is unknown gives rise to a non-parametric detection problem. More generally, it may be possible to describe the noise only qualitatively, as by saying that its expected value is 0 or that the p.d.f. of its amplitudes is an even function, the forms of its density functions remaining otherwise indeterminate. A class of p.d.f.s, restricted only in such a way and wanting values of an infinitude of parameters for their specification, is termed a *non-parametric class.*

Parametric detection is a matter of choosing between composite hypotheses, under which the p.d.f.s of the data depend on only a finite number of unknown parameters. It can be handled by the methods introduced in Chapter V, Section 1. If prior p.d.f.s of the parameters under the two hypotheses are given, the numerator and the denominator of the likelihood ratio can be averaged with respect to them, as in eq. (V, 1.8), and the decision is based on the value of the resulting ratio. If no prior p.d.f.s are to be had, least favorable ones can be postulated, or the principle of maximum likelihood can be applied. When only a finite number of parameters are unknown, their values can be estimated separately under each hypothesis, and a likelihood ratio can be determined from the estimates as in eq. (1.3).

Detection is particularly simple when the unknown parameters of the noise can be estimated independently of the presence or absence of a signal. Suppose that a coherent communication system transmits pulses of known form that are received in white Gaussian noise whose spectral density N is unknown, as might be the case if a jammer were trying to interfere by emitting broad-band noise. When the pulses are orthogonal and are received with equal energies, the optimum receiver does not even depend on the spectral density of the noise. When on–off pulses, $f(t)$ and 0, are used for sending binary messages, the output of a filter matched to the pulse $f(t)$ must be compared with a decision level proportional to $N^{\frac{1}{2}}$, as in eq. (IV, 1.11); but the probability of error is unaffected by prior ignorance of N, for N can be measured independently. (See Problem 3 at the end of this chapter.)

When the signal also depends on unknown parameters, or when more than simply the power level of the noise is unknown, the problem of estimating the unknown parameters, designing the detection system, and calculating the false-alarm and detection probabilities is much more complicated. Each such problem must be attacked individually, and there is little of general applicability that can be said.

(b) *Non-parametric Receivers*

(i) *Some preliminaries.* Besides the ever-present Gaussian thermal noise, input processes that cannot easily be described mathematically sometimes perturb a receiver. Randomly occurring impulses due to lightning, to sparks in ignition systems, or to faulty connections and switches may interfere with communications. A model of such "impulse noise" based on the simplest assumptions provides even first-order probability density functions only at the cost of some difficult calculations (Gilbert and Pollak, 1960), and to obtain joint p.d.f.s of higher order seems hardly possible. Underwater sound receivers pick up sporadic biological noise, strange croakings and cracklings that are difficult to describe statistically, yet impede the detection of weak signals. Such extraneous noise may not be stationary over a long enough period to allow empirical distributions to be measured with any precision. When neither theory nor experiment is able to furnish detailed statistics, the designer of a detection system must give up characterizing the noise by the usual array of p.d.f.s, and he must face the problem of how best to choose between non-parametric hypotheses.

With the distributions of the noise unknown, receivers can no longer be designed to meet a Bayes criterion. Although it may at times be sensible to admit prior p.d.f.s of a finite number of unknown parameters, it can hardly be meaningful to postulate prior distributions of the p.d.f.s $p_0(\mathbf{x})$ and $p_1(\mathbf{x})$ themselves. There is no way to determine the average risk of a detection strategy with respect to a non-parametric class of distributions, and hence no way of saying that one detector is better than another in the Bayes sense.

Of the Neyman–Pearson criterion all that is left is the directive to attain a specified false-alarm probability, and even this cannot always be achieved. A receiver whose false-alarm probability is the same for all noise distributions in a given non-parametric class is said to be a "non-parametric", "distribution-free", or "constant-false-alarm-rate" receiver. When the alternative hypothesis H_1 is non-parametric, there is no way to specify an average probability of detection and hence no way to maximize one.

The designer of a non-parametric receiver attempts to exploit the differences, often only qualitative, between the characteristics of the input under the two hypotheses, (H_0) "signal absent" and (H_1) "signal present". The values of the input, for instance, might be larger on the average, or more often positive, when a signal is present than when it is not. The designer seeks a receiver whose probability of detecting any of the expected signals is greater than the largest possible value of the false-alarm probability; such a receiver is said to be "unbiased". If nothing is known about the time dependence of the signals and the noise, the receiver should treat the values of the input at all instants in the same way; it should be invariant to permutations of samples of the input taken at different times. The already extensive development of non-parametric tests of hypotheses, described in books by Fraser (1957), Lehmann (1959), and Kendall and Stuart (1961), has guided the search for receivers with such properties as invariance and absence of bias. Our exposition will follow the survey by Carlyle and Thomas (1964).

If no distributions of the noise are available, nothing can be said about the correlations among values of the input at different times. How they should best be combined becomes uncertain, and matched filtering of the kind we described earlier cannot arise from a theory of non-parametric detection. The input must, however, be filtered in some way that will favor the signals to be detected, by, for instance, removing noise of frequencies outside the spectral band they are expected to occupy. We shall suppose this to have been done by "prefiltering" the input.

It is customary in non-parametric detection to assume that this prefiltered input is sampled at times far enough apart that the samples are statistically independent. For this it may suffice to take the samples at times separated by roughly the reciprocal of the bandwidth of the input filter. The signal is presumed either to last long enough for a number of such samples to fall within its continuance, or to be repeated with a period equal to the sampling interval. These samples, which we shall denote by $v_1, v_2, \ldots, v_n$, constitute the data on which the decision about the presence or absence of a signal will be based. One must beware, however, of the possibility that correlation among the samples will reduce the probability of detection in a receiver based on their independence.

(ii) *The t-test.* One approach to non-parametric detection is to pretend that the noise has a specific statistical structure, such as the Gaussian, design the receiver on that basis, and finally evaluate its performance for noise inputs different from what was assumed. As an illustration we shall suppose that the signal components of the data are known within a constant A of proportionality; we designate them by $Af_1, Af_2, \ldots, Af_n$. The expected value of the noise is taken as zero, and the noise and the signal are assumed to combine additively. Then the expected values of the samples are

$$\mathbf{E}(v_j \mid H_0) = 0, \quad \mathbf{E}(v_j \mid H_1) = Af_j,$$

with the n f_j's given. The p.d.f.s of the v_j's being unavailable, their variances are unknown.

If we pretend that the noise is Gaussian with mean value 0 and unknown variance σ^2, we can derive a procedure from the principle of maximum likelihood. The p.d.f.s of the samples under the two hypotheses are taken as

$$\begin{aligned} p_0(\mathbf{v}) &= (2\pi\sigma^2)^{-n/2} \exp\left[-\sum_{j=1}^{n} v_j^2/2\sigma^2\right], \\ p_1(\mathbf{v}) &= (2\pi\sigma^2)^{-n/2} \exp\left[-\sum_{j=1}^{n} (v_j - Af_j)^2/2\sigma^2\right]. \end{aligned} \tag{4.1}$$

The value of σ^2 is estimated under H_0 by maximizing $p_0(\mathbf{v})$; call this estimate σ_0^2. Estimates of A and σ^2 under H_1 are found by similarly maximizing $p_1(\mathbf{v})$; call the results $\hat{A}$ and σ_1^2. When they are substituted into $p_0(\mathbf{v})$ and $p_1(\mathbf{v})$ and the likelihood ratio is formed, it is found to be given simply by $(\sigma_0/\sigma_1)^n$, where

$$\begin{aligned} \sigma_0^2 &= n^{-1} \sum_{j=1}^{n} v_j^2, \quad \sigma_1^2 = n^{-1} \sum_{j=1}^{n} (v_j - \hat{A}f_j)^2, \\ \hat{A} &= \sum_{j=1}^{n} f_j v_j \Big/ \sum_{j=1}^{n} f_j^2. \end{aligned} \tag{4.2}$$

Comparing this likelihood ratio with a certain decision level is equivalent to comparing the statistic

$$t = \hat{A}n^{\frac{1}{2}} \big/ s, \quad s^2 = (n-1)^{-1} \sum_{i=1}^{n} (v_i - \hat{A}f_i)^2, \tag{4.3}$$

with some other decision level t_0. If the amplitude A is known to be positive, the receiver decides that a signal is present if $t > t_0$. If A might be either positive or negative, it is the absolute value $|t|$ that must surpass some other decision level t_0' in order for H_1 to be chosen. The quantity s^2 appearing in eq. (4.3) is an estimate of the variance σ^2 that happens to be unbiased under each hypothesis; $\mathbf{E}(s^2 \mid H_0) = \mathbf{E}(s^2 \mid H_1) = \sigma^2$.

If the values Af_i of the signal component of each sample are also unknown, one has no reason to assume that one value will be larger or smaller than any other. The receiver should then treat all the samples alike, and its processing should be invariant to a permutation of the samples v_j of the input. The statistic in eq. (4.3) can be endowed with this invariance by setting all the f_j's equal; and since the amplitude A is still to be estimated, the f_j's may as well be set equal to 1. The statistic in eq. (4.3) then becomes what is known to statisticians as "Student's t-statistic",

$$t = un^{\frac{1}{2}} / s, \quad u = n^{-1} \sum_{i=1}^{n} v_i, \quad s^2 = (n-1)^{-1} \sum_{i=1}^{n} (v_i - u)^2. \tag{4.4}$$

Here u is the "sample mean", and s is again the "sample standard deviation" of the data. If the components of the signal are expected to be positive, hypothesis H_1 is chosen when t exceeds a decision level t_0; this is known as the "one-sided t-test". If they may be either positive or negative, one requires the absolute value of t to surpass another level t_0'; this is the "two-sided t-test". If the noise is known to be Gaussian, the level t_0 or t_0' providing a specified false-alarm probability Q_0 can be obtained from tables of Student's t-distribution, which are available in most statistical handbooks. The probability of detecting a signal by the one-sided t-test can be determined from tables of the "non-central t-distribution" (Resnikoff and Lieberman, 1957). If the noise is not Gaussian, or if its first-order p.d.f. is unknown, the proper setting of the decision level cannot be found from the tables; and with the decision level set as for Gaussian noise, the false-alarm probability may exceed the specified value if the noise actually has some other distribution.

When the number n of samples is very large, the distribution of the statistic t is, by virtue of the Central Limit Theorem, approximately Gaussian for any ordinary distribution of the noise with mean 0. The variance of t is approximately equal to 1, and the decision levels t_0 and t_0' for a preassigned false-alarm probability are given by the equations

$$Q_0 \cong \operatorname{erfc} t_0, \quad Q_0 \cong 2 \operatorname{erfc} t_0'. \tag{4.5}$$

In this limit $n \to \infty$ the false-alarm probability is the same for all such noise distributions, and the receiver is said to be "asymptotically non-parametric". The probability of detection can as well be estimated in terms of the Gaussian distribution. When n is very large, the sample standard deviation s is nearly equal to the true standard deviation of the noise, and the expected value of the statistic t becomes

$$\mathbf{E}(t \mid H_1) = \left(A / \sigma n^{\frac{1}{2}}\right) \sum_{i=1}^{n} f_i \tag{4.6}$$

when the sample values of the signal are equal to Af_i, $i = 1, 2, \ldots, n$. The variance of t is approximately equal to 1 under hypothesis H_1 as well.

In this limit of a very large number n of samples, the receiver based on the t-test performs as well as one designed for detecting a constant signal in Gaussian noise of known variance σ^2 by using the same samples $v_1, v_2, \ldots, v_n$, provided that the signal really present is also constant. When the constant signal is known to be positive, this so-called "Neyman–Pearson" receiver simply compares the sample mean u with a suitable decision level. If the noise has a constant unilateral spectral density N over an input band of width W, samples of the input taken at intervals of $(2W)^{-1}$ seconds will be statistically independent. From a signal of duration T, a total number $n = 2TW$ of samples are available. The energy of the signal is now $E = A^2T$, and the variance of the noise is $\sigma^2 = NW$. The probability of detecting a constant positive signal by the Neyman–Pearson receiver, or when $n \gg 1$ by the t-test receiver, depends on the quantity in eq. (4.6), which is now equal to the familiar signal-to-noise ratio $d = (2E/N)^{\frac{1}{2}}$:

$$Q_d = 1 - \text{erfc}\,(d - t_0), \tag{4.7}$$

where t_0 is given by eq. (4.5).

When the number n of samples is finite, it is generally very difficult to evaluate the false-alarm and detection probabilities of the t-test receiver and of others proposed for detecting signals in noise of unknown distribution, especially when the noise that is actually supposed to be present for the evaluation is not Gaussian. It is therefore hard to compare the receivers for an extensive class of input distributions and determine the circumstances under which one might be preferred to another. For most of these receivers, however, the Central Limit Theorem can be invoked to certify that when the number n of samples is very large, the statistics upon which the receivers base their decisions have Gaussian distributions. The receivers can therefore simply be compared on the basis of their asymptotic relative efficiencies.

The asymptotic relative efficiency (a.r.e.) was introduced in Chapter VII, Section 2(d). One fixes both the false-alarm probability Q_0 and the detection probability Q_d, and for signals of equal strength one determines the numbers n_1 and n_2 of samples required by two receivers to attain the "reliability" (Q_0, Q_d). The a.r.e. of receiver 1 with respect to receiver 2 is equal to the limiting value of the ratio n_2/n_1 when the strength of the common signal is made to vanish and n_1 and n_2 go to infinity. To compare two receivers the a.r.e. should be calculated for various signals and for typical noise distributions. We have just seen that when the input signals are constant and positive, the a.r.e. of the t-test receiver with respect to the Neyman–Pearson receiver for these signals is equal to 1.

It should be borne in mind, however, that the a.r.e. provides a valid basis of comparison only when it is expected that the receivers will actually utilize a very large number of independent samples of the input. If the number n is finite and small, the receivers may behave quite differently from the predictions of the asymptotic theory. As we have seen, the t-test receiver is not non-parametric for finite numbers n; its false-alarm probability for a fixed decision level t_0 depends on the true p.d.f. of the noise.

(iii) *The sign test.* The example of the t-test receiver shows that a receiver utilizing the amplitudes of the samples v_i is unlikely ever to be non-parametric for finite n. There are two ways to avoid using the amplitudes to make the decisions. One is to discard all but the signs of the samples, the other to arrange the samples in order of their amplitudes and use their ranks in this arrangement. We shall first describe some receivers that work only with the signs of the input samples v_i.

If the noise is as often positive as negative, there will in the absence of a signal usually be nearly as many positive samples as negative. If the signal is known to be positive, therefore, a preponderance of positive samples will lead one to suspect its presence. The receiver can simply count the number n_+ of samples that are positive, choosing hypothesis H_1 when n_+ exceeds a certain decision level n_0. Such a receiver is said to carry out the "sign test".

The sign-test receiver is non-parametric over the class of noise p.d.f.s that are even functions of the amplitude, and indeed over the larger class for which the probability of a positive noise value equals $\frac{1}{2}$, $\Pr\{v > 0 \mid H_0\} = \frac{1}{2}$. The probability of there being more than n_0 positive samples under hypothesis H_0 is given by the binomial distribution,

$$Q_0 = \Pr\{n_+ > n_0 \mid H_0\} = 2^{-n} \sum_{i=n_0+1}^{n} \binom{n}{i}, \tag{4.8}$$

independently of the true form of the p.d.f. of the noise, provided only that its median amplitude is 0. For a fixed number n, however, only certain values of the false-alarm probability are accessible, and Q_0 cannot be less than 2^{-n} if signals are to be detected at all.

If the signal is constant, the p.d.f. of the amplitude of each sample will under hypothesis H_1 be the same for all; let us denote it by $p_1(v)$. The probability of detecting the signal is then also given by the binomial distribution,

$$Q_d = \sum_{j=n_0+1}^{n} \binom{n}{j} p^j (1-p)^{n-j}, \quad p = \Pr\{v > 0 \mid H_1\} = \int_0^{\infty} p_1(v)\, dv. \tag{4.9}$$

If $p > \frac{1}{2}$ for all possible signals, the sign-test receiver is unbiased; and it is invariant to permutations of the data $\{v_j\}$. Its performance can be evaluated by fixing the false-alarm probability and calculating the probability of detection as a function of signal strength for a variety of distributions of the noise.

It is often more instructive, however, to compare the performance of such a receiver with the Neyman–Pearson receiver or the t-test receiver. When the number of samples is finite and the noise is not Gaussian, it is difficult to calculate the false-alarm and detection probabilities of these receivers; and comparing them with the sign-test receiver or another necessitates vast numerical computations and the plotting and collation of their results. One resorts instead to the asymptotic relative efficiency as providing a simpler, more readily accessible and comprehensible basis of comparison, despite its drawbacks. Since the a.r.e. of the t-test receiver with respect to the Neyman–Pearson receiver equals 1 for all distributions, only the latter needs to be considered.

For the detection of a signal of constant, positive value in Gaussian noise, for instance, the sign-test receiver has an a.r.e. of $2/\pi = 0.637$ with respect to the Neyman–Pearson receiver (Hodges and Lehmann, 1956). Naturally, the Neyman–Pearson receiver is better for Gaussian noise. Kanefsky and Thomas (1965) have calculated the a.r.e. of these receivers for a number of other noise p.d.f.s. They found that if the p.d.f. of the noise is either highly asymmetrical or very much more peaked than the Gaussian, as seems to be the case with certain kinds of impulse noise, the a.r.e. exceeds 1 and the sign-test receiver is superior.

(iv) *Rank tests.* When the n samples Af_i of the signal are positive and the noise p.d.f. is an even function, $p_0(v) = p_0(-v)$, not only are there likely to be more positive samples v_i than negative when a signal is present, but the sample values of large absolute value are more likely to be positive than negative. This observation suggests a more elaborate and more efficient test based on ranking the data $\{v_i\}$. What follows assumes that nothing is known about the relative sizes of the samples of the signal and therefore takes them as equal. The test treats all samples in the same way and is invariant to their permutation.

Once all n samples have been received, they are arranged according to their absolute values,

$$|v_{i_1}| < |v_{i_2}| < \ldots < |v_{i_n}|,$$

where $i_1, i_2, \ldots, i_n$ is a permutation of the integers from 1 to n. The kth sample in this arrangement is assigned a "rank" equal to k. The receiver adds the ranks of those samples that are positive, forming the test statistic

$$r = \sum_{k=1}^{n} kU(v_{i_k}), \tag{4.10}$$

where henceforth in this section $U(x)$ is the unit step function, $U(x) = 0$, $x < 0$, $U(x) = 1$, $x \geqslant 0$. If the "rank statistic" r exceeds a decision level r_0, hypothesis H_1 is chosen. Carlyle and Thomas (1964) point out that the statistic r is also given by the expression

$$r = \sum_{i=1}^{n} \sum_{j=i}^{n} U(v_i+v_j), \tag{4.11}$$

which may be easier to implement in an electronic receiver.

If the signal may be either positive or negative, but maintains the same sign throughout, the receiver can determine the rank sum r of the positive samples and the rank sum $r' = \frac{1}{2}n(n+1)-r$ of the negative samples. If the larger of these exceeds a certain decision level r_0', the receiver asserts that a signal is present. With a positive signal r, with a negative signal r', tends to be large. Tests such as these are known as "Wilcoxon tests" (Wilcoxon, 1945).

If the p.d.f. of the noise is an even function, $p_0(v) = p_0(-v)$, all rankings of the n samples are equally likely under hypothesis H_0, and the probability that a given sample will be positive and have its rank appear in the sum r is equal to $\frac{1}{2}$. The false-alarm probability is obtained by examining all 2^n partitions of the integers from 1 to n into a primary set with m members ($1 \leqslant m \leqslant n$) and its complementary set with $(n-m)$ members. The number of primary sets whose sum exceeds the decision level r_0, divided by 2^n, equals the false-alarm probability for the receiver that tests only for a positive signal. The false-alarm probability for the second receiver is equal to 2^{-n} times twice the number of primary sets whose sum exceeds r_0'. Tables for determining the threshold have been provided by Bennett and Franklin (1954, p. 183). From what we have said it must be clear that the false-alarm probability is the same for all even p.d.f.s of the noise and that the receiver using either of these rank tests is non-parametric with respect to this class of distributions. For detecting a positive constant signal in Gaussian noise the a.r.e. of the first of the rank-test receivers with respect to the Neyman–Pearson receiver is $3/\pi = 0.955$. The a.r.e. of these receivers cannot fall below $108/125 = 0.864$ for any even noise distribution, and for certain distributions it may exceed 1 (Hodges and Lehmann, 1956). Thus the rank-test receiver, though complicated, performs well for a broad class of possible noise distributions.

If the signals to be detected are narrowband signals of the form

$$s(t) = A \operatorname{Rl} F(t)\, e^{i\Omega t + i\psi}, \tag{4.12}$$

with a known carrier frequency Ω and unknown phase ψ, a non-parametric receiver might be designed along the following lines. The prefiltered input is mixed with two locally generated sinusoids, $\cos \Omega t$ and $\sin \Omega t$. The outputs of the mixer, which are the two quadrature components of the input, are sampled at times far enough apart that the samples can be considered statistically independent. Denote the two sets of samples thus obtained by $v_{c1}, v_{c2}, \ldots, v_{cn}$ and $v_{s1}, v_{s2}, \ldots, v_{sn}$. These sets are individually ranked by their absolute values, so that

$$|v_{ci_1}| < |v_{ci_2}| < \ldots < |v_{ci_n}|, \qquad |v_{sj_1}| < |v_{sj_2}| < \ldots < |v_{sj_n}|,$$

where $(i_1, \ldots, i_n)$ and $(j_1, \ldots, j_n)$ are permutations of the integers from 1 to n. The rank sums

$$r_c = \sum_{k=1}^{n} kU(v_{ci_k}), \quad r_c' = \tfrac{1}{2}n(n+1) - r_c,$$

$$r_s = \sum_{k=1}^{n} kU(v_{sj_k}), \quad r_s' = \tfrac{1}{2}n(n+1) - r_s,$$

are formed. The receiver then compares the statistic $r_c''^2 + r_s''^2$ with a decision level r^2, where $r_c'' = \max(r_c, r_c')$, $r_s'' = \max(r_s, r_s')$; if the level is exceeded, a signal is declared present.

If no signal is present, the rank sums will all be roughly equal to their expected value $\frac{1}{4}n(n+1)$; but if a signal with some arbitrary phase ψ is present, one or the other, or both, outputs of the mixer will have a preponderance of positive or negative samples, and the statistic just given will, most likely, be larger. Unless the carrier frequency is known within about $2\pi/T$, where T is the time span of the set of samples, and unless the phases of the signals are all nearly the same, the quadrature components will change sign during the observation, the numbers of positive and negative samples in each set will be equalized, and the test will fail.

(v) *Receivers with a reference input.* Detection would be facilitated if the receiver could obtain a separate input exhibiting the same kind of noise as what corrupts the signals, but itself known to be free of any signals. If one is sure that the noise is stationary, this "reference input" can be collected before signalling begins. In most contemplated uses of non-parametric detection, however, stationarity cannot be presumed. It may then be possible to interrupt communication or echo-ranging periodically to sample the noise, or to take samples during intervals between signal pulses. Receivers provided with such a reference input are supposed to have available m independent samples $w_1, w_2, \ldots, w_m$ that represent only noise, besides the n independent input samples $v_1, v_2, \ldots, v_n$ that may or may not contain a signal.

Adapting from statistics what is variously known as the "Wilcoxon two-sample test" (Wilcoxon, 1945) and the "Mann–Whitney test" (Mann and Whitney, 1947), Capon (1959) analyzed a receiver that detects a constant signal causing the samples $v_1, v_2, \ldots, v_n$ to be generally larger than the reference samples $w_1, w_2, \ldots, w_m$. This signal might be a coherent signal that is always positive, or a quasiharmonic signal that has been passed with the noise through a non-linear rectifier before sampling. The receiver forms all mn possible pairs (v_i, w_j) with samples from the two inputs. It counts the number of pairs in which v_i exceeds w_j to form the statistic

$$V = (mn)^{-1} \sum_{i=1}^{n} \sum_{j=1}^{m} U(v_i - w_j). \tag{4.13}$$

If V exceeds a decision level V_0, the receiver decides that a signal is present. Alternatively, the receiver can arrange all $(m+n)$ samples in order of their values. The position of a sample in this ordering, starting from the smallest, is its rank. The sum of the ranks of the n samples v_i is linearly related to the statistic V and can be used instead. This receiver is non-parametric for all noise inputs for which the m samples w_i have the same p.d.f. as the n samples v_j under hypothesis H_0, and are statistically independent of them. Tables that can be used for setting the level V_0 have been published by Fix and Hodges (1955).

When both numbers n and m of samples are very large, the statistic V is approximately Gaussian. Capon (1959) showed that if the ratio m/n remains finite as m and n increase beyond all bounds and the signal strength vanishes, the asymptotic relative efficiency of this receiver with respect to a Neyman–Pearson receiver is $3/\pi = 0.955$ when the noise is Gaussian. Whatever the noise distribution, the a.r.e. cannot fall below $108/125 = 0.864$; for certain distributions it may be much greater than 1. The receiver is then much more sensitive than one designed to satisfy the Neyman–Pearson criterion for Gaussian noise. It is thus less affected than the Neyman–Pearson receiver by deviations from a Gaussian distribution.

The sign test that we described earlier counts the number of input samples $v_1, \ldots, v_n$ greater than the known median of the noise, taken there to be 0. If the median is unknown, as in the output of a non-linear rectifier whose input contains noise of uncertain power, it might be estimated from the reference input as $\hat{M}$, and the sign test could be applied to the n differences $v_i - \hat{M}$.

Hancock and Lainiotis (1965) have analyzed a receiver that can utilize a number m of reference samples much greater than the number n of possibly signal-bearing samples. It divides the reference samples into n groups of m/n samples each, determines the median $\hat{M}_i$ of each group, and performs a sign test on the n differences $v_i - \hat{M}_i$. With respect to a Neyman–Pearson receiver that similarly estimates an unknown median of the noise, this sign-test receiver has an a.r.e. of $2/\pi = 0.637$ in the presence of Gaussian noise.

(vi) *Two-input systems.* The non-parametric receivers considered so far have required a certain coherence in the signals, in the sense that the signals must consistently drive the sample values v_i toward more positive or more negative amplitudes. This coherence may not always exist, however. If the signal is a random process taking on both positive and negative values during the observation, or if the signals have random phases, the samples may have various signs, and it will be impossible to distinguish inputs containing signals from pure noise simply by looking at the signs of the samples.

The detection of stochastic signals, which, like random noise, can be described only by means of a collection of p.d.f.s, will be treated in Chapter XI by the parametric methods developed heretofore. At present we shall only mention that such signals arise in multipath communications, in sonar, and in radio astronomy. With these signals the inputs to the receiver may have an expected value of zero under both hypotheses, the principal differences being a greater power level and, possibly, a different spectral density under hypothesis H_1 from what is observed with the signals absent. If the statistics of the noise are unknown, it is difficult to take advantage of distinctions such as these.

If a reference noise input is available and known to be free of any signals, one might set up a receiver based on the Mann–Whitney–Wilcoxon test just described. The outputs of the prefilter would be applied to a quadratic rectifier before sampling, and one could expect the samples of the input being tested to be mostly larger than those of the reference input when a signal is present.

If the noise arises mainly in the receiver or nearby, it may be simpler to try picking up the signal with two receivers so placed that the signal components of the inputs to each are the same, while the noise components are independently random. The presence of a signal is then indicated by a correlation between the two inputs that is absent when there is no signal. Let the samples of the prefiltered inputs of the two receivers be $v_1, v_2, \ldots, v_n$ and $w_1, w_2, \ldots, w_n$. The samples in each set are supposed to be statistically independent among themselves.

The "sample correlation coefficient"

$$r = \frac{\sum_{i=1}^{n} (w_i - \bar{w})(v_i - \bar{v})}{\left[\sum_{i=1}^{n} (w_i - \bar{w})^2 \sum_{j=1}^{n} (v_j - \bar{v})^2\right]^{\frac{1}{2}}},$$

$$\bar{w} = n^{-1} \sum_{i=1}^{n} w_i, \quad \bar{v} = n^{-1} \sum_{i=1}^{n} v_i,$$

will tend to be small when there is no signal present, and a receiver might compare r with a decision level r_0, choosing H_1 when r is the larger. If there is a possibility of a constant, unknown phase shift between the signals at the two receivers, the absolute value $|r|$ should be compared with a level r_0', H_0 being chosen when $|r| < r_0'$. These receivers are only asymptotically non-parametric; for a finite number of samples of each input the decision levels r_0 and r_0' for a preassigned false-alarm probability will depend somewhat on the true distribution of the noise.

To eliminate this dependence on the distributions, the receiver should work with the signs or the ranks of the samples. The simplest system is the "polarity coincidence correlator" (p.c.c.), which has been analyzed by Wolff, Thomas, and Williams (1962), Ekre (1963), and Kanefsky and Thomas (1965). It bases its decisions on the signs of the products of the samples,

$$V = \sum_{i=1}^{n} U(v_i w_i),$$

where $U(x)$ is again the unit step function. If this statistic exceeds a decision level, the signs of the two sets of samples have a positive correlation, and the presence of a signal is indicated. This receiver is nonparametric for inputs that under H_0 are independent and have even p.d.f.s, $p_0(v) = p_0(-v)$, $p_0(w) = p_0(-w)$.

If the signals and the noise inputs are independent Gaussian random processes, the optimum receiver based on the Neyman–Pearson criterion simply combines the samples and adds the squares of their pairwise sums, comparing

$$\sum_{i=1}^{n} (v_i + w_i)^2$$

with a decision level. With respect to this detector the asymptotic relative efficiency of the p.c.c. is $2/\pi^2 = 0.202$, hardly a promising result. Nevertheless, for noise with certain types of asymmetrical distribution Kanefsky and Thomas (1965) have found this asymptotic relative efficiency to exceed 1. They were careful to point out, however, that unless the number n of samples is huge or the signal-to-noise ratio infinitesimal, use of the Central Limit Theorem to evaluate the polarity coincidence correlator with the types of noise p.d.f. they considered may seriously overestimate its relative efficiency.

(c) *Adaptive Detection*

At times the statistics of the noise are only vaguely known, and little more information about the signals is available than that they are expected to appear in a certain frequency band and at some time during a certain interval. To make matters worse, the characteristics of the noise, and perhaps of the signals as well, may change over a period of time, and whatever may be learned about them through observation may not be reliable for very long. It is then necessary to consider designing a receiver that modifies its structure continually so that it is always operating in the best possible way under its current circumstances, at least to the extent that it can determine them. Such a receiver may be called "adaptive". Receivers adaptive to various kinds of changing environment have been proposed and studied by numerous writers. Here we can do no more than indicate some of the lines along which this field of adaptive detection is developing.

Suppose that a signal occurring at random but well separated intervals is to be detected in Gaussian noise of uniform spectral density. The signal is known to occupy a certain spectral band of width W, but its form is otherwise unknown. The duration of the signal is of the order of T, and the product $M = 2TW$ is much greater than 1. If the shape of the signal were known, the receiver would be furnished with a filter matched to the signal, whose output would be continuously compared with a fixed decision level, as in Section 2 of this chapter. With the shape of the signal unknown, the receiver might instead try to create its own matched filter by estimating the signal component of its input whenever it believes a signal to be present. This is the principle of the adaptive receivers proposed by Glaser (1961), Jakowatz, Shuey, and White (1961), and Scudder (1965), among others. We shall only roughly sketch the operation of these receivers; details should be sought in the original papers.

In Glaser's receiver the input is filtered to remove components of the noise outside the band of the signals. The output of this filter is sampled at the Nyquist interval ($1/2W$ seconds) to generate a sequence $v_1, v_2, \ldots$ of input samples v_j. At any time $t/2W$—t an integer—the receiver examines the present sample and $M-1$ past samples of the input, $v_t, v_{t-1}, \ldots, v_{t-M+1}$, to decide whether they might contain a signal. By that time it has acquired a set of estimates $\hat{s}_1, \hat{s}_2, \ldots, \hat{s}_M$ of sample values of the signal at $M = 2TW$ uniformly spaced instants. These are used as weighting coefficients in the equivalent of a matched filter, generating the statistic $\gamma_t e_t + \delta_t g_t$, where

$$e_t = \sum_{j=t-M+1}^{t} v_j^2, \quad g_t = \sum_{j=t-M+1}^{t} s_{j-t+M} v_j .$$

The "correlations" g_t are produced by a tapped delay line, whose taps feed a set of amplifiers of variable gains proportional to the estimates $\hat{s}_k$.

The weighting coefficients γ_t, δ_t depend on the stage reached by the receiver in its process of adaptation, and they will differ from one trial of the procedure to another, although they are picked according to a fixed rule. At the start $\gamma_t = 1$, $\delta_t = 0$, for the receiver initially knows nothing about the signal and can base its decisions only on what corresponds to the energy of the input during the past T seconds.

The weighted statistic $\gamma_t e_t + \delta_t g_t$ is compared with a bias θ_t, also a function of the stage of adaptation. If $\gamma_t e_t + \delta_t g_t < \theta_t$, nothing happens. If the weighted statistic exceeds the bias, however, the receiver presumes that a signal is present and generates a new set of estimates $\hat{s}_j'$ of its values by making a linear combination of the previous estimates $\hat{s}_j$ and the current samples of the input,

$$\hat{s}_j' = \varepsilon_t v_{t-M+j} + (1-\varepsilon_t)\hat{s}_j .$$

These weights ε_t, $1-\varepsilon_t$ also depend on the stage of adaptation. A new stage is entered whenever the bias is surpassed.

If the input signal-to-noise ratio is large enough, the receiver will in this way gradually "learn" the sample values of the signal and build its own matched filter, with which it can subsequently detect the signal whenever it occurs. If the form of the signal changes gradually, the receiver can, to a certain extent, follow the change.

The receiver proposed by Jakowatz, Shuey, and White (1961) operates in much the same way, but the term e_t is omitted, and it is only the output g_t of the current matched filter that is compared with the bias. Details of selecting the weighting coefficients and the bias also differ. How soon this receiver starts learning a signal depends on values of the estimates $\{\hat{s}_j\}$ initially stored in the receiver. If these are unfavorable, it may take some time to come around to the proper set of values.

This receiver has been furnished with a means of learning a number of different signals that may interlace, but do not overlap. A number of matched filters are incorporated, each with its own set of weighting coefficients and its own bias. When a bias is surpassed, only the filter with the greatest output enters a new stage of adaptation and has its weighting coefficients modified. At high enough signal-to-noise ratios no more than one filter will learn a given signal. In a similar system described by Scudder (1965), the waveforms assigned by the transmitter to each symbol of an alphabet are drawn, once for all, from a Gaussian random process of known autocovariance, and the receiver employs a method of the type to be discussed in Chapter XI to estimate these waveforms.

These receivers are based to a large extent on the assumption that the noise is white and Gaussian, in that they aim toward at least an approximation of the filter matched to a signal mixed with such noise. They cannot be non-parametric for this reason. A receiver that avoids such an assumption about the noise and can be classed as non-parametric has been studied by Groginsky, Wilson, and Middleton (1966). It supposes that during each observation interval, in which the signal, when present, occurs at a fixed but unknown time, independent samples $(v_1, v_2, \ldots, v_m)$ and $(w_1, w_2, \ldots, w_n)$ of two inputs are available, only the first set of which can contain a signal. The two sets are combined and ranked according to their amplitudes, and a sequence $\mathbf{z} = (z_1, z_2, \ldots, z_{m+n})$ is generated according to the rule that $z_k = -m/n$ if the kth smallest amplitude is a w-sample, $z_k = 1$ if it is a v-sample.

The receiver works with a statistic

$$T(\mathbf{z}) = \sum_{k=1}^{m+n} a_k z_k$$

whose coefficients a_k are generated by the receiver from its inputs according to a certain rule. At the end of each observation interval, during which new sets of samples $\{v_j\}$, $\{w_j\}$ have been collected and treated, the statistic $T(\mathbf{z})$ is compared with a bias to decide if a signal is present. At each stage, whether the bias is surpassed or not, the coefficients a_k are modified to new values given by

$$a_k' = \alpha a_k + \beta T(\mathbf{z}) z_k .$$

The weights α and β and the bias are selected to provide non-parametric reception and high sensitivity, as discussed in the paper cited. Ultimately, if the signal-to-noise ratio is higher than a certain critical threshold, the receiver acquires a set of coefficients a_k such that $T(\mathbf{z})$ approximates an optimum rank statistic for detecting the signal. If the signal-to-noise ratio falls below the threshold, the receiver can never acquire the signal.

Systems such as these can be thought of as learning and, subsequently, recognizing patterns in a random environment. Just as theories of pattern recognition have drawn on decision theory and detection theory (Abramson and Braverman, 1962; Sebestyen, 1962), so have designers of adaptive receivers availed themselves of techniques of pattern recognition. Adaptive receivers are manifestly quite complicated and hardly amenable to mathematical analysis. False-alarm and detection probabilities cannot be calculated, and even asymptotic relative efficiencies are difficult to determine. What is done instead is to simulate the receivers on analogue or digital computers. Numerous trials with different initial conditions and different specimens of random noise are run off, and empirical statistics of the behavior of the receiver are collected and compared. Examples will be found in the articles cited. The experience thus gained will guide the designers of future adaptive receivers and may lead to a general theory of their properties and optimum structure.

PROBLEMS

1. The narrowband spectral density $\Psi(\omega)$ of a random process is not necessarily an even function of ω, and its Fourier transform is not necessarily real. Evaluate the covariance matrix of the four random variables $x = x(t)$, $y = y(t)$, $\dot{x} = dx/dt$, and $\dot{y} = dy/dt$, where $x(t)$ and $y(t)$ are the quadrature components of the process. All four variables are selected at the same point of time. Assuming that the process is Gaussian, write down the joint p.d.f. of these variables and determine the conditional p.d.f. $p(\dot{x}, \dot{y} \mid x, y)$ Using the method of Section 2(b), determine the rate at which the process $r(t) = [x(t)]^2 + [y(t)]^2$ crosses a level $r = a$. *Hint.* As before, show that $p(\dot{r} \mid x, y)$ depends on x and y only through $r = x^2 + y^2$.

2. A signal $s(t) = Af(t)$, $A > 0$, is repeated n times during successive intervals of duration T in order to transmit a "1" in a binary message; for a "0" nothing is sent. The receiver passes the n inputs $v_j(t)$ from these intervals through a filter matched to $f(t)$ and observes the outputs at the end of each interval. Suppose that the spectral density of the Gaussian white noise and the amplitude A of the signal as received are both unknown. Show that the principle of maximum likelihood prescribes a receiver that bases its decisions on the t-statistic of eq. (5.4).

3. A signal $s(t) = Af(t)$ of known shape, but unknown amplitude A, is received in white Gaussian noise of unknown spectral density N. A set of functions $f_1(t), f_2(t), \ldots,$ orthonormal among themselves and orthogonal to $f(t)$ over the observation interval $(0, T)$, is determined, as by the Gram–Schmidt orthogonalization process. The input $v(t)$ is passed through n parallel filters matched to n of these functions $f_j(t)$ to obtain the statistics

$$v_j = \int_0^T f_j(t)\, v(t)\, dt, \qquad = 1, 2, \ldots, n.$$

Show that an unbiased estimate of the spectral density N is

$$\hat{N} = (2/n) \sum_{j=1}^{n} v_j^2,$$

and that by taking n large enough, the variance of this estimate can be made as small as desired. Propose a receiver, based on the estimate $\hat{N}$ and on the output of a filter matched to $f(t)$, for detecting the signal $s(t)$, and show that if n is made large enough, this receiver is as reliable as one designed for detection in white noise of known spectral density N.

4. A signal of known form $s(t) = Af(t)$, but unknown positive amplitude A, is to be detected in Gaussian noise of autocovariance $\phi(t, u) = \sigma^2 \varrho(t, u)$, of which $\varrho(t, u)$ is known, but the variance σ^2 is not. $\varrho(0, 0) = 1$. As in Chapter IV, Section 4, make Karhunen–Loève expansions of the signal, the noise, and the input $v(t)$. Arrange the eigenvalues λ_k in descending order, and denote the associated eigenfunctions by $f_k(t)$. As data the n quantities

$$v_k = \int_0^T f_k(t)\, v(t)\, dt$$

are to be used. Design a maximum-likelihood receiver to detect the signal on the basis of estimates of the amplitude A and the variance σ^2. Show that if n is taken large enough, the reliability of this receiver will be as great as one designed for detection in noise of known variance σ^2.

5. Work out the following alternative version of the solution of Problem 4. Write the input $v(t)$, $0 < t < T$, as

$$v(t) = v_1(t) + v_2(t),$$

with $v_1(t)$ defined as

$$v_1(t) = f(t) \int_0^T g(s)\, v(s)\, ds \Big/ \int_0^T g(u) f(u)\, du,$$

where $g(t)$ is the solution of the integral equation

$$f(t) = \int_0^T \varrho(t, s)\, g(s)\, ds, \qquad 0 < t < T.$$

Show that $v_2(t)$ is statistically independent of $v_1(t)$ and that its probability density functions are the same whether the signal is present or not. Derive its covariance function. Use Problem 7 of Chapter VIII to determine the unknown variance σ^2 from $v_2(t)$, and use this variance in setting the decision level for the detection statistic. What should this detection statistic be? Calculate the false-alarm and detection probabilities.

6. In Problem 2 take the signals to be quasiharmonic, with independently random phases ψ_k during the n intervals, but with a common, though unknown, amplitude A,

$$s_k(t) = A \operatorname{Rl} F(t) \exp(i\Omega t + i\psi_k), \qquad k = 1, 2, \ldots, n.$$

The data are the real and imaginary parts, x_k and y_k, of the output of a filter matched to the signal,

$$x_k + iy_k = \int_0^T F^*(t)\, V_k(t)\, dt,$$

where the inputs are $v_k(t) = \operatorname{Rl} V_k(t) e^{i\Omega t}$. The noise is white and Gaussian of unknown spectral density. Work out under each hypothesis the maximum-likelihood estimates of the common variance of the n x_k's and the n y_k's, determine the maximum-likelihood estimates of the phases ψ_k and of the common amplitude A, and show that the maximum-likelihood detector is equivalent to one that compares the statistic

$$\left[\sum_{k=1}^{n}(x_k^2+y_k^2)^{\frac{1}{2}}\right]^2 \Big/ \sum_{k=1}^{n}(x_k^2+y_k^2)$$

with a suitable decision level.

7. The inputs $v(t)$ and $w(t)$ to two receivers are, under hypothesis H_0, independent Gaussian random processes; under hypothesis H_1 they contain a common signal component $s(t)$, which is also a realization of a Gaussian random process. Let these inputs be sampled at n such times that the sample values

$$(H_0): \quad v_k = n_k, \quad w_k = n_k'; \qquad (H_1): \quad v_k = s_k+n_k, \quad w_k = s_k+n_k',$$

$k = 1, 2, \ldots, n$, are independent. The n_k's and the n_k''s are then independent Gaussian random variables of mean 0 and variance σ^2. The s_k's are the same in both inputs and are themselves independent Gaussian random variables of mean 0 and variance S^2. Show that the likelihood-ratio receiver using these samples is equivalent to one that compares $\sum_{k=1}^{n}(v_k+w_k)^2$ with a decision level. Calculate the false-alarm and detection probabilities as functions of the decision level and of σ^2 and S^2. Work out their limiting forms as n increases beyond all bounds and the signal-to-noise ratio S^2/σ^2 approaches zero.

BIBLIOGRAPHY (IX)

1944 RICE, S. O., "The Mathematical Analysis of Random Noise", *Bell Sys. Tech. J.* **23,** 282–332 (July); **24,** 46–156 (Jan. 1945).

1945 WILCOXON, F., "Individual Comparisons by Ranking Methods", *Biometrics* **1,** 80–83 (June).

1947 MANN, H. B. and WHITNEY, D. R., "On a Test of whether One of Two Random Variables is Stochastically Larger than the Other", *Ann. Math. Stat.* **18,** 50–60.

1948 MIDDLETON, D., "Spurious Signals Caused by Noise in Triggered Circuits", *J. Appl. Phys.* **19,** 817–30 (Sept.).

1951 SIEGERT, A. J. F., "On the First-Passage Time Probability Problem", *Phys. Rev.* **81,** 617–23 (Feb. 15).

1954 BENNETT, C. A. and FRANKLIN, N. L., *Statistical Analysis in Chemistry and the Chemical Industry*, John Wiley & Sons, Inc., New York, N.Y.

1955 FIX, E. and HODGES, J. L., Jr., "Significance Probabilities of the Wilcoxon Test", *Ann. Math. Stat.* **26,** 301–12 (June).

1956 HODGES, J. L., Jr. and LEHMANN, E. L., "The Efficiency of Some Nonparametric Competitors of the *t*-Test", *Ann. Math. Stat.* **27,** 324–35 (June).

1957 FRASER, D. A. S., *Nonparametric Methods in Statistics*, John Wiley & Sons, Inc., New York, N.Y.

HELSTROM, C. W., "The Distributions of the Number of Crossings of a Gaussian Stochastic Process", *Trans. I.R.E.* **IT-3,** 232–7 (Dec.).

RESNIKOFF, G. J. and LIEBERMAN, G. J., *Tables of the Non-Central t-Distribution*, Stanford University Press, Stanford, Calif.

1958 RICE, S. O., "Distribution of the Duration of Fades in Radio Transmission: Gaussian Noise Model", *Bell Sys. Tech. J.* **37,** 581–635 (May).

SILVERMAN, R. A., "The Fluctuation Rate of the Chi Process", *Trans. I.R.E.* **IT-4** 30–34 (Mar.).

1959 CAPON, J., "A Nonparametric Technique for the Detection of a Constant Signal in Additive Noise", *IRE Wescon Convention Record*, pt. 4, 92–103.

HELSTROM, C. W., "A Note on a Markov Envelope Process", *Trans. I.R.E.* **IT–5**, 139–40 (Sept.).

LEHMANN, E. L. *Testing Statistical Hypotheses*, John Wiley & Sons, Inc. New York, N.Y.

1960 GILBERT, E. N. and POLLAK, H. O., "Amplitude Distribution of Shot Noise", *Bell Sys. Tech. J.* **39**, 333–50 (Mar.).

KELLY, E. J., REED, I. S. and ROOT, W. L., "The Detection of Radar Echoes in Noise", *J. Soc. Ind. Appl. Math.* **8**, (I) 309–41 (June); (II) 481–507 (Sept.).

MARCUM, J. I., "A Statistical Theory of Target Detection by Pulsed Radar", *Trans. I.R.E.* **IT–6**, 59–267 (Apr.).

1961 GLASER, E. M., "Signal Detection by Adaptive Filters", *Trans. I.R.E.* **IT–7**, 87–98 (Apr.).

JAKOWATZ, C. V., SHUEY, R. L. and WHITE, G. M., "Adaptive Waveform Recognition", *Proc. 4th London Symposium on Information Theory*, C. CHERRY, ed., Butterworths Scientific Publications, London, Eng., pp. 317–26.

KENDALL, M. G. and STUART, A., *The Advanced Theory of Statistics*, Hafner Publishing Co., New York, N.Y., vol. 2.

TIKHONOV, V. I., "The Markov Nature of the Envelope of Quasiharmonic Oscillations", *Radio Eng. & Electr. Phys.* **6**, no. 7, 961–71.

1962 ABRAMSON, N. and BRAVERMAN, D., "Learning to Recognize Patterns in a Random Environment", *Trans. I.R.E.* **IT–8**, S58–S63 (Sept.).

LONGUET–HIGGINS, M. S., "The Distribution of Intervals between Zeros of a Stationary Random Function", *Phil. Trans. Roy. Soc. (London)*, A **254**, 557–99 (May 24).

MCFADDEN, J. A., "On the Lengths of Intervals in a Stationary Point Process", *J. Roy. Stat. Soc. London* (B) **24**, no. 2, 364–82.

RAINAL, A. J., "Zero-Crossing Intervals of Gaussian Processes", *Trans. I.R.E.* **IT-8**, 372–8 (Oct.).

SEBESTYEN, G., *Decision-making Processes in Pattern Recognition*, Macmillan Co., New York, N.Y.

SLEPIAN, D., "The One-sided Barrier Problem for Gaussian Noise", *Bell Sys. Tech. J.* **41**, 463–501 (Mar.).

WOLFF, S. S., THOMAS, J. B. and WILLIAMS, T. R., "The Polarity-coincidence Correlator: a Nonparametric Detection Device", *Trans. I.R.E.* **IT-8**, 5–9 (Jan.).

1963 EKRE, H., "Polarity Coincidence Correlation Detection of a Weak Noise Source", *Trans. I.E.E.E.* **IT–9**, 18–23 (Jan.).

1964 CARLYLE, J. W. and THOMAS, J. B., "On Nonparametric Signal Detectors", *Trans. I.E.E.E.* **IT–10**, 146–52 (Apr.).

1965 CRAMÉR, H. and LEADBETTER, M. R., "The Moments of the Number of Crossings of a Level by a Stationary Normal Process", *Ann. Math. Stat.* **36**, 1656–63 (Dec.).

DALY, R. F. and RUSHFORTH, C. K., "Nonparametric Detection of a Signal of Known Form in Additive Noise", *Trans. I.E.E.E.* **IT-11**, 70–76 (Jan.).

HANCOCK, J. C. and LAINIOTIS, D. G., "On Learning and Distribution-free Coincidence Detection Procedures", *Trans. I.E.E.E.* **IT-11**, 272–81 (Apr.).

KANEFSKY, M. and THOMAS, J. B., "On Polarity Detection Schemes with Non-Gaussian Inputs", *J. Franklin Inst.* **280**, 120–38 (August).

KANEFSKY, M. and THOMAS, J. B., "On Adaptive Nonparametric Detection Systems using Dependent Samples", *Trans. I.E.E.E.* **IT-11**, 521–6 (Oct.).

SCUDDER, H. J., III, "Adaptive Communication Receivers", *Trans. I.E.E.E.* **IT-11**, 167–74 (Apr.).

YLVISAKER, N. D., "The Expected Number of Zeros of a Stationary Gaussian Process", *Ann. Math. Stat.* **36**, 1043–6 (June).

1966 CRAMÉR, H., "On the Intersections between the Trajectories of a Normal Stationary Stochastic Process and a High Level", *Arkiv för Mat.* **6**, no. 20, 337–49.

GROGINSKY, H. L., WILSON, L. R. and MIDDLETON, D., "Adaptive Detection of Signals in Noise", *Trans. I.E.E.E.* **IT-12**, 337–48 (July).

X
SIGNAL RESOLUTION

1. THE SPECIFICATION OF RECEIVERS

(a) *The Varieties of Resolution*

Up to now we have studied the detection only of individually identifiable signals. Radar targets, however, may be so close together that their echoes appear indistinguishable, and the receiver must decide whether to attribute its input to one signal or to several. A signal overlapping a weaker one of the same kind may well conceal it, as when the radar echo from a large bomber hides one from a small fighter plane nearby. The dreadful task of identifying a ballistic missile among a cloud of decoys requires the sorting out of a multitude of echo signals. The echo from a low-flying aircraft arrives in the midst of a throng of weak, random signals reflected from the ground; these create the interference known as "clutter". In a ground-mapping radar it is the detailed structure of the reflections themselves that is of interest.

The process of deciding whether the input to a receiver contains one signal or a number of adjacent signals is called *resolution*. The term is borrowed from optics, which has long been concerned with the efficient resolution of close images. One speaks of resolving the echoes of the fighter plane and the bomber, or of the decoys and the missile. A ground-mapping radar that accurately reproduces details of the terrain it scans is said to provide good resolution. The quality of signals determining whether they can be easily resolved is called their *resolvability*. Echoes of the same transmitted radar pulse from diverse targets may differ in several respects: in time of arrival τ because of a difference of target distances, in carrier frequency Ω by virtue of a difference of target velocities, and in the antenna azimuth θ for maximum amplitude, owing to a difference of target bearings. Any combination of such parameters may be utilized to resolve the signals.

The study of radar resolution falls into two parts, signal design and receiver design. Most attention has been given to the former, which seeks transmitted pulses whose echoes are most easily resolved. The latter, concerned with how the receiver should be modified to accommodate signals that may overlap, has been less widely developed, possibly because it is so complex. The tendency has been to accept the conventional plan of a radar receiver, which is essentially the maximum-likelihood receiver described in the previous chapter, and to provide it with filters matched to transmitted signals designed for good resolution.

There are various aspects under which the resolution of signals can be considered, and they are exemplified by the situations mentioned in the first paragraph. One can suppose that at most two signals might be present and that the receiver has either to detect a weak signal in the presence of a strong one or to decide whether two signals, one, or none is present in its input. Alternatively, the possibility that an arbitrary number of signals are present can be confronted, and one can ask the receiver to estimate the number of signals as well as their arrival times, frequencies, or other parameters. A third type of problem is the detection of a given signal against a background of many weak, random echoes such as make up the ground clutter; it can often be viewed as the detection of a signal in colored Gaussian noise. Ground mappers and similar radars can be regarded as measuring the scattering function of a surface or a volume of space, and their operation can be treated as the estimation of a random process. The first three of these aspects of resolution will be discussed in this chapter; the fourth is beyond the scope of this book.

In what follows we shall assume that the signals are corrupted by white Gaussian noise of unilateral spectral density N. The modifications needed to accommodate colored noise are mostly evident, but to make them is uninstructive. Although the problems of resolution will be analyzed from the standpoint of hypothesis testing, it will be found that for any useful progress, compromises must be made and something less than an optimum system must be accepted.

(b) *The Resolution of Two Signals*

(i) *Detection of two known signals.* In the most elementary and least common situation one or the other, or both or neither, of two signals $Af(t)$ and $Bg(t)$ may be present in the input $v(t)$ of the receiver. We suppose that the functions $f(t)$ and $g(t)$ are given, $f(t) \neq g(t)$, and that they are normalized so that

$$\int_0^T [f(t)]^2 \, dt = \int_0^T [g(t)]^2 \, dt = 1. \tag{1.1}$$

The former signal will be called "signal A", the latter "signal B". Signal B may be a copy of signal A arriving earlier or later, $g(t) = f(t+\tau)$, with a given delay τ. On the basis of the input $v(t)$ received during the observation interval $(0, T)$, the observer must choose one of four hypotheses: (H_0) neither signal A nor signal B is present, (H_1) signal A alone is present, (H_2) signal B alone is present, and (H_3) both signal A and signal B are present. A prescription for making this choice may be termed a "resolution strategy".

If there were no noise present, the observer could decide without error which of the hypotheses is true, by passing the input through properly matched filters and observing the output. It is easy to verify that the following two test statistics, among others, yield the desired information,

$$\begin{aligned} \hat{A} &= (1-\lambda^2)^{-1} \int_0^T [f(t) - \lambda g(t)]\, v(t)\, dt, \\ \hat{B} &= (1-\lambda^2)^{-1} \int_0^T [g(t) - \lambda f(t)]\, v(t)\, dt, \end{aligned} \tag{1.2}$$

where

$$\lambda = \int_0^T f(t)\, g(t)\, dt. \tag{1.3}$$

If hypothesis H_0 is true, $\hat{A} = \hat{B} = 0$; under hypothesis H_1, $\hat{A} = A$, $\hat{B} = 0$; under H_2, $\hat{A} = 0$, $\hat{B} = B$; and under H_3, $\hat{A} = A$, $\hat{B} = B$. If either of the quantities in eq. (1.2) vanishes, the corresponding signal is absent. From our work in Section 2 of Chapter IV we know that the quantity $\hat{A}$ can be generated by passing the input $v(t)$ through a filter matched to the signal $[f(t) - \lambda g(t)]/(1-\lambda^2)$, that is, through one with an impulse response

$$\begin{aligned} K_a(\tau) &= (1-\lambda^2)^{-1} [f(T-\tau) - \lambda g(T-\tau)], \quad && 0 < \tau < T, \\ &= 0, && \tau < 0, \quad \tau > T. \end{aligned} \tag{1.4}$$

A similar filter with impulse response $K_b(\tau)$, matched to the signal $[g(t) - \lambda f(t)]/(1-\lambda^2)$, can be used to form the statistic $\hat{B}$. The outputs of these filters at the end of the observation interval are the values of $\hat{A}$ and $\hat{B}$ desired.

If the input contains additive random noise $n(t)$, the statistics $\hat{A}$ and $\hat{B}$ do not vanish, even when the signals are absent; and the observer is faced with a statistical problem. He must set up some strategy—utilizing perhaps the test quantities $\hat{A}$ and $\hat{B}$, perhaps some other functionals of the input $v(t)$—by which to make a choice among the four hypotheses that meets some standard of long-run success. To derive this strategy we turn to the theory of statistical testing of hypotheses.

It is clear how the Bayes criterion of Chapter III can be applied to this problem if one is given a matrix of the costs C_{ij} of choosing hypothesis H_i when hypothesis H_j is really true, and if one is also given the prior probabilities of the four hypotheses and the prior p.d.f.s of the amplitudes A and B. The Bayes strategy involves calculating the average conditional risk $\bar{C}_i$ of each hypothesis, and the observer chooses the one whose conditional risk is the smallest. The conditional risks are defined as in Chapter III, Section 2(b). In our study of binary communication channels in Chapter VI we treated the choice between hypotheses H_1 and H_2 alone, assuming H_0 and H_3 impossible. The "overlap integral" in eq. (1.3) appeared there also, in the expression for the average probability of error.

When some or all of the prior probabilities and costs are unspecified, the same difficulties arise as in the simpler detection problems treated earlier, and the usual methods of testing hypotheses become inapplicable. Instead we adopt as a guide the method of maximum likelihood, introduced in the previous chapter to deal with the detection of a signal of unknown time of arrival. The resulting resolution strategy and its probabilities of success and failure shed some light on the resolvability of signals of this kind.

The maximum-likelihood detection of a signal in white, Gaussian noise, we found, is in effect based on the estimate of the amplitude of the signal, an estimate derived on the assumption that the input $v(t)$ actually contains a signal. If the estimated amplitude is too small, the result is attributed to a noise fluctuation, and the decision is made that no signal is present. Taking the same viewpoint here, we imagine that the input $v(t)$ contains both signals, and we form the maximum-likelihood estimates of their amplitudes A and B. If the estimate $\hat{A}$ of the amplitude of the first signal is too small, the system decides that the first signal is absent, and the second signal is treated in the same way. If both $|\hat{A}|$ and $|\hat{B}|$ exceed certain decision levels, both signals are declared to be present.

From what we learned in Chapter IV we can immediately write down the likelihood functional for the input $v(t)$ with respect to a choice between hypotheses H_0 and H_3,

$$\Lambda[v(t)] = \exp\left[\frac{A}{N}\int_0^T f(t)\,v(t)\,dt + \frac{B}{N}\int_0^T g(t)\,v(t)\,dt - (A^2+B^2+2\lambda AB)/2N\right]. \tag{1.5}$$

The estimates $\hat{A}$ and $\hat{B}$ that maximize this likelihood ratio are given in eq. (1.2), and they can be found by measuring the outputs, at the end of the observation interval, of filters with impulse responses $K_a(\tau)$ and $K_b(\tau)$. These estimates are to be tested to decide whether the values obtained might be the result of noise alone.

When signal A is absent, the estimate $\hat{A}$ of its amplitude from eq. (1.2) tends to be small. Limits are therefore placed on the values of $\hat{A}$ and $\hat{B}$, such that if either falls between them, the corresponding signal is declared absent. This procedure is equivalent to dividing the $(\hat{A}, \hat{B})$-plane into four regions R_0, R_1, R_2, and R_3 and choosing hypothesis H_k if the estimate point $(\hat{A}, \hat{B})$ falls into region R_k, $k = 0, 1, 2, 3$. The decision whether signal A is present is independent of the estimate $\hat{B}$, for $\hat{B}$ takes on the same value regardless of the true value of the amplitude A, which may even vanish without affecting $\hat{B}$. The choice among the four hypotheses is thus reduced to two independent choices concerning each of the signals; these can be made by comparing the absolute values $|\hat{A}|$ and $|\hat{B}|$ with some decision level b. The value of b is determined by the cost of making a mistake; that is, it depends on some preassigned false-alarm probability Q_0, which is just the probability $\Pr\{|\hat{A}| > b \mid H_0 \text{ or } H_2\}$ that the estimate $\hat{A}$ will fall within the regions R_1 or R_3 when the true amplitude A vanishes.

When signal A is present, whether signal B is present or not, the expected value of the estimate $\hat{A}$ is

$$\mathbf{E}(\hat{A} \mid H_1 \text{ or } H_3) = A; \tag{1.6}$$

otherwise it is zero. Similarly $\mathbf{E}(\hat{B} \mid H_2 \text{ or } H_3) = B$. The variances of these estimates are

$$\operatorname{Var} \hat{A} = \operatorname{Var} \hat{B} = N/2(1-\lambda^2), \tag{1.7}$$

and their covariance is

$$\{\hat{A}, \hat{B}\} = \mathbf{E}[(\hat{A}-A)(\hat{B}-B)] = -N\lambda/2(1-\lambda^2), \tag{1.8}$$

where N is the noise spectral density. These formulas are derived in the same manner as eq. (IV, 1.9). Under the null hypothesis that signal A is absent, the p.d.f. of the estimate $\hat{A}$ is

$$p_0(\hat{A}) = (1-\lambda^2)^{\frac{1}{2}}(\pi N)^{-\frac{1}{2}} \exp[-(1-\lambda^2)\hat{A}^2/N]. \tag{1.9}$$

If the observer decides that signal A is present whenever $|\hat{A}|$ is greater than the decision level b, the false-alarm probability Q_0 is

$$Q_0 = \Pr\{|\hat{A}| > b \mid A = 0\} = 2 \operatorname{erfc} [2(1-\lambda^2)b^2/N]^{\frac{1}{2}}, \tag{1.10}$$

$$\operatorname{erfc} x = (2\pi)^{-\frac{1}{2}} \int_x^\infty \exp(-t^2/2)\, dt.$$

From this formula the decision level yielding the preassigned false-alarm probability is determined.

The probability Q_d of detecting the signal A is also independent of the presence or absence of signal B. It is given by

$$\begin{gathered} Q_d = \Pr\{|\hat{A}| > b \mid A \neq 0\} = 1 - \operatorname{erfc} y_2 + \operatorname{erfc} y_1, \\ y_1 = [2(1-\lambda^2)A^2/N]^{\frac{1}{2}} + x, \quad y_2 = [2(1-\lambda^2)A^2/N]^{\frac{1}{2}} - x, \\ x = [2(1-\lambda^2)b^2/N]^{\frac{1}{2}}. \end{gathered} \tag{1.11}$$

For a fixed false-alarm probability Q_0 the probability Q_d of detection is an increasing function of the quantity $2E(1-\lambda^2)/N$, where $E = A^2$ is the signal energy received during the observation interval, in the appropriate units. The more the signals overlap, the nearer is the parameter λ to 1, and the larger is the signal-to-noise ratio $(2E/N)^{\frac{1}{2}}$ required to attain a given probability of detecting either of the signals. The dependence of the parameter λ on the form of the signals will be discussed in detail later.

If the two signals to be resolved are quasiharmonic signals,

$$\begin{aligned} s_a(t) &= A \operatorname{Rl} F(t) \exp(i\Omega t + i\phi_1), \\ s_b(t) &= B \operatorname{Rl} G(t) \exp(i\Omega t + i\phi_2), \end{aligned} \tag{1.12}$$

having independent and unknown phases and amplitudes, and occurring in the presence of white, Gaussian noise, the method of maximum likelihood can as well be applied. In place of eq. (1.5) the likelihood ratio is, by eq. (V, 2.5),

$$\Lambda[v(t); a, b] = \exp\{N^{-1} \operatorname{Rl} [a^*x + b^*y - \tfrac{1}{2}(|a|^2 + |b|^2 + 2\lambda ab^*)]\} \tag{1.13}$$

where we have put

$$\begin{gathered} a = A \exp i\phi_1, \quad b = B \exp i\phi_2, \\ x = \int_0^T F^*(t)\, V(t)\, dt, \quad y = \int_0^T G^*(t)\, V(t)\, dt, \\ \int_0^T |F(t)|^2\, dt = \int_0^T |G(t)|^2\, dt = 1, \quad \lambda = \int_0^T F(t)\, G^*(t)\, dt, \end{gathered} \tag{1.14}$$

and where $V(t)$ is the complex envelope of the input $v(t) = \operatorname{Rl} V(t)e^{i\Omega t}$. The likelihood ratio is to be maximized over the four variables A, ϕ_1, B, ϕ_2, or equivalently over a, a^*, b, and b^*. By writing out the exponent in terms of these and setting the derivatives with respect to a^* and b^* equal to zero, we find the equations

$$x = a + \lambda^* b, \quad y = b + \lambda a. \tag{1.15}$$

Maximization with respect to a and b gives the complex conjugate equations. Solving for the estimates $\hat{A} = |a|$, $\hat{B} = |b|$, we obtain

$$\hat{A} = (1-|\lambda|^2)^{-1}|x-\lambda^* y|, \quad \hat{B} = (1-|\lambda|^2)^{-1}|y-\lambda x|. \tag{1.16}$$

The estimate $\hat{A}$ can be found by passing the input $v(t)$ through a filter matched to a quasiharmonic signal with envelope $F(t)-\lambda G(t)$; the filter is followed by a linear rectifier. For the estimate $\hat{B}$ the filter is matched to a signal with the complex envelope $G(t)-\lambda^* F(t)$. The outputs of each of the rectifiers at the end of the observation interval are compared with a decision level γ, which can be so adjusted that if $\hat{A} < \gamma$, signal A is declared absent; if $\hat{B} < \gamma$, signal B is rejected. The false-alarm and detection probabilities are now given by

$$\begin{aligned} Q_0 &= \exp(-c^2/2), \quad & Q_d &= Q\big(d(1-|\lambda|^2)^{\frac{1}{2}}, c\big), \\ d &= (2E/N)^{\frac{1}{2}}, & c &= \gamma[(1-|\lambda|^2)/N]^{\frac{1}{2}}, \end{aligned} \tag{1.17}$$

with $Q(\alpha, \beta)$ the Q-function defined in Chapter V.

(ii) *The resolution of signals of unknown arrival time.* In what has just been said it has been assumed that the receiver knows exactly when both signals will arrive and is hence able to measure the outputs of the matched filters $K_a(\tau)$ and $K_b(\tau)$ at precisely the right instant. If the time at which a close pair of signals might arrive is unknown, however, some method must be found to determine it. The method will itself be affected by the noise, and the resolution of the two signals, or the detection of a weak signal near a strong one, will be more fallible. If the output of the matched filter for estimating the amplitude of signal B is read at the wrong instant, it may contain a component due to the presence of signal A, which may be large enough to exceed the decision level for B and cause a false indication that signal B is present. Only at the correct instant does the part of the output of $K_b(\tau)$ due to signal A vanish. As a result, the false-alarm probability Q_0 for signal B is increased, and to restore it to an acceptable value the decision level must be raised, reducing the probability of detecting signal B.

To determine the effect of uncertainty in the time of arrival of the signals, let us suppose that their complex envelopes are known except for amplitudes, phases, and a common epoch t_0. The two signals have the form

$$\begin{aligned} s_a(t) &= A \,\mathrm{Rl}\, F(t-t_0) \exp(i\Omega t + i\phi_1), \\ s_b(t) &= B \,\mathrm{Rl}\, G(t-t_0) \exp(i\Omega t + i\phi_2). \end{aligned} \tag{1.18}$$

This situation might arise when a small target is expected at a given distance from a large one, but the range of the pair of targets is known only very roughly. The envelopes would then be related by $G(t) = F(t-\tau)$ with τ, the relative delay of the echo signals, assumed known.

Again applying the principle of maximum likelihood, we suppose that the input $v(t)$ contains both signals, and we determine the maximum-likelihood estimates of the unknown parameters A, ϕ_1, B, ϕ_2, and t_0 as the values for which the likelihood ratio is largest. The likelihood ratio is given by eq. (1.13), except that the integrals in eq. (1.14) extend over the infinite range $-\infty < t < \infty$, and in the expressions for x and y, $F(t)$ is replaced by $F(t-t_0)$, $G(t)$ by $G(t-t_0)$. After maximization with respect to $a = A \exp i\phi_1$, $b = B \exp i\phi_2$, the likelihood ratio is

$$\Lambda[v(t); \hat{a}, \hat{b}; t_0] = \exp\left[\frac{|x|^2+|y|^2-2\,\mathrm{Rl}\,\lambda xy^*}{2N(1-|\lambda|^2)}\right], \tag{1.19}$$

where x and y are now functions of t_0. The value of t_0 maximizing this expression is the best estimate of the time of arrival of the pair of signals.

As in the detection of a single signal of unknown arrival time, it is possible to turn the dependence on t_0 into a variation in time by using filters matched to the two signals with a long delay T'. Their complex impulse responses are

$$\begin{aligned} k_a'(\tau) &= F^*(T'-\tau), & k_b'(\tau) &= G^*(T'-\tau), & &0 < \tau < T', \\ &= 0, & &= 0, & &\tau < 0, \quad \tau > T', \end{aligned} \tag{1.20}$$

and their outputs have complex envelopes $y_a(t)$ and $y_b(t)$ given by

$$y_a(t_0+T') = x(t_0), \quad y_b(t_0+T') = y(t_0) \tag{1.21}$$

for all t_0. These outputs can be combined to yield the function in eq. (1.19) as a time variation, and its crossing of a certain amplitude level set by the false-alarm probability indicates the presence of one or the other or both the signals, provides an estimate of the arrival time t_0, and causes the rectified combined outputs

$$(1-|\lambda|^2)^{-1}|y_a(t)-\lambda^* y_b(t)|, \quad (1-|\lambda|^2)^{-1}|y_b(t)-\lambda y_a(t)|$$

to be sampled to determine the maximum-likelihood estimates of the amplitudes A and B, as in eq. (1.16). If either of the estimates surpasses its decision level, the presence of the associated signal is indicated.

The reader can verify that if there were no noise present, the quantity $|x|^2+|y|^2-2\,\mathrm{Rl}\,\lambda xy^*$ in eq. (1.19) would be maximum for the true value t_0 of the time of arrival, provided that at least one of the signals were on hand. Thus it would provide the correct time at which to determine the maximum-likelihood estimates $\hat{A}$ and $\hat{B}$. If the estimate $\hat{B}$ then vanished, it would be known that signal B was absent. With noise in the receiver input, however, the estimate of the time t_0 will be in error, and the estimate of the amplitude B will be evaluated at the wrong time. If there is a strong signal A present, this estimate $\hat{B}$ may exceed the decision level even with $B = 0$, causing a false alarm.

It is difficult to determine the false-alarm and detection probabilities exactly for a system like this. An approximate calculation (Helstrom, 1957) showed that in the limit of large signal-to-noise ratio the minimum detectable energy for signal B in the presence of signal A is proportional to $\left(\overline{\omega^4} - \overline{\omega^2}^2\right)^{-1} \tau^{-4}$ for purely amplitude-modulated signals of mean frequency $\bar{\omega} = 0$, the moments of the frequency being defined as in Chapter I, Section 5. If on the other hand the time t_0 of arrival were known, this minimum detectable energy would be proportional to $(\overline{\omega^2}\tau^2)^{-1}$, as we shall see when we come to analyze the ambiguity function. Thus the minimum detectable energy increases much more rapidly, as the time separation τ vanishes, when the epoch t_0 is unknown.

The calculation of the minimum detectable energy just referred to began with the assumption that signal A is present with a large signal-to-noise ratio. The error in the estimate of the time t_0 was computed to first order in the noise voltage and substituted into the expression for the estimate $\hat{B}$, which yielded the error in that estimate due to the uncertainty in the time when the outputs of the matched filters are measured. To this error was added the error due to the noise $n(t)$ in determining $\hat{B}$ by eq. (1.16). The probabilities

$$Q_0 = \Pr\{\hat{B} > \gamma \mid B = 0\} \quad \text{and} \quad Q_d = \Pr\{\hat{B} > \gamma \mid B \neq 0\}$$

were then computed and used to determine the minimum detectable signal energy.

(iii) *The merging of two signals into one.*† The two signals to be resolved usually have the same form, but slightly different values of essential parameters such as arrival time and carrier frequency. We might write them as

$$s_j(t) = \text{Rl}\, a_j\, F(t; \boldsymbol{\theta}_j) \exp i\Omega t, \qquad j = 1, 2, \tag{1.22}$$

where $a_j = A_j \exp i\phi_j$, $j = 1, 2$, gives the amplitudes and phases of the signals, and $\boldsymbol{\theta}_1$ and $\boldsymbol{\theta}_2$ designate the additional parameters serving to distinguish them.

If the parameters $\boldsymbol{\theta}_1$ and $\boldsymbol{\theta}_2$ are nearly the same, the two signals might appear in the presence of the noise as a single signal,

$$s_3(t) = \text{Rl}\, b\, F(t; \boldsymbol{\theta}) \exp i\Omega t, \tag{1.23}$$

† This part may be omitted on first reading.

where b and θ have appropriate values. W. L. Root (1962) suggested taking the probability of such an apparent merging of the two signals into one as an inverse measure of their resolvability. The greater this probability, the less resolvable the signals.

Let us denote by H_0 the hypothesis that the two signals given by eq. (1.22) are present, and by H_1 the hypothesis that only the signal in eq. (1.23) has appeared. The likelihood ratio for the input $v(t) = \text{Rl}\, V(t)e^{i\Omega t}$ with respect to these two hypotheses is, for white Gaussian noise and fixed values of the parameters,

$$\begin{aligned} \Lambda[v(t); b, \theta; a_j, \theta_j] &= \exp N^{-1}\Big[\text{Rl} \int b^* F^*(t;\theta)\, V(t)\, dt - \tfrac{1}{2}|b|^2\Big] \\ &\div \exp N^{-1}\Big[\text{Rl} \int [a_1^* F^*(t;\theta_1) + a_2^* F^*(t;\theta_2)]\, V(t)\, dt \\ &- \tfrac{1}{2} \int |a_1 F(t;\theta_1) + a_2 F(t;\theta_2)|^2\, dt\Big] \end{aligned} \tag{1.24}$$

with the normalization

$$\int |F(t;\theta)|^2\, dt = 1 \tag{1.25}$$

for all θ. If the maximum value of this likelihood ratio exceeds 1, the observer is to decide that only one signal is present.

We are concerned here with evaluating the susceptibility of the pair of signals to being taken for a single signal, rather than with designing a receiver for optimum resolution. It is sensible, therefore, to assume the values of a_1, θ_1, a_2, and θ_2 given, and to maximize the likelihood ratio only with respect to b and θ. The maximizing values of these parameters b and θ will be accepted as the parameter values of the merged signal. We then take the probability that the resulting maximum value of the likelihood ratio exceeds 1 as an indication of the probability that the two signals will appear as one.

As we have seen before, the value of b making the likelihood ratio largest is

$$\hat{b} = \int F^*(t;\theta)\, V(t)\, dt,$$

and the likelihood ratio becomes

$$\begin{aligned} \max_b \Lambda[v(t)|\, b, \theta; a_j, \theta_j] &= \exp \Big\{(2N)^{-1} \Big|\int F^*(t;\theta)\, V(t)\, dt\Big|^2 \\ &- N^{-1}\, \text{Rl} \int [a_1^* F^*(t;\theta_1) + a_2^* F^*(t;\theta_2)]\, V(t)\, dt \\ &+ (2N)^{-1}[|a_1|^2 + |a_2|^2 + 2\text{Rl}\, \lambda(\theta_1, \theta_2) a_1 a_2^*]\Big\}, \end{aligned} \tag{1.26}$$

where as in eq. (1.14)

$$\lambda(\theta_1, \theta_2) = \int F(t;\theta_1)\, F^*(t;\theta_2)\, dt. \tag{1.27}$$

What is needed is the probability that

$$\max_{\theta} \max_{b} \Lambda[v(t) \,|\, b, \theta; a_j, \theta_j] > 1$$

under hypothesis H_0 that there are really two signals present. To find this probability requires the solution of a problem akin to the first-passage-time problem discussed in Section 2(c) of Chapter IX, and it will be very difficult. Root (1962) suggested replacing the aforementioned measure of resolvability by

$$P = \max_{\theta} \Pr \left\{ \max_{b} \Lambda[v(t) \,|\, b, \theta; a_j, \theta_j] > 1 \,|\, H_0 \right\},$$

which is easier to calculate.

Denoting the complex envelope of the noise by $N(t)$, we put into eq. (1.26)

$$V(t) = a_1 F(t; \theta_1) + a_2 F(t; \theta_2) + N(t) \tag{1.28}$$

and obtain

$$\begin{aligned} 2N \ln & \max_{b} \Lambda[v(t) \,|\, b, \theta; a_j, \theta_j] \\ &= |a_1|^2[|\lambda(\theta_1, \theta)|^2 - 1] + |a_2|^2[|\lambda(\theta_2, \theta)|^2 - 1] \\ &\quad + 2\text{Rl}\; a_1 a_2^*[\lambda(\theta_1, \theta)\, \lambda^*(\theta_2, \theta) - \lambda(\theta_1, \theta_2)] \\ &\quad + 2\text{Rl} \int \{[a_1^* \lambda^*(\theta_1, \theta) + a_2^* \lambda^*(\theta_2, \theta)]\, F^*(t; \theta) \\ &\quad - [a_1^* F^*(t; \theta_1) + a_2^* F^*(t; \theta_2)]\}\, N(t)\, dt \\ &\quad + \left| \int F^*(t; \theta)\, N(t)\, dt \right|^2. \end{aligned} \tag{1.29}$$

At high enough signal-to-noise ratios that there is a good probability of detecting the signals at all, the final quadratic term will be much smaller than the term linear in $N(t)$ and is neglected. The rest of the expression we denote by X and seek the probability that it is positive. Since $N(t)$ is Gaussian, so is X. Its mean and variance are

$$\begin{aligned} \mathbf{E}(X \,|\, H_0) = \bar{X} &= |a_1|^2\, [|\lambda(\theta_1, \theta)|^2 - 1] + |a_2|^2\, [|\lambda(\theta_2, \theta)|^2 - 1] \\ &\quad - 2\text{Rl}\; a_1 a_2^*[\lambda(\theta_1, \theta_2) - \lambda(\theta_1, \theta)\, \lambda^*(\theta_2, \theta)], \\ \text{Var}\, X &= -4N\bar{X}. \end{aligned} \tag{1.30}$$

Hence, the probability that X is positive is

$$\begin{aligned} \Pr\{X > 0 \,|\, H_0\} &= \text{erfc}\, u, \\ u^2 = \tfrac{1}{4}\{ & d_1^2[1 - |\lambda(\theta_1, \theta)|^2] + d_2^2[1 - |\lambda(\theta_2, \theta)|^2] \\ & + 2\, d_1\, d_2\, \text{Rl} \exp i(\phi_1 - \phi_2)\, [\lambda(\theta_1, \theta_2) - \lambda(\theta_1, \theta)\, \lambda^*(\theta_2, \theta)]\}, \\ d_i^2 = 2E_i/N, \quad & \phi_i = \arg a_i, \quad E_i = \tfrac{1}{2}\, |a_i|^2, \quad i = 1, 2. \end{aligned} \tag{1.31}$$

The resolvability of the signals can then be measured by $1-\text{erfc}\, u_{\min}$, where $u_{\min}$ is the minimum value of u as the phases ϕ_1, ϕ_2 and the parameters $\boldsymbol{\theta}$ vary over their respective domains. The smaller $u_{\min}$, the greater the probability $\text{erfc}\, u_{\min}$ that the two signals will appear merged into a single signal. The least favorable values of the phases ϕ_1 and ϕ_2 are those for which $\phi_1-\phi_2$ is the negative of the phase of $[\lambda(\boldsymbol{\theta}_1, \boldsymbol{\theta}_2)-\lambda(\boldsymbol{\theta}_1, \boldsymbol{\theta})\,\lambda^*(\boldsymbol{\theta}_2, \boldsymbol{\theta})]$, and we find

$$u^2_{\min} = \min_{\boldsymbol{\theta}} \tfrac{1}{4}\{d_1^2[1-|\lambda(\boldsymbol{\theta}_1, \boldsymbol{\theta})|^2]+d_2^2[1-|\lambda(\boldsymbol{\theta}_2, \boldsymbol{\theta})|^2] \\ -2\, d_1\, d_2|\lambda(\boldsymbol{\theta}_1, \boldsymbol{\theta}_2)-\lambda(\boldsymbol{\theta}_1, \boldsymbol{\theta})\,\lambda^*(\boldsymbol{\theta}_2, \boldsymbol{\theta})|\}. \tag{1.32}$$

It is in general difficult to find the value of $\boldsymbol{\theta}$ that minimizes u. We are mainly interested, however, in signals having parameter values $\boldsymbol{\theta}$ very close together, and it is instructive to expand the ambiguity function $\lambda(\boldsymbol{\theta}_1, \boldsymbol{\theta}_2)$ in a power series about its peak, where $\boldsymbol{\theta}_1 = \boldsymbol{\theta}_2$. For simplicity we shall consider only a single parameter θ as distinguishing the signals; it might, for instance, be their arrival time τ. We shall also suppose that the ambiguity function is a real-valued function of the difference $\theta_2-\theta_1$. Such will be the case with amplitude-modulated pulses arriving at distinct times,

$$\lambda(\theta_1, \theta_2) = \int F(t-\theta_2)\, F(t-\theta_1)\, dt = \lambda(\theta_2-\theta_1), \\ \lambda(\tau) = \int F(s)\, F(s-\tau)\, ds. \tag{1.33}$$

If we now put

$$\lambda(\theta_1, \theta_2) = 1+\tfrac{1}{2}\lambda''(\theta_2-\theta_1)^2+\tfrac{1}{24}\lambda''''(\theta_2-\theta_1)^4+\ \ldots, \tag{1.34}$$

where the primes indicate derivatives of $\lambda(\tau)$ with respect to τ, evaluated at $\tau = 0$, we find that through terms quadratic in $(\theta_1-\theta)$ and $(\theta_2-\theta)$, u is minimized for

$$\theta = (d_1\,\theta_1+d_2\,\theta_2)/(d_1+d_2), \tag{1.35}$$

which is a mean value of θ_1 and θ_2 weighted by the amplitudes of each signal. The residual value of u^2 then depends on terms of fourth order in the differences $\theta_1-\theta$ and $\theta_2-\theta$. Putting $\delta = (\theta_2-\theta_1)$, we find

$$u_{\min} = \frac{1}{4}\,\delta^2\left(\frac{d_1\, d_2}{d_1+d_2}\right)(\lambda''''-\lambda''^2)^{\frac{1}{2}}. \tag{1.36}$$

When θ is the signal epoch as in eq. (1.33), this becomes

$$u_{\min} = \frac{1}{4}\,\delta^2\left(\frac{d_1\, d_2}{d_1+d_2}\right)(\overline{\omega^4}-\overline{\omega^2}^2)^{\frac{1}{2}}, \tag{1.37}$$

where as before $\overline{\omega^n}$ is the nth moment of the spectrum of the signal envelope

$F(t)$, as defined in Chapter I, Section 5, and where the mean frequency $\bar{\omega}$ is taken as zero.

Considering signals of equal energies, $d_1 = d_2 = d = (2E/N)^{\frac{1}{2}}$, we learn that for a fixed resolvability, that is, for a specified probability that the two signals will appear as one, the energy E is inversely proportional to the fourth power of the interval between their arrivals. Further details of this theory of signal resolvability, including the effect of separation in both arrival time and carrier frequency, can be found in Root's paper (1962). We observe that in general, the resolvability of two signals depends strongly on the form of the ambiguity function $\lambda(\theta_1, \theta_2)$. The more sharply is this function peaked in the neighborhood of the points $\theta_1 = \theta_2$, the closer the parameter values can be and still allow signals of a fixed strength to be resolved with a given probability.

(c) *The Resolution of Many Signals*

(i) *Maximum-likelihood detection.* A radar may be called upon to detect echoes arriving at any time τ within an interval of long duration and having carrier frequencies Ω anywhere within a broad range of values about the frequency Ω_0 of the transmitted pulses. In addition, there may be times when a great many closely spaced targets are to be expected, and it will be necessary to determine both the number of targets and their ranges and range-rates. If the echo signals may overlap in time or frequency or both, the problem of resolving them is especially difficult.

One approach is to impose on the space of the essential parameters θ'' a rectangular grid of more or less uniformly spaced values, and to concentrate on the detection of the M signals

$$s_j(t) = A_j \text{Rl}\, F(t; \theta_j'') \exp(i\Omega t + i\phi_j), \quad j = 1, \ldots, M, \tag{1.38}$$

having parameters θ_j'' at the points of the grid. The signals $F(t; \theta_j'')$ are normalized as in eq. (1.25). The spacings of the points will correspond to the degree of resolution that one wishes to attain with respect to the essential parameters θ''.

As in part (i) of the previous section, the detection of these M signals can be treated by the method of maximum likelihood. It is assumed that the input $v(t) = \text{Rl}\, V(t)e^{i\Omega t}$ contains all M signals,

$$V(t) = \sum_{j=1}^{M} a_j F(t; \theta_j'')\, e^{i\Omega t} + N(t), \qquad a_j = A_j \exp(i\phi_j), \tag{1.39}$$

where $N(t)$ is the complex envelope of the noise. The complex amplitudes a_j of the signals are estimated by the method of maximum likelihood as

$$\hat{a}_j = \sum_{m=1}^{M} k_{jm} z_m, \qquad z_m = \int F^*(t; \theta''_m)\, V(t)\, dt, \tag{1.40}$$

where $\mathbf{K} = ||k_{jm}||$ is the matrix inverse to the matrix $\mathbf{\Lambda} = ||\lambda_{mn}||$ of the overlap integrals of the signals,

$$\lambda_{mn} = \lambda(\theta''_n, \theta''_m) = \int F^*(t; \theta''_m)\, F(t; \theta''_n)\, dt, \qquad \lambda_{mm} = 1. \tag{1.41}$$

The estimated amplitudes $\hat{A}_j = |\hat{a}_j|$ are then compared with decision levels γ_j; if $\hat{A}_j > \gamma_j$, the receiver decides that a signal having the parameter values θ_j is present. The real and imaginary parts of the complex quantities z_m are the quadrature components of the outputs, at the end of the observation interval, of a bank of M parallel filters matched to the signals $F(t; \theta''_j)$.

If there were no noise, and if the only signals permitted were those having parameter values θ''_j, this system could correctly identify which signals are present. If signals might arrive with intermediate values of the parameters θ'', however, two adjacent estimates $\hat{A}_j$ might exceed their decision levels γ_j, indicating the presence of two signals when only one is really there. This must be counted as an error of the system. Random noise will increase the probability of such errors, as well as introducing false alarms that signals are present when they are not.

If N is the unilateral spectral density of the noise, the covariances of the complex outputs a_j are

$$\{\hat{a}_j, \hat{a}^*_m\} = 2N\, k_{jm}, \quad \{\hat{a}_j, \hat{a}_m\} = 0, \tag{1.42}$$

and the false-alarm and detection probabilities for the nth signal are

$$Q_0 = \exp(-\xi_n^2/2), \quad Q_d = Q(D_n, \xi_n), \qquad \xi_n = \gamma_n(Nk_{nn})^{-\frac{1}{2}}, \quad D_n^2 = 2E_n/Nk_{nn}, \quad E_n = \tfrac{1}{2}\,|a_n|^2, \tag{1.43}$$

where again $Q(\alpha, \beta)$ is the usual Q-function, and E_n is the energy of the nth signal. If none of the signals overlap, $\lambda_{nm} = \delta_{nm}$, $k_{nn} = 1$, and the signals can be independently detected. The more the signals overlap, however, the greater the diagonal elements k_{nn} of the inverse matrix $\mathbf{K} = \mathbf{\Lambda}^{-1}$, and the smaller the probability of detecting each signal. The finer the resolution desired, the stronger must each signal be in order to maintain a specified pair of false-alarm and detection probabilities.

(ii) *Resolution from the Bayes viewpoint.* Let ζ_k be the prior probability that k signals are present in the input $v(t) = \text{Rl}\ V(t)\ e^{i\Omega t}$ to the receiver, with

$$\sum_{k=0}^{\infty} \zeta_k = 1. \tag{1.44}$$

When exactly k signals are present, the complex envelope of the input is

$$V(t) = \sum_{j=1}^{k} a_j F(t; \theta_j'') + N(t), \tag{1.45}$$

where $a_j = A_j \exp i\phi_j$ specifies the amplitude and phase and θ_j'' the essential parameters of the jth signal. There are m parameters $\theta_j = (A_j, \phi_j, \theta_j'')$ for each signal, and for the k signals they have a joint prior p.d.f. $z_k(\theta_1, \theta_2, \ldots, \theta_k)$. Again $N(t)$ is the complex envelope of the noise.

The posterior probability, given the input $v(t)$, that k signals are present is

$$p(k\,|\,v(t)) = C\zeta_k \Lambda_k[v(t)] \tag{1.46}$$

where

$$\Lambda_k[v(t)] = \int \ldots \int z_k(\theta_1, \ldots, \theta_k)\, \Lambda[v(t)\,|\,\theta_1, \ldots, \theta_k]\, d^m\theta_1 \ldots d^m\theta_k \tag{1.47}$$

is the average likelihood ratio for detecting k signals. When the noise is white and Gaussian,

$$\Lambda[v(t)\,|\,\theta_1, \ldots, \theta_k] \tag{1.48}$$
$$= \exp\left\{N^{-1}\,\text{Rl} \int \sum_{j=1}^{k} a_j^* F^*(t; \theta_j'')\, V(t)\, dt - (2N)^{-1} \int \left| \sum_{j=1}^{k} a_j F(t; \theta_j'') \right|^2 dt \right\}$$

must be substituted into eq. (1.47). The constant C in eq. (1.46) is such that the total probability equals 1,

$$C \sum_{k=0}^{\infty} \zeta_k \Lambda_k[v(t)] = 1.$$

A receiver devised on the basis of Bayes' rule and taking all errors as equally costly would decide that k signals are present if $\zeta_k \Lambda_k[v(t)] > \zeta_j \Lambda_j[v(t)]$, for all $j \neq k$. It would assign to the k signals those sets $\hat{\theta}_1, \ldots, \hat{\theta}_k$ for which the product

$$z_k(\theta_1, \ldots, \theta_k)\, \Lambda[v(t)\,|\,\theta_1, \ldots, \theta_k]$$

is maximum. Its design would require a knowledge of the prior probabilities, its implementation a complicated apparatus, and its evaluation an insuperably difficult calculation.

A slightly simpler system could dispense with the prior p.d.f.s $z_k(\theta_1, \ldots, \theta_k)$ by finding the maximum-likelihood estimates of the parameters $\theta_1, \ldots, \theta_k$ under the assumption that there really are k signals present. It would have to do so for all possible integral values of k by maximizing the likelihood ratio in eq. (1.48). Let the sets of parameters so estimated be $\hat{\theta}_1, \ldots, \hat{\theta}_k$. Then the receiver could judge the posterior probability that n signals are present to be

$$p(n \mid v(t)) = C'\zeta_n \Lambda_n[v(t) \mid \hat{\theta}_1, \ldots, \hat{\theta}_n],$$

where C' is independent of n and has such a value that the sum of these posterior probabilities equals 1. The receiver would pick the value of n for which $p(n \mid v(t))$ is largest, and it would report n signals present with parameter values $\hat{\theta}_1, \ldots, \hat{\theta}_n$. This maximization of the likelihood ratios might require scanning over a multidimensional parameter space or the use of a bank of parallel matched filters. Knowledge of the prior probabilities ζ_k is still necessary.

A somewhat similar system proposed by Nilsson (1961) takes the input signal to have the form

$$S(t) = \sum_{j=1}^{n} A_j s(t-\tau_j),$$

where the A_j's are the amplitudes and the τ_j's the delays of the echoes from point radar targets, $s(t)$ representing the transmitted pulse. A loss function of the form

$$L = \int [\hat{S}(t)-S(t)]^2 \, dt + \alpha_{ij}$$

is stipulated, where $\hat{S}(t)$ is the estimated signal and α_{ij} is the cost of deciding that there are i targets present when there are actually j. The receiver is to minimize the conditional expected value of L, given the input $v(t)$, as a function of the number n of signals and of their amplitudes and epochs. Required are assumptions about $S(t)$ as a stochastic process and knowledge of the prior probabilities ζ_k of the number k of signals. Further details can be found in Nilsson's paper (1961).

In view of the complexity of all these attempts to apply the methods of decision and estimation theory to the detection of a number of signals with unknown parameters, it is little wonder that radar receivers are built as though the echo signals never overlapped, and that most emphasis has been placed on the use of signals that in a certain sense are least likely to interfere with each other. The design of such signals will now be considered.

2. THE SPECIFICATION OF SIGNALS

(a) *General Properties of the Ambiguity Function*

(i) *Definitions.* Whenever it is necessary to distinguish or resolve two narrowband signals in the presence of white Gaussian noise, the structure of the receiver and its performance depend on the integrated product, or "cross-correlation", of the two signals. When the complex envelopes of the signals have a common form and the signals differ only in certain essential parameters $\boldsymbol{\theta}$, the cross-correlation is termed the "ambiguity function" of the signals and is written

$$\lambda(\boldsymbol{\theta}_1, \boldsymbol{\theta}_2) = \int_{-\infty}^{\infty} F(t; \boldsymbol{\theta}_1)\, F^*(t; \boldsymbol{\theta}_2)\, dt. \tag{2.1}$$

The normalization

$$\lambda(\boldsymbol{\theta}, \boldsymbol{\theta}) = \int_{-\infty}^{\infty} |F(t; \boldsymbol{\theta})|^2\, dt = 1 \tag{2.2}$$

for all values of the parameters $\boldsymbol{\theta}$ is customary.

In radar the parameters chiefly serving to distinguish two echo signals are their arrival times τ and the Doppler shifts w of their carrier frequencies from a common reference value. When the integration in eq. (2.1) is, as usual, carried out over the infinite range, the ambiguity function for these parameters depends only on the differences of the epochs and frequencies of the two signals. If the signals are assigned the epochs $-\frac{1}{2}\tau$ and $+\frac{1}{2}\tau$ and the carrier frequencies $\Omega-\frac{1}{2}w$, and $\Omega+\frac{1}{2}w$, their complex envelopes can be written

$$\begin{aligned} F(t; -\tfrac{1}{2}\tau, -\tfrac{1}{2}w) &= F(t-\tfrac{1}{2}\tau) \exp\,[-\tfrac{1}{2}iw\,(t-\tfrac{1}{2}\tau)], \\ F(t; \tfrac{1}{2}\tau, \tfrac{1}{2}w) &= F(t+\tfrac{1}{2}\tau) \exp[\tfrac{1}{2}iw(t+\tfrac{1}{2}\tau)], \end{aligned} \tag{2.3}$$

and the ambiguity function $\lambda(-\frac{1}{2}\tau, -\frac{1}{2}w; \frac{1}{2}\tau, \frac{1}{2}w)$ becomes simply

$$\lambda(\tau, w) = \int_{-\infty}^{\infty} F(t-\tfrac{1}{2}\tau)\, F^*(t+\tfrac{1}{2}\tau) e^{-iwt}\, dt. \tag{2.4}$$

Other definitions differing from this by a phase factor have been used, but the form in eq. (2.4) has because of its convenience become standard. With the complex envelope $F(t)$ normalized to 1 as in eq. (2.2), the ambiguity function takes on its peak value at the origin,

$$|\lambda(\tau, w)| \leqslant \lambda(0, 0) = 1, \tag{2.5}$$

as can be shown by means of the Schwarz inequality.

If we introduce the spectrum $f(\omega)$ of the complex envelope $F(t)$,

$$f(\omega) = \int_{-\infty}^{\infty} F(t)e^{-i\omega t}\, dt, \tag{2.6}$$

we find by substituting the inverse Fourier transform into eq. (2.5) that the ambiguity function looks quite similar in the frequency domain,

$$\lambda(\tau, w) = \int_{-\infty}^{\infty} f(\omega+\tfrac{1}{2}w)\, f^*(\omega-\tfrac{1}{2}w)\, e^{-i\omega\tau}\, d\omega/2\pi. \tag{2.7}$$

(ii) *The ambiguity surface.* The ambiguity function $\lambda(\tau, w)$ is in general complex, but the resolvability of two signals with a relative delay τ and a frequency difference w depends only on its magnitude $|\lambda(\tau, w)|$, which it is advantageous to imagine plotted as the height of a surface over the (τ, w)-plane. This quantity $|\lambda(\tau, w)|$ acquires further meaning if one considers a set of parallel filters used to detect a signal of unknown arrival time and Doppler shift in the presence of white, Gaussian noise, as described in Chapter IX, Section 3. We insert a test signal Rl $F(t)\, e^{i\Omega t}$ at time $t = 0$ and determine the resulting output from the filter matched to a signal Rl $F(t)\, e^{i(\Omega+w)t}$ with frequency shift w. If $-\tau$ denotes the time measured from the common delay T' of the filters, the rectified output of this filter is

$$\begin{aligned} R_w(T'-\tau) &= \left| \int F^*(T'-s)\, e^{-iw(T'-s)}\, F(T'-\tau-s)\, ds \right| \\ &= \left| \int F(u)\, F^*(u+\tau)\, e^{-iwu}\, du \right| = |\lambda(\tau, w)|, \end{aligned}$$

the noise having been omitted. If we suppose that the filters are matched for a dense set of frequencies $\Omega+w$, and if we picture their rectified responses $R_w(T'-\tau)$ to the signal Rl $F(t)\, e^{i\Omega t}$ plotted as a function of time τ and frequency shift w, they will appear to form a surface similar to the ambiguity surface.

For every signal the ambiguity surface is peaked at the origin (0, 0) of the (τ, w)-plane. A second signal arriving with separations τ in time and w in frequency that lie under this central peak will be difficult to distinguish from the first signal. For many types of signal the ambiguity function $|\lambda(\tau, w)|$ exhibits additional peaks elsewhere over the (τ, w)-plane. These "sidelobes" may conceal weak signals with arrival times and carrier frequencies far from those of the first signal. In a measurement of the arrival time and frequency of a single signal, the noise may cause one of the subsidiary peaks to appear higher than the main one, leading to gross errors in the result. The taller the sidelobes, the greater the probability of such errors, or "ambiguities", in Doppler shift and signal epoch. It is desirable, therefore, for the central peak of the ambiguity function to be narrow, and for there to be as few and as low sidelobes as possible.

(iii) *Restrictions on the ambiguity function.* If there existed a signal $F(t)$ whose ambiguity function equaled 1 at $\tau = 0$, $w = 0$ and zero everywhere else, it could be distinguished from another signal having the same form, but separated in time and frequency by displacements however small. The probability of error in resolving two such signals would be no greater than the false-alarm probability for detection. No such signal exists, however. Indeed, a function $\lambda(\tau, w)$ chosen arbitrarily will not necessarily be the ambiguity function of any signal. Even the magnitude $|\lambda(\tau, w)|$ is not at a designer's disposal, but must satisfy certain conditions.

An example of such a condition is the self-transform property of the squared magnitude $|\lambda(\tau, w)|^2$, due to Siebert (1958),

$$\int_{-\infty}^{\infty}\int_{-\infty}^{\infty} |\lambda(\tau, w)|^2 e^{-ix\tau+iyw}\, d\tau\, dw/2\pi = |\lambda(y, x)|^2. \tag{2.8}$$

To find a function $|\lambda(\tau, w)|$ possessing such a property, and having a form assuring good resolution besides, will be no easy task. Even if it can be found, one must still assign it such a phase arg $\lambda(\tau, w)$ that the function $|\lambda(\tau, w)|$ arg $\lambda(\tau, w) = \lambda(\tau, w)$ will be the ambiguity function of some signal $F(t)$. Only when the proper phase is known as well can the Fourier transform of $\lambda(\tau, w)$ with respect to w be taken to obtain

$$\int_{-\infty}^{\infty} \lambda(\tau, w)\, e^{iwu}\, dw/2\pi = F(u-\tfrac{1}{2}\tau)\, F^*(u+\tfrac{1}{2}\tau), \tag{2.9}$$

from which the signal envelope $F(t)$ can be found, within an arbitrary constant phase factor, by setting $u = \frac{1}{2}t$, $\tau = -t$, and normalizing as in eq. (2.2). Some further restrictions on the amplitude and phase of $\lambda(\tau, w)$, and on its real and imaginary parts, have been reported by Stutt (1964).

An informative corollary of the self-transform property in eq. (2.8) is derived by setting $x = 0$, $y = 0$,

$$\int_{-\infty}^{\infty}\int_{-\infty}^{\infty} |\lambda(\tau, w)|^2\, d\tau\, dw/2\pi = 1. \tag{2.10}$$

The total volume under the surface $|\lambda(\tau, w)|^2$ must be equal to 2π, no matter what the waveform of the signal. This condition prevents our making $|\lambda(\tau, w)|$ small everywhere in the (τ, w)-plane away from the origin. The magnitude $|\lambda(\tau, w)|$ will always have a peak over the point (0, 0), and if we try to make that peak more slender, the values of $|\lambda(\tau, w)|$ elsewhere in the (τ, w)-plane must rise in compensation. Much effort has been expended in searching for signals whose ambiguity function has a magnitude remaining below a specified level over as much of the (τ, w)-plane as possible.

(b) *Single Pulses*

The behavior of the ambiguity function near its peak at the origin can be discovered by expanding the integrand of eq. (2.4) into a double Taylor series in τ and w. Putting

$$F(t-\tfrac{1}{2}\tau) \doteq F(t)-\tfrac{1}{2}\tau F'(t)+\tfrac{1}{8}\tau^2 F''(t),$$
$$e^{-iwt} \doteq 1-iwt-\tfrac{1}{2}w^2t^2,$$

substituting into eq. (2.4), evaluating certain of the integrals in t by parts and using the definitions of the signal moments in Chapter I, Section 5, we obtain finally

$$\lambda(\tau, w) = 1-i\bar{\omega}\tau-i\bar{t}w-\tfrac{1}{2}\overline{\omega^2}\tau^2-\overline{\omega t}w\tau-\tfrac{1}{2}\overline{t^2}w^2, \tag{2.11}$$

and through quadratic terms the squared magnitude of the ambiguity function is

$$|\lambda(\tau, w)|^2 \doteq 1-(\Delta\omega^2\tau^2+2\,\Delta(\omega t)\,w\tau+\Delta t^2w^2), \tag{2.12}$$

where $\Delta\omega$ and Δt are the r.m.s. bandwidth and duration, and $\Delta(\omega t) = \overline{\omega t}-\bar{\omega}\bar{t}$ is the cross-moment of time and frequency, of the signal. Referring to eq. (I, 5.15) we see that for small values of τ and w the magnitude $|\lambda(\tau, -w)|$ is constant along contours similar to the uncertainty ellipse introduced there. Such an ellipse is sketched in Fig. I.7.

For the Gaussian pulse this similarity of the contours of constant magnitude $|\lambda(\tau, w)|$ holds for all values of τ and w. A signal whose complex envelope is

$$F(t) = (a^2/\pi)^{\frac{1}{4}} \exp\,[-(a^2-ib)\,t^2/2] \tag{2.13}$$

has an amplitude of the Gaussian shape proportional to $\exp(-a^2t^2/2)$ and an instantaneous frequency increasing linearly with time: $\phi'(t) = bt$ (cf. Chapter I, section 3). For this signal the ambiguity function has the magnitude

$$|\lambda(\tau, w)| = \exp\,\{-[(a^4+b^2)\,\tau^2-2b\tau w+w^2]/4a^2\}. \tag{2.14}$$

This function is constant along elliptical contours of the form

$$(a^4+b^2)\,\tau^2-2b\tau w+w^2]/4a^2 = \mu^2.$$

The area of each contour is equal to $4\pi\mu^2$, which is independent of the rate b of change of the instantaneous frequency. The effect of this linear frequency modulation on the pulse is only to rotate or shear the elliptical contours $|\lambda(\tau, w)| =$ constant without changing their area. An improvement in resolvability in one region due to the frequency modulation is accompanied by a deterioration in some other region.

In applications where negligible Doppler shifts are expected, it is only the behavior of the ambiguity function $\lambda(\tau, 0)$ along the τ-axis that is important; and this can be improved by making the rate b much greater than a^2. An advantage of the Gaussian signal is the absence of subsidiary peaks from its ambiguity function, which much reduces the risk of large errors in measuring its epoch and its frequency. Fowle *et al.* (1963) have extensively treated the generation and detection of the frequency-modulated Gaussian signal.

Linear frequency modulation found one of its first applications to the improvement of range resolution in the design of the "Chirp" radar (Klauder *et al.*, 1960). This radar transmits a rectangular pulse with a quadratic phase,

$$\begin{aligned} F(t) &= \exp(ibt^2/2), \qquad & -\tfrac{1}{2}T \leq t \leq \tfrac{1}{2}T, \\ &= 0, & |t| > \tfrac{1}{2}T, \end{aligned} \tag{2.15}$$

and the total phase change from beginning to end, $\frac{1}{4}bT^2$, is very large. The ambiguity function of this signal is

$$\begin{aligned} \lambda(\tau, w) &= \frac{2 \sin (b\tau + w)(T - |\tau|)/2}{(b\tau + w)\,T}, \qquad & |\tau| \leq T, \\ &= 0, & |\tau| > T. \end{aligned} \tag{2.16}$$

Resolution in range only is governed by the values along the τ-axis,

$$\lambda(\tau, 0) = \frac{2 \sin (b\tau T/2)}{b\tau T}, \qquad |\tau| \leq T, \tag{2.17}$$

a function that has a narrow peak at the origin $\tau = 0$. The width of this peak, measured between the first zeros, is $(2\pi/bT^2)T$, which when $bT^2 \gg 2\pi$ is much smaller than the duration T of the original signal.

This function $\lambda(\tau, 0)$ represents the output of a filter matched to the signal Rl $F(t)\, e^{i\Omega t}$ when only that signal is fed into it. Because it is much narrower when $bT^2 \gg 2\pi$ than the envelope of the signal itself, the matched filter is said to compress the pulse. Radars transmitting such frequency-modulated signals and receiving them with matched filters are called "pulse-compression" radars. The danger of high-voltage breakdown in the output circuitry of the transmitter limits the peak amplitude of a radar pulse, and the pulse-compression radar can send out signals of much greater total energy than one that simply produces a narrow amplitude-modulated pulse of the same r.m.s. bandwidth.

For certain combinations of delay τ and frequency shift w, however, the resolvability of the Chirp signal will be no better than that of an unmodulated rectangular pulse of the same duration T and the same energy. Along the line $w+b\tau = 0$, the ambiguity function of the Chirp signal is

$$\lambda(\tau, -b\tau) = (T-|\tau|)/T, \qquad |\tau| < T,$$

which is the same as the function $\lambda(\tau, 0)$ for the unmodulated pulse. As with the Gaussian signal, the frequency modulation displaces part of the volume under the ambiguity surface to a different part of the (τ, w)-plane. A Doppler-shifted Chirp signal can only with difficulty be distinguished from one that is merely delayed.

An instructive generalization of the Gaussian signal is the Hermite waveform whose complex envelope is, for any positive integer n,

$$F(t) = (a/n!)^{\frac{1}{2}}\pi^{-\frac{1}{4}} \exp(-a^2t^2/2)\, h_n\!\left(2^{-\frac{1}{2}}at\right), \tag{2.18}$$

where $h_n(x)$ is the Hermite polynomial defined in Chapter VII, Section 2(b). These signals have an oscillatory amplitude modulation, which changes sign n times before finally decaying to zero. Klauder (1960) and Wilcox (1960) showed that the ambiguity function of this signal is

$$\lambda(\tau, w) = \exp(-r^2/4)\, L_n(r^2/2), \qquad r^2 = (a^2\tau^2+a^{-2}w^2), \tag{2.19}$$

where $L_n(x)$ is the nth Laguerre polynomial, defined in Chapter I, Section 6. Around the central peak $|\lambda(\tau, w)|$ has elliptical ridges whose heights decrease from the center; between them are elliptical contours on which $\lambda(\tau, w) = 0$. Diagrams are to be found in the paper by Klauder (1960).

As n increases, the central peak of $|\lambda(\tau, w)|$ becomes narrower and narrower, but at the same time the r.m.s. bandwidth and the r.m.s. duration of the signals increase. Asymptotically for $n \gg 1$,†

$$\lambda(\tau, w) \sim J_0(r\sqrt{2n+1}), \qquad r = (a^2\tau^2+a^{-2}w^2)^{\frac{1}{2}},$$
$$0 < r \lesssim 2(2n+1)^{\frac{1}{2}}.$$

† A. Erdélyi *et al.* (1953), vol. 2, p. 199, eq. 10.15(2).

For large n, $\lambda(\tau, w)$ vanishes for values of τ and w on the ellipses

$$[(n+\tfrac{1}{2})(a^2\tau^2+a^{-2}w^2)]^{\frac{1}{2}} \cong 1.70,\ 3.90,\ 6.11,\ \ldots$$

The first elliptical ridge surrounding the central peak has a height of about 0.4, the one next to it a height of about 0.3. Far from the center the function $\lambda(\tau, w)$ is roughly sinusoidal, but with a slowly decreasing amplitude,

$$\lambda(\tau, w) \sim [2/(n+\tfrac{1}{2})\pi^2 r^2]^{\frac{1}{4}} \cos(r\sqrt{2n+1}-\tfrac{1}{4}\pi),$$
$$r = (a^2\tau^2+a^{-2}w^2)^{\frac{1}{2}}.$$

After n zeros, however, there is a final ridge, beyond which $\lambda(\tau, w)$ drops to zero. These ridges in $|\lambda(\tau, w)|$ render the signals liable to ambiguity in time and frequency.

These Hermite signals have r.m.s. bandwidths and durations given by

$$\Delta t^2 = (n+\tfrac{1}{2})\,a^{-2}, \qquad \Delta\omega^2 = (n+\tfrac{1}{2})\,a^2.$$

The central peak of their ambiguity function covers an area of about $9.1/(\Delta\omega\,\Delta t)$ for $n \gg 1$. The area of the (τ, w)-plane occupied by the entire ambiguity function, out to where it begins its final exponential descent to zero, is of the order of the product $\Delta\omega\,\Delta t$.

Indeed, it seems to be generally true for all amplitude-modulated signals that the area covered by the central peak is of the order of $(\Delta\omega\,\Delta t)^{-1}$, as is evident from eq. (2.12). The part of the ambiguity function significantly greater than zero covers an area of the order of $\Delta\omega\Delta t$, as can be deduced from the relations

$$\begin{aligned} \tfrac{1}{2}\iint \tau^2\,|\lambda(\tau, w)|^2\,d\tau\,dw/2\pi &= \Delta t^2, \\ \tfrac{1}{2}\iint w\tau\,|\lambda(\tau, w)|^2\,d\tau\,dw/2\pi &= -\Delta(\omega t), \\ \tfrac{1}{2}\iint w^2\,|\lambda(\tau, w)|^2\,d\tau\,dw/2\pi &= \Delta\omega^2, \end{aligned} \tag{2.20}$$

which can in turn be derived by making a power-series expansion of the exponential in the integrand of eq. (2.8) and applying eq. (2.12) to the right-hand side. For an amplitude-modulated pulse, for which $\Delta(\omega t) = 0$, the r.m.s. widths of the ambiguity function in τ and w are of the same order of magnitude as those of the signal itself in time and frequency. The product of these widths crudely measures the area of the entire ambiguity function.

In order for amplitude-modulated signals to provide good over-all resolution, therefore, they must have a large "time-bandwidth product"

$\Delta t\, \Delta\omega$. When $\Delta t\, \Delta\omega \gg 1$, the central peak of the ambiguity surface will be slender; and as the rest of the function takes up an area of the order of $\Delta t\, \Delta\omega$, $|\lambda(\tau, w)|$ cannot attain very large values outside the center and still meet the volume constraint given by eq. (2.10). The average level of $|\lambda(\tau, w)|$ in that region will be of the order of $(\Delta t\, \Delta\omega)^{-\frac{1}{2}}$.

It is not enough, however, to make $\Delta t\, \Delta\omega$ large by introducing frequency modulation. As Rihaczek (1965) emphasized, the areas in question then involve not $\Delta t\, \Delta\omega$, but

$$\{\Delta\omega^2 \Delta t^2 - [\Delta(\omega t)]^2\}^{\frac{1}{2}},$$

which also appears in the variances of the errors incurred in simultaneously measuring arrival time and frequency (eq. (VIII, 4.11)). Linear frequency modulation does not change this quantity at all; its only effect is to rotate or shear the ambiguity surface with respect to the τ- and w-axes. If signals might arrive with time and frequency separations anywhere in a broad area of the (τ, w)-plane, no over-all improvement of their resolution can be achieved in this way.

(c) *Pulse Trains*

(i) *The ambiguity function of a uniform train.* Thus far we have imagined the signal $F(t)$ as consisting of a single pulse. Certain radars, however, transmit a sequence of coherent pulses, constraining their phases to have a definite, known relationship to each other. Let us suppose that a train of M such coherent pulses $F_0(t)$ of equal amplitudes is received from a target, and let us study the form of its ambiguity function $\lambda(\tau, w)$. We shall assume that successive pulses overlap to a negligible degree. If we take the complex envelope of the signal as

$$F(t) = M^{-\frac{1}{2}} \sum_{k=1}^{M} F_0(t-kT_r), \qquad \int |F_0(t)|^2\, dt = 1, \tag{2.21}$$

where T_r is the repetition period between the pulses, the composite signal will be normalized to 1 as in eq. (2.2).

To calculate the ambiguity function we take the time delay in the range $[(p-\frac{1}{2})T_r, (p+\frac{1}{2})T_r]$, with p a positive integer or 0, and we put $\tau = \tau_0 + pT_r$, so that $|\tau_0| < \frac{1}{2}T_r$. There are then $(M-p)$ pulses in one train overlapping as many in the other; the kth pulse of one group overlaps the $(k+p)$th of the other. The ambiguity function becomes

$$\lambda(\tau, w) = M^{-1} \sum_{k=1}^{M} \sum_{k'=1}^{M} \int F_0(t-\tfrac{1}{2}\tau-kT_r)\, F_0^*(t+\tfrac{1}{2}\tau-k'T_r)\, e^{-iwt}\, dt$$

$$= M^{-1} \sum_{k=1}^{M} \sum_{k'=1}^{M} F_0(s-\tfrac{1}{2}\tau_0)\, F_0^*(s+\tfrac{1}{2}\tau_0+(p+k-k')\,T_r) \exp\big[-iw\cdot$$

$$(s+\tfrac{1}{2}pT_r+kT_r)\big]\, ds = M^{-1}\lambda_0(\tau_0, w) \sum_{k=1}^{M-p} \exp\big[-iw(\tfrac{1}{2}pT_r+kT_r)\big]$$

$$= M^{-1}\lambda_0(\tau_0, w) \exp\big[-i(\tfrac{1}{2}p+1)\, wT_r\big] \frac{1-\exp\,[-i(M-p)wT_r]}{1-\exp\,(-iwT_r)},$$

where $\lambda_0(\tau, w)$ is the ambiguity function of the individual pulses $F_0(t)$. Taking the absolute value of this expression, we find

$$|\lambda(\tau, w)| = \left| \frac{\sin\,(M-|p|)\, wT_r/2}{M \sin\,(wT_r/2)} \right| \cdot |\lambda_0(\tau-pT_r, w)|,$$

$$(p-\tfrac{1}{2})\, T_r < \tau < (p+\tfrac{1}{2})\, T_r, \qquad -M < p < M, \tag{2.22}$$

where now the integer p can be positive, negative, or zero. In particular,

$$|\lambda(pT_r, 0)| = 1-|p|/M, \qquad -M < p < M. \tag{2.23}$$

Along the τ-axis ($w = 0$) the ambiguity function consists of repetitions of the function $|\lambda_0(\tau, 0)|$ for the component pulses, with $(M-1)$ peaks on one side of the origin, $(M-1)$ on the other, and one in the center. The heights of these peaks decrease to each side, as given in eq. (2.23). The reason for this behavior is easily seen. Sets of pulses received separated in time by small multiples of the period T_r overlap, except for the pulses at the beginning of one train and at the end of the other. To resolve these composite signals, a receiver must use those pulses that do not overlap; and the more of them there are—the larger the index p—the more reliable is the resolution of the signal trains.

In the frequency (w-) direction the width of the peak of the ambiguity function $|\lambda_0(\tau, w)|$ of the component pulses $F_0(t)$ is of the order of $(\Delta_0 t)^{-1}$, where $\Delta_0 t$ is the r.m.s. duration of $F_0(t)$. As we have taken $T_r \gg \Delta_0 t$, $(\Delta_0 t)^{-1} \gg T_r^{-1}$. The factor with the sines multiplying $|\lambda_0(\tau-pT_r, w)|$ in eq. (2.22) breaks up this peak of $|\lambda_0(\tau-pT_r, w)|$ into a succession of narrower peaks having widths of the order of $2\pi/(M-|p|)T_r$ and spaced by $2\pi/T_r$. These peaks resemble the amplitude pattern of light reflected from a diffraction grating.

We fix our attention on the central set of peaks ($p = 0$) of the function $|\lambda(\tau, w)|$, for which the multiplying factor is

$$\left| \frac{\sin (MwT_r/2)}{M \sin (wT_r/2)} \right|.$$

This factor reaches a value of 1 whenever $w = 2k\pi/T_r$, k an integer, producing a peak whose width is of the order of $2\pi/MT_r$. Between the tall peaks are a number of ripples whose height is lower by a factor of M^{-1}. This "diffraction pattern" is superimposed on the original function $|\lambda_0(\tau, w)|$, breaking it up into many narrow peaks of width $2\pi/MT_r$ and period $2\pi/T_r$, both of which are much smaller than the width $(\Delta_0 t)^{-1}$ of $\lambda_0(\tau, w)$ in the w-direction. The r.m.s. duration of the signal is now of the order of $\Delta t \cong MT_r$, and the area of the (τ, w)-plane covered by the central peak of the ambiguity function is again of the order of $(\Delta t\, \Delta\omega)^{-1}$. The entire ambiguity function occupies a total area of about $\Delta t\, \Delta\omega$.

The breaking up of $|\lambda_0(\tau, w)|$ into peaks and valleys in the w-direction indicates that trains of pulses can be more effectively resolved in frequency than single pulses of the same total energy. This can be understood by observing that the coherent repetition M times of the pulse $F_0(t)$ causes its spectrum $f_0(\omega)$ to divide into a line spectrum. The lines are separated by $2\pi/T_r$, and their widths are about $2\pi/MT_r$. If the Doppler shifts due to the motions of the radar targets are such that these line spectra for the echoes interlace, filters can be constructed to resolve the signals with high probability. If the relative velocity of the targets is such that the shift w is an integral multiple of the repetition period, $w = 2k\pi/T_r$, on the other hand, the line spectra will overlap and resolution will be difficult unless the signals are far enough apart in time.

The measurement of the velocity of an isolated target, by estimating the Doppler shift of its radar echoes as described in Chapter VIII, can be made more accurately by utilizing a train of coherent pulses in place of a single pulse. However, the behavior of the function $|\lambda(\tau, w)|$ indicates that ambiguity will be introduced into the results, frequencies differing by multiples of $2\pi/T_r$ becoming indistinguishable. For a repetition period $T_r = 10^{-3}$ sec and a carrier frequency $\Omega_0 = 2\pi \cdot 3 \cdot 10^9$ sec^{-1} (3000 MHz), the ambiguity in target velocity amounts to $\Delta v = c/[2(\Omega_0/2\pi)T_r] = 112$ m.p.h., where c is the velocity of light.

The origin of this ambiguity is easily understood. Since the transmitted pulses are coherent, the receiver can measure the change in phase of the r.f. carrier from one reflected pulse to the next by comparing the phases of the echoes with that of a local oscillator synchronized with the transmitted phase. If a target with a velocity v moves a distance $d = vT_r$ in a pulse-repetition period, the r.f. phase of the carrier will change by an amount $\Delta\phi = \Omega_0(2d/c)$. The target velocity is then given by $v = (\Delta\phi/\Omega_0)(c/2T_r)$. As the receiver cannot distinguish phase changes differing by multiples of 2π, an ambiguity in the true velocity of some multiple of $(2\pi/\Omega_0)(c/2T_r)$ arises.

(ii) *The clear area.* If it is only the resolution of very close targets that is of concern, the best signal is one whose ambiguity function $|\lambda(\tau, w)|$ has as slender a central peak as possible, outside of which the function must take on the lowest possible values. We now know that a long train of narrow pulses has these properties. The area A_c occupied by the central peak is inversely proportional to the number M of pulses in the train,

$$A_c \sim 2\pi/MT_r\Delta_0\omega,$$

where T_r is the pulse repetition period and where $\Delta_0\omega$, the r.m.s. bandwidth of the component pulses, measures the width of their ambiguity function $|\lambda_0(\tau, w)|$ along the τ-axis. The level of the ambiguity function $|\lambda(\tau, w)|$ between the central peak and the adjacent peaks is of the order of M^{-1}, and by taking M large enough both this level and the area A_c can be made as small as desired.

The peaks nearest to the central one are separated from it by T_r along the τ-axis and by $2\pi/T_r$ along the w-axis. The area of the (τ, w)-plane over which $|\lambda(\tau, w)|$ can be made arbitrarily small is, therefore, of the order of $(2T_r)(4\pi/T_r) = 8\pi$. The question whether this so-called "clear area" can be made any broader by judicious choice of the signal waveform $F(t)$ has been answered in the negative by Price and Hofstetter (1965), who worked out bounds on the size of clear areas of various shapes.

(iii) *Non-uniform pulse trains.* With a long uniform pulse train the (τ, w)-plane is studded with a great many narrow peaks whose heights near the origin are almost equal to 1, and ambiguities abound. The first step that has been taken in trying to suppress them is to vary the relative phases of the pulses. The signal in eq. (2.21) is replaced by

$$F(t) = M^{-\frac{1}{2}} \sum_{k=1}^{M} a_k F_0(t-kT_r), \qquad \sum_{k=1}^{M} |a_k|^2 = M, \tag{2.24}$$

with the component pulses $F_0(t)$ normalized as before and assumed not to overlap. The amplitude factors a_k are complex; when only the relative phases are being altered, their absolute values $|a_k|$ equal 1. Instead of eq. (2.22) one now finds for the ambiguity function of the pulse train

$$|\lambda(\tau, w)| = \sum_{p=-(M-1)}^{M-1} |\lambda_0(\tau - pT_r, w)| \, C_p(wT_r),$$

$$C_p(x) = M^{-1} \left| \sum_{k=1}^{M-|p|} a_k a^*_{k+|p|} \, e^{-ikx} \right|, \qquad -M < p < M, \tag{2.25}$$

$$C_0(0) = 1.$$

If no Doppler shifts w greater than a fraction of $2\pi/T_r$ are expected, the designer needs to be concerned mainly with the behavior of the M quantities

$$C_p(0) = M^{-1} \left| \sum_{k=1}^{M-|p|} a_k a^*_{k+|p|} \right|,$$

which represent the convolution or "autocorrelation" of the sequence a_k with itself. The simplest choices for the a_k's are the numbers $+1$ and -1. In discussing the synchronization of long trains of pulses in a binary communication system, Barker (1953) recommended the use of sequences of M positive and negative pulses for whose amplitudes a_k

$$C_0(0) = 1, \quad C_p(0) \leq M^{-1}, \quad p \neq 0,$$

and he exhibited a number of such sequences. One of length 5 having this property is $+1, +1, +1, -1, +1$, for which

$$C_0 = 1, \quad C_1 = 0, \quad C_2 = \tfrac{1}{5}, \quad C_3 = 0, \quad C_4 = \tfrac{1}{5}.$$

It is very difficult to find long sequences with such an advantageous autocorrelation. In fact, Storer and Turyn (1961) showed that there exists none of odd length M greater than 13. The Barker sequence of length 13 is

$$+1,\ +1,\ +1,\ +1,\ +1,\ -1,\ -1,\ +1,\ +1,\ -1,\ +1,\ -1,\ +1.$$

Golomb and Scholtz (1965) have studied "generalized Barker sequences" in which the a_k's are the nth roots of 1, that is, powers of $e^{2\pi i/n}$, for integers n. They tabulated a number of these for various values of n and M, and for small values of M they stated for which integers n generalized Barker sequences exist.

If Doppler shifts w much larger than $2\pi/T_r$ may occur, one must investigate the functions $C_p(x)$ for all values of x in the interval $(0, 2\pi)$, which is their basic period. The pattern $C_p(0)$ of peak heights along the τ-axis will be repeated along all lines $w = 2\pi m/T_r$ parallel to the τ-axis, for positive and negative integers m. Even with Barker sequences, $C_p(x)$ may rise above the level M^{-1} for values of x between 0 and 2π. Indeed

$$\sum_{p=-(M-1)}^{M-1} \int_0^{2\pi} |C_p(x)|^2\, dx/2\pi = 1,$$

which indicates that $C_p(x)$ can be expected to reach heights of the order of $M^{-\frac{1}{2}}$ on the average.

Other sequences of amplitudes a_k investigated include trains of $+1$'s and -1's that can be generated by a binary shift register, particularly sequences of maximal length 2^n-1, where n is the number of stages in the shift register (Zierler, 1959). A bibliography of these studies has been given by Lerner (1963). Little seems to have been done with sequences a_k of non-uniform magnitudes $|a_k|$. In general, there is no way of finding a sequence $\{a_k\}$ whose functions $C_p(x)$ will have a specified set of properties. The most one can usually do is try a set of a_k's, compute $C_p(x)$ for $p = 0, 1, \ldots, M-1$ at a number of values of x in $(0, 2\pi)$, and see what it looks like.

The artifice of staggering the epochs and frequencies of the component pulses of the train has been treated by Rihaczek (1964). The usual result is that the clear area becomes filled, and the ambiguity function outside the central peak takes on a jagged structure with an average level of the order of $(\Delta t \Delta\omega)^{-\frac{1}{2}}$. Over-all resolution deteriorates. By reducing the heights of the outstanding peaks away from the origin, however, the risk of ambiguities—large errors in the measurement of carrier frequency and arrival time—is diminished.

3. THE DETECTION OF SIGNALS IN CLUTTER

(a) *The Spectrum of Clutter Interference*

A radar system is often called upon to detect a target echo in the presence of a great many other echoes from raindrops or from the surface of the ground or the sea. Interference of this kind is known as "clutter". In wartime strips of metal foil known as "chaff" or "window" are dropped from airplanes to confuse enemy radar by creating a similar interference. The reverberation encountered in sonar is another type of clutter. The task of a radar subjected to clutter might be considered as the resolution of a wanted signal from a number of undesirable ones that overlap it in time and frequency.

However, since the parameters of the extraneous signals are unpredictable, it is more convenient to view the clutter as a type of noise. An apt model pictures the clutter as composed of reflections of the transmitted pulse from a large number of small dispersed scatterers. Since the net voltage they produce at the receiver input is the sum of a large number of weak, random voltages, it can be described by a Gaussian distribution. Methods developed earlier for detecting a signal in colored Gaussian noise can be applied to finding the optimum detection system, which in turn can be analyzed to determine the probability of detection as a function of the strength and distribution of the clutter.

This clutter noise is not stationary, for the density of scatterers within the transmitted beam varies with the distance, and the total power they reflect is not uniform. However, because the density and other characteristics of the scatterers usually change only slightly over a distance of the order of several radar pulse lengths, the detectability of an echo signal in the midst of the clutter will be nearly the same as if the clutter had at all times the same statistical properties as in the vicinity of the signal. We can therefore treat the clutter as though it were stationary. As it is Gaussian and has zero mean, its probability density functions depend only on its spectral density.

If the scatterers are all at rest with respect to the transmitter, the composite echo signal takes the form Rl $S(t)\,e^{i\Omega t}$, where

$$S(t) = \sum_n z_n F(t-t_n). \tag{3.1}$$

Here $F(t)$ is the complex envelope of the narrowband transmitted pulse, z_n a complex number specifying the amplitude and phase of the nth echo, and t_n the epoch of the nth echo. We suppose the envelope $F(t)$ normalized as usual,

$$\int_{-\infty}^{\infty} |F(t)|^2\, dt = 1. \tag{3.2}$$

The z_n's and the t_n's are random variables independent from one scattering to another. The echo pulses arrive at a finite average rate, producing clutter with a finite average power equal, say, to P_c. As we learned in Chapter II, Section 3, noise of this kind has a spectral density proportional to the absolute square of the spectrum

$$f(\omega) = \int_{-\infty}^{\infty} F(t)\, e^{-i\omega t}\, dt \tag{3.3}$$

of each pulse. Hence the spectral density of the clutter is

$$\Psi(\omega) = \tilde{\Psi}(\omega-\Omega)+\tilde{\Psi}(\omega+\Omega), \tag{3.4}$$

where $\tilde{\Psi}(\omega)$ is the positive-frequency part of the spectral density as measured from the carrier frequency Ω, and

$$\tilde{\Psi}(\omega) = \tfrac{1}{2} P_c \,|f(\omega)|^2. \tag{3.5}$$

Usually the scatterers are not all at rest with respect to the transmitter. The transmitter may be on a moving airplane, and the scatterers may themselves be moving erratically, as when trees, bushes, and sea spray are blown about by the wind. In most cases the effect of such motions can be expressed by a convolution,

$$\tilde{\Psi}(\omega) = \tfrac{1}{2} \int_{-\infty}^{\infty} \Pi_c(w)\,|f(\omega - w)|^2 \,dw/2\pi, \tag{3.6}$$

where $\Pi_c(w)\,dw/2\pi$ is the power in the clutter reflected by scatterers inducing a frequency shift in an interval of width $dw/2\pi$ about the frequency $w/2\pi$. The total clutter power is

$$P_c = \int_{-\infty}^{\infty} \Pi_c(w)\,dw/2\pi. \tag{3.7}$$

For clutter due to reflections from wind-blown vegetation, the width of the distribution $\Pi_c(w)$ has been observed to be inversely proportional to the wavelength of the transmitted pulses. The product of this width and the wavelength is of the order of a few centimeters or tens of centimeters per second. Further details of the characteristics of clutter are to be found in Lawson and Uhlenbeck (1950), George (1952), McGinn and Pike (1960), and Skolnik (1962).

The complex autocovariance function $\tilde{\varphi}(\tau)$ of the clutter is the Fourier transform of $2\tilde{\Psi}(\omega)$, as in eq. (II, 6.3). Since eq. (3.6) has the form of a convolution, its Fourier transform is simply a product,

$$\tilde{\varphi}(\tau) = \lambda(\tau, 0)\, p_c(\tau), \tag{3.8}$$

where

$$\begin{aligned} \lambda(\tau, 0) &= \int_{-\infty}^{\infty} F(t - \tfrac{1}{2}\tau)\, F^*(t + \tfrac{1}{2}\tau)\,dt, \\ p_c(\tau) &= \int_{-\infty}^{\infty} \Pi_c(w)\, e^{-iwt}\,dw/2\pi, \qquad p_c(0) = P_c. \end{aligned} \tag{3.9}$$

Thus the complex autocovariance function of the clutter is the product of the ambiguity function $\lambda(\tau, 0)$ of the transmitted pulse and the Fourier transform of the density $\Pi_c(w)$ of the frequency shifts.

(b) *Detection of Single Pulses in Clutter*

Let the echo signal be represented by

$$s(t) = A \,\mathrm{Rl}\, F_s(t-\tau)\, e^{i\Omega t+i\phi}, \tag{3.10}$$

where A and ϕ are its unknown amplitude and phase, τ its epoch, and $F_s(t)$ its complex envelope, normalized as in eq. (3.2). If the signal is a version of the transmitted pulse with the Doppler shift w, as we shall generally presume here, $F_s(t) = F(t)e^{iwt}$.

We suppose that the receiver is working only with the return from a single transmitted pulse and is detecting echoes individually. The spreading of the spectral density given by eq. (3.6) can then be neglected, for the distribution $\Pi_c(w)$ is much narrower than the spectrum $f(\omega)$ of most radar pulses. By adopting as our reference carrier frequency Ω that of the clutter echoes, we can write the spectral density of the clutter as in eqs. (3.4) and (3.5). In addition to the clutter, the input to the receiver will contain white noise of unilateral spectral density N. As we said in Chapter II, Section 6, the white noise can be treated as narrowband noise whose spectral density is uniform over the range of frequencies occupied by the signal. Hence, the narrowband spectral density of the total input noise is

$$\tilde{\Phi}(\omega) = \tfrac{1}{2}N + \tilde{\Psi}(\omega) = \tfrac{1}{2}[N + P_c\,|f(\omega)|^2]. \tag{3.11}$$

As the arrival time of the signal is unknown, we employ the maximum likelihood detection strategy developed in Chapter IX. The input to the receiver is passed through a filter matched to a signal whose complex envelope is

$$\begin{aligned} Q(t) &= \int_{-\infty}^{\infty} q_s(\omega)\, e^{i\omega t}\, d\omega/2\pi, \\ q_s(\omega) &= f_s(\omega)/2\tilde{\Phi}(\omega) = [N + P_c\,|f(\omega)|^2]^{-1} f_s(\omega), \end{aligned} \tag{3.12}$$

where $f_s(\omega)$ is the Fourier transform of the signal envelope $F_s(t)$. The narrowband impulse response of the filter is

$$\begin{aligned} k(\tau) &= Q^*(T'-\tau), \qquad 0 < \tau < 2T', \\ &= 0, \qquad \tau < 0, \quad \tau > 2T', \end{aligned} \tag{3.13}$$

where T' is a delay long enough for the interval $-T' < t < T'$ to include most of the envelope $Q(t)$,

$$|Q(t)| \ll \max_{t'} |Q(t')|, \qquad |t| > T', \qquad -\infty < t' < \infty. \tag{3.14}$$

The output of this matched filter is rectified and compared with a decision level, which when surpassed indicates the presence of a signal.

If the delay T' is very long, the matched filter has for its complex narrow-›and transfer function $y(\omega)$, defined in Section 4 of Chapter I,

$$y(\omega) = q_s(\omega)\, e^{-i\omega T'} = [N+P_c\,|f(\omega)|^2]^{-1} f_s^*(\omega)\, e^{-i\omega T'}. \qquad (3.15)$$

[he spectrum of the echo pulse as it issues from the matched filter is

$$f_o(\omega) = A[N+P_c\,|f(\omega)|^2]^{-1}\,|f_s(\omega)|^2\, e^{-i\omega(T'+\tau)+i\phi}, \qquad (3.16)$$

vith frequencies still measured from the carrier frequency of the clutter.

In the situation least favorable for detection the target moves with the ame relative velocity as the scatterers, there is no relative frequency shift $w = 0$), and $f_s(\omega) = f(\omega)$. The amplitude $|f_o(\omega)|$ of the output spectrum is hen nearly constant for frequencies so near the carrier that ω is less than a 'cut-off frequency" ω_c given roughly by

$$P_c\,|f(\omega_c)|^2 \cong N.$$

We suppose the pulse spectrum symmetrical, $|f(\omega)| = |f(-\omega)|$, for sim-›licity.) At frequencies far from the carrier, for which $|\omega| > \omega_c$, the output pectrum $|f_o(\omega)|$ drops off to zero. The stronger the clutter power P_c com-›ared with the product of N and the bandwidth $\Delta\omega$ of the signal, the larger he cut-off frequency ω_c. The width of the output pulse $F_o(t)$ from the natched filter will be of the order of $2\pi/\omega_c$ and much smaller than $2\pi/\Delta\omega$, he approximate width of the echo signal. Thus the effect of the matched ilter in eq. (3.13) is to sharpen the returning echo pulses as much as pos-ible without too greatly enhancing the output resulting from the white ıoise. It is hoped that the signal echo will then stand out over the smaller choes due to the clutter.

The filter specified by eq. (3.15) for a signal with $w = 0$ is quite similar o the filters proposed by Urkowitz (1953), for which $y(\omega)$ equaled $[f(\omega)]^{-1}$ or $|\omega|$ less than a fixed cut-off frequency, beyond which $y(\omega)$ vanished. [he cut-off frequency was taken large enough to sharpen the signal pulses .s much as possible, yet not so large that the white noise generates an ex-essive output.

The performance of a detection system of this kind is described by its alse-alarm and detection probabilities, which can be calculated as in [hapter IX, Section 2. They are approximately

$$\begin{aligned} Q_0 &\cong (2\pi)^{-\frac{1}{2}}\beta T b \exp(-b^2/2), \\ Q_d &\cong Q(d, b), \end{aligned} \qquad (3.17)$$

vhere $Q(d, b)$ is Marcum's Q-function, b is proportional to the decision evel, T is the length of the observation interval, d is the signal-to-noise ratio, given by

$$d^2 = 2E \int_{-\infty}^{\infty} [N+P_c|f(\omega)|^2]^{-1}|f_s(\omega)|^2\, d\omega/2\pi, \tag{3.18}$$

and β is a bandwidth defined by

$$\beta^2 = \overline{\omega^2} - \bar{\omega}^2,$$
$$\overline{\omega^n} = \int_{-\infty}^{\infty} \omega^n |f_s(\omega)|^2 [\tilde{\Phi}(\omega)]^{-1}\, d\omega \Big/ \int_{-\infty}^{\infty} |f_s(\omega)|^2 [\tilde{\Phi}(\omega)]^{-1}\, d\omega. \tag{3.19}$$

This bandwidth will exist only if $|f_s(\omega)|^2$ decreases to 0 more rapidly than $|\omega|^{-3}$ as $|\omega| \to \infty$. In eq. (3.18) $E = \frac{1}{2}A^2$ is the signal energy, the normalization in eq. (3.2) being maintained.

For a fixed false-alarm probability, the probability of detection depends most strongly on the signal-to-noise ratio d given by eq. (3.18). If one alters the shape of the transmitted pulses, or even the transmitted power, to which P_c is proportional, the bandwidth β, and hence also the quantity b in eq. (3.17), must change. However, this variation in b has a much smaller effect on Q_d than the accompanying change in the signal-to-noise ratio d.

Let us study further the detectability of an echo with the same frequency as the clutter ($w = 0$). When $P_c \gg N\Delta\omega$, the integrand in eq. (3.18) is nearly constant for $|\omega| < \omega_c$, where again $P_c|f(\omega_c)|^2 \cong N$. For $|\omega| > \omega_c$ the integrand drops to zero. Therefore, the signal-to-noise ratio d is roughly given by

$$d^2 \cong (2E/P_c)\omega_c/\pi.$$

With both the signal energy E and the average clutter power P_c proportional to the power output P_t of the transmitter, the signal-to-noise ratio d depends on P_t only through the value of ω_c. If, for instance, $|f(\omega)|$ is proportional to $|\omega|^{-n}$ for large values of $|\omega|$, $|f(\omega)| \sim C_1|\omega|^{-n}$, we see from the equation

$$|C_1|^2 P_c |\omega_c|^{-2n} \cong N$$

that ω_c is proportional to $P_c^{1/2n}$, and hence to $P_t^{1/2n}$. The signal-to-noise ratio d determining signal detectability through eq. (3.17) is therefore proportional to $P_t^{1/4n}$. The larger n, the smaller the influence of a mere increase of transmitter power on the probability of detection.

If the detectability of the signal is to be nearly independent of the clutter power P_c, as eq. (3.18) shows, the relative frequency shift w must be great enough for $|f_s(\omega)|^2 = |f(\omega - w)|^2$ to have significant values only where $|f(\omega)|^2$ is very small. The spectra of signal and clutter should overlap as little as possible.

It is difficult in practice to use this maximum-likelihood detector because the clutter power P_c is not constant, but varies in time through the variation with distance of the density of the random scatterers. Since this variation is small in a time of the order of a pulse width, one can envision a system using a time-varying filter so designed that at each instant it is matched to the signal $Q(t)$, eq. (3.12), for the current value of P_c. Such a filter might be difficult to construct. An alternative is a set of many filters, each matched to $Q(t)$ for a particular value of P_c. The receiver would measure the clutter power independently and by switching arrange to use the filter matched for the nearest value of P_c.

(c) *Detection of Pulse Trains in Clutter*

Our remarks at the end of Section 2 lead us to believe that a long train of coherent pulses will be detectable in the midst of their own clutter for a smaller relative frequency shift w than required by a single pulse. The spectrum $f(\omega)$ of such a train with repetition period T_r consists of a series of narrow "lines" separated by $2\pi/T_r$. The width of each line is inversely proportional to the length of the train. For a sequence of M rectangular pulses of width T_p, for instance,

$$|f(\omega)|^2 = \frac{4 \sin^2 \frac{1}{2}\omega T_p}{M T_p \omega^2} \cdot \frac{\sin^2 \frac{1}{2} M\omega T_r}{\sin^2 \frac{1}{2}\omega T_r}. \tag{3.20}$$

The first factor on the right-hand side has a width in ω of the order of $2\pi/T_p \gg 2\pi/T_r$ and modulates the array of peaks standing at integral values of $2\pi/T_r$.

The clutter spectrum $\Psi(\omega)$ from such a coherent train will have a similar line structure. The widths of the lines will be of the order of either $2\pi/MT_r$ or the width of the distribution $\Pi_c(w)$, whichever is the greater. The relative frequency shift w between the echo signal and the clutter needs only to be large enough for their line spectra to stand clear of each other.

The narrowband transfer function $y(\omega)$ of the matched filter is now given by

$$y(\omega) = [N+2\Psi(\omega)]^{-1} f_s^*(\omega) e^{-i\omega T'} \tag{3.21}$$

when the delay T' is long. Here both $f_s^*(\omega)$ and $\Psi(\omega)$ have the line structure just described. The first factor in $y(\omega)$ can be realized approximately, when the clutter is strong, by a filter having a series of narrow stop-bands about the frequencies of the lines of the clutter spectrum. The widths of these stop-bands will be roughly equal to the widths of the spectral lines. Following this filter there will be a second one matched to the signal $F_s(t)$. It will be a "comb filter" with narrow pass-bands about the lines of the signal spectrum. As long as the shift w of the signal frequency with respect to the clutter frequencies is greater than the sum of the widths of the spectral lines of signal and clutter, the effective signal-to-noise ratio for detection will be approximately $(2E/N)^{\frac{1}{2}}$. If the shift w is unknown in advance, a bank of parallel filters, each matched to a signal with one of a dense set of frequency shifts w, can be provided. Only targets moving with the "blind velocities" relative to the scatterers will be effectively concealed by the clutter.

A stationary radar must filter out of the input to its receiver the transmitted carrier frequency and all angular frequencies differing from it by multiples of $2\pi/T_r$, at least over the range of expected Doppler shifts. One way of doing this is to pass the input through a delay line that retards it by T_r seconds, and to subtract the delayed input from the current input. The effective narrowband transfer function of this system is proportional to $y_1(\omega) = 1 - \exp(-i\omega T_r)$. For ω any multiple of $2\pi/T_r$, $y_1(\omega) = 0$. Signals having other frequency shifts will be passed by this filter, although with some attenuation. Such delay-line cancellation schemes are used in so-called "MTI" (moving-target indication) radars (Lawson and Uhlenbeck, 1950; Skolnik, 1962). The clutter echoes, which are nearly the same from pulse to pulse, are canceled by subtracting the delayed input; echoes from targets moving with speeds between the blind velocities are passed on to the indicator circuits. The relationship between such a scheme and the optimum detector has been treated by Wainstein and Zubakov (1962).

PROBLEMS

1. Calculate the ambiguity function $\lambda(\tau, w)$ for the signal

$$F(t) = (2\mu)^{-\frac{1}{2}} e^{-\mu t}, \quad t > 0; \qquad F(t) = 0, \quad t < 0.$$

2. Show that for signals of equal energies arriving in white Gaussian noise at known times separated by τ, the signal energy required to decide with given error probabilities which is present is proportional to $(\Delta\omega^2\tau^2)^{-1}$ for small values of τ.

3. Verify eqs. (1.30) and (1.36).

4. Prove Siebert's self-transform property, eq. (2.8).

5. Derive eq. (2.20) from the self-transform property.

6. Derive and sketch the absolute value of the Fourier transform $f(\omega)$ of the Chirp signal, eq. (2.15), for $bT^2 \ll 1$ and for $bT^2 \gg 1$. Verify eq. (2.16). Why is eq. (2.12) invalid for this signal?

7. For the thirteen-element Barker sequence on p. 364 calculate the autocorrelations $C_p(0)$ and $C_p(\pi)$ by eq. (2.25).

8. For a radar transmitted pulse of the form

$$F(t) = Cte^{-\mu t}, \quad t > 0; \qquad F(t) = 0, \quad t < 0,$$

calculate the signal-to-noise ratio d and the bandwidth β for detection in clutter, using the formulas in Section 3. Allow an arbitrary frequency shift w. For $w = 0$, describe the dependence of the signal-to-noise ratio on the transmitted power.

9. What is the dependence of the bandwidth β in eq. (3.19) on the transmitted power P_t when $P_c \gg N\,\Delta\omega$?

10. Define the cross-ambiguity function $\lambda_{12}(\tau, w)$ for signals with complex envelopes $F_1(t)$ and $F_2(t)$ by

$$\lambda_{12}(\tau, w) = \int_{-\infty}^{\infty} F_1(t-\tfrac{1}{2}\tau)\, F_2^*(t+\tfrac{1}{2}\tau)e^{-iwt}\, dt.$$

Prove the relation

$$\int_{-\infty}^{\infty}\int_{-\infty}^{\infty} \lambda_{12}(\tau-\delta, \phi+\lambda)\, \lambda_{34}^*(\tau+\delta, \phi-\lambda)e^{i(\tau y-\phi x)}\, d\tau\, \frac{d\phi}{2\pi}$$

$$= \lambda_{13}(x-\delta, y+\lambda)\, \lambda_{24}^*(x+\delta, y-\lambda).$$

Show how to obtain eq. (2.8) from this. What does the above relation become for $F_1(t) = F_2(t) = F_3(t) = F_4(t) = F(t)$ when $x = y = 0$? (Titlebaum, 1966).

BIBLIOGRAPHY (X)

1950 DWORK, B. M., "The Detection of a Pulse Superposed on Fluctuation Noise", *Proc. I.R.E.* **38**, 771–4 (July).

LAWSON, J. L. and UHLENBECK, G. E., *Threshold Signals*, McGraw-Hill Book Co., New York, N.Y.

1952 GEORGE, T. S., "Fluctuations of Ground Clutter Return in Airborne Radar Equipment", *Proc. I.E.E.* **99** (IV), 92–99 (Apr.).

1953 BARKER, R. H., "Group Synchronizing of Binary Digital Systems", in *Communication Theory*, W. JACKSON, ed., Butterworths Scientific Publications, London, England, pp. 273–87.

ERDÉLYI, A. *et al.*, *Higher Transcendental Functions*, 2 vols., McGraw-Hill Book Co., New York, N.Y.

URKOWITZ, H., "Filters for Detection of Small Radar Signals in Clutter", *J. Appl. Phys.* **24**, 1024–32 (Aug.).

WOODWARD, P. M., *Probability and Information Theory, with Applications to Radar*, McGraw-Hill Book Co., New York, N.Y., Pergamon Press Ltd., London, England.

1955 HELSTROM, C. W., "The Resolution of Signals in White, Gaussian Noise", *Proc. I.R.E.* **43**, 1111–18 (Sept.).

1956 SIEBERT, W. M., "A Radar Detection Philosophy", *Trans. I.R.E.* **IT-2**, 204–21 (Sept.).

1957 HELSTROM, C. W., *The Resolution of Pulsed Signals*, Westinghouse Research Labs., Pittsburgh, Pa., Report No. 8-1259-R6 (July 18).

1958 LERNER, R. M., "Signals with Uniform Ambiguity Functions", *I.R.E. Natl. Convention Record*, pt. 4, 27–36.

SIEBERT, W. M., "Studies of Woodward's Uncertainty Function", *M.I.T. Res. Lab. of Electronics, Quart. Rept.*, 90–94 (Apr.).

1959 STUTT, C. A., "A Note on Invariant Relations for Ambiguity and Distance Functions", *Trans. I.R.E.* **IT-5**, 164–7 (Dec.).

ZIERLER, N., "Linear Recurring Sequences", *J. Soc. Ind. Appl. Math.* **7,** 31–48 (Mar.).

1960 KLAUDER, J. R., "The Design of Radar Signals having both High Range Resolution and High Velocity Resolution", *Bell Sys. Tech. J.* **39,** 809–19 (July).

KLAUDER, J. R., PRICE, A. C., DARLINGTON, S. and ALBERSHEIM, W. J., "The Theory and Design of Chirp Radars", *Bell Sys. Tech. J.* **39,** 745–808 (July).

McGINN, J. W., Jr. and PIKE, E. W., "A Study of Sea Clutter Spectra", in *Statistical Methods of Radio Wave Propagation*, W. C. HOFFMAN, ed., Pergamon Press Ltd., London, England, pp. 49–92.

WILCOX, C. H., *The Synthesis Problem for Radar Ambiguity Functions*, Univ. of Wisconsin, Mathematics Research Center, Madison, Wis., Tech. Summary Rept. no. 157 (April).

1961 NILSSON, N. T., "On the Optimum Range Resolution of Radar Signals in Noise", *Trans. I.R.E.* **IT-7**, 245–253 (Oct.).

STORER, J. and TURYN, R., "On Binary Sequences", *Proc. Amer. Math. Soc.* **12,** 394–9.

1962 CRAIG, S. E., FISHBEIN, W. and RITTENBACH, O. E., "Continuous-Wave Radar with High Range Resolution and Unambiguous Velocity Determination", *Trans I.R.E.* **MIL-6**, 153-61 (Apr.).

ROOT, W. L., "Radar Resolution of Closely Spaced Targets", *Trans. I.R.E.* **MIL-6**, 197–204 (Apr.).

SKOLNIK, M. I., *Introduction to Radar Systems*, McGraw-Hill Book Co., New York, N.Y., chapter 4, 113–63; chapter 12, 521–69.

SUSSMAN, S. M., "Least-Square Synthesis of Radar Ambiguity Functions", *Trans. I.R.E.* **IT-8,** 246–54 (Apr.).

WAINSTEIN, L. A. and ZUBAKOV, V. D., *Extraction of Signals from Noise*, R. A. SILVERMAN, trans., Prentice-Hall, Inc., Englewood Cliffs, N.J., sections 39–42, pp. 205–22.

1963 FOWLE, E. N., CAREY, D. R., VANDER SCHUUR, R. E. and YOST, R. C., "A Pulse-Compression System employing a Linear FM Gaussian Signal", *Proc. I.E.E.E.* **51,** 304–12 (Feb.).

LERNER, R. M., "Report on Progress in Information Theory in the U.S.A., Communication and Radar—Section B, Radar Waveform Selection", *Trans. I.E.E.E.* **IT-9**, 246–8 (Oct.)

1964 RIHACZEK, A. W., "Radar Resolution Properties of Pulse Trains", *Proc. I.E.E.E.* **52,** 153–64 (Feb.).

STUTT, C. A., "Some Results on Real-Part/Imaginary-Part and Magnitude/Phase Relations in Ambiguity Functions", *Trans. I.E.E.E.* **IT-10,** 321–7 (Oct.)

1965 GOLOMB, S. W. and SCHOLTZ, R. A., "Generalized Barker Sequences", *Trans. I.E.E.E.* **IT-11,** 533–7 (Oct.).

KELLY, E. J. and WISHNER, R. P., "Matched-filter Theory for High-Velocity, Accelerating Targets", *Trans. I.E.E.E.* **MIL-9,** 56–69 (Jan.).

PRICE, R. and HOFSTETTER, E. M., "Bounds on the Volume and Height Distributions of the Ambiguity Function", *Trans. I.E.E.E.* **IT-11,** 207–14 (Apr.).

RIHACZEK, A. W., "Radar Signal Design for Target Resolution", *Proc. I.E.E.E.* **53,** 116–28 (Feb.).

1966 TITLEBAUM, E. L. "A Generalization of a Two-dimensional Fourier Transform Property for Ambiguity Functions", *Trans. I.E.E.E.* **IT-12,** 80–81 (Jan.).

XI
STOCHASTIC SIGNALS

1. THE STRUCTURE OF THE RECEIVER

(a) *Types of Stochastic Signals*

Our foregoing studies of detection have presumed that the receiver knows the form of the signals and may be ignorant only of parameters such as amplitude, phase, and time of arrival. It is sometimes impossible, however, to specify the detailed structure of the signal, which may differ from one instance to another. The designer may then have to imagine the signals to have been drawn from an ensemble of random processes with certain statistical properties. Such signals are known as "stochastic signals". Although their waveforms are usually complicated, it is not their complexity, but the unpredictability of their precise configurations that places them in this category.

Stochastic signals may have been generated in a random manner or, originally possessing a definite form, have been erratically distorted on the way to the receiver. A system for transmitting binary digits, for instance, might send a burst of random noise of fixed duration to represent each "1", with blank intervals standing for the "0"s. The signals would have the form

$$s(t) = \text{Rl}\, R(t)\, Z(t) e^{i\Omega t}, \tag{1.1}$$

where $R(t)$ is a fixed modulation, Ω the carrier frequency, and $Z(t)$ the complex envelope of a stationary random process of known complex autocovariance function $\phi(\tau)$,

$$\mathbf{E}[Z(t_1)\, Z^*(t_2)] = 2\phi(t_1 - t_2), \quad \mathbf{E}[Z(t_1)\, Z(t_2)] = 0. \tag{1.2}$$

The complex autocovariance function of the signal envelope $S(t)$ is then

$$\phi_s(t_1, t_2) = \tfrac{1}{2}\mathbf{E}[S(t_1)\, S^*(t_2)] = R(t_1)\, R(t_2)\, \phi(t_1 - t_2). \tag{1.3}$$

The jamming signals transmitted to incommode an enemy radar are sometimes of this nature; they can be generated by amplifying the output of certain noisy gas-discharge tubes. The signals that radio telescopes pick up from distant parts of the universe are stochastic and, usually, stationary for relatively long periods of time.

"Scatter-multipath" communication systems link stations far beyond each other's horizons by sending out signals to be reflected from the ionosphere. From each determinate transmitted pulse there arrive a large number of weak signals that have traveled paths of slightly different lengths, along which they have suffered a variety of attenuations and distortions. The sum of all these signals strongly resembles a stochastic process (Price, 1956; Price and Green, 1958; Bello, 1963). In radar astronomy, transmitted signals are reflected from a planet or the sun at a large number of scattering points, and the combination of all the echoes again creates a stochastic signal (Price and Green, 1960).

When each transmitted pulse Rl $F(t)e^{i\Omega t}$ is reflected without distortion from a multitude of moving scatterers that introduce Doppler shifts w_m and are so located that the total delays between transmitter and receiver are τ_k, the received signal is Rl $S(t)e^{i\Omega t}$ and

$$S(t) = \sum_{k,m} z_{km} F(t-\tau_k) \exp{(iw_m t)}. \tag{1.4}$$

Here z_{km} is a complex number representing the amplitude and phase of the signal with delay τ_k and shift w_m. The complex autocovariance of the received signal is

$$\begin{aligned}\phi_s(t_1, t_2) = \tfrac{1}{2} \sum_{k,m} \sum_{k',m'} \mathbf{E}(z_{km}z^*_{k'm'})\cdot \\ F(t_1-\tau_k)\, F^*(t_2-\tau_{k'}) \exp{(iw_m t_1 - iw_{m'} t_2)},\end{aligned} \tag{1.5}$$

where $\mathbf{E}$ denotes an expected value with respect to the ensemble of scatterings. If separate scatterings are assumed statistically independent,

$$\phi_s(t_1, t_2) = \tfrac{1}{2} \sum_{k,m} \mathbf{E}|z_{km}|^2 F(t_1-\tau_k)\, F^*(t_2-\tau_k) \exp iw_m(t_1-t_2). \tag{1.6}$$

When the scatterers are small and dense, this sum can be written as an integral by introducing a function $\sigma(\tau, w)$ defined by

$$\sigma(\tau, w)\, d\tau\, dw/2\pi = \tfrac{1}{2} \sum_{k,m} \mathbf{E}|z_{km}|^2,$$

in which the summation is taken over those scatterers resulting in a delay between τ and $\tau+d\tau$ and a frequency shift between $w/2\pi$ and $(w+dw)/2\pi$. Then

$$\phi_s(t_1, t_2) = \iint \sigma(\tau, w)\, F(t_1-\tau)\, F^*(t_2-\tau) \exp iw(t_1-t_2)\, d\tau\, dw/2\pi. \tag{1.7}$$

The signals may not be reflected by rigidly moving scatterers, but may pass through a medium in which they induce atomic or ionic transitions that reradiate energy at the incident frequency. The result is a scattered wave that has been chopped up into many random pieces. From each elementary volume of the medium comes a random process whose amplitude is proportional to the instantaneous amplitude of the irradiating signal. The received signal is the sum of all these random emissions and can be written as $s(t) = \text{Rl}\, S(t)e^{i\Omega t}$, with

$$S(t) = \sum_k F(t-\tau_k-\tau_k')\, z_k(t-\tau_k'), \tag{1.8}$$

where τ_k is the delay from the transmitter to the region in which the kth process is emitted, and τ_k' is the delay from there to the receiver. The complex autocovariance of this signal is

$$\begin{aligned}\phi_s(t_1, t_2) &= \tfrac{1}{2}\mathbf{E}[S(t_1)S^*(t_2)] \\ &= \tfrac{1}{2}\sum_{k,\,m} F(t_1-\tau_k-\tau_k')\, F^*(t_2-\tau_m-\tau_m')\, \mathbf{E}[z_k(t_1-\tau_k')\, z_m^*(t_2-\tau_m')].\end{aligned} \tag{1.9}$$

If the emissions from separate regions can be considered uncorrelated, we can put

$$\tfrac{1}{2}\mathbf{E}[z_k(t_1-\tau_k')\, z_m^*(t_2-\tau_m')] = \psi_k(t_1-t_2)\, \delta_{km}$$

and write eq. (1.9) as

$$\phi_s(t_1, t_2) = \sum_k F(t_1-\tau_k-\tau_k')\, F^*(t_2-\tau_k-\tau_k')\, \psi_k(t_1-t_2).$$

The time difference t_1-t_2 appears in ψ_k because the individual emissive processes can be assumed stationary. Again passing to the limit of many small regions of dense but weak processes, we can collect the emissions from all regions for which the total delay $\tau_k+\tau_k'$ lies between τ and $\tau+d\tau$ and assign them the complex autocovariance function $\psi(\tau, t_1-t_2)\, d\tau$, finally writing the complex autocovariance function of the received signal as

$$\phi_s(t_1, t_2) = \int \psi(\tau, t_1-t_2)\, F(t_1-\tau)\, F^*(t_2-\tau)\, d\tau. \tag{1.10}$$

The autocovariance function in eq. (1.7) results if one puts

$$\psi(\tau, t) = \int \sigma(\tau, w)e^{iwt}\, dw/2\pi,$$

as when the emitted signals are sinusoids with frequency shifts w and random phases. Autocovariance functions of the general form of eq. (1.10) are assigned by Price and Green (1960) to the echoes expected in radar astronomy. If $\psi(\tau, t)$ as a function of τ is significant over a range of values of τ much longer than the pulse $F(t)$, the target is called a "deep fluctuating" one; if $\psi(\tau, t) = \psi(t)\delta(\tau-\tau_0)$, it is termed a "fluctuating point target", which is in effect much thinner than the incident signal.

The autocovariance functions in eqs. (1.3), (1.7), and (1.10) exemplify those characterizing different kinds of stochastic signals. We shall assume furthermore that the signals are realizations of Gaussian processes of expected value 0. The joint p.d.f. of any set of samples of the signals $s(t)$ taken at arbitrary times has a Gaussian form like that in eq. (II, 4.2). We take the signals and noise to be quasiharmonic and the processes in question to be of the circular Gaussian type described in Chapter II, Section 6.

The stochastic signals, when present, are received in the midst of Gaussian noise, to which we attribute a complex autocovariance function $\phi_0(t_1, t_2)$. For stationary noise $\phi_0(t_1, t_2)$ is a function only of $t_1 - t_2$. If the noise is white, with unilateral spectral density N,

$$\phi_0(t_1, t_2) = N\delta(t_1 - t_2).$$

Stochastic signals are sometimes picked up not by a single antenna, but by a number of antennas or "sensors" located at different points of space. Many seismometers may be distributed over a broad area for the detection of seismic waves such as might come from an earthquake or a nuclear explosion; and arrays of ultrasonic sensors have been constructed for receiving acoustic signals under water, as in sonar. Both seismic and sonar signals can be represented as stochastic processes, and techniques for processing the outputs of such arrays can be derived from the principles of detection theory. Instead of a single input $v(t)$, there are now a number of inputs, the signal and noise components of which are correlated both temporally and spatially. The methods we shall describe here can be extended to cope with multiple inputs, but with some increase of mathematical complexity. For the application to seismology we refer the reader to the December 1965 issue of the *Proceedings of the I.E.E.E.*; for the application to sonar we cite the paper by Middleton and Groginsky (1965). Further references are to be found in both.

The detection of stochastic signals seems first to have been treated by Davis (1954) and Youla (1954). The approach through the theory of hypothesis testing was taken by Middleton (1957). The task of the receiver is viewed as one of choosing between two hypotheses about its input $v(t) = \text{Rl}\, V(t)\, e^{i\Omega t}$. Under hypothesis H_0, $V(t) = N(t)$, where $N(t)$ is the complex envelope of Gaussian narrowband noise of complex autocovariance $\phi_0(t_1, t_2)$. Under hypothesis H_1, $V(t) = S(t) + N(t)$, where $S(t)$ is a realization of a narrowband Gaussian process of complex autocovariance $\phi_s(t_1, t_2)$. The signals and noise being independent, the complex autocovariance function of the input $v(t) = \text{Rl}\, V(t) e^{i\Omega t}$ is, under hypothesis H_1,

$$\tfrac{1}{2}\mathbf{E}[V(t_1)\, V^*(t_2)] = \phi_1(t_1, t_2) = \phi_s(t_1, t_2) + \phi_0(t_1, t_2). \qquad (1.11)$$

The input $v(t)$ is observed during an interval $(0, T)$.

As we learned in Chapter III, the best strategy for the receiver is to form the likelihood ratio between the joint p.d.f.s of samples of the input under the two hypotheses. The likelihood ratio is compared with a decision level that depends on the criterion of choice—Bayes, minimax, or Neyman–Pearson—that the designer has adopted. We now proceed to the calculation of the likelihood ratio.

(b) *The Likelihood Ratio*

(i) *Sampling the input.* In calculating the likelihood ratio for the choice between hypotheses H_0 and H_1 we might sample the input $v(t)$ or its complex envelope $V(t)$ at uniformly spaced instants as in Chapter IV, Section 3. It is more convenient, however, to work with the Fourier coefficients of an expansion of $V(t)$ in a series of orthonormal functions $f_k(t)$,

$$V(t) = \sum_{k=1}^{\infty} V_k f_k(t), \quad 0 \leqslant t \leqslant T, \tag{1.12}$$

in which the V_k's are complex numbers given by

$$\begin{aligned} V_k &= \int_0^T f_k^*(t)\, V(t)\, dt, \\ \int_0^T f_k^*(t) f_m(t)\, dt &= \delta_{km}. \end{aligned} \tag{1.13}$$

For the most part the orthonormal set $\{f_k(t)\}$ can be arbitrary, although in special circumstances particular choices are instructive. It is said to form a "basis" for the vector representation of the input $v(t)$.

The samples V_k can be generated, if necessary, by passing the input $V(t)$ through a bank of filters matched to the signals $\text{Rl}\, f_k(t)e^{i\Omega t}$ and measuring their outputs at the end of the observation interval. We suppose that the receiver is going to base its decision on the first M of the coefficients V_1, $V_2, \ldots, V_M$. Later we shall let M grow beyond all bounds.

The process $V(t)$ is circular Gaussian under each hypothesis, and so are the coefficients V_k. For notational convenience we collect them into a column vector $\mathbf{V}$ of M components. Its "Hermitian transpose" is the row vector $\mathbf{V}^+ = (V_1^*, V_2^*, \ldots, V_M^*)$. The complex covariances of the samples V_k form a matrix

$$\boldsymbol{\phi}_j = \tfrac{1}{2}\mathbf{E}[\mathbf{V}\mathbf{V}^+ \,|\, H_j] = ||\phi_{km}^{(j)}||$$

under hypothesis H_j, $j = 0, 1$, where

$$\phi_{km}^{(j)} = \tfrac{1}{2}\mathbf{E}[V_k V_m^* \mid H_j]$$
$$= \tfrac{1}{2}\int_0^T \int_0^T f_k^*(t_1)\, f_m(t_2)\, \mathbf{E}[V(t_1)\, V^*(t_2) \mid H_j]\, dt_1\, dt_2 \tag{1.14}$$
$$= \int_0^T \int_0^T f_k^*(t_1)\, \phi_j(t_1, t_2)\, f_m(t_2)\, dt_1\, dt_2.$$

In the absence of a deterministic signal,

$$\mathbf{E}[V_k \mid H_j] = 0, \tag{1.15}$$

and the joint p.d.f. of the real and imaginary parts of the samples can be written, as in eq. (II, 6.15),

$$p_j(\mathbf{V}) = (2\pi)^{-M} |\det \boldsymbol{\phi}_j|^{-1} \exp\left[-\tfrac{1}{2}\sum_{k=1}^{M}\sum_{m=1}^{M} V_k^* \mu_{km}^{(j)} V_m\right]$$
$$= (2\pi)^{-M} |\det \boldsymbol{\phi}_j|^{-1} \exp(-\tfrac{1}{2}\mathbf{V}^+ \boldsymbol{\mu}_j \mathbf{V}), \tag{1.16}$$

where $\boldsymbol{\mu}_j = \|\mu_{km}^{(j)}\|$ is the matrix inverse to $\boldsymbol{\phi}_j$,

$$\boldsymbol{\mu}_j = \boldsymbol{\phi}_j^{-1}, \qquad \sum_{m=1}^{M} \mu_{km}^{(j)} \phi_{mn}^{(j)} = \delta_{kn},$$

and $\det \boldsymbol{\phi}_j$ is the determinant of the matrix $\boldsymbol{\phi}_j$.

(ii) *Forming the likelihood ratio.* The likelihood ratio $\Lambda_M(\mathbf{V})$ based on the M coefficients V_k, $k = 1, 2, \ldots, M$, is thus

$$\Lambda_M(\mathbf{V}) = p_1(\mathbf{V})/p_0(\mathbf{V}) = \det(\boldsymbol{\phi}_0 \boldsymbol{\phi}_1^{-1}) \exp[\tfrac{1}{2}\mathbf{V}^+(\boldsymbol{\mu}_0 - \boldsymbol{\mu}_1)\mathbf{V}]. \tag{1.17}$$

The exponential function being monotone, the choice between the two hypotheses H_0 and H_1 can just as well be based on the statistic

$$U_M = \tfrac{1}{2}\mathbf{V}^+(\boldsymbol{\mu}_0 - \boldsymbol{\mu}_1)\mathbf{V} = \tfrac{1}{2}\sum_{k=1}^{M}\sum_{m=1}^{M} V_k^*(\mu_{km}^{(0)} - \mu_{km}^{(1)}) V_m. \tag{1.18}$$

If U_M exceeds a certain decision level, hypothesis H_1 is chosen. What we must now do is write U_M in such a form that the transition to an infinite number of samples is easy.

We define a function $h_M(t, s)$ by

$$h_M(t, s) = \sum_{k=1}^{M}\sum_{m=1}^{M} h_{km}^{(M)} f_k(t)\, f_m^*(s), \qquad h_{km}^{(M)} = \mu_{km}^{(0)} - \mu_{km}^{(1)}, \tag{1.19}$$

in terms of which the statistic U_M can be written

$$U_M = \tfrac{1}{2}\int_0^T \int_0^T V^*(t)\, h_M(t, s)\, V(s)\, dt\, ds, \tag{1.20}$$

as can easily be seen by substituting eq. (1.19) into eq. (1.20) and using eq. (1.13) to reduce it to eq. (1.18). The matrix

$$\mathbf{H}_M = \|h_{km}^{(M)}\| = \boldsymbol{\mu}_0 - \boldsymbol{\mu}_1$$

satisfies the equation

$$\boldsymbol{\phi}_0 \mathbf{H}_M \boldsymbol{\phi}_1 = \boldsymbol{\phi}_1 - \boldsymbol{\phi}_0$$

or

$$\sum_{n=1}^{M} \sum_{p=1}^{M} \phi_{kn}^{(0)} h_{np}^{(M)} \phi_{pm}^{(1)} = \phi_{km}^{(1)} - \phi_{km}^{(0)}. \tag{1.21}$$

If we now define the "truncated" autocovariances $\phi_j^{(M)}(t, s)$ by

$$\phi_j^{(M)}(t, s) = \sum_{k, m=1}^{M} \phi_{km}^{(j)} f_k(t) f_m^*(s), \qquad j = 0, 1, \tag{1.22}$$

we see by eq. (1.21) that the function $h_M(t, s)$ satisfies the integral equation

$$\phi_1^{(M)}(t, s) - \phi_0^{(M)}(t, s) = \int_0^T \int_0^T \phi_0^{(M)}(t, r)\, h_M(r, u)\, \phi_1^{(M)}(u, s)\, dr\, du; \tag{1.23}$$

it is only necessary to substitute for $h_M(r, u)$ from eq. (1.19) and use the orthonormality of the functions $f_k(t)$.

When the number M of coefficients used by the receiver is increased beyond all bounds, the truncated autocovariances of eq. (1.22) become the true ones as given by eq. (1.14),

$$\phi_j(t, s) = \sum_{k, m=1}^{\infty} \phi_{km}^{(j)} f_k(t) f_m^*(s).$$

The function $h_M(t, s)$ goes into a function $h(t, s)$ that by eq. (1.23) is the solution of the integral equation

$$\phi_1(t, s) - \phi_0(t, s) = \phi_s(t, s) = \int_0^T \int_0^T \phi_0(t, r)\, h(r, u)\, \phi_1(u, s)\, dr\, du, \tag{1.24}$$

provided the solution exists; and the test statistic U_M becomes the statistic

$$U = \tfrac{1}{2} \int_0^T \int_0^T V^*(t)\, h(t, s)\, V(s)\, dt\, ds. \tag{1.25}$$

It is this quadratic functional of the input that will be compared with a decision level U_0 to decide whether a signal is present or not.

Like the matrices $\boldsymbol{\mu}_0$ and $\boldsymbol{\mu}_1$, the matrix $\mathbf{H}_M$ is Hermitian. Eq. (1.21) could just as well have been written

$$\boldsymbol{\phi}_1 \mathbf{H}_M \boldsymbol{\phi}_0 = \boldsymbol{\phi}_1 - \boldsymbol{\phi}_0,$$

and the function defined in eq. (1.19) has the Hermitian property

$$h_M(t, s) = h_M^*(s, t),$$

which is shared by the limiting form $h(t, s) = h^*(s, t)$. This is a necessary condition in order for the test statistic U to be real.

The solution of eq. (1.24) can proceed in two stages. One defines an intermediate function $g(t, s)$ by

$$g(t, s) = \int_0^T \phi_0(t, r)\, h(r, s)\, dr, \tag{1.26}$$

whereupon eq. (1.24) becomes

$$\phi_s(t, s) = \int_0^T g(t, u)\, \phi_1(u, s)\, du. \tag{1.27}$$

This equation is solved for $g(t, s)$, after which the previous equation (1.26) is solved for $h(t, s)$. If during the observation interval the signal and the noise are stationary random processes with rational spectral densities, the methods described in Chapter IV and Appendix E can be applied. When in particular the observation interval is much longer than the correlation times of both signal and noise, the dominant term in the solution is a function only of $(t-s)$ and is given by

$$\begin{aligned} h(t, s) &\cong \eta(t-s), \\ \eta(\tau) &= \int_{-\infty}^{\infty} [\Phi_s(\omega)/\Phi_0(\omega)\, \Phi_1(\omega)] e^{i\omega\tau}\, d\omega/2\pi. \end{aligned} \tag{1.28}$$

The decision level U_0 for the Bayes criterion is determined as the solution of the equation

$$\lim_{M\to\infty} \det(\boldsymbol{\phi}_0 \boldsymbol{\phi}_1^{-1}) \exp U_0 = \Lambda_0,$$

where Λ_0 depends on the costs and prior probabilities as in eq. (III, 2.10). Hence

$$U_0 = \ln \Lambda_0 + \lim_{M\to\infty} \ln \det(\boldsymbol{\phi}_1 \boldsymbol{\phi}_0^{-1}). \tag{1.29}$$

Later we shall find a way of calculating the limiting value of the determinant $\det(\boldsymbol{\phi}_1\boldsymbol{\phi}_0^{-1})$, which is known as the "Fredholm determinant" of the integral equation (1.24). For the Neyman–Pearson criterion it is necessary, in order to set the decision level, first to calculate the false-alarm probability Q_0 as a function of U_0 and then to equate it to the preassigned value. The next section will deal with the calculation of the false-alarm and detection probabilities.

(iii) *Detection in white noise.* If the noise is white, the kernel $h(t, s)$ of the test statistic U satisfies the somewhat simpler integral equation

$$N^{-1}\phi_s(t, s) = Nh(t, s) + \int_0^T \phi_s(t, v)\, h(v, s)\, dv, \tag{1.30}$$

which is a Fredholm integral equation of the second kind. It is then convenient to use as basis functions $f_j(t)$ the eigenfunctions of the autocovariance of the signal,

$$\lambda_j f_j(t) = \int_0^T \phi_s(t, s)\, f_j(s)\, ds, \tag{1.31}$$

whereupon the kernel $h(t, s)$ can be written

$$h(t, s) = \sum_{n=1}^{\infty} \frac{\lambda_n f_n(t)\, f_n^*(s)}{N(\lambda_n + N)}\,. \tag{1.32}$$

Related to the integral equation (1.30) is the more general equation

$$NL(t, s; u) + u \int_0^T \phi_s(t, v)\, L(v, s; u)\, dv = N\delta(t-s) \tag{1.33}$$

for the so-called "resolvent kernel" of the covariance function $\phi_s(t, s)$ (Courant–Hilbert, 1931, ch. 3). In particular,

$$h(t, s) = N^{-2} \int_0^T L(t, r; 1)\, \phi_s(r, s)\, dr. \tag{1.34}$$

In part (d) of this section we shall present an example of the solution of eq. (1.33). Associated with it is the Fredholm determinant

$$D(u) = \prod_{n=1}^{\infty} (1 + u\lambda_n/N). \tag{1.35}$$

The integral equation (1.33) has no solution for values of u equal to $-N/\lambda_k$, which are the zeros of the Fredholm determinant.

(iv) *The threshold detector.* A detector based on the statistic U of eq. (1.25) depends on the relative strengths of signals and noise, which may not be known in advance. If the signals are weak enough, the optimum detector will not differ much from the threshold detector, which measures the threshold statistic

$$U_\theta = \tfrac{1}{2} \int_0^T \int_0^T V^*(t)\, h_\theta(t, s)\, V(s)\, dt\, ds, \tag{1.36}$$

where $h_\theta(t, s)$ is the solution of the integral equation

$$\phi_s(t, s) = \int_0^T \int_0^T \phi_0(t, r)\, h_\theta(r, u)\, \phi_0(u, s)\, dr\, du. \tag{1.37}$$

This equation results when $\phi_1(t, r)$ on the right-hand side of eq. (1.24) becomes equal to $\phi_0(t, r)$ as the signal strength is reduced to zero. The relative strength of the signals now enters the test statistic only as a constant of proportionality, which can be directly eliminated. For detection in white noise, the threshold kernel is given immediately by

$$h_\theta(t, s) = N^{-2}\, \phi_s(t, s) \tag{1.38}$$

and corresponds to the first term of a solution of eq. (1.30) by iteration.

If both signal and noise are stationary during an observation interval much longer than their correlation times, the solution of eq. (1.37) is approximately

$$h_\theta(r, u) \cong \eta_\theta(r-u) = \int_{-\infty}^{\infty} H_\theta(\omega) e^{i\omega(r-u)}\, d\omega/2\pi,$$

$$H_\theta(\omega) = \Phi_s(\omega)/[\Phi_0(\omega)]^2,$$

$\Phi_0(\omega)$ and $\Phi_s(\omega)$ being the spectral densities of noise and signal, respectively.

(c) *Realizations of the Optimum and Threshold Detectors*

(i) *Time-variable filters.* Both the optimum and the threshold detectors are based on real quadratic functionals of the same type, and the ways we are about to describe of constructing the former will apply to the latter as well. It is necessary first to have calculated the appropriate kernel, $h(t, s)$ or $h_\theta(t, s)$.

Price (1956) showed how the test statistic U can be generated by means of a properly matched time-variable or non-stationary linear filter. Because $h(t, s) = h^*(s, t)$, the statistic can be written

$$U = \mathrm{Rl} \int_0^T V^*(t)\, dt \int_0^t h(t, s)\, V(s)\, ds = \mathrm{Rl} \int_0^T V^*(t)\, W(t)\, dt,$$

$$W(t) = \int_0^t h(t, s)\, V(s)\, ds. \tag{1.39}$$

For each value of t, the function $W(t)$ is a weighted average of the input that has arrived before the time t. It can be produced by passing the input through a time-variable linear filter whose narrowband impulse response is

$$k_t(\tau) = h(t, t-\tau), \quad 0 < \tau < t,$$
$$= 0, \qquad \tau > t.$$

The output of this filter at time t is Rl $W(t)e^{i\Omega t}$, where

$$W(t) = \int_0^\infty k_t(\tau)\, V(t-\tau)\, d\tau$$
$$= \int_0^t h(t, t-\tau)\, V(t-\tau)\, d\tau = \int_0^t h(t, s)\, V(s)\, ds.$$

The output of the time-variable filter is multiplied at each instant by the input Rl $V(t)e^{i\Omega t}$, and the high-frequency components of the product are removed by filtering. By writing out these factors in terms of sin Ωt and cos Ωt and multiplying them, it is easy to show that their product is

$$\text{Rl}\, V(t)e^{i\Omega t} \cdot \text{Rl}\, W(t)e^{i\Omega t} = \tfrac{1}{2}\text{Rl}\, W(t)\, V^*(t) + \text{terms of frequency } 2\Omega.$$

The product is integrated by a low-pass filter with impulse response

$$K(\tau) = 1, \quad 0 < \tau < T; \quad K(\tau) = 0, \quad \tau > T,$$

whose output at time T is

$$\tfrac{1}{2}\text{Rl} \int_0^T W(t)\, V^*(t)\, dt = \tfrac{1}{2}U.$$

The operation of this system is illustrated in Fig. XI.1. The required multiplication can be most easily accomplished by passing the sum Rl $[V(t)+W(t)]e^{i\Omega t}$ through a quadratic rectifier, the output of which is

$$|V(t)+W(t)|^2 = |V(t)|^2 + 2\, \text{Rl}\, V^*(t)\, W(t) + |W(t)|^2.$$

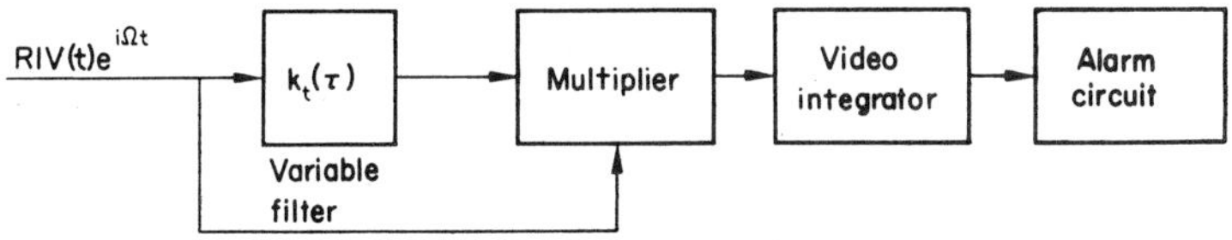

FIG. XI.1. Optimum detector of stochastic signals.

The separately rectified outputs $|W(t)|^2$ and $|V(t)|^2$ are subtracted to leave the product desired.

A second way of generating the test statistic U employs a time-variable filter followed by a quadratic rectifier and an integrator (Middleton, 1960b). The output of the filter has the complex envelope

$$X(t) = \int_0^T m(t, s)\, V(s)\, ds,$$

and this output is rectified and integrated to produce

$$U = \tfrac{1}{2} \int_0^T |X(t)|^2 \, dt.$$

In order for this quantity to equal the test statistic as given by eq. (1.25), the weighting function $m(t, s)$ must satisfy the integral equation

$$\int_0^T m^*(x, t) \, m(x, s) \, dx = h(t, s), \quad t, s \in (0, T), \tag{1.40}$$

where $h(t, s)$ is the solution of the integral equation (1.24) or, for the threshold statistic, (1.37).

Kailath (1960a) has shown how to solve this type of non-linear integral equation. Let γ_k be the eigenvalues of the kernel $h(t, s)$, and let $g_k(t)$ be the corresponding orthonormal eigenfunctions,

$$\gamma_k g_k(t) = \int_0^T h(t, s) \, g_k(s) \, ds.$$

Then $h(t, s)$ can be written as

$$h(t, s) = \sum_{k=1}^{\infty} \gamma_k g_k(t) \, g_k^*(s),$$

and the solution of eq. (1.40) is

$$m(t, s) = \sum_{k=1}^{\infty} \gamma_k^{\frac{1}{2}} g_k(t) \, g_k^*(s),$$

as can be shown by substituting it into eq. (1.40) and using the orthonormality of the eigenfunctions $g_k(t)$. For detection in white noise one can use eq. (1.32) for $h(t, s)$ and write the weighting function of the filter as

$$m(t, s) = \sum_{n=1}^{\infty} \left[\frac{\lambda_n}{N(\lambda_n + N)} \right]^{\frac{1}{2}} f_n(t) \, f_n^*(s).$$

Since the filter generating $X(t)$ must use all of the input $V(t)$ over the interval $(0, T)$, it cannot be realized without a delay of at least T seconds.

(ii) *The radiometer.* If the signal is an echo from a fluctuating point target, its autocovariance function $\phi_s(t, s)$ can be determined from eq. (1.10) by inserting $\psi(\tau, t) = \psi(t) \, \delta(\tau - \tau_0)$, and it is

$$\phi_s(t, s) = F(t - \tau_0) \, \psi(t - s) \, F^*(s - \tau_0), \tag{1.41}$$

where τ_0 is the delay to and from the target. Suppose now that the threshold statistic in eq. (1.37) is to be used in a receiver to detect this target in white noise. It is given by the equation

$$\begin{aligned} U_\theta &= \tfrac{1}{2}N^{-2}\int_0^T\int_0^T V^*(t)\,F(t-\tau_0)\,\psi(t-s)\,F^*(s-\tau_0)\,V(s)\,dt\,ds \\ &= \iint Y^*(t)\,\psi(t-s)\,Y(s)\,dt\,ds/2N^2, \end{aligned} \tag{1.42}$$

where $Y(t) = F^*(t-\tau_0)\,V(t)$ can be formed by multiplying the input by a locally generated replica of the transmitted signal with the proper time delay, assumed known. In the second integral the integrations need to be carried out only over intervals during which the signal might arrive and $Y(t) \neq 0$.

The realizations we have just described in part (i) might now be applied to U_θ of eq. (1.42), the function $\psi(t-s)$ taking the place of $h(t, s)$ and $Y(t)$ the place of $V(t)$. In particular we might employ the second realization, for which it is necessary to solve an equation similar to eq. (1.40). If the range of integration is extended to span the entire time axis, $-\infty < t < \infty$, the solution becomes a function only of the difference of the two arguments, and the equation itself takes the form

$$\int_{-\infty}^{\infty} g^*(x-t)\,g(x-s)\,dx = \psi(t-s). \tag{1.43}$$

Introducing the Fourier transforms

$$G(\omega) = \int_{-\infty}^{\infty} g(t)\,e^{-i\omega t}\,dt, \quad \Psi(\omega) = \int_{-\infty}^{\infty} \psi(t)\,e^{-i\omega t}\,dt, \tag{1.44}$$

we find by the convolution theorem

$$|G(\omega)|^2 = \Psi(\omega),$$

and $G(\omega)$ can be taken as

$$G(\omega) = |\Psi(\omega)|^{\frac{1}{2}} \exp i\chi(\omega),$$

the phase $\chi(\omega)$ being chosen so that a filter of impulse response $g(\tau)$ is physically realizable, with $g(\tau) = 0$, $\tau < 0$. The test statistic then becomes

$$U_\theta = \tfrac{1}{2}N^{-2}\int_{-\infty}^{\infty} dt \left| \int_{-\infty}^{\infty} g(t-s)\,F(s-\tau_0)\,V(s)\,ds \right|^2.$$

A device generating the statistic U_θ in this approximate way was proposed by Price and Green (1960) for detecting signals in radar astronomy. They called it a "radiometer". In practice, they pointed out, it will not be necessary to integrate the outputs of the filter or the rectifier over a very long interval in order to achieve a good approximation to the threshold detector.

If the target is "deep" and the autocovariance of the echo signals is given as in eq. (1.10), it is merely necessary to construct a parallel bank of these radiometers, each "matched" to the transmitted signal with one of a dense set of delays τ_0. The impulse responses $g(\tau)$ may differ from one filter to another. Price and Green (1960) termed this more elaborate device a "Rake radiometer", for it is reminiscent of a similar device used in the detection of signals in a multipath communication system, the so-called "Rake receiver" (Price and Green, 1958).

(d) *An Example*

To illustrate the ideas of this section and the next it is instructive to have before us the simple example of a stationary stochastic signal with the autocovariance function

$$\phi_s(r, t) = \phi_0 e^{-\mu|r-t|}. \tag{1.45}$$

The signal is received in the presence of white Gaussian noise of unilateral spectral density N. The modulation $R(t)$, eq. (1.1), is taken as constant, and the signals, which are also Gaussian processes, can be generated by passing white noise through a narrowband simply resonant circuit of bandwidth μ. They are observed during the interval $(0, T)$. This case has been analyzed by Price (1956) and others.

For future use it will be convenient to have the solution of the integral equation

$$Nh(r, t; u)+u \int_0^T \phi_s(r, s)\, h(s, t; u)\, ds = N^{-1}\phi_s(r, t), \tag{1.46}$$

which is related to eq. (1.33). In fact, the solution of eq. (1.33) is

$$L(t, s; u) = \delta(t-s)-Nuh(t, s; u). \tag{1.47}$$

The kernel of the test statistic is $h(t, s) = h(t, s; 1)$, by eq. (1.30).

The integral equation (1.46) takes the form of eq. (IV, 5.1) when we identify the kernel as

$$\phi(r-s) = N\delta(r-s)+u\phi_s(r-s),$$

and the method outlined in Chapter IV, Section 5 can be applied. The Fourier transform

$$\Phi(\omega) = \int_{-\infty}^{\infty} \phi(\tau) e^{-i\omega\tau} \, d\tau$$

of the kernel is a rational function of frequency,

$$\Phi(\omega) = N + u\Phi_s(\omega) = N + 2\mu\phi_0 u(\omega^2+\mu^2)^{-1} = N(\omega^2+\beta^2)/(\omega^2+\mu^2),$$
$$\beta^2 = \mu^2 + 2\mu\phi_0 u/N,$$

where $\Phi_s(\omega)$ is the spectral density of the signal.

The solution of the integral equation has the form given in eq. (IV, 5.7). Corresponding to $q_0(t)$ there is the solution $h_0(t-s)$ of eq. (1.46) when the limits of integration are $-\infty$ and $+\infty$ instead of 0 and T, and this solution is the Fourier transform of

$$\int_{-\infty}^{\infty} h_0(t) e^{-i\omega t} \, dt = N^{-1}\Phi_s(\omega)/\Phi(\omega) = 2\mu\phi_0 N^{-2}(\omega^2+\beta^2)^{-1},$$
$$h_0(t-u) = (\mu\phi_0/\beta N^2) e^{-\beta|t-u|}.$$

The terms of eq. (IV, 5.7) with delta functions are now absent because the degrees of the numerator and the denominator of $\Phi(\omega)$ are equal. Hence the solution has the form

$$h(r, t; u) = (\mu\phi_0/\beta N^2) e^{-\beta|r-t|} + Ae^{\beta r} + Be^{-\beta r}, \tag{1.48}$$

where A and B are functions of t.

To determine the unknown functions $A(t)$ and $B(t)$, we substitute eq. (1.48) into eq. (1.46). When we carry out the integration and use the definition of β, we find that all the terms in $e^{\beta r}$ and $e^{-\beta r}$ cancel, as does the term on the right-hand side of eq. (1.46). We are left only with terms proportional either to $e^{\mu r}$ or to $e^{-\mu r}$. Setting the coefficients of each of these functions separately equal to zero, we obtain two simultaneous linear equations for A and B, which are solved in the usual way and yield

$$A = \frac{\mu\phi_0(\beta-\mu)\,[(\beta+\mu)e^{\beta t} + (\beta-\mu)e^{-\beta t}]e^{-\beta T}}{N^2\beta[(\beta+\mu)^2 e^{\beta T} - (\beta-\mu)^2 e^{-\beta T}]},$$
$$B = \frac{\mu\phi_0(\beta-\mu)\,[(\beta+\mu)e^{-\beta(t-T)} + (\beta-\mu)e^{\beta(t-T)}]}{N^2\beta[(\beta+\mu)^2 e^{\beta T} - (\beta-\mu)^2 e^{-\beta T}]}. \tag{1.49}$$

Substituting these into eq. (1.48) and treating the regions $r < t$ and $r > t$ separately, we combine terms to derive the solution

$$h(r, t; u) = \frac{\mu\phi_0[(\beta+\mu)e^{\beta r} + (\beta-\mu)e^{-\beta r}]\,[(\beta+\mu)e^{\beta(T-t)} + (\beta-\mu)e^{-\beta(T-t)}]}{N^2\beta[(\beta+\mu)^2 e^{\beta T} - (\beta-\mu)^2 e^{-\beta T}]},$$
$$0 \leqslant r \leqslant t \leqslant T. \tag{1.50}$$

The solution for $0 \leqslant t \leqslant r \leqslant T$ is found by interchanging r and t in this expression. The kernel of the detection statistic in eq. (1.25) is given by eq. (1.50) when one determines β from

$$\beta^2 = \mu^2 + 2\mu\phi_0/N.$$

Substituting into eq. (1.39) we get the test statistic

$$U = (\mu\phi_0/N^2\beta)\,[(\beta+\mu)^2 e^{\beta T} - (\beta-\mu)^2 e^{-\beta T}]^{-1} \cdot \mathrm{Rl} \int_0^T V^*(s)\,[(\beta+\mu)e^{\beta(T-s)} + (\beta-\mu)e^{-\beta(T-s)}] \cdot \int_0^s [(\beta+\mu)e^{\beta t} + (\beta-\mu)e^{-\beta t}]\,V(t)\,dt\,ds.$$

In the present example the threshold detector for stochastic signals having the autocovariance function in eq. (1.45) is based on the approximation in eq. (1.38) and furnishes the statistic

$$U_\theta = (\phi_0/N^2)\,\mathrm{Rl} \int_0^T V^*(t)\,dt \int_0^t e^{-\mu(t-s)}\,V(s)\,ds$$
$$= (\phi_0/N^2)\,\mathrm{Rl} \int_0^T V^*(t)\,dt \int_0^t e^{-\mu\tau}\,V(t-\tau)\,d\tau.$$

If the input is turned on at time $t = 0$, the term

$$\int_0^t e^{-\mu\tau}\,V(t-\tau)\,d\tau$$

is proportional to the envelope of the output of a narrowband simply resonant circuit of bandwidth μ tuned to the carrier frequency Ω. This output is multiplied by the input $v(t) = \mathrm{Rl}\,V(t)e^{i\Omega t}$ in the manner described in part (c), and the product is integrated over a period of duration T. Such a threshold detection system can be made independent of the true signal power $\phi_s(0, 0)$, which may not be known in advance; the optimum system depends on the strengths of both signals and noise.

Unfortunately, there seems to be no such simple approximation in the general case when the signal-to-noise ratio is large. In the present example we see from eq. (1.50) that for large signal-to-noise ratio and long integration time T ($\beta T \gg 1$), the dominant term in the kernel $h(r, t)$ is proportional to $e^{-\beta|r-t|}$. Hence the optimum detection system is nearly the same as the threshold receiver, except that the bandwidth of the input filter is $(2\mu\phi_0/N)^{\frac{1}{2}}$ instead of μ. In the next section we shall attack the problem of calculating the false-alarm and detection probabilities for such receivers.

(e) *The Estimation of a Stochastic Signal*

An illuminating interpretation of the optimum receiver appears on considering the best linear estimate of the complex envelope $S(t)$ of the signal at an arbitrary instant t in the interval $(0, T)$. By the "best linear estimate" we mean an estimate of the form

$$\hat{S}(t) = \int_0^T M(t; s)\, V(s)\, ds$$

that minimizes the expected value of the squared error

$$\mathcal{E} = \tfrac{1}{2}\,\mathbf{E}[\hat{S}(t) - S(t)]^2,$$

when the signal is actually present. The estimate is formed by a linear operator on the input $v(t)$ as observed during the entire interval $(0, T)$.

The mean squared error can be written as

$$\mathcal{E} = \tfrac{1}{2}\,\mathbf{E}\left\{|S(t)|^2 - \int_0^T M^*(t; s)\, S(t)\, V^*(s)\, ds - \text{c.c.} \right.$$
$$\left. + \int_0^T \int_0^T M^*(t; s')\, M(t; s'')\, V(s'')\, V^*(s')\, ds'\, ds'' \right\},$$

where "c.c." denotes the complex conjugate of the immediately preceding term. Here $V(t) = S(t) + N(t)$ is the complex envelope of the input. We assume that the signal $\text{Rl}\, S(t) e^{i\Omega t}$ and the noise $\text{Rl}\, N(t) e^{i\Omega t}$ are statistically independent. In terms of the autocovariances defined in part (a), the mean squared error is then

$$\mathcal{E} = \phi_s(0, 0) - \int_0^T M^*(t; s)\, \phi_s(t, s)\, ds - \text{c.c.}$$
$$+ \int_0^T \int_0^T M^*(t; s')\, M(t; s'')\, \phi_1(s'', s')\, ds'\, ds''.$$

We now want to show that the error is minimized when the estimating kernel is the solution $g(t, s)$ of eq. (1.27), and to do so we rewrite the error using that equation,

$$\mathcal{E} = \phi_s(0, 0) - \int_0^T \int_0^T g^*(t, s')\, g(t, s'')\, \phi_1(s', s'')\, ds'\, ds''$$
$$+ \int_0^T \int_0^T [M^*(t; s') - g^*(t, s')]\, [M(t; s'') - g(t, s'')]\, \phi_1(s'', s')\, ds'\, ds''.$$

Because the function $\phi_1(s'', s')$ is positive definite, the last term in the squared error is always positive; and the error will be greater than need be unless $M(t; s) = g(t, s)$. Hence, the best estimate of the signal at time

t is

$$\hat{S}(t) = \int_0^T g(t, s)\, V(s)\, ds, \tag{1.51}$$

where $g(t, s)$ is the solution of eq. (1.27).

If we now substitute for $g(t, s)$ from eq. (1.26) we obtain

$$\hat{S}(t) = \int_0^T \int_0^T \phi_0(t, r)\, h(r, s)\, V(s)\, dr\, ds = \int_0^T \phi_0(t, r)\, \hat{Q}(r)\, dr, \tag{1.52}$$

where we have defined the function $\hat{Q}(t)$ by

$$\hat{Q}(t) = \int_0^T h(t, s)\, V(s)\, ds. \tag{1.53}$$

In terms of it the optimum test statistic is given by eq. (1.25) as

$$U = \tfrac{1}{2} \int_0^T \hat{Q}^*(t)\, V(t)\, dt. \tag{1.54}$$

If we compare eqs. (1.52) and (1.54) with eqs. (IV, 3.8) and (IV, 3.7) as these would be written for complex signals, we find that the optimum detector for the stochastic signals $s(t) = \text{Rl}\ S(t)e^{i\Omega t}$ can be described in the following way (Kailath, 1960b). The receiver first forms the best linear estimate of the signal envelope $S(t)$ under the presumption that the signal is present. It then passes the input $v(t) = \text{Rl}\ V(t)e^{i\Omega t}$ through the optimum detector of a known signal having the same form as the estimate Rl $\hat{S}(t)$ $e^{i\Omega t}$. That is, it "correlates" the input envelope $V(t)$ with the solution $\hat{Q}(t)$ of the integral equation (1.52). We are reminded of the principle of maximum likelihood, which states that to detect a signal depending on unknown parameters—here the values of the signal itself—one should first assume that the signal is present, form the maximum-likelihood estimate of the parameters, and then proceed as though the signal parameters actually equaled the estimates. For a signal in Gaussian noise the maximum-likelihood estimate of its values is just the linear estimate derived here.

2. THE PERFORMANCE OF THE RECEIVER

(a) *The Distributions of the Test Statistic*

(i) *The characteristic function.* Both the optimum detector and the threshold detector of a stochastic signal have the same structure. They determine the value of a quadratic functional

$$U = \tfrac{1}{2} \int_0^T \int_0^T V^*(r)\, h(r, s)\, V(s)\, dr\, ds \tag{2.1}$$

and compare it with a decision level U_0. Here $V(t)$ is the complex envelope of the input to the receiver, and $h(t, s)$ is a kernel whose form depends on which detector is adopted. For the optimum detector, $h(t, s)$ is the solution of the integral equation (1.24); for the threshold detector it is the solution of eq. (1.36).

The probability of detecting a particular signal is the probability that U exceeds U_0 when that signal is present. Since what signal might be present is unknown when the signals are stochastic, the only meaningful way to measure the effectiveness of the receiver is to average that probability over all signals of the ensemble.

It is useful to know the average probability of detection not only for the ensemble of signals for which the detector was designed, but also for ensembles of signals of arbitrary average energy. We therefore introduce the hypothesis H_γ that a signal is present that was drawn from an ensemble in which the autocovariance is $\gamma\phi_s(t, s)$, and we shall attempt to calculate the p.d.f. $p_\gamma(U)$ of the test statistic under that hypothesis. The complex autocovariance of the process Rl $V(t)e^{i\Omega t}$ under H_γ is

$$\begin{aligned} \tfrac{1}{2}\mathbf{E}[V(t_1)\, V^*(t_2) \mid H_\gamma] &= \phi_\gamma(t_1, t_2), \\ \phi_\gamma(t_1, t_2) &= \phi_0(t_1, t_2) + \gamma\phi_s(t_1, t_2). \end{aligned} \tag{2.2}$$

The probability of detection is

$$Q_d(\gamma) = \int_{U_0}^{\infty} p_\gamma(U)\, dU, \tag{2.3}$$

for signals of an arbitrary average energy $\gamma\phi_s(0, 0)T$; for signals of the designed strength it is $Q_d(1)$. The false-alarm probability is $Q_0 = Q_d(0)$.

The problem of finding the p.d.f. of a quadratic functional of a random process arose when Kac and Siegert (1947) analyzed the filtered output of a quadratic rectifier whose input is Gaussian noise. Let the input to the rectifier be Rl $V(t)e^{i\Omega t}$. Its filtered output at time t is

$$U(t) = \int_{-\infty}^{t} K(t-r)\, |V(r)|^2\, dr, \tag{2.4}$$

where $K(\tau)$ is the impulse response of the filter after the rectifier. If we put

$$h(r, s) = K(t-r)\, \delta(r-s) \tag{2.5}$$

into eq. (2.1) and change the limits of integration from 0 and T to $-\infty$ and t, we obtain eq. (2.4). Our subsequent formulas can similarly be modified to apply to the quadratic rectifier by changing the limits of integration in this way.

Among other treatments of the distribution of a quadratic functional of Gaussian noise we cite the work of Siegert (1957), Grenander, Pollak, and Slepian (1959), Turin (1960), and Middleton (1960a, ch. 17). The usual procedure is to derive first the characteristic function (ch.f.) of U and then, when possible, make a Fourier transformation to obtain the probability density function. This is the course we too shall follow.

As in Section 1, part (b), we shall first work with the M Fourier coefficients, the "samples" $V_1, V_2, \ldots, V_M$ as specified by eq. (1.13). They are circular Gaussian random variables and are collected into the column vector $\mathbf{V}$. In addition we define the $M \times M$ matrix $\mathbf{H} = ||h_{mn}||$ through the equations

$$h_{mn} = \int_0^T \int_0^T f_m^*(t)\, h(t, s)\, f_n(s)\, dt\, ds, \tag{2.6}$$

where the basis functions $\{f_k(t)\}$ are the same as before. The quadratic functional U is replaced by the Hermitian quadratic form

$$U_M = \tfrac{1}{2}\mathbf{V}^+\mathbf{H}\mathbf{V} = \tfrac{1}{2}\sum_{j=1}^{M}\sum_{k=1}^{M} V_j^* h_{jk} V_k, \tag{2.7}$$

which approximates it. We similarly derive the $M \times M$ matrices $\boldsymbol{\phi}_0$, $\boldsymbol{\phi}_s$, and $\boldsymbol{\phi}_\gamma = \boldsymbol{\phi}_0 + \gamma\boldsymbol{\phi}_s$ from the autocovariance functions $\phi_0(r, t)$, $\phi_s(r, t)$, and $\phi_\gamma(r, t)$.

At the end we shall pass to the limit $M \to \infty$, and it will be simple to convert our matrix equations to integral equations. For instance, to a matrix product such as $\mathbf{H}\boldsymbol{\phi}_\gamma$ will correspond the function of two variables

$$\int_0^T h(t, r)\, \phi_\gamma(r, u)\, dr.$$

It will be unnecessary to indicate explicitly the dependence of our matrices on the number M of the Fourier coefficients we are using.

The characteristic function of the statistic U_M is, under hypothesis H_γ,

$$f_\gamma(w) = \mathbf{E}[\exp iwU_M \,|\, H_\gamma] = \int_{-\infty}^{\infty} \cdots \int_{-\infty}^{\infty} \exp\left(\tfrac{1}{2}\, iw\mathbf{V}^+\mathbf{H}\mathbf{V}\right) p_\gamma(\mathbf{V}) \prod_{k=1}^{M} dV_{kx}\, dV_{ky}, \tag{2.8}$$

where $p_\gamma(\mathbf{V})$ is the circular Gaussian distribution of the real and imaginary parts of the variables $V_j = V_{jx} + iV_{jy}$, $j = 1, 2, \ldots, M$. As in Chapter II, Section 6, this distribution is

$$p_\gamma(\mathbf{V}) = (2\pi)^{-M} |\det \boldsymbol{\phi}_\gamma|^{-1} \exp\left(-\tfrac{1}{2}\mathbf{V}^+\boldsymbol{\phi}_\gamma^{-1}\mathbf{V}\right), \tag{2.9}$$

where in concise notation

$$\boldsymbol{\phi}_\gamma = \tfrac{1}{2}\,\mathbf{E}(\mathbf{V}\mathbf{V}^+ \mid H_\gamma);$$

explicitly, the elements of the covariance matrix $\boldsymbol{\phi}_\gamma$ are

$$\phi_{\gamma,jk} = \tfrac{1}{2}\,\mathbf{E}(V_j V_k^* \mid H_\gamma) = \int_0^T \int_0^T f_j^*(t)\, \phi_\gamma(t,s)\, f_k(s)\, dt\, ds, \tag{2.10}$$

which follows from eqs. (1.13) and (2.2). The multivariate Gaussian integral in eq. (2.8) can be evaluated by means of the normalization integral for a circular Gaussian p.d.f., and it yields

$$\begin{aligned} f_\gamma(w) &= |\det \boldsymbol{\phi}_\gamma|^{-1}| \det(\boldsymbol{\phi}_\gamma^{-1} - iw\mathbf{H})|^{-1} \\ &= |\det(\mathbf{I} - iw\mathbf{H}\boldsymbol{\phi}_\gamma)|^{-1}, \end{aligned} \tag{2.11}$$

I being the identity matrix. After the passage to the limit $M \to \infty$, the p.d.f. of the statistic U can in principle be obtained as the inverse Fourier transform

$$p_\gamma(U) = \int_{-\infty}^{\infty} f_\gamma(w) e^{-iwU}\, dw/2\pi. \tag{2.12}$$

This limiting process is awkward with the characteristic function in the form of a determinant, and first we write it in a different way. The determinant of any matrix **A** can be expressed as

$$\det \mathbf{A} = \exp(\mathrm{Tr} \ln \mathbf{A}), \tag{2.13}$$

where "Tr" stands for the trace of the matrix following it, the sum of the diagonal elements,

$$\mathrm{Tr}\,\mathbf{B} = \sum_{j=1}^{M} B_{jj}.$$

As customarily, functions of matrices are understood in terms of their Taylor series expansions. To verify eq. (2.13), one writes the determinant of **A** as the product of its eigenvalues $a_1, a_2, \ldots, a_M$,

$$\det \mathbf{A} = a_1 a_2 \ldots a_M = \exp\left(\sum_{j=1}^{M} \ln a_j\right).$$

The M quantities $\ln a_j$ are the eigenvalues of the matrix ln **A**, and as the trace of a matrix is equal to the sum of its eigenvalues, eq. (2.13) follows.

We can therefore put for eq. (2.11)

$$f_\gamma(w) = \exp\left[-\mathrm{Tr} \ln(\mathbf{I} - iw\mathbf{H}\boldsymbol{\phi}_\gamma)\right], \tag{2.14}$$

and this in turn can be expressed as

$$f_\gamma(w) = \exp i \operatorname{Tr} \int_0^w (\mathbf{I} - iu\mathbf{H}\boldsymbol{\phi}_\gamma)^{-1} \mathbf{H}\boldsymbol{\phi}_\gamma \, du$$
$$= \exp i \int_0^w \operatorname{Tr} \mathbf{L}_\gamma(-iu) \, du, \tag{2.15}$$

where the matrix $\mathbf{L}_\gamma(v) = ||L_{\gamma, km}(v)||$ is defined by the equation

$$\mathbf{L}_\gamma(v) = (\mathbf{I} + v\mathbf{H}\boldsymbol{\phi}_\gamma)^{-1} \mathbf{H}\boldsymbol{\phi}_\gamma$$

or

$$\mathbf{L}_\gamma(v) + v\mathbf{H}\boldsymbol{\phi}_\gamma \mathbf{L}_\gamma(v) = \mathbf{H}\boldsymbol{\phi}_\gamma. \tag{2.16}$$

To show the equivalence of eqs. (2.14) and (2.15), expand the integrand of the latter in a series of powers of u and integrate term by term to obtain the series for the logarithm in eq. (2.14).

We are now ready to pass to the limit $M \to \infty$. We define a function $L_\gamma(r, s; v)$ by

$$L_\gamma(r, s; v) = \lim_{M \to \infty} \sum_{k=1}^{M} \sum_{m=1}^{M} f_k(r) \, L_{\gamma, km}(v) \, f_m^*(s). \tag{2.17}$$

The limiting process transforms eq. (2.16) into the integral equation

$$L_\gamma(r, s; v) + v \int_0^T \int_0^T h(r, t) \, \phi_\gamma(t, y) \, L_\gamma(y, s; v) \, dt \, dy = \int_0^T h(r, t) \, \phi_\gamma(t, s) \, dt. \tag{2.18}$$

In addition, by setting $r = s$ in eq. (2.17), integrating over the interval $(0, T)$, and using the orthonormality of the basis functions, we find

$$\int_0^T L_\gamma(r, r; v) \, dr = \lim_{M \to \infty} \sum_{k=1}^{M} \sum_{m=1}^{M} L_{\gamma, km}(v) \, \delta_{mk} = \lim_{M \to \infty} \operatorname{Tr} \mathbf{L}_\gamma(v).$$

After all these manipulations we can use eq. (2.15) to write the ch.f. of the test statistic U of eq. (2.1) as

$$f_\gamma(w) = \mathbf{E}(e^{iwU} \mid H_\gamma) = \exp i \int_0^w du \int_0^T L_\gamma(r, r; -iu) \, dr. \tag{2.19}$$

To calculate it one must first solve the integral equation (2.18), substitute the solution into eq. (2.19), and carry out the integrations. It is apparent that taking the Fourier transform of the result in order to obtain the p.d.f. of U will not be easy. In most cases some approximations must be made.

(ii) *The optimum detector*. For the optimum detector the kernel $h(r, s)$ is the solution of the integral equation (1.24). We can use for the matrix **H** the one defined by eq. (1.19), which can be expressed as

$$\mathbf{H} = \boldsymbol{\phi}_0^{-1} - \boldsymbol{\phi}_1^{-1} = \boldsymbol{\phi}_0^{-1}\boldsymbol{\phi}_s\boldsymbol{\phi}_1^{-1} = \boldsymbol{\phi}_1^{-1}\boldsymbol{\phi}_s\boldsymbol{\phi}_0^{-1}, \qquad \boldsymbol{\phi}_1 = \boldsymbol{\phi}_0 + \boldsymbol{\phi}_s. \tag{2.20}$$

For the special values $\gamma = 0$ and $\gamma = 1$, an integral equation simpler than eq. (2.18) can then be obtained by substituting

$$\mathbf{H}\boldsymbol{\phi}_0 = \boldsymbol{\phi}_1^{-1}\boldsymbol{\phi}_s, \quad \mathbf{H}\boldsymbol{\phi}_1 = \boldsymbol{\phi}_0^{-1}\boldsymbol{\phi}_s$$

into eq. (2.16). We leave it for the reader to show that

$$\mathbf{L}_1(u) = \mathbf{L}_0(u-1) = (\boldsymbol{\phi}_0 + u\boldsymbol{\phi}_s)^{-1}\boldsymbol{\phi}_s, \tag{2.21}$$

so that after the passage to the limit, $L_1(r, s; u) = L_0(r, s; u-1)$ is the solution of the integral equation

$$\int_0^T [\phi_0(r, t) + u\phi_s(r, t)]\, L_1(t, s; u)\, dt = \phi_s(r, s), \qquad 0 < (r, s) < T. \tag{2.22}$$

It is unnecessary to have first solved eq. (1.24) for $h(t, s)$ in order to evaluate the optimum detector under hypotheses H_0 and H_1.

By integrating eq. (2.21) over $0 < u < 1$, we obtain

$$\int_0^1 \mathbf{L}_1(u)\, du = \ln\, [\boldsymbol{\phi}_0 + u\boldsymbol{\phi}_s]\Big|_{u=0}^{u=1} = \ln\, (\boldsymbol{\phi}_1\boldsymbol{\phi}_0^{-1}),$$

and by eq. (2.13) the Fredholm determinant we mentioned in connection with eq. (1.29) is

$$\det\, (\boldsymbol{\phi}_1\boldsymbol{\phi}_0^{-1}) = \exp\left[\mathrm{Tr} \int_0^1 \mathbf{L}_1(u)\, du\right] \to \exp \int_0^T \int_0^1 L_1(r, r; u)\, dr\, du = B. \tag{2.23}$$

Denoting the limiting expression on the right-hand side of this equation by B, we find from eq. (1.17) that the logarithm of the likelihood ratio of the optimum statistic U is

$$\ln \Lambda(U) = \ln\, [p_1(U)/p_0(U)] = U - \ln B, \tag{2.24}$$

from which the reader can show that

$$f_1(w) = B^{-1} f_0(w - i). \tag{2.25}$$

It does not seem possible in general to eliminate the kernel $h(t, s)$ from eq. (2.18) when γ does not equal 0 or 1. An exception is when the noise is white. By using as basis functions the eigenfunctions of the signal autocovariance, defined by eq. (1.31), one can put both matrices $\boldsymbol{\phi}_0$ and $\boldsymbol{\phi}_s$ simultaneously into diagonal form, to deduce that $\boldsymbol{\phi}_0^{-1}\boldsymbol{\phi}_s = N^{-1}\boldsymbol{\phi}_s$, where N is the unilateral spectral density of the noise. By eq. (2.20) and some matrix transformations, eq. (2.16) is reduced to

$$[\boldsymbol{\phi}_1 + v\boldsymbol{\phi}^{(1)}]\mathbf{L}_\gamma(v) = \boldsymbol{\phi}^{(1)}, \quad \boldsymbol{\phi}^{(1)} = \boldsymbol{\phi}_s + (\gamma/N)\boldsymbol{\phi}_s^2.$$

In the limit $M \gg 1$ the integral equation

$$NL_\gamma(r, t; v) + \int_0^T [\phi_s(r, s) + v\phi^{(1)}(r, s)]\, L_\gamma(s, t; v)\, ds = \phi^{(1)}(r, t) \quad (2.26)$$

is obtained for $L_\gamma(r, s; v)$, where

$$\phi^{(1)}(r, t) = \phi_s(r, t) + (\gamma/N) \int_0^T \phi_s(r, u)\, \phi_s(u, t)\, du. \quad (2.27)$$

Comparing eq. (2.26) for $\gamma = 0$ with eq. (1.46), we find that the function $h(r, t; u)$ for which we solved in the example in part (d) of Section 1 is

$$h(r, t; u) = N^{-1}L_0(r, t; u-1) = N^{-1}L_1(r, t; u).$$

(iii) *The Fredholm determinant.* If we write the determinant in eq. (2.11) in terms of the eigenvalues of the matrix $(\mathbf{I} - iw\mathbf{H}\boldsymbol{\phi}_\gamma)$, using eq. (1.32), we obtain in the limit $M \to \infty$

$$f_\gamma(w) = \prod_{n=1}^{\infty} \left[1 - \frac{iw\lambda_n(N+\gamma\lambda_n)}{N(\lambda_n+N)}\right]^{-1}.$$

Hence for $\gamma = 0$ and $\gamma = 1$ we find the simple relations

$$f_0(w) = D(1)/D(1-iw), \quad f_1(w) = 1/D(-iw), \quad (2.28)$$

where the Fredholm determinant $D(u)$ is defined as in eq. (1.35) for detection in white noise. That Fredholm determinant is now

$$D(u) = \exp\left[\int_0^u dv \int_0^T L_1(t, t; v)\, dt\right] \quad (2.29)$$

by virtue of eqs. (2.19) and (2.28).

A simpler formula for the Fredholm determinant was derived by Siegert (1957). In the present context it is

$$D(u) = \exp\left[u \int_0^T L_t(t, t; u)\, dt\right], \quad (2.30)$$

where $L_t(r, s; u)$ is the solution of the integral equation for $L_1(r, s; u)$ with the upper limit T replaced by t,

$$NL_t(r, s; u)+u \int_0^t \phi_s(r, v)\, L_t(v, s; u)\, dv = \phi_s(r, s),$$
$$0 < (r, s) < t.$$

By using the solution $h(r, t; u) = N^{-1}L_1(r, t; u)$ obtained in part (d) of Section 1, the reader can verify by either eq. (2.29) or eq. (2.30) that the Fredholm determinant associated with the signal autocovariance $\phi_s(r, t) = \phi_0 e^{-\mu|r-t|}$ is

$$D(u) = \frac{(\beta+\mu)^2 e^{\beta T}-(\beta-\mu)^2 e^{-\beta T}}{4\mu\beta e^{\mu T}}, \quad \beta^2 = \mu^2+2\mu\phi_0 u/N. \tag{2.31}$$

The numerator of $D(u)$ appears in the denominator of the solution for $h(r, t; u)$ in eq. (1.50), and as we stated before, the solution will not exist for such values of u that the Fredholm determinant $D(u)$ vanishes. These are the values $u = -N/\lambda_n$, where λ_n are the eigenvalues of the signal autocovariance. By setting $D(u)$ in eq. (2.31) equal to zero and solving for $u = -N/\lambda_n$, one obtains the eigenvalues derived in Chapter IV, Section 5, part (b) for this exponential covariance.

(iv) *The threshold detector.* For the threshold detector, $\mathbf{H} = \boldsymbol{\phi}_0^{-1}\boldsymbol{\phi}_s\boldsymbol{\phi}_0^{-1}$, and eq. (2.16) becomes

$$\mathbf{L}_\gamma^\theta(u) = [\boldsymbol{\phi}_0+u\boldsymbol{\phi}^{(1)}]^{-1}\boldsymbol{\phi}^{(1)}, \quad \boldsymbol{\phi}^{(1)} = \boldsymbol{\phi}_s\boldsymbol{\phi}_0^{-1}\boldsymbol{\phi}_\gamma. \tag{2.32}$$

From the matrix $\mathbf{L}_\gamma^\theta(u)$ one will pass to the limit $M \to \infty$ to obtain the function $L_\gamma^\theta(r, s; u)$, in terms of which the characteristic function of the threshold statistic will be

$$f_\gamma^\theta(w) = \mathbf{E}[\exp iwU_\theta \,|\, H_\gamma] = \exp\left[i\int_0^w dv \int_0^T L_\gamma^\theta(r, r; -iv)\, dr\right]. \tag{2.33}$$

Only for $\gamma = 0$ is the integral equation for $L_\gamma^\theta(r, s; u)$ any simpler than eq. (2.18). From eq. (2.32) one finds

$$\mathbf{L}_0^\theta(u) = (\boldsymbol{\phi}_0+u\boldsymbol{\phi}_s)^{-1}\boldsymbol{\phi}_s = \mathbf{L}_1(u),$$

where by eq. (2.21) $\mathbf{L}_1(u)$ is the matrix appropriate to the optimum detector under hypothesis H_1. Hence $L_0^\theta(r, t; u) = L_1(r, t; u)$ and

$$p_0^\theta(U) = p_1(U). \tag{2.34}$$

The threshold statistic U_θ has under hypothesis H_0 the same p.d.f. as the optimum statistic under hypothesis H_1.

For other signal strengths than $\gamma = 0$ the calculation of the characteristic function of the threshold statistic is no simpler than for the optimum statistic. When the noise is white, however, we obtain from eq. (2.32) by using

$\boldsymbol{\phi}_0^{-1}\boldsymbol{\phi}_s = N^{-1}\boldsymbol{\phi}_s$ the integral equation

$$NL_\gamma^\varrho(r, t; u)+u\int_0^T \phi^{(1)}(r, s)\, L_\gamma^\varrho(s, t; u)\, ds = \phi^{(1)}(r, t), \qquad 0 < (r, t) < T, \tag{2.35}$$

where $\phi^{(1)}(r, t)$ is again given by eq. (2.27). This equation may be compared with eq. (2.26) for the auxiliary function $L_\gamma(r, t; v)$ for the optimum detector.

(v) *The output of the quadratic rectifier.* Let the input to the quadratic rectifier be the stationary narrowband Gaussian random process Rl $V(t)e^{i\Omega t}$ with the complex autocovariance $\phi(\tau)$. The output of the rectifier is filtered as specified by eq. (2.4). The p.d.f. of the filtered output U, which is also stationary, is the Fourier transform of the characteristic function

$$f(w) = \mathbf{E}(e^{iwU}) = \exp\left[i\int_0^w dv \int_{-\infty}^t L(r, r; -iv)\, dr\right],$$

where the function $L(r, s; u)$ is the solution of the integral equation

$$\begin{aligned} L(r, s; u)+u\int_{-\infty}^t \int_{-\infty}^t K(t-r)\,\delta(r-p)\,\phi(p-v)\,L(v, s; u)\,dp\,dv \\ = \int_{-\infty}^t K(t-r)\,\delta(r-p)\,\phi(p-s)\,dp, \end{aligned} \tag{2.36}$$

which has been obtained by substituting eq. (2.5) into eq. (2.18) and changing the limits of integration as mentioned in connection with eqs. (2.4) and (2.5). By introducing new variables we can write eq. (2.36) as

$$L(t-\varrho, t-\sigma; u)+uK(\varrho)\int_0^\infty \phi(\tau-\varrho)\,L(t-\tau, t-\sigma; u)\,d\tau = K(\varrho)\,\phi(\sigma-\varrho).$$

If we now define a new function $G(\varrho, \sigma; u)$ by

$$L(t-\varrho, t-\sigma; u) = K(\varrho)\, G(\varrho, \sigma; u),$$

we find that the ch.f. is given by

$$f(w) = \exp\left[i\int_0^w dv \int_0^\infty K(\varrho)\, G(\varrho, \varrho; -iv)\, d\varrho\right] \tag{2.37}$$

with $G(\varrho, \sigma; u)$ the solution of the integral equation

$$G(\varrho, \sigma; u)+u\int_0^\infty K(\tau)\,\phi(\tau-\varrho)\,G(\tau, \sigma; u)\,d\tau = \phi(\sigma-\varrho). \tag{2.38}$$

This method of determining the ch.f. was presented by Siegert (1954).

Unfortunately, it is only for the quadratic rectifier that the ch.f. can be found in so straightforward a way as this. Linear rectifiers and most other non-linear devices resist simple analysis.

(b) *The Gram–Charlier Series*

To obtain the p.d.f. of the statistic U it is necessary to carry out an inverse Fourier transformation of the ch.f. $f_\gamma(w)$, and this is seldom possible by any analytical means. Approximations must be made, and the rest of this section will deal with a few of them.

The most direct method of approximating the probability $Q_d(\gamma)$ of detection utilizes the Gram–Charlier series introduced in Chapter VII, Section 2. The coefficients of that series involve the cumulants of the distribution, which are the coefficients of $(iw)^m/m!$ in an expansion of $\ln f_\gamma(w)$,

$$\ln f_\gamma(w) = \sum_{m=0}^{\infty} \varkappa_m (iw)^m/m!. \tag{2.39}$$

For a quadratic functional the cumulants can be found by first solving the integral equation (2.18) by iteration,

$$\begin{aligned} L_\gamma(r, s; u) = &\int h(r, t)\, \phi_\gamma(t, s)\, dt \\ &-u \iiint h(r, t')\, \phi_\gamma(t', v')\, h(v', t'')\, \phi_\gamma(t'', s)\, dt'\, dv'\, dt'' \\ &+u^2 \int \ldots \int h(r, t')\, \phi_\gamma(t', v')\, h(v', t'')\, \phi_\gamma(t'', v'')\, h(v'', t''')\cdot \\ &\qquad \phi_\gamma(t''', s)\, dt'\, dv'\, dt''\, dv''\, dt''' - + \ldots . \end{aligned} \tag{2.40}$$

The limits on all integrals are 0 and T. When this is substituted into eq. (2.19), we obtain

$$\begin{aligned} \ln f_\gamma(w) = &\, iw \iint h(r, t)\, \phi_\gamma(t, r)\, dt\, dr \\ &+\tfrac{1}{2}(iw)^2 \iiiint h(r, t')\, \phi_\gamma(t', v')\, h(v', t'')\, \phi_\gamma(t'', r)\, dt'\, dv'\, dt''\, dr \\ &+\tfrac{1}{3}(iw)^3 \int \ldots \int h(r, t')\, \phi_\gamma(t', v')\, h(v', t'')\, \phi_\gamma(t'', v'')\, h(v'', t''') \\ &\qquad \phi_\gamma(t''', r)\, dt'\, dv'\, dt''\, dv''\, dt'''\, dr + \ldots . \end{aligned} \tag{2.41}$$

The coefficients of the remaining terms are $n^{-1}(iw)^n$, their forms an obvious extension of those just given.

If the kernel $h(r, s)$ of the quadratic functional is known, the cumulants can be determined directly and substituted into eq. (VII, 2.23) to obtain the p.d.f. of the statistic U. From this, by means of eqs. (VII, 2.25), (VII, 2.26) we get the probability of detection,

$$\begin{aligned} Q_d(\gamma) = &\tfrac{1}{2} - \phi^{-1}(Y) + \tfrac{1}{6}(\varkappa_3/\sigma^3)\, \phi^{(2)}(Y) - \tfrac{1}{24}(\varkappa_4/\sigma^4)\, \phi^{(3)}(Y) \\ &+ \tfrac{1}{120}(\varkappa_5/\sigma^5)\, \phi^{(4)}(Y) - \tfrac{1}{720}(\varkappa_6 + 10\varkappa_3^2)\, \sigma^{-6} \phi^{(5)}(Y) + \ldots, \\ Y = (U - \bar{U}_\gamma)/\sigma_U, &\quad \bar{U}_\gamma = \mathbf{E}(U \mid H_\gamma), \quad \sigma_U^2 = \mathrm{Var}_\gamma\, U. \end{aligned} \tag{2.42}$$

This series will in general converge rapidly when the observation time T is much longer than the correlation times of the signal and the noise, whereupon the distribution of the statistic U is nearly Gaussian. The mean, variance, and third cumulant of U are, from eq. (2.41),

$$\begin{aligned} \mathbf{E}(U \mid H_\gamma) &= \bar{U}_\gamma = \iint h(t_1, t_2)\, \phi_\gamma(t_2, t_1)\, dt_1\, dt_2, \\ \mathrm{Var}_\gamma\, U &= \iiiint h(t_1, t_2)\, \phi_\gamma(t_2, t_3)\, h(t_3, t_4)\, \phi_\gamma(t_4, t_1)\, dt_1\, dt_2\, dt_3\, dt_4, \qquad (2.43) \\ \varkappa_3 &= \mathbf{E}[(U - \bar{U}_\gamma)^3 \mid H_\gamma] = 2 \int \ldots \int h(t_1, t_2)\, \phi_\gamma(t_2, t_3)\, h(t_3, t_4) \cdot \\ &\qquad \phi_\gamma(t_4, t_5)\, h(t_5, t_6)\, \phi_\gamma(t_6, t_1)\, dt_1\, dt_2\, dt_3\, dt_4\, dt_5\, dt_6 . \end{aligned}$$

This method was used by Emerson (1953) to approximate the p.d.f. of the filtered output of a quadratic rectifier. To evaluate the optimum or the threshold detector of stochastic signals, one must first have calculated the kernel $h(t, s)$, which is itself the solution of an integral equation.

For detection of stochastic signals in white noise, the ch.f. depends on the solution of the integral equation (2.26). Iteration applied to this equation does not yield a series of powers of u, however, and unless $h(t, s)$ is given in closed form, the cumulants themselves can be determined only approximately. With the threshold detector in white noise, on the other hand, the ch.f. can be found from the solution of eq. (2.34), and this equation does provide the cumulants when it is solved by iteration. One obtains the following expansion of the logarithm of the characteristic function

$$\begin{aligned} \ln f_\gamma^\theta(w) = {} & iw \int \phi^{(1)}(r, r)\, dr/N + \tfrac{1}{2}(iw)^2 \iint \phi^{(1)}(r, s)\, \phi^{(1)}(s, r)\, dr\, ds/N^2 \\ & + \tfrac{1}{3}(iw)^3 \iiint \phi^{(1)}(r, s)\, \phi^{(1)}(s, t)\, \phi^{(1)}(t, r)\, dr\, ds\, dt/N^3 + \ldots, \end{aligned} \qquad (2.44)$$

where $\phi^{(1)}(r, t)$ is given by eq. (2.27). For the false-alarm probability one sets $\gamma = 0$, $\phi^{(1)}(r, t) = \phi_s(r, t)$, and the formulas are simplified.

Applying this method to the threshold detector of signals whose autocovariance is that given by eq. (1.45), we find under hypothesis H_0 the cumulants

$$\begin{aligned} \mathbf{E}(U \mid H_0) &= \bar{U}_0 = \phi_0 T/N, \\ \mathrm{Var}_0\, U &= \tfrac{1}{2}(\phi_0/\mu N)^2 (2\mu T - 1 + e^{-2\mu T}), \qquad (2.45) \\ \varkappa_3 &= \mathbf{E}[(U - \bar{U}_0)^3 \mid H_0] = 3(\phi_0/\mu N)^3 [(\mu T - 1) + (\mu T + 1)e^{-2\mu T}]. \end{aligned}$$

For $\mu T \gg 1$ the quantity $\varkappa_3/\sigma^3$ is approximately equal to $3(\mu T)^{-\frac{1}{2}}$, and we can expect the Gram–Charlier series to be accurate in the limit $\mu T \gg 1$. The formulas for the cumulants under hypothesis H_γ are cumbersome and we give only the mean and the variance,

$$\mathbf{E}(U\,|\,H_\gamma) = (\phi_0 T/N)\left[1+\left(\frac{\gamma\phi_0 T}{N}\right)\frac{2\mu T-1+e^{-2\mu T}}{2\mu^2T^2}\right],$$

$$\begin{aligned}\mathrm{Var}_\gamma\, U = (\phi_0 T/N)^2\left\{\frac{2\mu T-1+e^{-2\mu T}}{2\mu^2T^2}+3\left(\frac{\gamma\phi_0 T}{N}\right)\frac{\mu T-1+(\mu T+1)e^{-2\mu T}}{\mu^3T^3}\right.\\ \left.+\frac{3}{2}\left(\frac{\gamma\phi_0 T}{N}\right)^2\frac{2\mu T-3+(3+4\mu T+2\mu^2T^2)e^{-2\mu T}}{\mu^4T^4}\right\} = \sigma_\gamma^2. \quad (2.46)\end{aligned}$$

The false-alarm and detection probabilities when $\mu T \gg 1$ are approximately

$$\begin{aligned}Q_0 \cong \mathrm{erfc}\, x, \quad Q_d \cong 1-\mathrm{erfc}\, y, \quad y = \frac{\sigma_0}{\sigma_\gamma}\left(\frac{\bar{U}_\gamma-\bar{U}_0}{\sigma_0}+x\right),\\ (\bar{U}_\gamma-\bar{U}_0)/\sigma_0 = D_\gamma \cong \bar{E}/N(\mu T)^{\frac{1}{2}}, \quad \bar{E} = \gamma\phi_0 T,\\ \sigma_0/\sigma_\gamma \cong (1+3\beta+3\beta^2)^{-\frac{1}{2}}, \quad \beta = \bar{E}/\mu TN,\end{aligned} \quad (2.47)$$

where $\bar{E}$ is the average total received signal energy. The longer the interval over which that energy is spread, the smaller the probability of detecting the signal.

(c) *Detectability for Short Observation Times*

Let $\varrho_k(\gamma)$ be the eigenvalues of the matrix $\mathbf{H\Phi}_\gamma$. Then from eq. (2.11) the ch.f. can be written

$$f_\gamma(w) = \prod_{k=1}^{\infty}[1-iw\varrho_k(\gamma)]^{-1}. \quad (2.48)$$

The poles of the function $f_\gamma(w)$ lie at the points $w = -i/\varrho_k(\gamma)$ in the complex plane. Formally the p.d.f. of the statistic U can be written in terms of the residues of $f_\gamma(w)$ at those poles,

$$p_\gamma(U) = -i\sum_{k=1}^{\infty}\mathrm{Res}\, f_\gamma(w)\Big|_{w=-i/\varrho_k}\exp(-U/\varrho_k). \quad (2.49)$$

For the optimum detector of a signal in white noise, by part (a, iii) of this section,

$$\varrho_k(\gamma) = \frac{\lambda_k(N+\gamma\lambda_k)}{N(N+\lambda_k)}, \quad (2.50)$$

where $\lambda_1, \lambda_2, \ldots,$ are the eigenvalues of the autocovariance $\phi_s(r, t)$ as determined by eq. (1.31). Let these be arranged in descending order, with λ_1 the largest. Then if all other eigenvalues are much smaller than λ_1, the term

$$\left[1-\frac{iw\lambda_1(N+\gamma\lambda_1)}{N(N+\lambda_1)}\right]^{-1}$$

dominates the ch.f. $f_\gamma(w)$, and the p.d.f. of the statistic U is approximately

$$p_\gamma(U) = [\varrho_1(\gamma)]^{-1} \exp [-U/\varrho_1(\gamma)]. \tag{2.51}$$

Thus the false-alarm and detection probabilities are approximately

$$\begin{aligned} Q_0 &\cong \exp [-U_0(\lambda_1+N)/\lambda_1], \\ Q_d(\gamma) &\cong \exp [-U_0N(N+\lambda_1)/\lambda_1(N+\gamma\lambda_1)], \end{aligned} \tag{2.52}$$

where U_0 is the decision level for the statistic U. Eliminating U_0, we find

$$Q_d(\gamma) \cong Q_0^{1/r}, \quad r = 1+\gamma\lambda_1/N. \tag{2.53}$$

In the example treated before, with the autocovariance of the signal given by eq. (1.45), we see by inspecting Fig. IV.6 that the first eigenvalue is much greater than all the others when $\mu T \ll 1$, that is, when the observation time is much shorter than the correlation time of the signal. The largest eigenvalue is then, as in this example, accurately given by the Rayleigh–Ritz method as

$$\begin{aligned} \lambda_1 &= \min_{f(\cdot)} \int_0^T \int_0^T \phi_s(r, t) \overset{*}{f}(r) f(t)\, dr\, dt \Big/ \int_0^T |f(t)|^2\, dt \\ &= T^{-1} \int_0^T \int_0^T \phi_s(r, t)\, dr\, dt, \end{aligned}$$

in which we have used a constant trial function $f(t)$. For a stationary signal $\gamma\lambda_1 \cong \bar{E}$, the total average energy of the signal, and the probability of detection is approximately

$$Q_d(\gamma) \cong Q_0^{1/r}, \quad r = 1+\bar{E}/N. \tag{2.54}$$

The same result is obtained for the threshold detector.

In Fig. XI.2 we have plotted the probability of detection as a function of the "signal-to-noise ratio" $\bar{E}/N = \gamma\phi_0 T/N$ for a few values of the false-alarm probability, in the limit in which the product of signal bandwidth and observation time is very small. In this case the system is effectively using only one statistically independent sample of the signal in making a decision whether it is present. To improve the detectability of the signals, the observation time must be much longer.

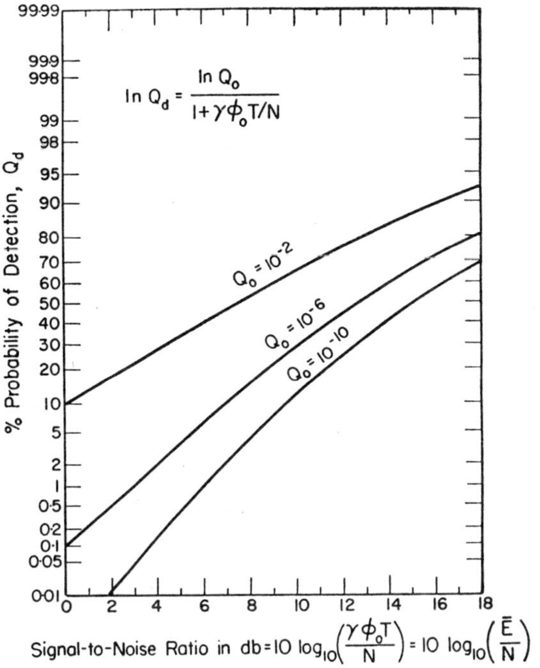

FIG. XI.2. Detectability of stochastic signals: short observation time.

(d) *The Probability Distribution for Small Values of the Statistic*†

If the characteristic function of the output U is given explicitly, it is possible to study the behavior of the probability density function of the test statistic U for small values of U, for the p.d.f. at small values of U is related to the form of the characteristic function $f(w)$ as w goes to infinity along the positive imaginary axis. For this purpose it is convenient to use the Laplace transform of the p.d.f. in place of its Fourier transform; it is simply a matter of rotating the complex plane through ninety degrees.

We shall consider the p.d.f. under hypothesis H_0 of the threshold statistic, which we have seen is the same as the p.d.f. under H_1 of the optimum test statistic. According to eq. (2.28) its Laplace transform is

$$\mathscr{L}p_0^\theta(U) = \int_0^\infty p_0^\theta(U)e^{-Uz}\,dU = 1/D(z), \tag{2.55}$$

and it can be recovered by the inverse Laplace transform

$$p_0^\theta(U) = \int_{C-i\infty}^{C+i\infty} \frac{e^{Uz}}{D(z)}\frac{dz}{2\pi i},$$

† Part (d) may be omitted on first reading.

in which the integration is taken along a contour $z = C+iy$, $-\infty < y < \infty$, that passes to the right of all the poles of the integrand. The Laplace transform of the cumulative distribution

$$P_0^\theta(U) = \int_0^U p_0^\theta(U')\, dU'$$

of the threshold statistic is in turn given by

$$\int_0^\infty P_0^\theta(U)e^{-Uz}\, dU = 1/zD(z), \tag{2.56}$$

as can be shown by partial integration. In terms of the cumulative distribution the false-alarm probability is

$$Q_0^\theta = 1-P_0^\theta(U_0),$$

U_0 being the decision level with which the threshold statistic is compared.

In the example of Section 1, part (d), the Fredholm determinant $D(z)$, given in eq. (2.31), behaves like $z^{\frac{1}{2}} \exp\left(az^{\frac{1}{2}}\right)$ for large, real values of z, where a is a positive constant; and the Laplace transform of the cumulative distribution $P_0^\theta(U)$ must therefore behave like $z^{-\frac{3}{2}} \exp\left(-az^{\frac{1}{2}}\right)$ in the same region. If we can find a function of U whose Laplace transform has this dependence for large z, it will approximate the distribution $p_0^\theta(U)$ for small values of U. The reason for this is that when in the definition in eq. (2.56) z is large and real, the integrand is significantly large only for very small values of U, e^{-Uz} vanishing rapidly as U increases. Thus the form of the transform for large, real values of z must reflect the character of the distribution $p_0^\theta(U)$ for small values of U.

A series possessing the desired transformation properties is

$$P_0^\theta(U) = U^k\, e^{-A/U}[b_0+b_1(U/A)+b_2(U/A)^2+\ \ldots]. \tag{2.57}$$

The Laplace transform of this series is, by eq. (29), p. 146 of Erdélyi *et al.* (1954), vol. 1,

$$\begin{aligned}\mathcal{L}P_0^\theta(U) = 1/zD(z) &= 2(A/z)^{(k+1)/2}\, \{b_0K_{k+1}(2\sqrt{Az})\\ &+b_1(Az)^{-\frac{1}{2}}\, K_{k+2}(2\sqrt{Az})+b_2(Az)^{-1}\, K_{k+3}(2\sqrt{Az})+\ \ldots\},\end{aligned} \tag{2.58}$$

where $K_n(x)$ is the modified Bessel function of the second kind. To work out the form of the above transform for large values of z we use the asymptotic form of the modified Bessel functions (Erdélyi *et al.* (1953), vol. 2, p. 86, eq. (7)),

$$K_n(x) \sim (\pi/2x)^{\frac{1}{2}}\, e^{-x} \sum_{m=0}^{\infty} (n, m)\, (2x)^{-m},$$

where (n, m) is the Neumann symbol

$$(n, 0) = 1; \qquad (n, m) = 2^{-2m}(4n^2-1^2)\,(4n^2-3^2)\,\ldots\,[4n^2-(2m-1)^2]/m!.$$

Substituting into eq. (2.58) we find for large values of z

$$1/zD(z) \sim \pi^{\frac{1}{2}}\,(Az)^{-\frac{1}{4}}\,(A/z)^{(k+1)/2}\,\exp\left[-2(Az)^{\frac{1}{2}}\right]\cdot \left\{b_0+(Az)^{-\frac{1}{2}}\,[b_1+\tfrac{1}{4}(k+1,\,1)b_0]+\ \ldots\right\}. \tag{2.59}$$

In order to determine the coefficients b_k to be used in eq. (2.57), we must expand the function $1/zD(z)$ for large values of z and compare it with the corresponding terms of eq. (2.59). In the example worked out in Section 1, large values of z correspond to large values of β. With the present approximations we can neglect the term in $e^{-\beta T}$ in eq. (2.31). After some labor we find, with $N=1$,

$$1/zD(z) \sim \frac{2}{z}(2m/x)^{\frac{1}{2}}\,\exp\!\left[m-(2mx)^{\frac{1}{2}}\right]\left[1-(1+\tfrac{1}{4}m)\,(2m/x)^{\frac{1}{2}}+\ \ldots\right],$$
$$m = \mu T, \quad x = \phi_0 Tz.$$

Comparing with eq. (2.59) we find $k = 3/2$, $A = m/2$, and we finally obtain the expansion

$$\begin{aligned} P_1(U_0) &= P_0^{\theta}(U_0) = 1-Q_d(1) = 1-Q_0^{\theta} \\ &\sim 4(2/\pi m)^{\frac{1}{2}}\,(U_0/\phi_0 T)^{\frac{3}{2}}\,\exp\left(m-\frac{m\phi_0 T}{2U_0}\right)\cdot \\ &\quad \left[1-\frac{m^2+4m+6}{2m}(U_0/\phi_0 T)+\ \ldots\right], \\ &\qquad m = \mu T. \end{aligned} \tag{2.60}$$

We can expect the series in brackets to be valid only when $(U_0/\phi_0 T)$ is much less than the smaller of μT and $(\mu T)^{-1}$. The p.d.f.s $p_1(U) = p_0^{\theta}(U)$ can be found by differentiating eq. (2.60) with respect to U_0, or by applying the same procedure to $1/D(z)$; they turn out to be proportional to $U^{-\frac{1}{2}}\exp\left(-\mu\phi_0 T^2/2U\right)$.

A method for determining expansions of the form of eq. (2.57) when the characteristic function is not known explicitly would be useful; to our knowledge such a method has not been published. It requires an analysis of the resolvent kernel $L_1(r, t; u)$ for large values of u. However, we can acquire some understanding of the behavior of p.d.f.s like $p_0^{\theta}(U)$ for small values of U by examining our result for the signal autocovariance $\phi_s(r, t) = \phi_0 e^{-\mu|r-t|}$. On account of the exponential factor $\exp\left(-\mu\phi_0 T^2/2U\right)$, the p.d.f. remains very small for small values of U, becoming significantly large only when (U/ϕ_0T) grows to something of the order of μT. The larger the product of observation time and input signal bandwidth, the wider this range of improbable values of (U/ϕ_0T). This behavior is to be expected, for the receiver integrates quantities that are always positive, and very small values of their sum become the more unlikely, the longer this integration proceeds. When the product of observation time and bandwidth is very large, on the other hand, the system is effectively summing a large number of independent random variables, and the p.d.f. of the sum is nearly Gaussian. The Gaussian approximation, eq. (2.42), is best for values of U_0 in the neighborhood of the mean. For small values of U_0 the cumulative distribution is most closely approximated by the series in eq. (2.57), and for large values of U it becomes proportional to the exponential function $\exp(-U_0/\lambda_1)$, where λ_1 is the largest eigenvalue of the signal autocovariance $\phi_s(r, t)$.

(e) *The Question of Singularity*

When we studied the detection of a deterministic signal in colored Gaussian noise, we found that under certain circumstances the theory predicted that the signal could be detected with zero probability of error. This situation, known as the "singular case of perfect detection", arises, for instance, if the spectral density of the noise vanishes in a region of frequencies where the spectrum of the signal remains finite. The same possibility of perfect detection must be considered in dealing with stochastic signals.

Usually one's model of the signal and the noise is at least partly conjectural, and its accuracy cannot be completely verified. The model is often one that has been simplified to make it mathematically tractable. If upon an analysis based on it, the singular case turns up and the signals appear to be perfectly detectable, the model must be at fault, for nature never permits complete freedom from the hazard of error. Our treatment of the problem of singularity will necessarily be crude. For rigorous derivations the reader must look to the references we shall cite.

A stochastic signal will be perfectly detectable only if the p.d.f.s of the statistic U_M under hypotheses H_0 and H_1 recede so far from each other as M goes to infinity that they no longer overlap. It will then be possible to set the decision level U_0 at such a point between them that $Q_0 = 0$ and $Q_d = 1$. As the statistic U_M is a quadratic form in Gaussian random variables, however, its p.d.f. will be finite at all positive values of U_M under both hypotheses. The only way by which the p.d.f.s $p_0(U_M)$ and $p_1(U_M)$ can cease to overlap as M goes to infinity, therefore, is for the difference of the means

$$\Delta \bar{U}_M = \mathbf{E}(U_M \mid H_1) - \mathbf{E}(U_M \mid H_0)$$

to become ever larger with respect to the standard deviations of U_M. Conversely, the p.d.f.s will continue to overlap if the ratio

$$(\Delta \bar{U}_M)^2 / \mathrm{Var}_0\, U_M$$

remains finite as M grows beyond all bounds. It is the limiting value of this ratio that settles the question of singularity.

By eqs. (1.18) and (1.14)

$$\begin{aligned}\Delta \bar{U}_M &= \mathrm{Tr}\, \mathbf{H}\boldsymbol{\phi}_s = \mathrm{Tr}\, (\boldsymbol{\phi}_s \boldsymbol{\phi}_0^{-1} \boldsymbol{\phi}_s \boldsymbol{\phi}_1^{-1}) \\ &= \mathrm{Tr}\, \left(\boldsymbol{\phi}_s^{\frac{1}{2}} \boldsymbol{\phi}_0^{-1} \boldsymbol{\phi}_s^{\frac{1}{2}} \boldsymbol{\phi}_s^{\frac{1}{2}} \boldsymbol{\phi}_1^{-1} \boldsymbol{\phi}_s^{\frac{1}{2}}\right),\end{aligned}$$

where we have used the rule $\mathrm{Tr}\, \mathbf{AB} = \mathrm{Tr}\, \mathbf{BA}$ for any two matrices $\mathbf{A}$ and $\mathbf{B}$. Here $\boldsymbol{\phi}_s^{\frac{1}{2}}$ is the square root of the positive-definite matrix $\boldsymbol{\phi}_s$. It can be found if necessary by first diagonalizing $\boldsymbol{\phi}_s$ by a unitary transformation, taking the square-roots of the diagonal elements of the transformed matrix—the eigenvalues of $\boldsymbol{\phi}_s$—and performing the inverse unitary transformation.

By Schwarz's inequality the traces of the Hermitian matrices $\mathbf{A} = \boldsymbol{\phi}_s^{\frac{1}{2}} \boldsymbol{\phi}_0^{-1} \boldsymbol{\phi}_s^{\frac{1}{2}}$ and $\mathbf{B} = \boldsymbol{\phi}_s^{\frac{1}{2}} \boldsymbol{\phi}_1^{-1} \boldsymbol{\phi}_s^{\frac{1}{2}}$ satisfy the relation

$$\begin{aligned}(\mathrm{Tr}\, \mathbf{AB})^2 &= \left(\sum_{i,j=1}^{M} A_{ij} B_{ij}^* \right)^2 \le \sum_{i,j=1}^{M} |A_{ij}|^2 \sum_{i,j=1}^{M} |B_{ij}|^2 \\ &= \mathrm{Tr}\, \mathbf{AA}^+ \; \mathrm{Tr}\, \mathbf{BB}^+ .\end{aligned}$$

Hence

$$\begin{aligned}(\Delta \bar{U}_M)^2 &\le \mathrm{Tr}\, \boldsymbol{\phi}_s^{\frac{1}{2}} \boldsymbol{\phi}_0^{-1} \boldsymbol{\phi}_s^{\frac{1}{2}} \boldsymbol{\phi}_s^{\frac{1}{2}} \boldsymbol{\phi}_0^{-1} \boldsymbol{\phi}_s^{\frac{1}{2}} \; \mathrm{Tr}\, \boldsymbol{\phi}_s^{\frac{1}{2}} \boldsymbol{\phi}_1^{-1} \boldsymbol{\phi}_s^{\frac{1}{2}} \boldsymbol{\phi}_s^{\frac{1}{2}} \boldsymbol{\phi}_1^{-1} \boldsymbol{\phi}_s^{\frac{1}{2}} \\ &= \mathrm{Tr}\, \boldsymbol{\phi}_s \boldsymbol{\phi}_0^{-1} \boldsymbol{\phi}_s \boldsymbol{\phi}_0^{-1} \; \mathrm{Tr}\, \boldsymbol{\phi}_s \boldsymbol{\phi}_1^{-1} \boldsymbol{\phi}_s \boldsymbol{\phi}_1^{-1} = (\mathrm{Var}_1\, U_M)(\mathrm{Var}_0\, U_M),\end{aligned}$$

and the ratio $(\Delta \bar{U}_M)^2 / \mathrm{Var}_0\, U_M$ is bounded by

$$\mathrm{Var}_1\, U_M = \mathrm{Tr}\, \boldsymbol{\phi}_s \boldsymbol{\phi}_0^{-1} \boldsymbol{\phi}_s \boldsymbol{\phi}_0^{-1}.$$

If, therefore, $\mathrm{Var}_1 U_M$ stays finite as M goes to infinity, the detection cannot be perfect.

Root (1963) studied the singularity of the detection of stochastic signals in terms of the eigenvalues ε_k of the matrix $\boldsymbol{\phi}_0^{-\frac{1}{2}} \boldsymbol{\phi}_1 \boldsymbol{\phi}_0^{-\frac{1}{2}}$, by means of which the variance of the test statistic under hypothesis H_1 can be written

$$\mathrm{Var}_1\, U_M = \mathrm{Tr}\, \boldsymbol{\phi}_0^{-\frac{1}{2}} \boldsymbol{\phi}_s \boldsymbol{\phi}_0^{-\frac{1}{2}} \boldsymbol{\phi}_0^{-\frac{1}{2}} \boldsymbol{\phi}_s \boldsymbol{\phi}_0^{-\frac{1}{2}} = \sum_{k=1}^{M} (\varepsilon_k - 1)^2,$$

and he showed that if this sum remains finite as M goes to infinity, the detection process is liable to error. Pitcher (1966) has proved that a sufficient condition for this non-singularity is that the solution $h(t, s)$ of the integral equation (1.24) exist and be continuous in t and s. Further treatment can be found in papers by Hájek (1962) and Kadota (1964, 1965). Slepian (1958) presented some simple and illuminating examples of singular detection.

It is generally difficult to judge on the basis of the autocovariances $\phi_s(t, s)$ and $\phi_0(t, s)$ of signal and noise whether these conditions are fulfilled. Matters are somewhat simpler when both signal and noise are segments of stationary processes and their autocovariances are functions only of $\tau = t-s$, $\phi_s(\tau)$ and $\phi_0(\tau)$. Yaglom (1963) showed that when both have rational spectral densities $\Phi_s(\omega)$ and $\Phi_0(\omega)$, detection will be imperfect if and only if

$$\lim_{\omega\to\infty} \Phi_1(\omega)/\Phi_0(\omega) = 1, \quad \Phi_1(\omega) = \Phi_0(\omega)+\Phi_s(\omega). \tag{2.61}$$

This will always be the case when the signal has finite power and the noise contains a component that is white.

We can understand the condition in eq. (2.61) by observing first that the solution of eq. (1.24) will contain a term of the form $\eta(t-s)$ given by eq. (1.28), along with some delta-functions and their derivatives to take care of the end-points of the interval $(0, T)$ and, possibly, some exponential functions. This term will contribute to $\mathrm{Var}_1 U_M$, when T is large, approximately

$$T \int_{-\infty}^{\infty} [\Phi_s(\omega)/\Phi_0(\omega)]^2 \, d\omega/2\pi.$$

Middleton (1961) showed that the remaining terms are always finite. If the condition in eq. (2.61) is satisfied, $\mathrm{Var}_1 U_M$ will indeed be finite when the spectral densities are rational, and the detection will entail a probability of error that vanishes only when the strength of the signal itself grows beyond all bounds.

3. SUMMARY

In this book we have introduced the statistical theory of signal detection in terms of the simplest of three kinds of problem, signal detection, parameter estimation, and signal resolution; and we have presented mathematical methods for solving them. Not all applications of the theory are so easy; rather, the opposite is the case, but the understanding acquired by studying elementary examples is a guide to the analysis of more complicated situations.

Applying the theory to a new problem involves several steps. First of all, one specifies the hypotheses to be tested and the kinds of measurements to be used in deciding among them. Are there only two hypotheses, as in ordinary signal detection, or several, as in multi-signal communications; and are these hypotheses simple or composite? One describes what is known about past occurrence of the hypothetical circumstances and, when possible, fixes prior probabilities for the hypotheses and prior probability density functions of any unknown parameters. The probability distributions of the measurements under each hypothesis are determined by experiment or theory, and for this one must study the "noise" that interferes with the decision in a random, unpredictable way.

Second, a decision criterion is chosen. The Bayes criterion requires knowledge of the prior probabilities of the hypotheses and assessment of the cost of each possible decision under each hypothesis. If sufficient prior information is not at hand, one may instead select the minimax criterion and look for least favorable distributions. When cost evaluations are unavailable, the Neyman–Pearson criterion or an appropriate modification may be adopted. The selection of a criterion is naturally influenced by the observer's policies and by the uses to which the decisions are to be put.

Third, on the basis of the chosen criterion the best decision strategy is determined. In geometrical language, the "space" of the measured data is divided into decision regions, each associated with a choice of one of the hypotheses. In an estimation problem the desired estimates are such functions of the data as satisfy the ruling criterion. A system is then designed to process the data and indicate the selected hypothesis or form the estimate. At this stage it is often necessary to make approximations to simplify the strategy and the system. To avoid excessive complexity, strict adherence to a criterion must sometimes be relaxed.

Finally, the efficiency of the decision strategy and of the system that realizes it is determined. False-alarm and detection probabilities, variances of errors of parameter estimates, and minimax or Bayes risks are calculated. The results permit comparison of the new system with existing ones. Here again mathematical difficulties often arise, and approximations must be made.

We first applied this theory to the detection of a completely known signal in the midst of Gaussian noise, with the decision about its presence or absence to be based on measurement of the receiver input voltage $v(t)$

during a given observation interval. This is a problem of choosing one of two hypotheses, both of them simple because the joint probability density functions of samples of the input are independent of any unknown parameters. We found that all three criteria—Bayes, minimax, and Neyman–Pearson—lead to the same strategy, the calculation of a likelihood ratio and its comparison with some fixed number. The strategy can be carried out by passing the input $v(t)$ through a certain linear filter and comparing its output at the end of the observation interval with a decision level.

Next we treated the detection of a quasiharmonic signal, all of whose parameters except the phase are known. We introduced the concept of the least favorable distribution of an unknown parameter and adopted a modified Neyman–Pearson criterion requiring the probability of detection, averaged over the least favorable distribution, to be maximized for a given false-alarm probability. The detection system then consisted of a filter matched to any one of the possible signals, followed by a rectifier and a comparison device. Since this system can be built independently of the value of the signal amplitude, it serves also to detect quasiharmonic signals of unknown amplitude. Optimum choices among multiple hypotheses and methods of combining a number of independent observations were subsequently treated.

When we attempted to apply the modified Neyman–Pearson criterion to the detection of a quasiharmonic signal of unknown arrival time, the resulting system was complicated, and it provided poor detection even at high signal-to-noise ratios. Although the Neyman–Pearson criterion, combined with the least favorable prior distributions of the unknown parameters, provides a solution independent of prior knowledge, it was unsatisfactory in this case because of its emphasis on the weakest signals, which the observer has no hope of detecting. The designer prefers a system that performs best at such signal-to-noise ratios that a useful probability of detection can be attained with a low false-alarm probability.

To this end we introduced the method of maximum likelihood, bringing it in first as a way of estimating signal parameters. We showed how one can set up a Bayes criterion for estimation when one knows prior probability density functions of the unknown parameters and the cost of errors. Seeking an estimation strategy applicable when this prior knowledge is missing, we came upon the method of maximum likelihood, whereby those estimates of the unknown parameters are selected that maximize the joint probability density function of the observations. It was put to use in the estimation of the time of arrival and the carrier frequency of a signal received in the midst of Gaussian noise.

Returning to the detection of a signal of unknown amplitude, phase, and arrival time, we adopted the following procedure. The assumption is made that the receiver input contains a signal of the given form, and the maximum-likelihood estimates of the parameters of this signal are calculated. The estimates are then tested to decide whether their values might have arisen from an input containing only noise. This decision was found to depend only on the estimate of amplitude, comparison of which with some fixed decision level is used to accept or reject the hypothesis that a signal is present. The calculation of the false-alarm and detection probabilities of this system required our finding the rate of crossing of an amplitude level by a stochastic process. The maximum-likelihood detector, which closely resembles an ordinary radar receiver, is inferior for small signal-to-noise ratios to the Neyman–Pearson system derived earlier, but it is more efficient at such signal strengths that there is some hope of detection with low false-alarm probability.

Turning now to signal resolution, we looked at the problem of deciding whether one or both or neither of two signals is present in a given receiver input. Here we must choose among not two, but four hypotheses. The decision can be made under the Bayes criterion by choosing the hypothesis with minimum posterior risk, but the associated costs and prior probabilities must be known, and often they are not. In view of the difficulty of applying a Neyman–Pearson criterion to this problem, we resorted to the method of maximum likelihood, obtaining a resolution strategy that, if not always practical, gave us at least some understanding of the signal characteristics on which resolution depends. These were studied in terms of the ambiguity function $\lambda(\tau, w)$, for signals with a relative delay τ and a relative frequency shift w. Finally we applied detection theory to the problem of detecting stochastic signals, whose form can be described only statistically.

The theory of signal detection requires the designer of a receiver to take into account the statistics of the interfering noise. It not only provides a framework for utilizing prior knowledge and assessments of costs, but also indicates how to proceed in their absence. Evaluation of the strategy prescribed by the theory in terms of Bayes risks or false-alarm and detection probabilities furnishes a standard of performance against which present systems can be judged, and the theoretically optimum systems guide the designer in improving existing devices.

PROBLEMS

1. Find the characteristic function of the quadratic form $U_M = \frac{1}{2}\mathbf{V}^+\mathbf{H}\mathbf{V}$ when the components of the M-dimensional column vector $\mathbf{V}$ are circular Gaussian random variables V_k with mean values S_k and covariances as given in eq. (XI, 1.14).

2. Using the result of Problem 1 show that if $V(t)$ is a circular Gaussian random process of mean $S(t)$ and complex autocovariance $\phi(t, s)$, the characteristic function of the quadratic functional

$$U = \frac{1}{2}\int_0^T \int_0^T V^*(t)\, h(t, s)\, V(s)\, dt\, ds$$

is

$$f(w) = f_0(w) \exp\left[\tfrac{1}{2}iw \int_0^T \int_0^T \int_0^T S^*(t)\, L(t, s; -iw)\, h(s, u)\, S(u)\, ds\, dt\, du\right],$$

where $f_0(w)$ is the characteristic function for the process of mean zero, and $L(t, s; v)$ is the solution of an integral equation similar to eq. (XI, 2.18).

3. Linearly polarized light whose electric field vector is proportional to Rl $V(t)e^{i\Omega t}$ impinges normally on a photosensitive surface. The probability that n photoelectrons are emitted in an interval $(0, T)$ is

$$p_n(T) = \langle \lambda^n e^{-\lambda}/n!\rangle, \qquad \lambda = \alpha \int_0^T |V(t)|^2\, dt,$$

where α is proportional directly to the quantum efficiency of the surface and inversely to the energy $h\Omega/2\pi$ of each quantum of the light, h being Planck's constant (Mandel, 1958). The angular brackets indicate an average over the ensemble of complex functions $V(t)$, which for ordinary light are circular Gaussian processes of complex autocovariance $\phi(\tau) = \frac{1}{2}\mathrm{E}[V(t)\, V^*(t-\tau)]$ and mean zero. Show how to calculate the generating function

$$f(s, T) = \sum_{n=0}^{\infty} s^n p_n(T)$$

of the numbers n of photoelectrons in terms of $\phi(\tau)$. Determine the mean and the variance of the number of photoelectrons from this generating function.

4. For an arbitrary quadratic functional of the type given by eq. (2.1) calculate the equivalent signal-to-noise ratio D_M (eq. (VII, 2.36)). Show that this equivalent signal-to-noise ratio is maximum when $h(t, s)$ is equal to the kernel $h_0(t, s)$ of the threshold statistic as given by eq. (1.37). *Hint.* Use the Schwarz inequality for traces, p. 409.

BIBLIOGRAPHY (XI)

1931 Courant, R. and Hilbert, D., *Methoden der mathematischen Physik*, J. Springer Verlag, Berlin. English translation, Interscience Publishers, New York, N.Y. (1953).

1947 Kac, M. and Siegert, A. J. F., "On the Theory of Noise in Radio Receivers with Square Law Detectors", *J. Appl. Phys.* **18**, 383–97 (Apr.).

1953 Emerson, R. C., "First Probability Densities for Receivers with Square Law Detectors", *J. Appl. Phys.* **24**, 1168–76 (Sept.).

ERDÉLYI, A., *et al.*, *Higher Transcendental Functions*, McGraw-Hill Book Co., New York, N.Y.

1954 DAVIS, R. C., "The Detectability of Random Signals in the Presence of Noise", *Trans. I.R.E.* **PGIT-3**, 52–62 (Mar.).

ERDÉLYI, A., *et al.*, *Integral Transforms*, McGraw-Hill Book Co., New York, N.Y.

SIEGERT, A. J. F., "Passage of Stationary Processes through Linear and Non-Linear Devices", *Trans. I.R.E.* **PGIT-3**, 4–25 (Mar.).

YOULA, D. C., "The Use of the Method of Maximum-likelihood in Estimating Continuous-modulated Intelligence which has been Corrupted by Noise", *Trans. I.R.E.* **PGIT-3**, 90–105 (Mar.).

1956 PRICE, R., "Optimum Detection of Random Signals in Noise, with Application to Scatter-multipath Communication", *Trans. I.R.E.* **IT-2**, no. 4, 125–35 (Dec.).

1957 MIDDLETON, D., "On the Detection of Stochastic Signals in Additive Normal Noise—Part I", *Trans. I.R.E.* **IT-3**, 86–121 (June).

SIEGERT, A. J. F., "A Systematic Approach to a Class of Problems in the Theory of Noise and Other Random Phenomena—Part II, Examples", *Trans. I.R.E.* **IT-3**, 38–44 (Mar.).

1958 MANDEL, L., "Fluctuations of Photon Beams and their Correlations", *Proc. Phys. Soc. (London)* **72,** 1037–48 (Dec.).

PRICE, R. and GREEN, P. E., Jr., "A Communication Technique for Multipath Channels", *Proc. I.R.E.* **46,** 555–70 (Mar.).

SLEPIAN, D., "Some Comments on the Detection of Gaussian Signals in Gaussian Noise", *Trans. I.R.E.* **IT-4,** no. 2, 65–68 (June).

1959 GRENANDER, U., POLLAK, H. O. and SLEPIAN, D., "The Distribution of Quadratic Forms in Normal Variates: A Small Sample Theory with Applications to Spectral Analysis", *J. Soc. Ind. Appl. Math.* **7,** 374–401.

1960 KAILATH, T. (a), "Solution of an Integral Equation Occurring in Multipath Communication Problems", *Trans. I.R.E.* **IT-6,** 412 (June).

KAILATH, T. (b), "Correlation Detection of Signals Perturbed by a Random Channel", *ibid.*, pp. 361–6.

MIDDLETON, D. (a), *Statistical Communication Theory*, McGraw-Hill Book Co., New York, N.Y.

MIDDLETON, D. (b), "On New Classes of Matched Filters and Generalizations of the Matched Filter Concept", *Trans. I.R.E.* **IT-6,** 349–60 (June).

PRICE, R. and GREEN, P. E. Jr., *Signal Processing in Radar Astronomy—Communication via Fluctuating Multipath Media*, Lincoln Laboratory, M.I.T., Lexington, Mass., Tech. Rept. no. 234 (Oct. 6).

TURIN, G., "The Characteristic Function of Hermitian Quadratic Forms in Complex Variables", *Biometrika* **47,** nos. 1 and 2, 199–201.

1961 MIDDLETON, D., "On Singular and Nonsingular Optimum (Bayes) Tests for the Detection of Normal Stochastic Signals in Normal Noise", *Trans. I.R.E.* **IT-7,** 105–13 (Apr.).

RUDNICK, P., "Likelihood Detection of Small Signals in Stationary Noise", *J. Appl. Phys.* **32,** 140–3 (Feb.).

1962 HÁJEK, J., "On Linear Statistical Problems in Stochastic Processes", *Czech. Math. J.* **12** (87), 404–43.

1963 BELLO, P. A., "Characterization of Randomly Time-variant Linear Channels", *Trans. I.E.E.E.* **CS-11,** 360–93 (Dec.).

ROOT, W. L., "Singular Gaussian Measures in Detection Theory", *Proceedings of the Symposium on Time Series Analysis*, M. Rosenblatt, ed., John Wiley & Sons, Inc., New York, N.Y., 292–315.

YAGLOM, A. M., "On the Equivalence and Perpendicularity of Two Gaussian Probability Measures in Function Space", *ibid.*, pp. 327–46.

1964 KADOTA, T., "Optimum Reception of Binary Gaussian Signals", *Bell Sys. Tech. J.* **43,** 2767–2810 (Nov.).

1965 KADOTA, T., "Optimum Reception of Binary Sure and Gaussian Signals", *Bell Sys. Tech. J.* **44,** 1621–58 (Oct.).

MIDDLETON, D. and GROGINSKY, H. L., "Detection of Random Acoustic Signals by Receivers with Distributed Elements: Optimum Receiver Structures for Normal Signal and Noise Fields", *J. Acoust. Soc. Am.* **38,** 727–37 (Nov.).

1966 PITCHER, T. S., "An Integral Expression for the Log Likelihood Ratio of Two Gaussian Processes", *SIAM J. Appl. Math.* **14,** 228–33 (Mar.).

APPENDIX A

INTEGRAL TRANSFORMS

IN THIS appendix we shall present a few useful formulas and techniques for dealing with Fourier and Laplace transforms. For a thorough treatment of this subject the student is referred to textbooks, some of which are listed in the bibliography; only the simpler aspects will be used in this work. In particular we shall not attempt to give strict conditions under which the formulas hold; we assume that all the functions involved are sufficiently well behaved for the various integrals to exist.

Given a function $F(t)$ that drops to zero sufficiently rapidly as t goes to $-\infty$ or $+\infty$, we can define its *Fourier transform* by the formula

$$f(\omega) = \int_{-\infty}^{\infty} F(t)\, e^{-i\omega t}\, dt. \tag{A.1}$$

From the transform $f(\omega)$ the original function can be recovered by an inverse Fourier transformation†

$$F(t) = \int_{-\infty}^{\infty} f(\omega)\, e^{i\omega t}\, d\omega/2\pi. \tag{A.2}$$

The Fourier integral is an extension of the concept of the Fourier series used to analyze periodic functions. As the period T of the periodic function increases, the lines of its Fourier spectrum, which are separated by $(2\pi/T)$, become closer and closer together, approaching the "continuous spectrum" $f(\omega)$ of eqs. (A.1) and (A.2). For a more precise description of this transition from the Fourier series to the Fourier integral, the reader should consult a text such as Churchill's (1941).

For example, if $F(t) = e^{-\alpha|t|}$, $f(\omega) = 2\alpha/(\alpha^2+\omega^2)$. To determine the inverse transform in this case we must evaluate the integral

$$F(t) = \int_{-\infty}^{\infty} \frac{2\alpha\, e^{i\omega t}}{(\alpha^2+\omega^2)} \frac{d\omega}{2\pi}. \tag{A.3}$$

† Different textbooks dispose the factor $(1/2\pi)$ in different ways, some assigning a factor of $(1/\sqrt{2\pi})$ to each of the above integrals. The choice made here seemed to be most convenient for our purposes.

This integral can be evaluated by the technique of contour integration (Copson, 1935, Chapter 6); we shall outline the calculation. For $t > 0$ one considers the contour integral

$$I = \int_C \frac{e^{izt}}{z^2+\alpha^2}\,dz, \qquad z = x+iy,$$

where the contour C is a semicircle of radius R lying in the upper half-plane and centered at the origin, along with a part of the x-axis from $-R$ to $+R$ (see Fig. A.1). According to the calculus of residues, the value of this integral I is $2\pi i$ times the sum of the residues of the integrand at all

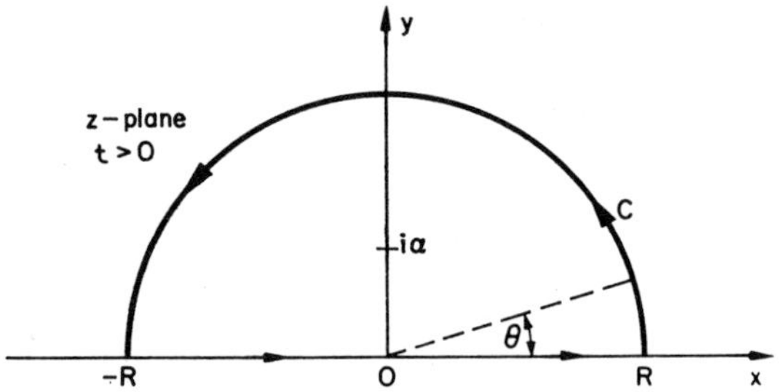

FIG. A.1. Contour of integration for eq. (A.3).

poles lying inside the contour. In this problem there is only one such pole, the one at $z = i\alpha$. The residue at that pole is

$$\lim_{z\to i\alpha} (z-i\alpha)\frac{e^{izt}}{z^2+\alpha^2} = e^{-\alpha t}/2i\alpha.$$

Therefore, the value of the contour integral I is $2\pi i \cdot e^{-\alpha t}/2i\alpha = (\pi/\alpha)e^{-\alpha t}$. Breaking up the integral I into its parts along the x-axis and along the semicircle, one finds

$$I = \int_{-R}^{R} \frac{e^{ixt}}{x^2+\alpha^2}\,dx + \int_0^{\pi} \frac{e^{iRte^{i\theta}}}{\alpha^2+R^2e^{2i\theta}}\, iRe^{i\theta}\,d\theta = I_1+I_2,$$

for on the semicircle $z = Re^{i\theta}$ and $dz = iRe^{i\theta}\,d\theta$, $0 < \theta < \pi$.

We now let the radius R increase without limit. The first integral I_1 approaches the one in eq. (A.3) that we are seeking. We must only show that the second integral I_2 vanishes as $R \to \infty$. Its absolute value is

$$|I_2| \leqslant \int_0^{\pi} \left| \frac{Re^{iRte^{i\theta}}e^{i\theta}}{R^2e^{2i\theta}+\alpha^2} \right| d\theta = R\int_0^{\pi} \frac{e^{-Rt\sin\theta}\,d\theta}{|R^2e^{2i\theta}+\alpha^2|}.$$

Here we have used the fact that the absolute value of an integral is less than or equal to the integral of the absolute value of the integrand. The denominator above is at least equal to $R^2-\alpha^2$, and $e^{-Rt\sin\theta} \leqslant 1$ because $t > 0$, so that we find

$$|I_2| \leqslant \frac{\pi R}{R^2-\alpha^2}.$$

Therefore, we can make the term I_2 as small as we like by taking the radius R large enough; $I_2 \to 0$ as $R \to \infty$. Our result is

$$\int_{-\infty}^{\infty} \frac{e^{ixt}dx}{x^2+\alpha^2} = (\pi/\alpha)\, e^{-\alpha t}, \qquad t > 0.$$

For $t < 0$ the contour must be taken as a large semicircle around the lower half of the z-plane, along with the same part of the x-axis as before. The pole used then lies at $z = -i\alpha$, and its residue is

$$\lim_{z \to -i\alpha} (z+i\alpha) \frac{e^{izt}}{z^2+\alpha^2} = -e^{\alpha t}/2i\alpha.$$

An additional minus sign appears because the contour is now traced clockwise, and one obtains the result $F(t) = e^{\alpha t}$, $t < 0$. The contour need not be completed by a semicircle. Any curve will do, provided its minimum distance from the origin is finally increased beyond all bound; the semicircle is merely the simplest to handle.

In Chapter I, eq. (1.6), we presented the Fourier transform, or spectrum, of a rectangular pulse. It is instructive to work out the inverse transformation of this spectrum. We must then evaluate the integral

$$\int_{-\infty}^{\infty} \frac{1-e^{-i\omega T}}{i\omega} e^{i\omega t}\, d\omega/2\pi = \frac{1}{2\pi i} \int_{-\infty}^{\infty} [e^{i\omega t}-e^{i\omega(t-T)}]\, d\omega/\omega. \qquad \text{(A.4)}$$

For $t < 0$ we can again complete the contour in the lower half of the plane of the complex variable $z = x+iy$ (Fig. A.2) by drawing a large semicircle Γ of radius R. We let the contour C' consist of the real axis ($x = \text{Rl}\, z$), indented in a small semicircle γ of radius r below the origin, and the large semicircle Γ around the lower half-plane. Then

$$\frac{1}{2\pi i}\int_{C'} e^{izt}\, dz/z = \frac{1}{2\pi i}\int_{-R}^{-r} e^{ixt}\, dx/x + \frac{1}{2\pi i}\int_{\gamma} e^{izt}\, dz/z + \frac{1}{2\pi i}\int_{r}^{R} e^{ixt}\, dx/x$$
$$+\frac{1}{2\pi i}\int_{\Gamma} e^{izt}\, dz/z = 0,$$

because there are no singularities of the integrand within the contour. Now on the semicircle γ we find, as its radius becomes very small,

$$\lim_{r\to 0}\frac{1}{2\pi i}\int_{\gamma} e^{izt}\,dz/z = \frac{1}{2\pi i}\lim_{r\to 0}\int_{\pi}^{2\pi} e^{irte^{i\theta}}\,id\theta = \frac{1}{2}.$$

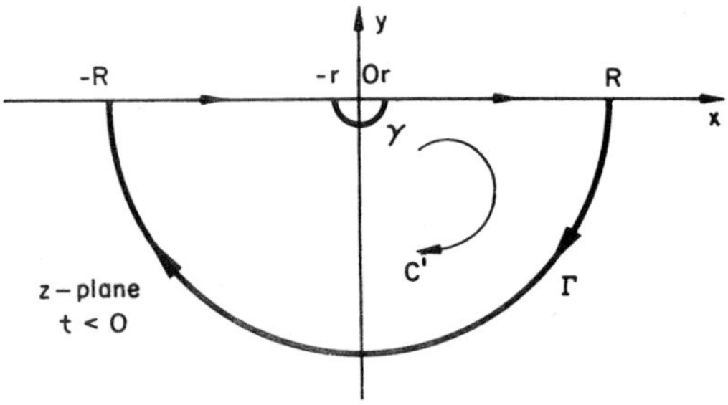

FIG. A.2. Contour of integration for eq. (A.4).

On the large semicircle Γ, on the other hand, as $R \to \infty$,

$$\left|\frac{1}{2\pi i}\int_{\Gamma} e^{izt}\,dz/z\right| \leqslant \frac{1}{2\pi}\int_{0}^{-\pi} e^{-Rt\sin\theta}\,d\theta = \frac{1}{\pi}\int_{0}^{\pi/2} e^{-R|t|\sin\theta}\,d\theta$$

$$< \frac{1}{\pi}\int_{0}^{\pi/2} e^{-2R|t|\theta/\pi}\,d\theta = \frac{1-e^{-R|t|}}{2R|t|} \to 0,$$

$$R \to \infty, \quad t < 0,$$

where we have used the fact that for $0 < \theta < \pi/2$, $\sin\theta > 2\theta/\pi$. Letting P stand for the principal value of the integral, we get

$$\frac{1}{2\pi i}P\int_{-\infty}^{\infty} e^{ixt}\,dx/x = \lim_{\substack{r\to 0\\ R\to\infty}}\left[\frac{1}{2\pi i}\int_{-R}^{-r} e^{ixt}\,dx/x + \frac{1}{2\pi i}\int_{r}^{R} e^{ixt}\,dx/x\right]$$

$$= -\frac{1}{2} \quad \text{for} \quad t < 0.$$

For $t > 0$ we complete the contour with a large semicircle around the upper half-plane. There is now a pole of the integrand inside C, so that

$$\frac{1}{2\pi i}\int_{C} e^{izt}\,dz/z = \operatorname*{Res}_{z=0} e^{izt}/z = 1.$$

We use the same reasoning as before to show that the integral around the large semicircle vanishes as its radius R goes to infinity, and we get

$$\frac{1}{2\pi i} P \int_{-\infty}^{\infty} e^{ixt}\, dx/x = \frac{1}{2}, \qquad t > 0.$$

The second term in eq. (A.4) similarly yields

$$\frac{1}{2\pi i} P \int_{-\infty}^{\infty} e^{ix(t-T)}\, dx/x = \begin{cases} -\frac{1}{2}, & t < T, \\ \frac{1}{2}, & t > T. \end{cases}$$

Subtracting these results we obtain

$$\frac{1}{2\pi i} P \int_{-\infty}^{\infty} [e^{ixt} - e^{ix(t-T)}]\, dx/x = \begin{cases} 0, & t < 0, \\ 1, & 0 < t < T, \\ 0, & t > T. \end{cases}$$

Since this integrand has no singularities in the range of integration, the principal value of the integral coincides with the value of the ordinary Riemann integral, yielding the result in eq. (1.5).

The technique of contour integration that we have used to evaluate the integrals in eqs. (A.3) and (A.4) shows us that in general if the function $F(t)$ vanishes for $t < 0$, its transform $f(\omega)$ must have no singularities in the lower half of the complex ω-plane, that is, in Im $\omega < 0$. The transfer functions $Y(\omega)$ of the linear filters discussed in Chapter I, Section 2 possess this property.

The manipulation of Fourier transforms is greatly aided by the formula

$$\int_{-\infty}^{\infty} e^{i\omega t}\, d\omega/2\pi = \delta(t), \tag{A.5}$$

where $\delta(t)$ is the Dirac delta-function, defined by

$$\int_{-\infty}^{\infty} f(x)\, \delta(x-a) dx = f(a) \tag{A.6}$$

for any function $f(x)$ continuous at $x = a$. Equation (A.5) is seen to be consistent with the equations (A.1) and (A.2).

As an example of the use of this formula, let us work out the Fourier transform of the *convolution* $G(t)$ of the functions $F_1(t)$ and $F_2(t)$, defined by

$$G(t) = \int_{-\infty}^{\infty} F_1(s)\, F_2(t-s)\, ds. \tag{A.7}$$

Substituting the transform formula (A.2) for each of the functions $F_1(t)$ and $F_2(t)$, we find

$$G(t) = \int_{-\infty}^{\infty}\int_{-\infty}^{\infty}\int_{-\infty}^{\infty} f_1(\omega_1)\, e^{i\omega_1 s} f_2(\omega_2)\, e^{i\omega_2(t-s)}\, ds\, d\omega_1\, d\omega_2/(2\pi)^2$$

$$= \int_{-\infty}^{\infty}\int_{-\infty}^{\infty} f_1(\omega_1) f_2(\omega_2)\, e^{i\omega_2 t}\, \delta(\omega_1-\omega_2)\, d\omega_1\, d\omega_2/2\pi$$

$$= \int_{-\infty}^{\infty} f_1(\omega) f_2(\omega)^{i\omega t}\, d\omega/2\pi.$$

Thus we see that the Fourier transform of the convolution of two functions is given by the product of the transforms of the functions,

$$\int_{-\infty}^{\infty} G(t)\, e^{-i\omega t}\, dt = f_1(\omega) f_2(\omega), \tag{A.8}$$

which is known as the "convolution theorem". As a special case of this result we have Parseval's formula

$$\int_{-\infty}^{\infty} |F(t)|^2\, dt = \int_{-\infty}^{\infty} |f(\omega)|^2\, d\omega/2\pi, \tag{A.9}$$

where either $F(t)$ or $f(\omega)$ can be complex functions.

We can use the convolution theorem to solve a simple integral equation of the form

$$s(t) = \int_{-\infty}^{\infty} \phi(t-u)\, q(u)\, du, \qquad -\infty < t < \infty, \tag{A.10}$$

for the unknown function $q(t)$. Let the Fourier transforms of $s(t)$, $q(t)$, and $\phi(t)$ be $S(\omega)$, $Q(\omega)$, and $\Phi(\omega)$ respectively. Then by eq. (A.8) we get

$$S(\omega) = \Phi(\omega)\, Q(\omega),$$

so that the solution of the integral equation is

$$q(t) = \int_{-\infty}^{\infty} \frac{S(\omega)}{\Phi(\omega)}\, e^{i\omega t}\, d\omega/2\pi. \tag{A.11}$$

Another useful fact is that the Fourier transform of the nth derivative of the function $F(t)$ is $(i\omega)^n$ times the transform of $F(t)$ itself,

$$(i\omega)^n f(\omega) = \int_{-\infty}^{\infty} \frac{d^n F(t)}{dt^n}\, e^{-i\omega t}\, dt, \tag{A.12}$$

provided the derivative and its transform exist; this is not the case for the examples treated earlier. To prove eq. (A.12) one differentiates eq. (A.2) n times respect to t and takes the inverse Fourier transform.

For functions $F(t)$ that vanish for $t < 0$ it is often convenient to use the *Laplace transform*, defined by the equation

$$\mathcal{L}F(t) = g(p) = \int_0^\infty F(t)\, e^{-pt}\, dt. \tag{A.13}$$

It is related to the Fourier transform of $F(t)$ by the formula

$$g(i\omega) = f(\omega).$$

The inverse Laplace transform is given by

$$F(t) = \mathcal{L}^{-1}g(p) = \frac{1}{2\pi i}\int_C g(p)\, e^{pt}\, dp, \tag{A.14}$$

where the contour of integration C is taken along a line parallel to the imaginary axis of the complex p-plane and to the right of all singularities of the function $g(p)$.

The p-plane for Laplace transforms is just the ω-plane for Fourier transforms rotated a quarter turn to the left. The techniques of contour integration discussed before can be used to evaluate inverse Laplace transforms as well. Often it is more convenient to look up the inverse transform in a set of tables, such as the extensive one of Erdélyi *et al.* (1954). As an example, the Laplace transform of the function $f(t) = e^{-\beta t}$, $t > 0$, is $g(p) = 1/(p+\beta)$.

For Laplace transforms the basic convolution formula is

$$\mathcal{L}\int_0^t K(\tau) f(t-\tau)\, d\tau = \mathcal{L}K(\tau)\cdot\mathcal{L}f(t). \tag{A.15}$$

It can be proved by using the definition in eq. (A.13) and changing the order of integration,

$$\int_0^\infty e^{-pt}\int_0^t K(\tau)\, f(t-\tau)\, d\tau\, dt = \int_0^\infty d\tau \int_\tau^\infty e^{-pt}K(\tau) f(t-\tau)\, dt$$

$$= \int_0^\infty d\tau K(\tau)\, e^{-p\tau}\int_0^\infty e^{-ps} f(s)\, ds, \qquad s = t-\tau.$$

This formula is useful in applying Laplace transforms to the solution of problems in transients in electrical networks, where $K(\tau)$ represents the impulse response of the network and $f(t)$ is a signal applied to the network beginning at $t = 0$ (see Chapter I, Section 2). On the other hand, if one is given the differential equations of a linear passive network, they can often be easily solved by using the basic formula

$$\mathcal{L}\, d^nF(t)/dt^n = p^n g(p) - p^{n-1}F(0) - p^{n-2}F'(0) - \dots - F^{(n-1)}(0), \quad F^{(k)}(t) = d^kF(t)/dt^k. \tag{A.16}$$

This formula enables one to transform the set of differential equations into a set of algebraic equations for the Laplace transforms of the currents or voltages of the network. For these techniques, see any book on Laplace transform theory or electrical transients.

BIBLIOGRAPHY (A)

1935 COPSON, E. T., *An Introduction to the Theory of Functions of a Complex Variable*, Oxford University Press, London, England.

1941 CHURCHILL, R. V., *Fourier Series and Boundary-Value Problems*, McGraw-Hill Book Co., New York, N.Y.

1942 GARDNER, M. F. and BARNES, J. L., *Transients in Linear Systems*, John Wiley & Sons, Inc., New York, N.Y.

1951 SNEDDON, I. N., *Fourier Transforms*, McGraw-Hill Book Co., New York, N.Y.

TRANTER, C. J., *Integral Transforms in Mathematical Physics*, Methuen, London, England (2nd ed., 1956).

1953 GUILLEMIN, E. A., *Introductory Circuit Theory*, John Wiley & Sons, Inc., New York, N.Y.

MCLACHLAN, N. W., *Complex Variable Theory and Transform Calculus*, Cambridge University Press, Cambridge, England.

1954 ERDÉLYI, A., *et al.*, *Integral Transforms*, vol. 1, McGraw-Hill Book Co., New York, N.Y.

1955 VAN DER POL, B. and BREMMER, H., *Operational Calculus Based on the Two-Sided Laplace Integral*, Cambridge University Press, Cambridge, England.

1961 DOETSCH, G., *Guide to the Applications of Laplace Transforms*, D. Van Nostrand Co., Princeton, N.J.

1962 PAPOULIS, A., *The Fourier Integral and its Applications*, McGraw-Hill Book Co., New York, N.Y.

1963 BROWN, W. M., *Analysis of Linear Time-invariant Systems*, McGraw-Hill Book Co., New York, N.Y.

APPENDIX B

CHARACTERISTIC FUNCTIONS

(a) *The Characteristic Function of a Single Random Variable*

Characteristic functions of random variables are discussed in many books on the theory of probability. For a more thorough treatment than we can give here, as well as for expository material on other topics in probability and random processes, we refer the reader to the texts listed in the bibliography at the end of this appendix.

For a random variable x whose probability density function is $p(x)$, the characteristic function (ch.f.) is defined by

$$h(z) = \mathbf{E}(e^{izx}) = \int_{-\infty}^{\infty} p(x)\, e^{izx}\, dx, \tag{B.1}$$

for all values of z at which this integral exists. The ch.f. is simply the Fourier transform of the probability density function (p.d.f.), and if it is known, the p.d.f. can be found from the inverse transform

$$p(x) = \int_{-\infty}^{\infty} h(z)\, e^{-izx}\, dz/2\pi. \tag{B.2}$$

By the normalization integral for a probability density function, $h(0) = 1$.

The ch.f. is related to the moments of the distribution of x. If into eq. (B.1) we substitute the power-series expansion of the exponential function e^{izx} and integrate term by term, we obtain

$$h(z) = 1+m_1(iz)+m_2(iz)^2/2!+m_3(iz)^3/3!+ \ldots +m_n(iz)^n/n!+\ldots,$$

$$m_k = \mathbf{E}(x^k) = \int_{-\infty}^{\infty} x^k p(x)\, dx, \tag{B.3}$$

provided this series converges in some region about the origin $z = 0$. The coefficient of $(iz)^n/n!$ is the nth moment of the distribution. Indeed, the function $h(-iu) = \mathbf{E}(e^{ux})$ is called the "moment generating function" of x. For some distributions, such as the Cauchy,

$$p(x) = a/\pi(a^2+x^2), \quad h(z) = e^{-a|z|}, \quad (z \text{ real})$$

an expansion such as that in eq. (B.3) cannot be made, for moments beyond a certain order—here the first—do not exist.

When the logarithm of the ch.f. is expanded in powers of (iz), the coefficients are called the "cumulants" $\varkappa_n$ of the random variable (or of the distribution),

$$\ln h(z) = \varkappa_1(iz)+\varkappa_2(iz)^2/2!+ \ldots +\varkappa_n(iz)^n/n!+\ldots. \tag{B.4}$$

The cumulant, of any order, of the sum of a number of independent random variables is equal to the sum of the cumulants, of the same order, of the individual variables, whence the name. The reader can easily show that

$$\begin{aligned} \varkappa_1 &= \mathbf{E}(x) = m_1, & \varkappa_2 &= m_2-m_1^2 = \text{Var}\, x, \\ \varkappa_3 &= \mathbf{E}(x-m_1)^3, & \varkappa_4 &= \mathbf{E}(x-m_1)^4-3[\text{Var}\, x]^2, \end{aligned} \tag{B.5}$$

by using the series expansion of $\ln(1+u)$, $u = izm_1+(iz)^2m_2/2!+\ldots$

One of the chief uses of the characteristic function is to find the p.d.f. of the sum of a number of independent random variables. Let

$$s = x_1+x_2+ \ldots +x_n.$$

Then if $x_1, x_2, \ldots, x_n$ are independent, the ch.f. $h_s(z)$ of s is

$$\begin{aligned} h_s(z) &= \mathbf{E} \exp(izs) = \mathbf{E} \exp iz(x_1+x_2+ \ldots +x_n) \\ &= \mathbf{E} \exp izx_1 \mathbf{E} \exp izx_2 \ldots \mathbf{E} \exp izx_n = h_1(z)\, h_2(z) \ldots h_n(z), \end{aligned} \tag{B.6}$$

where $h_j(z)$ is the ch.f. of x_j, $j = 1, 2, \ldots, n$. From $h_s(z)$ one obtains the p.d.f. of the sum s by an inverse Fourier transformation.

For example, if x_j has the Cauchy distribution,

$$p_j(x_j) = a_j/\pi(x_j^2+a_j^2), \qquad j = 1, 2, \ldots, n,$$

the ch.f. of the sum $s = x_1+x_2+ \ldots +x_n$ is

$$h_s(z) = \prod_{j=1}^{n} \exp(-a_j|z|) = \exp\left[-\left(\sum_{j=1}^{n} a_j\right)|z|\right].$$

Hence, the p.d.f. of the sum s also has the Cauchy form,

$$p(s) = A/\pi(s^2+A^2), \quad A = \sum_{j=1}^{n} a_j.$$

The p.d.f. of the sum of any functions of a number of independent random variables can be found in a similar way. The ch.f. of the density function $p(f)$ of a function $f(x)$ of a random variable x is

$$h_f(z) = \int_{-\infty}^{\infty} p(f)e^{izf}\, df = \int_{-\infty}^{\infty} p(x)e^{izf(x)}\, dx,$$

since $p(f)\,df = p(x)\,dx$ for $f = f(x)$. For instance, the ch.f. of the sum of squares of a number of independent random variables is the product of ch.f.s of the form

$$h_{x^2}(z) = \int_{-\infty}^{\infty} p(x) \exp(izx^2)\, dx.$$

It is by this method that we calculate the p.d.f. of the statistic L in eq. (VII, 2.1).

(b) *The Joint Characteristic Functions of a Gaussian Variable*

For a number of random variables $x_1, x_2, \ldots, x_n$ with the joint p.d.f. $p(x_1, x_2, \ldots, x_n)$, the joint ch.f. is defined as

$$\begin{aligned} h(z_1, z_2, \ldots, z_n) &= \mathbf{E} \exp i(z_1x_1+z_2x_2+ \ldots +z_nx_n) \\ &= \int_{-\infty}^{\infty} \ldots \int_{-\infty}^{\infty} p(x_1, x_2, \ldots, x_n) \exp i(z_1x_1+ \ldots +z_nx_n)\, dx_1 \ldots dx_n. \end{aligned} \tag{B.7}$$

For a joint Gaussian p.d.f.

$$\begin{aligned} &p(x_1, x_2, \ldots, x_n) \\ &= (2\pi)^{-n/2} \,|\det \boldsymbol{\phi}|^{-\frac{1}{2}} \exp\left[-\tfrac{1}{2}\sum_{i=1}^{n}\sum_{j=1}^{n} \mu_{ij}(x_i-\bar{x}_i)(x_j-\bar{x}_j)\right], \end{aligned} \tag{B.8}$$

where as in Chapter II, Section 4

$$\begin{aligned} \bar{x}_i &= \mathbf{E}(x_i), \qquad \phi_{ij} = \{x_i, x_j\} = \mathbf{E}(x_i-\bar{x}_i)(x_j-\bar{x}_j), \\ \boldsymbol{\phi} &= \|\phi_{ij}\|, \qquad \boldsymbol{\mu} = \|\mu_{ij}\| = \boldsymbol{\phi}^{-1}, \end{aligned} \tag{B.9}$$

the joint characteristic function is

$$h(z_1, \ldots, z_n) = \exp\left[i\sum_{k=1}^{n} \bar{x}_k z_k - \tfrac{1}{2}\sum_{j=1}^{n}\sum_{k=1}^{n} \phi_{jk}z_jz_k\right]. \tag{B.10}$$

To prove this we substitute from eq. (B.8) into eq. (B.7) and introduce the new integrating variables $y_j = x_j - \bar{x}_j$, $j = 1, \ldots, n$,

$$\begin{aligned} h(z_1, z_2, \ldots, z_n) &= (2\pi)^{-n/2}\,|\det \boldsymbol{\phi}|^{-\frac{1}{2}} \int_{-\infty}^{\infty} \ldots \int_{-\infty}^{\infty} \exp\left(-\tfrac{1}{2}\sum_{k,j}\mu_{kj}y_ky_j\right)\cdot \\ \exp\left[i\sum_k z_k(y_k+\bar{x}_k)\right] dy_1 \ldots dy_n &= \exp\left(i\sum_k z_k\bar{x}_k\right)\cdot(2\pi)^{-n/2}\,|\det \boldsymbol{\phi}|^{-\frac{1}{2}}\cdot \\ \int_{-\infty}^{\infty} \ldots \int_{-\infty}^{\infty} &\exp\left(-\tfrac{1}{2}\sum_{k,j}\mu_{kj}y_ky_j + i\sum_k z_ky_k\right) dy_1 \ldots dy_n. \end{aligned} \tag{B.11}$$

To evaluate the multiple integral, the axes of the y-space are rotated to such a position that the quadratic form in the exponent is reduced to a sum of squares. In matrix notation that quadratic form is $\tilde{\mathbf{Y}}\boldsymbol{\mu}\mathbf{Y}$, where $\mathbf{Y}$ is the column vector of the y_j's and $\tilde{\mathbf{Y}}$ is the row vector $(y_1, y_2, \ldots, y_n)$. New variables $u_1, u_2, \ldots, u_n$, whose column vector is denoted by $\mathbf{U}$, are introduced by the orthogonal transformation matrix $\mathbf{T}$,

$$\mathbf{U} = \mathbf{TY}, \quad \mathbf{Y} = \tilde{\mathbf{T}}\mathbf{U}, \quad \tilde{\mathbf{T}}\mathbf{T} = \mathbf{T}\tilde{\mathbf{T}} = \mathbf{I},$$

where $\tilde{\mathbf{T}}$ is the transpose of $\mathbf{T}$ and $\mathbf{I}$ is the $n \times n$ identity matrix.

The transformation $\mathbf{T}$ is chosen so that

$$Q = \tilde{\mathbf{Y}}\boldsymbol{\mu}\mathbf{Y} = \tilde{\mathbf{U}}\mathbf{T}\boldsymbol{\mu}\tilde{\mathbf{T}}\mathbf{U} = \tilde{\mathbf{U}}\boldsymbol{\Lambda}\mathbf{U},$$

where $\boldsymbol{\Lambda}$ is a diagonal matrix with diagonal elements λ_j, $j = 1, 2, \ldots, n$, $\boldsymbol{\Lambda} = ||\lambda_j \delta_{jk}||$. Then

$$Q = \sum_{j=1}^{n} \lambda_j u_j^2 .$$

We can also put

$$\sum_k z_k y_k = \tilde{\mathbf{Z}}\mathbf{Y} = \tilde{\mathbf{Z}}\tilde{\mathbf{T}}\mathbf{U} = \tilde{\mathbf{W}}\mathbf{U} = \sum_k w_k u_k ,$$

where $\mathbf{W} = \mathbf{TZ}$ is the transformed vector $\mathbf{Z}$. The multiple integral in eq. (B.11) then breaks up into a product

$$\int_{-\infty}^{\infty} \cdots \int_{-\infty}^{\infty} = \prod_{j=1}^{n} \int_{-\infty}^{\infty} \exp\left(-\tfrac{1}{2}\lambda_j u_j^2 + i w_j u_j\right) du_j$$

$$= \prod_{j=1}^{n} (2\pi/\lambda_j)^{\frac{1}{2}} \exp\left(-w_j^2/2\lambda_j\right).$$

Since $\det \mathbf{T} = 1$,

$$\det \boldsymbol{\mu} = \det \mathbf{T}\boldsymbol{\mu}\tilde{\mathbf{T}} = \det \boldsymbol{\Lambda} = \prod_{j=1}^{n} \lambda_j = |\det \boldsymbol{\phi}|^{-1},$$

and the determinant in front of the integral in eq. (B.11) is canceled. The exponent now contains the quadratic form

$$R = \sum_{j=1}^{n} w_j^2/\lambda_j = \tilde{\mathbf{W}}\boldsymbol{\Lambda}^{-1}\mathbf{W} = \tilde{\mathbf{Z}}\tilde{\mathbf{T}}\boldsymbol{\Lambda}^{-1}\mathbf{TZ} = \tilde{\mathbf{Z}}\boldsymbol{\phi}\mathbf{Z} = \sum_{j=1}^{n} \sum_{k=1}^{n} \phi_{jk} z_j z_k ,$$

and we obtain the formula in eq. (B.10).

Just as the moments of the first-order p.d.f. can be obtained from the ch.f. $h(z)$, so can joint moments such as $\mathbf{E}(x_1 x_2)$ be determined from the joint ch.f., whose multiple power series expansion is

$$h(z_1, z_2, \ldots, z_n) = 1 + \sum_{k=1}^{n} (iz_k)\bar{x}_k + \tfrac{1}{2} \sum_{k=1}^{n} \sum_{m=1}^{n} (iz_k)(iz_m)\, \mathbf{E}(x_k x_m) + \ldots \tag{B.12}$$

The power series for the exponential function in eq. (B.11) shows, for instance, that for the joint Gaussian p.d.f.

$$\mathbf{E}(x_j x_k) = \phi_{jk} + \bar{x}_j \bar{x}_k .$$

Taking the mean values as zero for simplicity, we can similarly derive the formula

$$\mathbf{E}(x_1 x_2 x_3 x_4) = \overline{x_1 x_2}\,\overline{x_3 x_4} + \overline{x_1 x_3}\,\overline{x_2 x_4} + \overline{x_1 x_4}\,\overline{x_2 x_3} .$$

The moment of the product of an even number $2m$ of Gaussian random variables of mean value 0 is the sum of $(2m)!/2^m m!$ terms, each of which is the product of the expected values of pairs of all the variables, with a different pairing in each term.

The requirement that the joint p.d.f.s of a set of random variables be consistent, as exemplified by eq. (II, 1.2), is reflected in a relationship among the joint ch.f.s of the distributions. If $h_n(z_1, \ldots, z_n)$ is the ch.f. of $x_1, \ldots, x_n$,

$$h_{n-1}(z_1, \ldots, z_{n-1}) = h_n(z_1, \ldots, z_{n-1}, 0).$$

The ch.f. of a subset of random variables is obtained by replacing the z's corresponding to the missing variables by zeros.

In Section 4 of Chapter II we stated that if the p.d.f. of an arbitrary linear combination of random variables has the Gaussian form, their joint p.d.f. is also Gaussian. Let such a linear combination of $x_1, x_2, \ldots, x_n$ be

$$\xi = \sum_{j=1}^{n} a_j x_j .$$

If ξ is Gaussian, its ch.f. must have the form

$$\mathbf{E} e^{iz\xi} = \exp\left(iz\bar{\xi} - \tfrac{1}{2}z^2 \operatorname{Var} \xi\right), \quad \bar{\xi} = \mathbf{E}(\xi).$$

For any random variables, however,

$$\bar{\xi} = \sum_{j=1}^{n} a_j \bar{x}_j , \qquad \operatorname{Var} \xi = \sum_{j=1}^{n} \sum_{k=1}^{n} a_j a_k \phi_{jk} ,$$

where $\phi_{jk} = \{x_j, x_k\}$ is the covariance of x_j and x_k. Hence,

$$\mathbf{E} \exp\left(iz \sum_{j=1}^{n} a_j x_j\right) = \exp\left(iz \sum_{j=1}^{n} a_j \bar{x}_j - \tfrac{1}{2}z^2 \sum_{j=1}^{n} \sum_{k=1}^{n} a_j a_k \phi_{jk}\right).$$

Since the a_j's are arbitrary, we can put $za_j = z_j$ and obtain

$$\mathbf{E} \exp\left(i \sum_{j=1}^{n} z_j x_j\right) = \exp\left[i \sum_{j=1}^{n} z_j \bar{x}_j - \tfrac{1}{2} \sum_{j=1}^{n} \sum_{k=1}^{n} \phi_{jk} z_j z_k\right]$$

for all values of $z_1, z_2, \ldots, z_n$. By eq. (B.10) this is the characteristic function of the joint Gaussian p.d.f. in eq. (B.8), and our assertion that the distribution of $x_1, x_2, \ldots, x_n$ is Gaussian has been verified. The converse statement, that the p.d.f. of any linear combination of Gaussian random variables is itself Gaussian, is as easily demonstrated.

BIBLIOGRAPHY (B)

1928 FRY, T. C., *Probability and Its Engineering Uses*, D. Van Nostrand Co., Princeton, N.J.; 2nd ed., 1965.

1946 CRAMÉR, H., *Mathematical Methods of Statistics*, Princeton University Press, Princeton, N.J.

1950 KOLMOGOROV, A. N., *Foundations of the Theory of Probability*, Chelsea Publishing Co., New York, N.Y.

MOOD, A. M., *Introduction to the Theory of Statistics*, McGraw-Hill Book Co., New York, N.Y.

1951 MUNROE, M. E., *Theory of Probability*, McGraw-Hill Book Co., New York, N.Y.

1953 DOOB, J. L., *Stochastic Processes*, John Wiley & Sons, Inc., New York, N.Y.

1955 LOÈVE, M., *Probability Theory*, D. Van Nostrand Co., Princeton, N.J.

1957 FELLER, W., *An Introduction to Probability Theory and Its Applications*, Vol. I, John Wiley & Sons, Inc., New York, N.Y.

1958 DAVENPORT, W. B. and ROOT, W. L., *An Introduction to the Theory of Random Signals and Noise*, McGraw-Hill Book Co., New York, N.Y.

1960 PARZEN, E., *Modern Probability Theory and Its Applications*, John Wiley & Sons, Inc., New York, N.Y.

1965 PAPOULIS, A., *Probability, Random Variables, and Stochastic Processes*, McGraw-Hill Book Co., New York, N.Y.

PFEIFFER, P. E., *Concepts of Probability Theory*, McGraw-Hill Book Co., New York, N.Y.

APPENDIX C

THE COVARIANCES OF FOURIER COEFFICIENTS OF A RANDOM PROCESS

TO REDUCE the integral in eq. (II, 2.5) we divide the square $0 < t_1 < T$, $0 < t_2 < T$ into two parts by drawing the diagonal $t_1 = t_2$ through the origin. In one half $t_1 > t_2$, and we put $t_2 = t_1 - \tau$; in the other $t_1 < t_2$, and we put $t_1 = t_2 - \tau$. Then we obtain

$$\mathbf{E}(c_n c_m^*) = T^{-2} \int_0^T \phi(\tau)\, d\tau \int_\tau^T dt_1 \exp(i\omega_m t_1 - i\omega_n t_1 + i\omega_n \tau)$$

$$+ T^{-2} \int_0^T \phi(\tau)\, d\tau \int_\tau^T dt_2 \exp(i\omega_m t_2 - i\omega_m \tau - i\omega_n t_2)$$

$$= T^{-2} \int_0^T \phi(\tau)\, d\tau\, [\exp(i\omega_n \tau) + \exp(-i\omega_m \tau)] \cdot$$

$$[\exp i(\omega_m - \omega_n)T - \exp i(\omega_m - \omega_n)\tau]/i(\omega_m - \omega_n)$$

$$= T^{-2} \int_0^T \phi(\tau) \exp[\tfrac{1}{2} i(\omega_m - \omega_n)T] \{\exp[\tfrac{1}{2} i(\omega_n + \omega_m)\tau]$$

$$+ \exp[-\tfrac{1}{2} i(\omega_n + \omega_m)\tau]\} \{\exp[\tfrac{1}{2} i(\omega_m - \omega_n)(T - \tau)]$$

$$+ \exp[-\tfrac{1}{2} i(\omega_m - \omega_n)(T - \tau)]\}\, d\tau / i(\omega_m - \omega_n)$$

$$= (4/T) \int_0^T \phi(\tau) \cos[\tfrac{1}{2}(\omega_m + \omega_n)\tau] \frac{\sin \tfrac{1}{2}(\omega_m - \omega_n)(T - \tau)}{(\omega_m - \omega_n)T} \cdot$$

$$\exp[\tfrac{1}{2} i(\omega_m - \omega_n)T]\, d\tau.$$

For $m = n$, on the other hand, the integrations over t_1 and t_2 give simply

$$\mathbf{E}(|c_n|)^2 = T^{-2} \int_0^T \phi(\tau)\, d\tau\, [\exp i\omega_n \tau - \exp(-i\omega_n \tau)](T - \tau)$$

$$= (2/T) \int_0^T \phi(\tau) \left(1 - \frac{\tau}{T}\right) \cos \omega_n \tau\, d\tau.$$

These are eqs. (II, 2.6) and (II, 2.7).

APPENDIX D

THE CIRCULAR GAUSSIAN DENSITY FUNCTION

TO PROVE that eq. (6.15) of Chapter II indeed represents the joint p.d.f. of the $2M$ variables $x_1, \ldots, x_M, y_1, \ldots, y_M$ we shall show how it can be reduced to the conventional form. We take the mean values of all the variables equal to zero; no generality is lost thereby.

The calculation is simplest in matrix notation. We write the $(2M)$-element column vector made up of the real random variables x_m and y_m, arranged vertically, as

$$\begin{pmatrix} \mathbf{x} \\ \mathbf{y} \end{pmatrix},$$

where $\mathbf{x}$ is the M-element column vector of the x_m's and $\mathbf{y}$ the M-element column vector of the y_m's. The $2M \times 2M$ matrices $\boldsymbol{\phi}'$ and $\boldsymbol{\mu}'$ are similarly written in block form as

$$\boldsymbol{\phi}' = \begin{pmatrix} \boldsymbol{\phi}_x & -\boldsymbol{\phi}_y \\ \boldsymbol{\phi}_y & \boldsymbol{\phi}_x \end{pmatrix}, \quad \boldsymbol{\mu}' = \begin{pmatrix} \boldsymbol{\mu}_x & -\boldsymbol{\mu}_y \\ \boldsymbol{\mu}_y & \boldsymbol{\mu}_x \end{pmatrix}, \tag{D.1}$$

where the elements of $\boldsymbol{\phi}_x = ||\phi_{x,\,mn}||$ and $\boldsymbol{\phi}_y = ||\phi_{y,\,mn}||$ are defined by eq. (II, 6.14).

Let $\mathbf{T}$ be the unitary matrix

$$\mathbf{T} = 2^{-\frac{1}{2}} \begin{bmatrix} \mathbf{I} & i\mathbf{I} \\ \mathbf{I} & -i\mathbf{I} \end{bmatrix} \tag{D.2}$$

with $\mathbf{I}$ the $M \times M$ identity matrix. (A scalar in front of a matrix multiplies each element of the matrix.) The adjoint of $\mathbf{T}$ is

$$\mathbf{T}^+ = 2^{-\frac{1}{2}} \begin{bmatrix} \mathbf{I} & \mathbf{I} \\ -i\mathbf{I} & i\mathbf{I} \end{bmatrix} \tag{D.3}$$

and by the rules of matrix multiplication,

$$\mathbf{T}\mathbf{T}^+ = \mathbf{T}^+\mathbf{T} = \begin{bmatrix} \mathbf{I} & \mathbf{0} \\ \mathbf{0} & \mathbf{I} \end{bmatrix} \tag{D.4}$$

where $\mathbf{0}$ is the $M \times M$ matrix of zeros. In terms of this unitary matrix $\mathbf{T}$ we find

$$\begin{bmatrix} \mathbf{z} \\ \mathbf{z}^* \end{bmatrix} = 2^{\frac{1}{2}}\mathbf{T} \begin{bmatrix} \mathbf{x} \\ \mathbf{y} \end{bmatrix}, \quad (\mathbf{z}^+ \; \mathbf{z}^{*+}) = 2^{\frac{1}{2}}(\mathbf{x}^+ \; \mathbf{y}^+)\,\mathbf{T}^+, \tag{D.5}$$

where $\mathbf{z}$ is the column vector with elements $z_m = x_m + iy_m$. The row vector $\mathbf{z}^+$ has as elements $\mathbf{z}_m^*$, and $\mathbf{z}^{*+} = (z_1, z_2, \ldots, z_M)$.

Because the matrix $\boldsymbol{\mu}$ is Hermitian, $\boldsymbol{\mu} = \boldsymbol{\mu}^+$, the quadratic form in the exponent in eq. (II, 6.15), with $\zeta_m = 0$, can be written

$$Q = \sum_{m=1}^{M} \sum_{n=1}^{M} z_m^* \mu_{mn} z_n = \tfrac{1}{2}(\mathbf{z}^+ \; \mathbf{z}^{*+}) \begin{bmatrix} \boldsymbol{\mu} & \mathbf{0} \\ \mathbf{0} & \boldsymbol{\mu}^* \end{bmatrix} \begin{bmatrix} \mathbf{z} \\ \mathbf{z}^* \end{bmatrix}$$
$$= (\mathbf{x}^+ \; \mathbf{y}^+)\, \mathbf{T}^+ \begin{bmatrix} \boldsymbol{\mu} & \mathbf{0} \\ \mathbf{0} & \boldsymbol{\mu}^* \end{bmatrix} \mathbf{T} \begin{bmatrix} \mathbf{x} \\ \mathbf{y} \end{bmatrix}. \tag{D.6}$$

Using eqs. (D. 2) and (D. 3) and the rules of matrix multiplication, we find

$$\mathbf{T}^+ \begin{bmatrix} \boldsymbol{\mu} & \mathbf{0} \\ \mathbf{0} & \boldsymbol{\mu}^* \end{bmatrix} \mathbf{T} = \begin{bmatrix} \boldsymbol{\mu}_x & -\boldsymbol{\mu}_y \\ \boldsymbol{\mu}_y & \boldsymbol{\mu}_x \end{bmatrix} = \boldsymbol{\mu}', \tag{D.7}$$

and the quadratic form becomes

$$Q = (\mathbf{x}^+ \; \mathbf{y}^+) \begin{bmatrix} \boldsymbol{\mu}_x & -\boldsymbol{\mu}_y \\ \boldsymbol{\mu}_y & \boldsymbol{\mu}_x \end{bmatrix} \begin{bmatrix} \mathbf{x} \\ \mathbf{y} \end{bmatrix}$$
$$= \mathbf{x}^+ \boldsymbol{\mu}_x \mathbf{x} - \mathbf{x}^+ \boldsymbol{\mu}_y \mathbf{y} + \mathbf{y}^+ \boldsymbol{\mu}_y \mathbf{x} + \mathbf{y}^+ \boldsymbol{\mu}_x \mathbf{y} \tag{D.8}$$
$$= \sum_{m=1}^{M} \sum_{n=1}^{M} [\mu_{x,\,mn}(x_m x_n + y_m y_n) + \mu_{y,\,mn}(y_m x_n - x_m y_n)].$$

Because $\boldsymbol{\phi} = \boldsymbol{\mu}^{-1}$, $\mathbf{T}^{-1} = \mathbf{T}^+$, and

$$\boldsymbol{\phi}' = \mathbf{T}^+ \begin{bmatrix} \boldsymbol{\phi} & \mathbf{0} \\ \mathbf{0} & \boldsymbol{\phi}^* \end{bmatrix} \mathbf{T}, \tag{D.9}$$

we find

$$\boldsymbol{\phi}'^{-1} = \mathbf{T}^+ \begin{bmatrix} \boldsymbol{\mu} & \mathbf{0} \\ \mathbf{0} & \boldsymbol{\mu}^* \end{bmatrix} \mathbf{T} = \boldsymbol{\mu}', \tag{D.10}$$

so that the matrix $\boldsymbol{\mu}'$ of the quadratic form Q is indeed the inverse of the covariance matrix $\boldsymbol{\phi}'$ of the $2M$ variables $x_1, \ldots, x_M, y_1, \ldots, y_M$. In addition, since $\det \mathbf{T} = -i$, $\det \mathbf{T}^+ = i$,

$$\det \boldsymbol{\phi}' = \det \mathbf{T}^+ \det \begin{bmatrix} \boldsymbol{\phi} & \mathbf{0} \\ \mathbf{0} & \boldsymbol{\phi}^* \end{bmatrix} \det \mathbf{T} = |\det \boldsymbol{\phi}|^2. \tag{D.11}$$

Putting eqs. (D.8) and (D.11) into eq. (II, 6.15), we find the usual form for the joint p.d.f. of the $2M$ random variables,

$$p(x_1, \ldots, x_M, y_1, \ldots, y_M) = (2\pi)^{-M} |\det \boldsymbol{\phi}'|^{-\frac{1}{2}} e^{-Q/2}. \tag{D.12}$$

A useful integral involving the circular Gaussian distribution is

$$(2\pi)^{-M}|\det \boldsymbol{\phi}|^{-1} \int_{-\infty}^{\infty} \cdots \int_{-\infty}^{\infty} \exp\left[-\tfrac{1}{2}\sum_{m=1}^{M}\sum_{n=1}^{M} z_m^* \mu_{mn} z_n + \tfrac{1}{2}\sum_{m=1}^{M}(v_m^* z_m + w_m z_m^*)\right]\prod_{m=1}^{M} dx_m\, dy_m \qquad \text{(D.13)}$$

$$= \exp\left(\tfrac{1}{2}\sum_{m=1}^{M}\sum_{n=1}^{M} v_m^* \phi_{mn} w_n\right),$$

where $\boldsymbol{\mu}$ is a Hermitian matrix, $\boldsymbol{\phi} = \boldsymbol{\mu}^{-1}$, and the v_m's and the w_m's are arbitrary complex numbers.

To derive this result we introduce the $2M$ complex numbers $(s_1', \ldots, s_M', s_1'', \ldots, s_M'')$, which make up the column vector

$$\mathbf{s} = \begin{bmatrix} \mathbf{s}' \\ \mathbf{s}'' \end{bmatrix}$$

composed of the two M-element column vectors $\mathbf{s}'$ and $\mathbf{s}''$ of the s_j' and s_j'', respectively. They are defined by the transformation

$$\mathbf{s} = \begin{bmatrix} \mathbf{s}' \\ \mathbf{s}'' \end{bmatrix} = 2^{-\frac{1}{2}}\mathbf{T}^{+}\begin{bmatrix} \mathbf{w} \\ \mathbf{v}^* \end{bmatrix} = \frac{1}{2}\begin{bmatrix} \mathbf{v}^* + \mathbf{w} \\ i(\mathbf{v}^* - \mathbf{w}) \end{bmatrix} \qquad \text{(D.14)}$$

in terms of the v_m's and the w_m's. In addition, if we use the tilde to denote the transpose of a vector or a matrix—without complex conjugation of the elements—we can write the row vector

$$(\tilde{\mathbf{v}}^* \ \tilde{\mathbf{w}}) = 2^{\frac{1}{2}}(\tilde{\mathbf{s}}' \ \tilde{\mathbf{s}}'')\mathbf{T}^{+}, \qquad \text{(D.15)}$$

and by eq. (D.5) the second summation in the exponent in eq. (D.13) is

$$\frac{1}{2}(\tilde{\mathbf{v}}^* \ \tilde{\mathbf{w}})\begin{bmatrix} \mathbf{z} \\ \mathbf{z}^* \end{bmatrix} = (\tilde{\mathbf{s}}' \ \tilde{\mathbf{s}}'')\begin{bmatrix} \mathbf{x} \\ \mathbf{y} \end{bmatrix} = \tilde{\mathbf{s}}'\mathbf{x} + \tilde{\mathbf{s}}''\mathbf{y}. \qquad \text{(D.16)}$$

By eqs. (D.8), (D.11) the integral to be evaluated is now

$$I = (2\pi)^{-M}|\det \boldsymbol{\phi}'|^{-\frac{1}{2}} \int_{-\infty}^{\infty} \cdots \int_{-\infty}^{\infty} \exp\left[-\tfrac{1}{2}Q + \sum_{j=1}^{M}(s_j' x_j + s''y_j)\right]\prod_{k=1}^{M} dx_k\, dy_k$$

and by eq. (B.10) this is

$$I = \exp(\tfrac{1}{2}\tilde{\mathbf{s}}\boldsymbol{\phi}'\mathbf{s}), \quad \tilde{\mathbf{s}} = (\tilde{\mathbf{s}}' \ \tilde{\mathbf{s}}'').$$

The quadratic form in the exponent can be written

$$\tilde{\mathbf{s}}\boldsymbol{\phi}'\mathbf{s} = (\tilde{\mathbf{s}}'\ \tilde{\mathbf{s}}'') \begin{bmatrix} \boldsymbol{\phi}_x & -\boldsymbol{\phi}_y \\ \boldsymbol{\phi}_y & \boldsymbol{\phi}_x \end{bmatrix} \begin{bmatrix} \mathbf{s}' \\ \mathbf{s}'' \end{bmatrix}$$

$$= (\tilde{\mathbf{s}}'\ \tilde{\mathbf{s}}'')\, \mathbf{T}^{+} \begin{bmatrix} \boldsymbol{\phi} & \mathbf{0} \\ \mathbf{0} & \boldsymbol{\phi}^* \end{bmatrix} \mathbf{T} \begin{bmatrix} \mathbf{s}' \\ \mathbf{s}'' \end{bmatrix} = \tfrac{1}{2}(\tilde{\mathbf{v}}^*\ \tilde{\mathbf{w}}) \begin{bmatrix} \boldsymbol{\phi} & \mathbf{0} \\ \mathbf{0} & \boldsymbol{\phi}^* \end{bmatrix} \begin{bmatrix} \mathbf{w} \\ \mathbf{v}^* \end{bmatrix}$$

$$= \tfrac{1}{2}(\tilde{\mathbf{v}}^*\boldsymbol{\phi}\mathbf{w} + \tilde{\mathbf{w}}\boldsymbol{\phi}^*\mathbf{v}^*) = \tilde{\mathbf{v}}^*\boldsymbol{\phi}\mathbf{w} = \sum_{m=1}^{M} \sum_{n=1}^{M} v_m^* \phi_{mn} w_n ,$$

which is the exponent in eq. (D.13). Here we have used eqs. (D.9), (D.14), and (D.15). The characteristic function in eq. (II, 6.17) can be derived from eq. (D.13) by replacing v_m^* by iw_m^* and w_m by iw_m.

APPENDIX E

SOLUTION OF AN INTEGRAL EQUATION

INTEGRAL equations of the form

$$s(t) = \int_{T_1}^{T_2} \phi(t-u)\, q(u)\, du, \quad T_1 \leqslant t \leqslant T_2, \tag{E.1}$$

occur in the theory of detecting both known and stochastic signals, as well as in the theory of least-squares prediction, estimation, and filtering. Here we shall describe a method of solving eq. (E.1) when the Fourier transform

$$\Phi(\omega) = \int_{-\infty}^{\infty} \phi(\tau) e^{-i\omega\tau}\, d\tau \tag{E.2}$$

of the kernel $\phi(\tau)$ is a non-negative rational function of ω^2. The kernel is then the autocovariance of noise of the type we have called "leucogenic". Such noise can be generated by passing white noise through a filter composed of resistors, inductors, and capacitors. Various techniques for the solution of equations like (E.1) are to be found in the books and papers cited in the bibliography.

The spectral density $\Phi(\omega)$ has n poles im_k, $k = 1, 2, \ldots, n$, above the real ω-axis and n poles $-im_k$ below it. There are $2m$ zeros, ih_j, $-ih_j$, $j = 1, 2, \ldots, m$, of the spectral density, m above and m below the real ω-axis. The real parts of the h_j's and the m_k's are taken as positive. We define the polynomials

$$H(z) = \prod_{j=1}^{m} (z-h_j), \quad D(z) = \prod_{k=1}^{n} (z-m_k), \tag{E.3}$$

which permit us to factor the spectral density into the form

$$\Phi(\omega) = C \frac{H(i\omega)\, H(-i\omega)}{D(i\omega)\, D(-i\omega)}\, . \tag{E.4}$$

Bear in mind that the zeros of $H(i\omega)$ and $D(i\omega)$ lie below the real axis of the complex ω-plane; those of $H(-i\omega)$ and $D(-i\omega)$ lie above it. If $m = 0$, the polynomial $H(z)$ is replaced by 1, and the terms involving its zeros are omitted from the equations to follow. It is assumed that $\Phi(\omega)$ does not vanish at any real values of ω and that all the zeros h_j are distinct.

(i) $T_1 = -\infty, \quad T_2 = +\infty.$

When the integration in eq. (E.1) is taken over the infinite interval, we write the equation as

$$s(t) = \int_{-\infty}^{\infty} \phi(t-u)\, q_0(u)\, du. \tag{E.5}$$

It can be solved by Fourier transforms, as shown in Appendix A, and the solution is

$$\begin{aligned} q_0(t) &= \int_{-\infty}^{\infty} Q_0(\omega) e^{i\omega t}\, d\omega/2\pi, \\ Q_0(\omega) &= S(\omega)/\Phi(\omega), \end{aligned} \tag{E.6}$$

where

$$S(\omega) = \int_{-\infty}^{\infty} s(t)\, e^{-i\omega t}\, dt \tag{E.7}$$

is the Fourier transform of the "signal" $s(t)$. We assume that $S(\omega)$ vanishes, as $|\omega|$ goes to ∞, faster than $\Phi(\omega)$ does, so that $q_0(t)$ exists.

(ii) $T_1 \neq -\infty, \quad T_2 = +\infty.$

When the integration is carried over a semi-infinite interval—T_1 is usually 0—the integral equation is commonly known as the "Wiener–Hopf" equation. We denote its solution by $q_+(t)$,

$$s(t) = \int_{T_1}^{\infty} \phi(t-u)\, q_+(u)\, du, \quad T_1 \leqslant t < \infty. \tag{E.8}$$

The equation must be satisfied only over the interval (T_1, ∞); what values the function on the right-hand side takes on in the interval $(-\infty, T_1)$ do not matter. When the kernel $\phi(\tau)$ is of the exponential type being considered here, the solution can be written in the form

$$\begin{aligned} q_+(t) &= q_0(t) + g_+^0(t), \\ g_+^0(t) &= \sum_{j=0}^{n-m-1} a_j^0 \delta^{(j)}(t-T_1) + \sum_{j=1}^{m} c_j^0 \exp[-h_j(t-T_1)], \\ &\qquad T_1 \leqslant t < \infty. \end{aligned} \tag{E.9}$$

Here $\delta^{(j)}(t-u)$ is the jth derivative of the delta-function,

$$\delta^{(j)}(t-u) = \frac{d^j}{dt^j}\,\delta(t-u),$$

$$\int_a^b \delta^{(j)}(t-u)\, f(u)\, du = f^{(j)}(t) = \frac{d^j}{dt^j} f(t), \qquad a < t < b. \tag{E.10}$$

The delta-function $\delta(t-T_1)$ and its derivatives are assumed to be located just inside the interval of integration, so that they contribute their full weights when integrated with a function that is continuous and differentiable within the interval, as in

$$\int_{T_1}^{\infty} f(t)\, \delta^{(j)}(t-T_1)\, dt = (-1)^j f^{(j)}(T_1). \tag{E.11}$$

If $m = n$, the delta-functions do not appear in the solution, eq. (E.9); if $m = 0$, the exponential terms are absent.

The term $g_+^0(t)$ in the solution compensates for the breaking off of the integration at a finite lower limit T_1. We shall now give formulas for determining the coefficients a_j^0 and c_j^0 therein when the signal is the complex wave $s(t) = e^{ivt}$. The solution for any other signal whose Fourier transform is $S(\omega)$ can be found by multiplying the solution for this special case by $S(v)\, dv/2\pi$ and integrating over $-\infty < v < \infty$. The values of $s(t)$ in the interval $(-\infty, T_1)$ are irrelevant and can be adjusted if necessary so that the spectrum $S(\omega)$ exists and has a convenient form.

For $s(t) = e^{ivt}$ the solution of eq. (E.8) is

$$q_+(t) = [\Phi(v)]^{-1} e^{ivt} + \int_{-\infty}^{\infty} G_+^0(\omega)\, e^{i\omega t}\, d\omega/2\pi, \tag{E.12}$$

where

$$\begin{aligned} G_+^0(\omega) &= \left\{ \sum_{j=0}^{n-m-1} a_j^0 (i\omega)^j + \sum_{j=1}^{m} \frac{c_j^0}{h_j + i\omega} \right\} \exp(-i\omega T_1) \\ &= \frac{D(iv)}{CH(iv)\,(i\omega - iv)} \left[\frac{D(-i\omega)}{H(-i\omega)} - \frac{D(-iv)}{H(-iv)} \right] \exp[i(v-\omega)T_1] \end{aligned} \tag{E.13}$$

is the Fourier transform of the function $g_+^0(t)$ in eq. (E.9). Since $G_+^0(\omega)$ has no poles in the lower half of the ω-plane, its Fourier transform $g_+^0(t)$ vanishes for $t < T_1$ as required by eq. (E.9). By the method of partial fractions the rational function of ω on the right-hand side of eq. (E.13) can be decomposed in order to obtain the coefficients a_j^0, c_j^0. We now give explicit formulas for them.

By integrating the function $G^0_+(\omega) \exp(i\omega T_1)$ counterclockwise along a closed path C_j surrounding only the pole at $\omega = ih_j$, we find that the coefficient c^0_j is given by the formula

$$
\begin{aligned}
c^0_j &= \int_{C_j} G^0_+(\omega) \exp(i\omega T_1)\, d\omega/2\pi \\
&= \frac{D(iv)}{CH(iv)} \frac{D(h_j)}{H'(h_j)(h_j+iv)} \exp(ivT_1),
\end{aligned}
\tag{E.14}
$$

in which $H'(z) = dH(z)/dz$. In the vicinity of the pole, the function $H(-i\omega)$ is approximately

$$H(-i\omega) \doteq -i(\omega - ih_j)\, H'(h_j),$$

and eq. (E.14) follows from the residue theorem for complex integration.

We now define the function $M(z)$ as the polynomial part of the rational function $D(z)/H(z)$. That is,

$$D(z) = H(z)\, M(z) + \bar{D}(z), \tag{E.15}$$

where $\bar{D}(z)$ is a polynomial of degree at most $(m-1)$. In addition we define the polynomial

$$\tilde{M}(x; z) = \frac{M(x) - M(z)}{x - z}. \tag{E.16}$$

Then the polynomial

$$A^0(\omega) = \sum_{j=0}^{n-m-1} a^0_j (i\omega)^j \tag{E.17}$$

is given by

$$
\begin{aligned}
A^0(\omega) &= G^0_+(\omega) \exp(i\omega T_1) - \sum_{j=1}^{m} c^0_j (h_j + i\omega)^{-1} \\
&= -\frac{D(iv)}{CH(iv)} \tilde{M}(-iv; -i\omega) \exp(ivT_1).
\end{aligned}
\tag{E.18}
$$

This result is derived by substituting eq. (E.14) for c^0_j and combining the terms by means of the formula

$$\frac{D(z)}{H(z)} = M(z) + \sum_{j=1}^{m} \frac{D(h_j)}{H'(h_j)(z - h_j)}, \tag{E.19}$$

which holds because both sides have the same poles with equal residues and behave identically at infinity.

It remains to prove that eqs. (E.12) and (E.13) are correct. In this we take $T_1 = 0$ to simplify the equations. We assume first that the angular frequency v of the signal has an infinitesimal positive imaginary part. Then we can define a function $r(t)$ by

$$\begin{aligned} r(t) &= e^{ivt}/\Phi(v), \quad t > 0, \\ &= 0, \quad t < 0, \end{aligned} \tag{E.20}$$

whose Fourier transform is

$$R(\omega) = [\Phi(v)]^{-1} (i\omega - iv)^{-1}.$$

The Fourier transform of $r(t)+g_+^0(t)$ is then $R(\omega)+G_+^0(\omega)$, and that of

$$\int_0^\infty \phi(t-u)\, q_+(u)\, du = \int_{-\infty}^\infty \phi(t-u)\, [r(u)+g_+^0(u)]\, du$$

is

$$\Phi(\omega)\,[R(\omega)+G_+^0(\omega)] = \frac{CH(i\omega)\,H(-i\omega)}{D(i\omega)\,D(-i\omega)} \cdot$$

$$\left\{\frac{1}{\Phi(v)\,(i\omega-iv)} + \frac{D(iv)}{CH(iv)\,(i\omega-iv)} \left[\frac{D(-i\omega)}{H(-i\omega)} - \frac{D(-iv)}{H(-iv)}\right]\right\}$$

$$= \frac{D(iv)\,H(i\omega)}{H(iv)\,(i\omega-iv)\,D(i\omega)}\,.$$

Hence

$$\int_0^\infty \phi(t-u)\, q_+(u)\, du = \int_{-\infty}^\infty \frac{D(iv)\,H(i\omega)}{H(iv)\,(i\omega-iv)\,D(i\omega)}\, e^{i\omega t}\, d\omega/2\pi.$$

For $t > 0$ the contour of integration can be completed around the upper half of the complex ω-plane, for reasons presented in Appendix A. Since $\operatorname{Im} v > 0$, the integrand has a single pole within the contour, at the point $\omega = v$, and the residue theorem shows that for $t > 0$ the right-hand side of the equation is equal to e^{ivt} as required.

Inspection of the solution in eqs. (E.12) and (E.13) shows that it remains a regular function of v as $\operatorname{Im} v$ vanishes, and it must therefore hold for real values of v as well. As stated previously, the solution for an arbitrary Fourier transformable signal is obtained by a superposition of these solutions weighted by the spectrum $S(v)$ of the signal.

For later reference we present the solution $q_-(t)$ of the equation

$$s(t) = \int_{-\infty}^{T_2} \phi(t-u)\, q(u)\, du, \quad -\infty < t \leq T_2, \tag{E.21}$$

again with $s(t) = e^{ivt}$. Now

$$q_{-}(t) = [\Phi(v)]^{-1} e^{ivt} + g_{-}^{0}(t),$$

$$g_{-}^{0}(t) = \sum_{j=0}^{n-m-1} b_j^0 \delta^{(j)}(t-T_2) + \sum_{j=1}^{m} d_j^0 \exp[-h_j(T_2-t)], \qquad -\infty < t \leqslant T_2, \tag{E.22}$$

where $g_{-}^{0}(t)$ is the Fourier transform of

$$\begin{aligned} G_{-}^{0}(\omega) &= \int_{-\infty}^{T_2} g_{-}^{0}(t)\, e^{-i\omega t}\, dt \\ &= \frac{D(-iv)}{CH(-iv)\,(iv-i\omega)} \left[\frac{D(i\omega)}{H(i\omega)} - \frac{D(iv)}{H(iv)}\right] \exp[i(v-\omega)T_2]. \end{aligned} \tag{E.23}$$

Here

$$d_j^0 = \frac{D(-iv)}{CH(-iv)\,(h_j-iv)}\, \frac{D(h_j)}{H'(h_j)} \exp(ivT_2) \tag{E.24}$$

and

$$B^0(\omega) = \sum_{j=0}^{n-m-1} b_j^0 (i\omega)^j = -\frac{D(-iv)}{CH(-iv)} \tilde{M}(iv;\, i\omega) \exp(ivT_2). \tag{E.25}$$

The delta-functions in eq. (E.22) are located inside the interval of integration, infinitesimally to the left of the endpoint $t = T_2$.

(iii) *Finite limits*

The solution of the integral equation (E.1) when both limits are finite can be most simply stated in terms of the solutions $q_{+}(t)$ and $q_{-}(t)$ of the Wiener–Hopf equations for the right- and left-hand semi-infinite intervals. It takes the form

$$q(t) = q_0(t) + g(t),$$

$$\begin{aligned} g(t) = &\sum_{j=0}^{n-m-1} [a_j \delta^{(j)}(t-T_1) + b_j \delta^{(j)}(t-T_2)] \\ &+ \sum_{j=1}^{m} \{c_j \exp[-h_j(t-T_1)] + d_j \exp[-h_j(T_2-t)]\}. \end{aligned} \tag{E.26}$$

Again, if $n = m$ the delta-functions, if $m = 0$ the exponentials, are missing. The coefficients c_j, d_j are determined by solving the $2m$ linear equations

$$\begin{aligned} c_k - \frac{D(h_k)}{H'(h_k)} \sum_{j=1}^{m} \frac{H(-h_j) \exp(-h_j T)}{D(-h_j)\,(h_j+h_k)}\, d_j &= c_k^0, \\ d_k - \frac{D(h_k)}{H'(h_k)} \sum_{j=1}^{m} \frac{H(-h_j) \exp(-h_j T)}{D(-h_j)\,(h_j+h_k)}\, c_j &= d_k^0. \end{aligned} \tag{E.27}$$

One can easily substitute for the d_k's from the second set of equations into the first set, reducing the number of equations immediately to m.

The coefficients a_k, b_k are then obtained from the polynomials

$$\begin{aligned}
A(\omega) &= \sum_{k=0}^{n-m-1} a_k(i\omega)^k = -\frac{\tilde{D}(-i\omega;\,-iv)}{\Phi(v)\,D(-iv)}\exp(ivT_1) \\
&\quad -\sum_{j=1}^{m}\left[c_j\frac{\tilde{D}(h_j;\,-i\omega)}{D(h_j)}+d_j\frac{\tilde{D}(-h_j;\,-i\omega)}{D(-h_j)}\exp(-h_jT)\right], \\
B(\omega) &= \sum_{k=0}^{n-m-1} b_k(i\omega)^k = -\frac{\tilde{D}(i\omega;\,iv)}{\Phi(v)\,D(iv)}\exp(ivT_2) \qquad \text{(E.28)} \\
&\quad -\sum_{j=1}^{m}\left[c_j\frac{\tilde{D}(-h_j;\,i\omega)}{D(-h_j)}\exp(-h_jT)+d_j\frac{\tilde{D}(h_j;\,i\omega)}{D(h_j)}\right],
\end{aligned}$$

where $T = T_2-T_1$ and

$$\tilde{D}(x;\,z) = \frac{D(x)-D(z)}{x-z}. \qquad \text{(E.29)}$$

The coefficients of $(i\omega)$ on the right-hand side of these two equations should vanish for powers of $(i\omega)$ greater than $n-m-1$. This serves as a check on the numerical work. The polynomials in eq. (E.28) apply to the signal $s(t) = e^{ivt}$. For a general signal they must be multipled by the spectrum $S(v)$ and integrated, as before. The sets of equations (E.27) hold for an arbitrary signal $s(t)$ when the coefficients c_k^0 and d_k^0 are determined as in part (ii) for the same signal.

To prove that we have the correct solution is a lengthy process. We start by combining eqs. (E.1) and (E.8),

$$\int_{T_1}^{T_2}\phi(t-u)\,[q(u)-q_+(u)]\,du = \int_{T_2}^{\infty}\phi(t-u)\,q_+(u)\,du, \qquad T_1 \leqslant t \leqslant T_2. \qquad \text{(E.30)}$$

The function that equals $q(t)-q_+(t)$ in the interval (T_1, T_2) and vanishes outside the interval has a Fourier transform $\Delta(\omega)$ that can be determined from eqs. (E.9) and (E.26),

$$\begin{aligned}
\Delta(\omega) &= [A(\omega)-A^0(\omega)]\exp(-i\omega T_1)+B(\omega)\exp(-i\omega T_2) \\
&\quad +\sum_{j=1}^{m}\{(c_j-c_j^0)\,[\exp(-i\omega T_1)-\exp(-h_jT-i\omega T_2)]\,(h_j+i\omega)^{-1} \\
&\quad +d_j[\exp(-i\omega T_2)-\exp(-h_jT-i\omega T_1)]\,(h_j-i\omega)^{-1}\}, \qquad \text{(E.31)}
\end{aligned}$$

where $T = T_2 - T_1$. The left-hand side of eq. (E. 30) is equal at all times t to

$$\int_{-\infty}^{\infty} \Phi(\omega)\Delta(\omega)\, e^{i\omega t}\, d\omega/2\pi.$$

Because the autocovariance $\phi(\tau)$ consists of decaying exponentials $\exp(-m_k|\tau|)$, the right-hand side of eq. (E.30) yields for $t < T_2$ only terms proportional to $\exp[-m_k(T_2 - t)]$, where $\pm im_k$ are the poles of the spectral density $\Phi(\omega)$, with Rl $m_k > 0$.

When the left-hand side of eq. (E.30) is evaluated for $T_1 \leq t \leq T_2$, it cannot, therefore, contain any terms proportional to $\exp[-m_k(t-T_1)]$; and the terms with the factor $\exp(-i\omega T_1)$ in the Fourier transform

$$\Phi(\omega)\, \Delta(\omega) = \frac{CH(i\omega)\, H(-i\omega)}{D(i\omega)\, D(-i\omega)} \Delta(\omega)$$

of the left-hand side may have no poles in the upper half-plane. Hence, the function

$$\frac{H(-i\omega)}{D(-i\omega)} \left\{ A(\omega) - A^0(\omega) + \sum_{j=1}^{m} \left[\frac{c_j - c_j^0}{h_j + i\omega} - \frac{d_j}{h_j - i\omega} \exp(-h_j T) \right] \right\}$$

may have poles only at the points $\omega = -ih_j$ in the lower half-plane, and it must, therefore, be equal to

$$\sum_{k=1}^{m} \beta_k/(h_k - i\omega),$$

where the β_k are constants yet to be determined.

If we integrate both sides of the equation

$$A(\omega) - A^0(\omega) + \sum_{j=1}^{m} \left[\frac{c_j - c_j^0}{h_j + i\omega} - \frac{d_j}{h_j - i\omega} \exp(-h_j T) \right] = \frac{D(-i\omega)}{H(-i\omega)} \sum_{k=1}^{m} \frac{\beta_k}{h_k - i\omega} \tag{E.32}$$

along a closed contour surrounding only the pole at $\omega = -ih_j$, we find by Cauchy's integral formula

$$\frac{D(-h_j)}{H(-h_j)} \beta_j = -d_j \exp(-h_j T). \tag{E.33}$$

Integrating the same equation along a closed contour C_k surrounding only the pole at $\omega = ih_k$, we get

$$c_k - c_k^0 = \int_{C_k} \frac{D(-i\omega)}{H(-i\omega)} \sum_{j=1}^{m} \frac{\beta_j}{h_j - i\omega} \frac{d\omega}{2\pi} = -\frac{D(h_k)}{H'(h_k)} \sum_{j=1}^{m} \frac{\beta_j}{h_j + h_k}. \tag{E.34}$$

Substituting eq. (E.33) into eq. (E.34), we obtain the first of the two sets of equations (E.27).

We next use the equation

$$\frac{1}{H(-i\omega)}\sum_{k=1}^{m}\frac{\beta_k}{h_k-i\omega}=\sum_{j=1}^{m}\left[\frac{c_j-c_j^0}{D(h_j)(h_j+i\omega)}-\frac{d_j\exp(-h_jT)}{D(-h_j)(h_j-i\omega)}\right], \tag{E.35}$$

which must hold because both sides have the same poles and, by virtue of eqs. (E.33) and (E.34), the same residues at those poles. If eq. (E.35) is combined with eq. (E.32), one finds after some algebra

$$A(\omega)=A^0(\omega)-\sum_{j=1}^{m}\left[(c_j-c_j^0)\frac{\tilde{D}(h_j;\,-i\omega)}{D(h_j)}+d_j\frac{\tilde{D}(-h_j;\,-i\omega)}{D(-h_j)}\exp(-h_jT)\right]. \tag{E.36}$$

From eq. (E.13), however,

$$A^0(\omega)+\sum_{j=1}^{m}\frac{c_j^0}{h_j+i\omega}=\frac{D(iv)}{CH(iv)(i\omega-iv)}\left[\frac{D(-i\omega)}{H(-i\omega)}-\frac{D(-iv)}{H(-iv)}\right]\exp(ivT_1), \tag{E.37}$$

and from eq. (E.14)

$$\begin{aligned}\sum_{j=1}^{m}\frac{c_j^0}{D(h_j)(h_j+i\omega)}&=\frac{D(iv)}{CH(iv)}\sum_{j=1}^{m}\frac{\exp(ivT_1)}{H'(h_j)(h_j+iv)(h_j+i\omega)}\\&=\frac{D(iv)}{CH(iv)(i\omega-iv)}\left[\frac{1}{H(-i\omega)}-\frac{1}{H(-iv)}\right]\exp(ivT_1),\end{aligned} \tag{E.38}$$

so that

$$\begin{aligned}A^0(\omega)&+\sum_{j=1}^{m}c_j^0\frac{D(h_j)-D(-i\omega)}{D(h_j)(h_j+i\omega)}\\&=\frac{D(iv)}{CH(iv)(i\omega-iv)}\left[\frac{D(-i\omega)}{H(-iv)}-\frac{D(-iv)}{H(-iv)}\right]\exp(ivT_1)\\&=-\frac{D(iv)\tilde{D}(-i\omega;\,-iv)}{CH(-iv)H(iv)}\exp(ivT_1),\end{aligned} \tag{E.39}$$

the remaining terms having cancelled out. Subtracting this equation from eq. (E.36), we obtain the first part of eq. (E.28).

The remaining equations are obtained in the same way, but one must work with solution $q_-(t)$ of eq. (E.21) instead of with $q_+(t)$.

(iv) *The Homogeneous Integral Equation*

The problem of finding the eigenvalues λ_j of the homogeneous integral equation

$$f(t) = \lambda \int_0^T \psi(t-u) f(u) \, du, \quad \text{(E.40)}$$

the Fourier transform

$$\Psi(\omega) = \int_{-\infty}^{\infty} \psi(\tau) e^{-i\omega\tau} \, d\tau \quad \text{(E.41)}$$

of whose kernel is a rational function of ω^2, was treated by Youla (1957). An equation similar to his can be obtained by the method just outlined. By writing eq. (E.40) as

$$0 = \int_0^T f(u) [\delta(t-u) - \lambda\psi(t-u)] \, du, \quad \text{(E.42)}$$

we reduce it to eq. (E.1) with

$$\Phi(\omega) = 1 - \lambda\Psi(\omega), \quad s(t) = 0.$$

If the function $\Psi(\omega)$ approaches a constant or zero as $|\omega|$ goes to infinity, the degree of the numerator of $\Phi(\omega)$ equals the degree of the denominator, $m = n$, and the solution of eq. (E.42) contains only exponential functions. The zeros h_j of $H(z)$ are now functions of the eigenvalue λ. When λ is an eigenvalue of eq. (E.40), the determinant of the coefficients of the $2m$ simultaneous linear equations (E.27) must vanish when applied to the solution of eq. (E.42); otherwise the solution will be identically zero. If we define the matrix $\mathbf{R} = \|R_{ij}\|$ by

$$R_{ij} = \frac{D(h_i) H(-h_j)}{H'(h_i) D(-h_j)(h_i+h_j)} \exp(-h_j T), \quad \text{(E.43)}$$

we require

$$0 = \det(\mathbf{I}-\mathbf{R}^2) = \det(\mathbf{I}-\mathbf{R}) \det(\mathbf{I}+\mathbf{R}), \quad \mathbf{I} = \|\delta_{ij}\|.$$

Hence $\det(\mathbf{I}\pm\mathbf{R}) = 0$, and the solution of this determinantal equation—it is transcendental—provides the eigenvalues λ of the homogeneous equation (E. 40).

(v) *An Example*

As an example let us take the integral equation studied in Chapter XI, Section 1(d), which we write as

$$\int_0^T [\delta(t-s)+(u\phi_0/N)e^{-\mu|t-s|}]\,h(s,r;u)\,ds = (\phi_0/N^2)e^{-\mu|t-r|}, \qquad 0<t<T. \tag{E.44}$$

By comparison with eq. (E.1) we see that the kernel is

$$\phi(\tau) = \delta(\tau)+(u\phi_0/N)e^{-\mu|\tau|}, \quad \Phi(\omega) = 1+\frac{2u\mu\phi_0}{N(\mu^2+\omega^2)} = \frac{\beta^2+\omega^2}{\mu^2+\omega^2}, \tag{E.45}$$
$$\beta^2 = \mu^2+2u\mu\phi_0/N.$$

Hence $H(z) = z-\beta$, $D(z) = z-\mu$, $C = 1$, $h_j = \beta$, $m = n = 1$. The "signal" is now

$$s(t) = (\phi_0/N^2)e^{-\mu|t-r|}, \tag{E.46}$$

and its spectrum is

$$S(v) = \frac{2\mu\phi_0 e^{-ivr}}{N^2(\mu^2+v^2)}. \tag{E.47}$$

From eq. (E.14) we find

$$c_0 = (2\mu\phi_0/N^2)(\beta-\mu)\int_{-\infty}^{\infty}\frac{e^{-ivr}}{(\beta^2+v^2)(\mu+iv)}\frac{dv}{2\pi}. \tag{E.48}$$

Since $0<r<T$, we evaluate this integral by completing the contour around the lower half-plane and taking the residue of the integrand at $v = -i\beta$. The result is

$$c_0 = \frac{\mu\phi_0}{\beta N^2}\frac{\beta-\mu}{\beta+\mu}e^{-\beta r}. \tag{E.49}$$

Similarly from eq. (E.24) we get

$$d_0 = (2\mu\phi_0/N^2)(\beta-\mu)\int_{-\infty}^{\infty}\frac{e^{iv(T-r)}}{(\mu-iv)(\beta^2+v^2)}\frac{dv}{2\pi}. \tag{E.50}$$

With $r<T$ the contour must be completed around the upper half-plane, and the residue is taken at the pole $v = i\beta$, with the result

$$d_0 = \frac{\mu\phi_0}{\beta N^2}\frac{\beta-\mu}{\beta+\mu}e^{-\beta(T-r)}. \tag{E.51}$$

The simultaneous equations (E. 27) are now simply

$$c - \frac{\beta-\mu}{\beta+\mu} e^{-\beta T} d = c_0,$$
$$d - \frac{\beta-\mu}{\beta+\mu} e^{-\beta T} c = d_0, \qquad \text{(E.52)}$$

and their solution is

$$c = \left[1 - \left(\frac{\beta-\mu}{\beta+\mu}\right)^2 e^{-2\beta T}\right]^{-1} \left(c_0 + \frac{\beta-\mu}{\beta+\mu} e^{-\beta T} d_0\right),$$
$$d = \left[1 - \left(\frac{\beta-\mu}{\beta+\mu}\right)^2 e^{-2\beta T}\right]^{-1} \left(d_0 + \frac{\beta-\mu}{\beta+\mu} e^{-\beta T} c_0\right), \qquad \text{(E.53)}$$

into which eqs. (E. 48) and (E. 51) must be substituted. There are no delta-functions in the solution because $m = n$. The term $q_0(t)$ in the solution is given by

$$q_0(t) = \int_{-\infty}^{\infty} \frac{S(v)}{\Phi(v)} e^{ivt}\, dv/2\pi$$
$$= \frac{2\mu\phi_0}{N^2} \int_{-\infty}^{\infty} \frac{e^{iv(t-r)}}{\beta^2+v^2} \frac{dv}{2\pi} = \frac{\mu\phi_0}{\beta N^2} e^{-\beta|t-r|}. \qquad \text{(E.54)}$$

By combining eqs. (E.53), (E.54), and (E.26) the solution as given in eq. (XI, 1.50) is finally obtained.

BIBLIOGRAPHY (E)

1949 WIENER, N., *Extrapolation, Interpolation, and Smoothing of Stationary Time Series*, John Wiley & Sons, Inc., New York, N.Y., Section 3.2, pp. 84–86.

1950 BODE, H. W. and SHANNON, C. E., "A Simplified Derivation of Linear Least-Square Smoothing and Prediction Theory", *Proc. I.R.E.* **38**, 417–25 (Apr.).

ZADEH, L. A. and RAGAZZINI, J. R., "An Extension of Wiener's Theory of Prediction", *J. Appl. Phys.* **21**, 645–55 (July).

1952 ZADEH, L. A. and RAGAZZINI, J. R., "Optimum Filters for the Detection of Signals in Noise", *Proc. I.R.E.* **40**, 1223–31 (Oct.).

1956 LANING, J. H. and BATTIN, R. H., *Random Processes in Automatic Control*, Mc Graw-Hill Book Co., New York, N.Y., Section 8.4, pp. 309–29.

1957 YOULA, D., "The Solution of a Homogeneous Wiener-Hopf Integral Equation Occurring in the Expansion of Second-Order Random Functions", *Trans. I.R.E.* **IT-3**, 187–93 (Sept.).

1958 DARLINGTON, S., "Linear Least-Squares Smoothing and Prediction", *Bell Sys. Tech. J.* **37**, 1221–94 (Sept.).

LEE, Y. W., *Statistical Theory of Communication*, John Wiley & Sons, Inc., New York, N.Y., Chapter 14, pp. 355–95.

1960 MIDDLETON, D., *An Introduction to Statistical Communication Theory*, McGraw-Hill Book Co., New York, N.Y., Appendix 2, pp. 1082–1102.

1962 WAINSTEIN, L. A. and ZUBAKOV, V. D., *Extraction of Signals from Noise*, R. A. SILVERMAN, trans., Prentice-Hall Inc., Englewood Cliffs, N.J., Section 11, pp. 56–61.

1963 WHITTLE, P., *Prediction and Regulation by Linear Least-Squares Methods*, The English Universities Press, Ltd., London, England.

1965 MULLIKIN, T. W. and SELIN, I., "The Likelihood Ratio Filter for the Detection of Gaussian Signals in White Noise", *Trans. I.E.E.E.* **IT-11**, 513–15 (Oct.).

PUGACHEV, V. S., *Theory of Random Functions and Its Application to Control Problems*, Pergamon Press, Ltd., Oxford, England, Section 132, pp. 659–70.

1966 KAILATH, T., "Some Integral Equations with 'Nonrational' Kernels", *Trans. I.E.E.E.* **IT-12**, 442–7 (Oct.).

APPENDIX F

THE Q-FUNCTION

THE probability density function

$$q(\alpha, x) = x \exp\left[-\tfrac{1}{2}(x^2+\alpha^2)\right] I_0(\alpha x) \tag{F.1}$$

is called the "non-central Rayleigh" or the "Rician" density function. It describes the distribution of the distance from a point in a plane to the origin when the Cartesian coordinates of the point are independent Gaussian random variables of unit variance and expected values $\alpha \cos \psi$ and $\alpha \sin \psi$, ψ an arbitrary angle. The complementary cumulative distribution

$$Q(\alpha, \beta) = \Pr(x > \beta) = \int_{\beta}^{\infty} q(\alpha, x)\, dx \tag{F.2}$$

is known as the "Q-function". Some of its properties were given by Rice (1944), and it was extensively calculated and utilized by Marcum (1948, 1950). In this appendix we shall list some of its properties, with brief derivations of most of them. Advice about numerical computation of the Q-function has been given by Brennan and Reed (1965). A recent tabulation is by Bark *et al.* (1964).

Particular values of the Q-function are

$$Q(\alpha, 0) = 1, \quad Q(0, \beta) = \exp(-\beta^2/2). \tag{F.3}$$

The normalization equation $Q(\alpha, 0) = 1$ gives us the useful integral

$$\int_0^{\infty} x \exp(-ax^2/2)\, I_0(bx)\, dx = a^{-1} \exp(b^2/2a) \tag{F.4}$$

by a change of variables.

The generating function of the even moments of the distribution is

$$\int_0^{\infty} \exp(ux^2)\, q(\alpha, x)\, dx = (1-2u)^{-1} \exp\left[\alpha^2 u/(1-2u)\right] \tag{F.5}$$

by eq. (F.4). The resemblance of this formula to the generating function of the Laguerre polynomials,

$$L_n(z) = (n!)^{-1} e^z \frac{d^n}{dz^n}(z^n e^{-z}),$$

gives us the moments of even order,

$$\mathbf{E}(x^{2n}) = 2^n n!\, L_n(-\alpha^2/2). \tag{F.6}$$

In particular

$$\mathbf{E}(x^2) = 2+\alpha^2, \quad \mathbf{E}(x^4) = 8+8\alpha^2+\alpha^4. \tag{F.7}$$

The moments of all orders are most conveniently written in terms of the confluent hypergeometric function,

$$\mathbf{E}(x^m) = 2^{m/2}\Gamma(\tfrac{1}{2}m+1)\, {}_1F_1(-\tfrac{1}{2}m;\, 1;\, -\alpha^2/2), \tag{F.8}$$

which reduces to eq. (F.6) when $m = 2n$. In particular

$$\mathbf{E}(x) = \tfrac{1}{2}(2\pi)^{\frac{1}{2}} \exp(-\alpha^2/4)\, [(1+\tfrac{1}{2}\alpha^2)\, I_0(\alpha^2/4)+\tfrac{1}{2}\alpha^2 I_1(\alpha^2/4)], \tag{F.9}$$

which can be obtained by expressing the Bessel functions as confluent hypergeometric functions,

$$I_0(x/2) = e^{-x/2}\, {}_1F_1(\tfrac{1}{2};\, 1;\, x), \quad I_1(x/2) = \tfrac{1}{4}xe^{-x/2}\, {}_1F_1(\tfrac{3}{2};\, 3;\, x),$$

and applying the recurrence relations for the hypergeometric functions (Erdélyi *et al.*, 1953, chapter VI, p. 254). See also Rice (1944), eq. (4.2–3).

The partial derivatives of the Q-function are

$$\frac{\partial Q(\alpha, \beta)}{\partial \alpha} = \beta \exp[-(\alpha^2+\beta^2)/2]\, I_1(\alpha\beta), \tag{F.10}$$

which is obtained by differentiating the defining equation and integrating by parts, and

$$\frac{\partial Q(\alpha, \beta)}{\partial \beta} = -\beta \exp[-(\alpha^2+\beta^2)/2]\, I_0(\alpha\beta). \tag{F.11}$$

The formula

$$Q(\alpha, \beta)+Q(\beta, \alpha) = 1+\exp[-\tfrac{1}{2}(\alpha^2+\beta^2)]\, I_0(\alpha\beta) \tag{F.12}$$

can be proved by noting that the first partial derivatives of both sides with respect to α are equal, by eqs. (F.10) and (F.11). Since the formula holds at $\alpha = 0$ by eq. (F.3), it must hold for all values of α.

The equation

$$Q(\alpha, \beta) = \exp[-\tfrac{1}{2}(\alpha^2+\beta^2)] \sum_{n=0}^{\infty} (\alpha/\beta)^n\, I_n(\alpha\beta) \tag{F.13}$$

holds at $\alpha = 0$ by virtue of eq. (F.3), and its partial derivative with respect to α agrees with eq. (F.10), as can be shown by using

$$\frac{d}{d\alpha}[\alpha^n I_n(\alpha\beta)] = \beta\alpha^n I_{n-1}(\alpha\beta).$$

Hence, it is valid for all values of α. Combining eqs. (F.13) and (F.12) and interchanging α and β, one gets

$$Q(\alpha, \beta) = 1-\exp\left[-\tfrac{1}{2}(\alpha^2+\beta^2)\right] \sum_{n=1}^{\infty} (\beta/\alpha)^n I_n(\alpha\beta). \tag{F.14}$$

This formula was attributed by Rice (1944) to W. R. Bennett.

The following asymptotic formulas are given by Rice (1944),

$$\begin{aligned} Q(\alpha, \beta) &\cong \operatorname{erfc}(\beta-\alpha) \\ &\quad -(2\alpha)^{-1}(2\pi)^{-\frac{1}{2}}\left[1-\frac{\beta-\alpha}{4\alpha}+\frac{1+(\beta-\alpha)^2}{8\alpha^2}\right]\exp\left[-\frac{1}{2}(\beta-\alpha)^2\right], \\ &\qquad \alpha\beta \gg 1, \quad \alpha \gg |\beta-\alpha|. \end{aligned} \tag{F.15}$$

For $\alpha\beta \gg 1, \alpha-\beta \gg 1$,

$$\begin{aligned} Q(\alpha, \beta) &\cong 1-(\alpha-\beta)^{-1}(\beta/2\pi\alpha)^{\frac{1}{2}}\exp\left[-\frac{1}{2}(\alpha-\beta)^2\right]\cdot \\ &\qquad \left[1-\frac{3(\alpha+\beta)^2-4\beta^2}{8a\beta(\alpha-\beta)^2}+\ldots\right] \\ &\cong 1-(\beta/\alpha)^{\frac{1}{2}}\operatorname{erfc}(\alpha-\beta)\left[1-\frac{\beta+3\alpha}{8\alpha\beta(\alpha-\beta)}+\ldots\right]. \end{aligned} \tag{F.16}$$

If one substitutes the asymptotic form of the Bessel function $I_0(\alpha x)$ into the defining equation (F.2) and integrates twice by parts, one gets

$$\begin{aligned} Q(\alpha, \beta) &= (\beta/\alpha)^{\frac{1}{2}}\operatorname{erfc}(\beta-\alpha)\cdot \\ &\quad \left[1+\frac{\beta+3\alpha}{8\alpha\beta(\beta-\alpha)}+\ldots\right], \quad \alpha\beta \gg 1, \quad \beta-\alpha \gg 1. \end{aligned} \tag{F.17}$$

In these formulas one may wish to use the asymptotic form of the error-function integral

$$\operatorname{erfc} x \cong (2\pi)^{-\frac{1}{2}}x^{-1}\exp(-x^2/2)(1-x^{-2}+\ldots), \quad x \gg 1.$$

The following equations are due to Maximon (1956),

$$\begin{aligned} \int_0^\infty q(a, x)\,dx \int_{rx}^{\infty} q(b, y)\,dy &= \int_0^\infty q(a, x)\,Q(b, rx)\,dx \\ &= (1+r^2)^{-1}\{r^2[1-Q(v_1, v_2)]+Q(v_2, v_1)\} \\ &= 1-Q(v_1, v_2)+(1+r^2)^{-1}\exp\left[-\frac{a^2r^2+b^2}{2(1+r^2)}\right] I_0\left(\frac{abr}{1+r^2}\right) \\ &= Q(v_2, v_1)-\frac{r^2}{1+r^2}\exp\left[-\frac{a^2r^2+b^2}{2(1+r^2)}\right] I_0\left(\frac{abr}{1+r^2}\right), \\ v_1 = ar(1+r^2)^{-\frac{1}{2}}, &\quad v_2 = b(1+r^2)^{-\frac{1}{2}}. \end{aligned} \tag{F.18}$$

To derive them one establishes first that they hold for $b = 0$ ($v_2 = 0$). Using eqs. (F.3), (F.4) we find

$$\int_0^\infty q(a, x)\, Q(0, rx)\, dx$$

$$= \int_0^\infty x \exp\left[-\tfrac{1}{2}(x^2+a^2)\right] I_0(ax) \exp\left(-\tfrac{1}{2}r^2x^2\right) dx$$

$$= (1+r^2)^{-1} \exp\left[-a^2r^2/2(1+r^2)\right].$$

One next shows that the derivatives of both sides with respect to b are equal, whence it follows that eq. (F.18) holds for all values of b. Call the function on the left-hand side $L(a, b)$, that on the right-hand side $R(a, b)$. By eq. (F.10)

$$\partial L/\partial b = \int_0^\infty q(a, x)\, rx \exp\left[-\tfrac{1}{2}(r^2x^2+b^2)\right] I_1(rbx)\, dx$$

$$= \exp\left[-\frac{1}{2}(a^2+b^2)\right] \frac{\partial}{\partial b} \int_0^\infty x \exp\left[-\frac{1}{2}(1+r^2)x^2\right] I_0(ax)\, I_0(rbx)\, dx$$

$$= \exp\left[-\frac{1}{2}(a^2+b^2)\right] \frac{\partial}{\partial b} \left\{(1+r^2)^{-1} \exp\left[\frac{a^2+b^2r^2}{2(1+r^2)}\right] I_0\left(\frac{abr}{1+r^2}\right)\right\}.$$

(Cf. Erdélyi *et al.*, vol. 2, p. 50, eq. (7.7.3(25)).) Thus

$$\partial L/\partial b = (1+r^2)^{-2}\left[br^2 I_0\left(\frac{abr}{1+r^2}\right) + arI_1\left(\frac{abr}{1+r^2}\right)\right] \exp\left[-\frac{a^2r^2+b^2}{2(1+r^2)}\right].$$

Differentiating the first form of the right-hand side with respect to b one gets, by eqs. (F. 10), (F. 11),

$$\partial R/\partial b = (1+r^2)^{-1}\left\{\frac{ar}{1+r^2} \exp\left[-\frac{1}{2}(v_1^2+v_2^2)\right] I_1(v_1v_2)\right.$$

$$\left. + \frac{r^2b}{1+r^2} \exp\left[-\frac{1}{2}(v_1^2+v_2^2)\right] I_0(v_1v_2)\right\} = \partial L/\partial b,$$

as was to be shown. An extensive collection of formulas of the type of eq. (F.18) has been given by Price (1964).

A trigonometrical integral for the Q-function can be found by substituting into eq. (F.13) the integrals

$$I_n(\alpha\beta) = \int_0^{2\pi} \cos n\theta\, e^{\alpha\beta\cos\theta}\, d\theta/2\pi,$$

interchanging summation and integration, and summing,

$$Q(\alpha, \beta) = \exp\left[-\tfrac{1}{2}(\alpha^2+\beta^2)\right]\cdot \int_0^{2\pi} \frac{1-(\alpha/\beta)\cos\theta}{1-2(\alpha/\beta)\cos\theta+(\alpha/\beta)^2}\, e^{\alpha\beta\cos\theta}\, d\theta/2\pi. \tag{F.19}$$

BIBLIOGRAPHY (F)

1944 Rice, S. O., "The Mathematical Analysis of Random Noise", *Bell Sys. Tech. J.* **23,** 282–332 (July); **24,** 46–156 (Jan. 1945). Reprinted in *Noise and Stochastic Processes*, N. Wax, ed., Dover Publications, Inc., New York, N.Y. (1954).

1948 Marcum, J. I., *A Statistical Theory of Target Detection by Pulsed Radar*, Rand Corp. Rept. RM-753 (July 1). Reprinted in *Trans. I.R.E.* **IT-6,** 145–267 (Apr. 1960).

1950 Marcum, J. I., *A Table of Q-Functions*, Rand Corp. Rept. RM–339 (Jan. 1).

1953 Erdélyi, A., *et al.*, *Higher Transcendental Functions*, 2 vols., McGraw-Hill Book Co., New York, N.Y.

1955 Helstrom, C. W., "The Resolution of Signals in White, Gaussian Noise", *Proc. I.R.E.* **43,** 1111–18 (Sep.).

1956 Maximon, L. C., "On the Representation of Indefinite Integrals Containing Bessel Functions by Simple Neumann Series", *Proc. Amer. Math. Soc.* **7,** 1054–62.

1964 Bark, L. S., Bolshev, L. N., Kuznetsov, P. I. and Cherenkov, A. P., *Tables of the Rayleigh–Rice Distributions*, Computation Center of the U.S.S.R., Academy of Sciences, U.S.S.R., vol. 28.

Price, R., "Some Non-Central *F*-Distributions Expressed in Closed Form", *Biometrika* **51,** nos. 1 and 2, 107–22.

1965 Brennan, L. E. and Reed, I. S., "A Recursive Method of Computing the *Q*-Function", *Trans. I.E.E.E.* **IT-11,** 312–13 (Apr.).

1966 Schwartz, M., Bennett, W. R., and Stein, S., *Communication Systems and Techniques*, McGraw-Hill Book Co., New York, N.Y., Appendix A, pp. 585–9.

APPENDIX G

ERROR PROBABILITY FOR A CHANNEL WITH TWO NON-ORTHOGONAL SIGNALS OF RANDOM PHASES

ACCORDING to Chapter VI, Section 2(b), we want the probability that $R_1 > R_0$, where

$$R_i = \left| \int_0^T Q_i^*(t)\, V(t)\, dt \right|, \quad i = 0, 1, \tag{G.1}$$

and $V(t) = F_1(t) + N(t)$, $N(t)$ being the complex envelope of Gaussian random noise of autocovariance

$$\phi(\tau) = \text{Rl}\, \tilde{\phi}(\tau) e^{i\Omega\tau}. \tag{G.2}$$

Here $Q_0(t)$ and $Q_1(t)$ are solutions of the integral equations

$$F_i(t) = \int_0^T \tilde{\phi}(t-u)\, Q_i(u)\, du, \quad 0 < t < T, \quad i = 0, 1. \tag{G.3}$$

The signals are so chosen that

$$\int_0^T Q_1^*(t)\, F_1(t)\, dt = \int_0^T Q_0^*(t)\, F_0(t)\, dt = d^2. \tag{G.4}$$

For detection in white noise this means that the signals are received with equal energies E, and $d^2 = 2E/N$.

We introduce the complex random variables

$$z_j = x_j + iy_j = \int_0^T Q_j^*(t)\, V(t)\, dt, \quad j = 0, 1. \tag{G.5}$$

The distribution of their real and imaginary parts x_0, y_0, x_1, and y_1 is conveniently written in terms of z_0 and z_1 in the manner introduced in Chapter II, Section 6. Their expected values are

$$\begin{aligned} \mathbf{E}(z_0 | H_1) &= \zeta_0 = e^{i\psi} \int_0^T Q_0^*(t)\, F_1(t)\, dt = \lambda d^2 e^{i\psi}, \\ \mathbf{E}(z_1 | H_1) &= \zeta_1 = e^{i\psi} \int_0^T Q_1^*(t)\, F_1(t)\, dt = d^2 e^{i\psi}, \end{aligned} \tag{G.6}$$

where the complex numb er λ is defined by

$$\lambda = d^{-2} \int_0^T Q_0^*(t)\, F_1(t)\, dt = d^{-2} \int_0^T \int_0^T Q_0^*(t)\, \tilde{\phi}(t-u)\, Q_1(u)\, dt\, du. \quad (G.7)$$

The variances and covariances of x_0, y_0, x_1, and y_1 can be obtained from the relations

$$\begin{aligned} \{z_0, z_0^*\} = \{z_1, z_1^*\} &= \mathbf{E} \int_0^T \int_0^T Q_0^*(t_1)\, Q_0(t_2)\, N(t_1)\, N^*(t_2)\, dt_1\, dt_2 \\ &= 2 \int_0^T \int_0^T Q_0^*(t_1)\, Q_0(t_2)\, \tilde{\phi}(t_1 - t_2)\, dt_1\, dt_2 \qquad (G.8) \\ &= 2 \int_0^T Q_0^*(t)\, F_0(t)\, dt = 2d^2, \end{aligned}$$

$$\{z_0, z_1^*\} = 2 \int_0^T \int_0^T Q_0^*(t_1)\, Q_0(t_2)\, \tilde{\phi}(t_1 - t_2)\, dt_1\, dt_2 = 2\lambda\, d^2. \quad (G.9)$$

The covariance matrix of the complex variables z_0, z_1, as defined in eq. (II, 6.14), is

$$\boldsymbol{\phi} = \begin{bmatrix} d^2 & \lambda\, d^2 \\ \lambda^*\, d^2 & d^2 \end{bmatrix}, \quad (G.10)$$

and its inverse is

$$\boldsymbol{\mu} = d^{-2}(1-|\lambda|^2)^{-1} \begin{bmatrix} 1 & -\lambda \\ -\lambda^* & 1 \end{bmatrix}, \quad (G.11)$$

with $\det \boldsymbol{\phi} = d^4(1-|\lambda|^2)$. Thus the joint p.d.f. of x_0, y_0, x_1, y_1 can be written as in eq. (II, 6.15),

$$p(x_0, y_0, x_1, y_1) = \tilde{p}(z_0, z_1) = (2\pi)^{-2}\, d^{-4}(1-|\lambda|^2)^{-1} \cdot \exp\left[-\frac{|z_0-\zeta_0|^2 + |z_1-\zeta_1|^2 - 2\, \mathrm{Rl}\, \lambda(z_0^* - \zeta_0^*)(z_1-\zeta_1)}{2d^2(1-|\lambda|^2)} \right]. \quad (G.12)$$

It is convenient to introduce two new complex variables by a linear transformation that diagonalizes the quadratic form in the exponent of $\tilde{p}(z_0, z_1)$. They are

$$u = \left[\frac{\lambda^* z_0 - (1+k) z_1}{kd[2(1+k)]^{\frac{1}{2}}} \right] e^{-i\psi}, \quad v = \left[\frac{(1+k) z_0 - \lambda z_1}{kd[2(1+k)]^{\frac{1}{2}}} \right] e^{-i\psi}, \quad (G.13)$$

with $k = (1-|\lambda|^2)^{\frac{1}{2}}$. Their expected values are

$$\begin{aligned} U &= \mathbf{E}(u|H_1) = -d[(1+k)/2]^{\frac{1}{2}} = -\mu_1, \\ V &= \mathbf{E}(v|H_1) = -d(\lambda/|\lambda|)\, [(1-k)/2]^{\frac{1}{2}} = -(\lambda/|\lambda|)\mu_2, \qquad (G.14) \\ \mu_1 &= d[(1+k)/2]^{\frac{1}{2}}, \quad \mu_2 = d[(1-k)/2]^{\frac{1}{2}}, \end{aligned}$$

and their complex covariances are

$$\{u, u^*\} = \{v, v^*\} = 1, \quad \{u, v^*\} = 0, \tag{G.15}$$

as the reader can easily show from eqs. (G.6), (G.8), and (G.9). Thus the joint p.d.f. of the real and imaginary parts of u and v is

$$\tilde{p}(u, v) = (2\pi)^{-2} \exp\{-\tfrac{1}{2}[|u-U|^2+|v-V|^2]\} \tag{G.16}$$

in the circular Gaussian form.

The probability sought, that $R_1 > R_0$, equals the probability that $R_1^2 - R_0^2 = |z_1|^2 - |z_0|^2 > 0$. But from eq. (G.13) we can show that

$$|u|^2 - |v|^2 = (kd^2)^{-1}(|z_1|^2 - |z_0|^2),$$

so that

$$\Pr(R_1 > R_0) = \Pr\{|u|^2 - |v|^2 > 0\} = \Pr\{|u| > |v|\}. \tag{G.17}$$

This last probability is simplest to calculate because u and v are independent.

If we put $u = xe^{i\gamma}$, $v = ye^{i\delta}$, and convert the joint p.d.f. in eq. (G.16) to polar coordinates, it becomes

$$p(x, y, \gamma, \delta) = (2\pi)^{-2}\, xy \exp\{-\tfrac{1}{2}[|xe^{i\gamma} - U|^2 + |ye^{i\delta} - V|^2]\}, \tag{G.18}$$

and the joint p.d.f. of x and y is obtained by integrating γ and δ over the interval $(0, 2\pi)$. Since $|U| = \mu_1$, $|V| = \mu_2$, we get a product of familiar functions,

$$p(x, y) = q(\mu_1, x)\, q(\mu_2, y). \tag{G.19}$$

The probability of correct reception is now

$$\Pr(R_1 > R_0) = \Pr(x > y) = \int_0^\infty q(\mu_2, y)\, dy \int_y^\infty q(\mu_1, x)\, dx, \tag{G.20}$$

and this can be evaluated by eq. (F.18) with $b = \mu_1$, $a = \mu_2$, $r = 1$, $v_1 = 2^{-\frac{1}{2}}\mu_2$, $v_2 = 2^{-\frac{1}{2}}\mu_1$, with the result

$$\begin{aligned}
&\Pr(R_1 > R_0) \\
&= \tfrac{1}{2}[1 - Q(\tfrac{1}{2}d\sqrt{1-k}, \tfrac{1}{2}d\sqrt{1+k}) + Q(\tfrac{1}{2}d\sqrt{1+k}, \tfrac{1}{2}d\sqrt{1-k})] \\
&= 1 - Q(\tfrac{1}{2}d\sqrt{1-k}, \tfrac{1}{2}d\sqrt{1+k}) + \tfrac{1}{2}\exp(-d^2/4)\, I_0(|\lambda|\, d^2/4), \\
&\qquad k = (1-|\lambda|^2)^{\frac{1}{2}}.
\end{aligned} \tag{G.21}$$

An alternative derivation of this formula was given by the writer (1955).

AUTHOR INDEX

SUBJECT INDEX

OTHER TITLES IN THE SERIES IN ELECTRONICS AND INSTRUMENTATION

Vol. 1 *Signal Noise and Resolution in Nuclear Counter Amplifiers*
by A. B. GILLESPIE
Vol. 2 *Scintillation Counters*
by J. B. BIRKS
Vol. 3 *Probability and Information Theory with Applications to Radar*
by P. M. WOODWARD
Vol. 4 *Physics and Applications of Secondary Electron Emission*
by H. BRUINING
Vol. 5 *Millimicrosecond Pulse Techniques* (2nd Edition)
by I. A. D. LEWIS and F. H. WELLS
Vol. 6 *Introduction to Electronic Analogue Computers* (2nd Edition)
by C. A. A. WASS and K. C. GARNER
Vol. 7 *Scattering and Diffraction of Radio Waves*
by J. R. MENTZER
Vol. 8 *Space-charge Waves and Slow Electromagnetic Waves*
by A. H. W. BECK
Vol. 9 *Statistical Theory of Signal Detection* (2nd Edition)
by CARL W. HELSTROM
Vol. 10 *Laplace Transforms for Electronic Engineers* (2nd Edition)
by J. G. HOLBROOK
Vol. 11 *Frequency Modulation Theory—Application to Microwave Links*
by J. FAGOT and PH. MAGNE
Vol. 12 *Theory of Microwave Valves*
by S. D. GVOZDOVER
Vol. 13 *Electronic Computers*
by A. I. KITOV and N. A. KRINITSKII
Vol. 14 *Topics in Engineering Logic*
by M. NADLER
Vol. 15 *Environmental Testing Techniques for Electronics and Materials*
by G. W. A. DUMMER and N. B. GRIFFIN
Vol. 16 *Fundamentals of Microwave Electronics*
by V. N. SHEVCHIK
Vol. 17 *Static Electromagnetic Frequency Changers*
by L. L. ROZHANSKII
Vol. 18 *Problems in the Design and Development of 750 MW Turbogenerators*
by V. P. ANEMPODISTOV, E. G. KASHARSKII and I. D. URUSOV
Vol. 19 *Controlled-delay Devices*
by S. A. DOGANOVSKII and V. A. IVANOV
Vol. 20 *High Sensitivity Counting Techniques*
by D. E. WATT and D. RAMSDEN
Vol. 21 *Asynchronized Synchronous Machines*
by M. M. BOTVINNIK